# KNOWLEDGE AND POWER

# KNOWLEDGE
# and
# POWER ESSAYS ON
# SCIENCE AND GOVERNMENT

EDITED BY *Sanford A. Lakoff*

Fp

THE FREE PRESS, NEW YORK

*Collier-Macmillan Limited, London*

*ACKNOWLEDGMENTS*

For permission to reprint material in this book the courtesy of the following journals is acknowledged with gratitude:

*Science* for Daniel S. Greenberg, "Mohole: The Project That Went Awry"; and McGeorge Bundy, "The Scientists and National Policy."

*Minerva* and *Physics Today* for Alvin M. Weinberg, "Priorities in Scientific Research."

Collier-Macmillan Canada Ltd., Toronto, Ontario

Library of Congress Catalog Card Number: 66-23079

*Printing Number*
*2   3   4   5   6   7   8   9   10*

THE ASSOCIATION of knowledge and power—*scientia et potentia*—posed dramatically by Sir Francis Bacon at the dawn of modern history, has long been an idea fascinating to imaginative minds. In our time it is not only an idea but a reality. But like all bold ideas that come to fruition in social life, this one too takes far more complicated and unexpected forms in reality than in conception. Knowledge does not always provide power; it sometimes only breeds confusion. Power is not necessarily enhanced by the pursuit of knowledge; it may only be rendered obsolete. A large research project may yield no particularly useful results and yet subtract considerably from the resources available to meet pressing social needs. Developments in science and technology often upset previous balances of power and sometimes create problems that even ostensibly powerful nations are incapable of solving. In mythology a king may call upon his Merlin to solve such a problem and receive a clear and presumably scientific answer; but what are politicians to do in a democracy when they call upon scientists for advice and find that, like other mortals, these too disagree?

Contradictions such as these in the relationship of knowledge to power are so commonplace today that we almost ignore them. One day we watch tensely, with feelings of elation and relief, as our astronauts complete a successful mission in space. The next day we listen sympathetically as a congressman complains that we ought not to be spending five billion dollars a year to reach the moon while poverty and disease remain unrelieved on earth. One moment we learn with joy and admiration of some new triumph of medical science—an advance in preventative medicine, an artificial organ, a new surgical technique—which will prolong life; the next we are warned that the rise in population made possible by medical progress poses a grave threat to civilization. Wonder drugs are found to have miraculous effects in some respects and terrible side effects in others. Pesticides improve crop yields but soon threaten, by their very success, to impair the environment in other no less important respects. By withdrawing personnel and facilities from other uses, the very investments in science that confer immediate benefits in terms of international power and prestige weaken the process of innovation in the civilian sector of the economy upon which national power depends in the long run. Nor are these the last of the paradoxes we and our progeny will have to confront in the effort to put to use the processes and results of scientific creativity. Future advances in genetics and climate control, for example, may pose dilemmas even more difficult than these, and the problem of allocating scarce resources is likely to grow still more pressing in the future.

All the while, in subtle but profound ways, the increasing involvement of society in the underwriting and direction of research and development raises general issues of public policy. When universities and industries come to depend upon government subvention, new relationships must be worked out if the autonomy of the private sector and the public interest are both to be protected. When scientific advice becomes a crucial component of vital decisions in foreign and domestic policy, the role of the adviser in the decision-making process must be clarified and defined if the adviser is to be free to give an independent judgment and if policy is to be decided by responsible representatives.

Political questions such as these demand study—and they are being studied with increasing depth and frequency. Only a few years ago, when a colleague and I decided to introduce a course on science and government, it was hard to find enough good material to assign. Now there are a number of such courses being taught throughout the country, and no single volume could possibly contain all the worthwhile studies that are now regularly produced in this general area. In this collection I have tried to assemble a number of those that seem to me and to others familiar with the literature to offer a solid and wide-ranging view of the field. The fifteen essays here presented are diverse in nature and in topic, as befits a subject with so many ramifications. I have reluctantly excluded many other valuable studies, on the grounds that they are readily available elsewhere or are too large and detailed to survive condensation. A substantial list of such studies is appended in the form of a Select Bibliography.

For assistance in the preparation of this volume, I am especially indebted to a number of colleagues. My friend and collaborator, J. Stefan Dupré, who would have been coeditor of this volume had not Canadian affairs monopolized even his prodigious energies, worked with me to initiate the project. W. Eric Gustafson also contributed to laying the groundwork. Don K. Price was helpful throughout as a ready source of sound advice. Carl Kaysen and Robert C. Wood also made helpful suggestions. Victor J. Stein of Varian Associates helped me to avoid unnecessary duplication in canvassing for contributions. Martin Kessler, Herbert Cohen, and Charles Christensen of The Free Press have been most helpful. William S. Comanor and Harvey M. Sapolsky kindly called my attention to significant acquisitions of the Science and Public Policy Library at the Littauer School, Harvard. My deepest gratitude must go, however, to the contributors to this volume.

For the support of my own research and writing, I am especially indebted to various institutions. The essay on the Oppenheimer case was written for a graduate seminar at Harvard in 1955 and was afterward awarded a Bowdoin Prize. I am indebted to the members of the prize committee for their encouragement, particularly to the late Perry Miller. The essay on the "third culture" derives from lectures in a course at Harvard and, in particular, from a Gabrielson Lecture given at Colby College in Waterville, Maine, in the spring of 1963. The paper on "The Scientific Establishment and American Pluralism" was originally delivered in November 1964, as one in a series of lectures on science and government initiated by Professor Paul J. Piccard at Florida State University in Tallahassee, Florida. It has been further developed with the aid of a subsidy from a National Science Foundation institutional grant to the State University of New York. During the academic year 1963–64, I was able to engage in research and writing in this general area thanks to a generous fellowship from the George and Eliza Gardner Howard Foundation, administered under the direction of Dean R. Bruce Lindsay of Brown University. During this period I benefited from many interviews with government administrators in the Bureau of the Budget, the Office of Science and Technology, and other agencies concerned with the federal government's programs in science. I should like particularly to thank William D. Carey and J. Lee Westrate. I acknowledge the assistance of these benefactors and sources of information with keen appreciation. In the preparation of this volume I have been assisted by my wife, Evelyn Lakoff, my typists, Elma Leavis, Joan Erdman, and Barbara Kornfield, and my colleague, Ashley L. Schiff. I acknowledge all this help with keen appreciation.

I have taken an editor's liberty to dedicate this collection of essays to Don K. Price in recognition of his preeminent contribution to the understanding of the modern relations of science and government. All students of these relations owe him a profound debt of gratitude.

*Sanford A. Lakoff*

STATE UNIVERSITY OF NEW YORK AT STONY BROOK

For Don K. Price

# CONTENTS

PART 3   Knowledge and Power: The Overview

      ALAN T. WATERMAN

12. Criteria for Scientific Choice                               406
      ALVIN M. WEINBERG

13. The Scientist and National Policy                            420
      MC GEORGE BUNDY

14. Future Needs for the Support of Basic Research               432
      HARVEY BROOKS

15. Knowledge and Power:                                         469
    *Science in the Service of Society*
      PHILIP H. ABELSON

    SELECT BIBLIOGRAPHY                                          483

    INDEXES                                                      495

# The Third Culture:

## *Science in Social Thought*

SANFORD A. LAKOFF

FUTURE historians of intellectual life in the middle years of the twentieth century are destined to discover that some of the most passionate polemics of the times were reserved for a perplexing and largely unsatisfying argument over what were called the "two cultures." For their benefit, it should perhaps be pointed out that the two cultures are the humanities and the natural sciences and that the argument boils down to the question of whether a civilized and responsible man in this century can consider himself properly educated if he stresses either of these "cultures" (or sets of disciplines) to the virtual exclusion of the other.

So stated, the controversy may well strike the historians as too simpleminded to warrant serious debate. Surely it will puzzle them to learn that so many people of intelligence became zealous partisans in a debate that could be resolved in favor of either side only by imposing a hopelessly narrow redefinition upon something so plastic and manifold as the pursuit of knowledge. It should not surprise us, therefore, if, with the advantage of perspective, the historians of the future treat it as an example of Dialogue Among the Over-committed. It would then come to rest among other such curiosities of intellectual history as the debate over transubstantiation, the *querrelle des anciens et modernes* in the Enlightenment, and, in more recent times, the great struggle to decide once and for all whether the world was created by God or merely insinuated by Him through evolution.

We may envy the historian his ability to dispose of our problem so neatly. Our job is more difficult—just because it *is* our problem. Like it or not, we must admit that the controversy over the two cultures has raged on uncontrolled for some years, like a fire being fought by two rival volunteer companies, each more anxious to hose down the other than to put out the fire. Until lately, those of us who are professional intellectuals but not students of either literature or nature have been put in the position of dismayed onlookers. At last, however, our existence has been recognized. C. P. Snow, whose provocative Rede Lecture started the fire in the first place, has announced that in addition to the two cultures he had designated originally, there is also a third—the culture that comprises the social scientists and everyone else, regardless of profession, who becomes concerned "with how human beings are living and have lived—and concerned, not in terms of legend, but of fact." This culture, Snow maintains, has emerged from the increasing awareness of the critical importance of science and technology for every aspect of civilized life. The peculiar importance of the third culture, he believes, is that through its concern with the human implications of scientific change the debate over the two cultures may now "be shifted in a direction which will be more profitable to us all."[1]

Snow's suggestion of a way out of the two-cultures controversy must surely meet with universal appreciation. Nevertheless, it is by no means certain that the third culture actually exists as a separate and integral entity (any more than do the other two) or that insofar as it does exist it can be expected to perform the noble mission to which it has now been summoned. Social scientists are hardly in agreement among themselves either over the methods appropriate to their work or about the substantive issues that need to be studied. Some are more convinced than others of the degree to which their disciplines can be made rigorously scientific, in the same sense as physics and chemistry are scientific, by the use of quantitative techniques and predictive standards of validity. Indeed some would even contend that human drives and responses to environment are largely or at least significantly invariant to changes in scientific understanding and technological facilities. And some define the study of behavior to include not only primal hordes and mature industrial societies but even properly trained pigeons and rats, which share with man the learning process that is sometimes regarded as the infrastructure of all behavior and organization.

This confusion, or disagreement, within the ranks of the social scientists is of course symptomatic of the general state of modern intelligence. The very development of the social sciences, like that of the natural sciences and humanities, as relatively distinct fields of inquiry, is an aspect of a slow but relentless drift, away from the virtually undifferentiated pursuit of truth in earlier times to the highly specialized and widely ramified intellectualism of modern times.

For the longest span of Western cultural history it would have been almost impossible to distinguish one kind of intellectual work from another, with the single great exception of the distinction between philosophy and revealed religion, a distinction arising in ancient Greece and powerfully reenforced by the Christian assertion of the unique and transcendental character of faith and revelation. This undifferentiated, sometimes eclectic, tradition was shaken in the seventeenth century by advances in natural science. Even though it continued to be the fashion to speak of all men of learning as "philosophers," whether they concerned themselves with "moral" or "natural" philosophy, increasingly those who devoted themselves to studying the natural universe came to stand apart—because of their methods, because of the objectivity and measurability of their results—from those who could only speculate upon the purposes of existence from inconclusive experience or subjective inspiration.

Since the emergence of the natural sciences as autonomous disciplines, some of the keenest philosophic minds have sought to reunite the disparate paths of knowledge by providing them all with a common method and a common sense of limitation. Hume and Kant in an earlier time, and Whitehead, Russell, and Michael Polanyi[2] in recent years, have all pursued this objective. Notwithstanding their theoretical achievements, these philosophical efforts have failed to inhibit the fracturing of intellect that arose from and around the advances of the natural scientists. If anything, the succeeding centuries have witnessed a continuing and crescive dissolution of intellectual unity, to the point where even the natural sciences are now a multitude of separate estates, a network of subcultures.

Indeed, ironic as it is, what unity there is among the natural scientists has in part been an artificial unity imposed by the growing division between them and students of the humanities. Being read out of the club by their colleagues in arts and letters at least gave the scientists a common feeling of rejection. As Snow has pointed out, in England the separation between the two cultures has been particularly evident in the educational system and in the cultural milieu influenced by the schools. Those in the camp of the humanists generally chose to define culture in such a way as to exclude science, or at least to shunt it off toward the margin of knowledge that mattered. They even appropriated the designation of "intellectual" as their own special title. Their right to set the standards of education was so widely recognized that it was only considered legitimate for a man of learning to deal with science if he dabbled in it as a hobby. Gertrude Himmelfarb reports that when Charles Darwin went to study at Oxford and turned out to have no particular inclination for classical studies, his family decided that the only honorable vocation left open to him was the clergy. If not for the intervention of Darwin's uncle, Josiah Wedgewood, his father would have refused permission for young Charles to take that famous voyage of the *Beagle* during which he determined to become a natural scientist.[3] Darwin's upbringing illustrates the existence of two cultures; his doctrines had the effect of deepening the rift. For it was in the epic warfare between science and religion — however misconceived the entire tempest may seem in retrospect — that still more members of the humanist camp became convinced of the incompatibility of science and traditional values.

Even though by now the wounds of that unfortunate war are largely healed and even though scientists and humanists are for the most part not enemies, neither are they as familiar with each other's work as was once the case, or as committed to the same common preoccupations. This much of C. P. Snow's thesis is surely true, and we are obligated to him for bringing it to our attention. At the same time it is also quite clear, as a number of his critics have pointed out, that Snow's truth is really only an aspect of a larger truth. The lack of communication between scientists and humanists is only one instance of a much more general failure of communication among professionals and artisans of every description. Now almost everyone whose job demands more than manual dexterity, and whose commitment to his work is serious, is in some sense a member of a separate culture. A microbiologist and an electronics engineer will have as little to say to each other in their professional capacities as a humanist and a scientist, or for that matter, as a sculptor and a musicologist. In short, do we have two cultures or do we have a multitude of cultures?

If there is a common ground on which all these specialists may still consider themselves members of a single overriding intellectual community, it is the one on which they must consider together the uses to which their separate labors are put. In this dialogue the social scientists, for all their disagreements with each other, must play a unique guiding role. In this sense there is in fact a third culture, although it is by no means a child of the 1960's or of the 1940's or indeed of the twentieth century. The concern for the human implications of scientific and technological change grew up alongside modern science. It was fathered by those prescient spirits of an earlier time who realized that the progress of knowledge would entail a momentous departure from a past common to all the branches of the human species — a past overgrown with magic and supernaturalism and mired in ignorance of the natural universe; a past in which fear and hostility, dependence and oppression, seemed unavoidable alternatives. Then and since, many intellectuals have become preoccupied with the effort to investigate the relationship between the state of science and the state of society, to foresee if possible what benefits and what dangers might follow from the ethically neutral power that the progress of science would confer. The record of this effort is worth retracing, both for what it may teach us about the social conditions of our own times and for what we may learn about the ways of examining the impact of science on man and society explored before us.

## The Legitimation of Modern Science

> Bacon, like Moses, led us forth at last,
> The barren wilderness he past,
> Did on the very border stand
> Of the bless'd promised land,
> And from the mountain top of his exalted wit
> Saw it himself and show'd us it.
>     ABRAHAM COWLEY, "Ode to the Royal Society"

The first major effort to examine the social consequences of scientific progress was surely the one made in the seventeenth century by the brilliant essayist and lord chancellor to King James I, Sir Francis Bacon. It was in this century — "the insurgent century," as Charles Singer describes it[4] — that science came to mean not simply a collection of items of information and scattered theories but a grand challenge along a broad front to accepted beliefs and established institutions. The preceding century had seen a number of bold departures from long-held but crude beliefs, notably by Copernicus and Bruno in astronomy and Vesalius in anatomy, but as yet these could be regarded as isolated and tentative ventures. It was left to the scientists of the seventeenth century to put up an unmistakable rival to the hold on opinion, educated and popular, of classical philosophy and organized religion. This challenge resulted from the combined work of no less formidable an array of talented scientists than Galileo, Kepler, Descartes, Huyghens, Gilbert, Hooke, Boyle, Leibnitz, Harvey, and the illustrious Newton. Taken as a whole, the effect of their work was so impressive in so many directions that by the start of the eighteenth century science had — in fact, if not in the eyes of the church — all but legally displaced theology as queen of the disciplines. Francis Bacon was a witness and, in an indirect way, a contributor, to these developments, and he had an exceptionally keen grasp of the social changes they portended.

Bacon saw that what distinguished the discoveries of seventeenth-century science from so much of what had been done in the past was both a new emphasis on rigorous method and a fresh motivation toward the pursuit of truth. He understood well that it had become possible to think of science as a unique source of truth because science was an instrument of inquiry rather than a collection of information, a way of knowing which, if used with exacting care, might serve to overcome arbitrary bias and human error. He also sensed that those who were developing this new instrument shared a common sense of mission. For although science might be chosen as vocation or avocation from a number of particular motives, behind all of them lay the achievements of the Renaissance in stimulating the desire for knowledge, the joy of discovery, the will to personal accomplishment and fame, the indulgence of sheer curiosity. Behind them also lay the Reformation, for to reject Rome was often to reject Scholasticism and sometimes to adopt a theology glorifying God as the creator of a wonderful universe. And coupled with these spiritual preparations were the incentives due to the revival of trade which provided special impetus for innovation in agriculture, the extractive industries, textiles, and navigation.

Bacon also realized that despite the extent to which the ground had been favorably prepared for the emergence of modern science, there were at the same time obstacles to be overcome—resistances deeply embedded in European civilization. Even as late as the seventeenth century the atmosphere was by no means entirely congenial. Science continued to be associated with astrology, necromancy, and the black arts, as was evident in the persistence of the Faust legend and in the concern over alchemy, which was said to involve not only the seductions of a pseudoscience but also those of spiritual heresy. Science was suspected, as in the older myth of Prometheus, of representing a defiance of limit, of standing for the wish to make man more significant than the Creator intended. Scientific research might even be thought to involve a pact with the devil or at any rate an attempt to penetrate mysteries God had chosen not to reveal to man.

It happened that cosmology was one of the earliest fields of investigation in which modern science made great and startling contributions, largely because the opportunities for more precise and more extensive observations became available through the development of better instruments. Inasmuch as the anatomy of the heavens was a matter in which the Church had always taken a considerable interest, sanctioning some theories and rejecting others, it is perhaps understandable that the century of modern science should have been opened with the martyrdom of Bruno, who was convinced not only that the received theories were wrong but that the authorities who promulgated them hardly deserved to be obeyed. Shortly thereafter Galileo became entangled with the self-appointed ecclesiastical guardians of cosmological knowledge. His case, however, was not as clear cut. Galileo was censured not only because certain of his findings contradicted doctrines considered essential to faith and not only because he persisted in discussing these findings as possibly true (that is, as hypotheses) rather than as fanciful speculations, but also because he became enmeshed in a political controversy between secular and spiritual authorities. Moreover, he was condemned not precisely for discussing forbidden doctrines in the abstract, but, to use the modern phrase, for teaching and advocating them. As the inquisitors put it:

> We say, pronounce, sentence, and declare that you, the said Galileo, by reason of the matters adduced in trial, and by you confessed as above, have rendered yourself in the judgment of this holy office vehemently suspected of heresy, namely, of having believed and held the doctrine—which is false and contrary to the sacred and divine Scriptures—that the Sun is the center of the world and does not move from east to west and that the Earth moves and is not the center of the world; and that an opinion may be held and defended as probable after it has been declared and defined to be contrary to the Holy Scripture; and that consequently you have incurred all the censures and penalties imposed and promulgated in the sacred canons and other constitutions, general and particular, against such delinquents. From which we are content that you be absolved, provided that, first, with a sincere heart and unfeigned faith, you abjure, curse, and detest before us the aforesaid errors and heresies and every other error and heresy contrary to the Catholic and Apostolic Roman Church in the form to be prescribed by us for you.[5]

It is in the light of such hostility to science, rather than by considering the factors promoting the favorable reception of modern science, that we can best appreciate the efforts of Bacon. As a philosopher of science, Bacon made a now-famous contribution to the development of the scientific method; but what is perhaps not as well appreciated is Bacon's contribution to the *legitimation* of modern science.

Bacon set for himself the double mission of placating the external enemies of science and of prescribing canons of evidence and a method of research so that scientists themselves could steer clear of charlatans and pseudoscience. It was Bacon's achievement to have successfully devoted his literary and logical gifts not so much to science itself—for Bacon's additions to science as a body of knowledge are nil—but to the effort to establish a climate of opinion in which science might flourish; in which, indeed, knowledge would be considered the greatest source of power.

He strove to make science legitimate in two different ways, as can be seen from the titles of his two major works, *The Advancement of Learning* (1605) and the *Novum Organum* (1620). The first was designed to clear the way for science by putting it on the side of humane learning; the second to lay down the rules by which truly scientific work could be distinguished from ill-founded pretensions. The strategic situation of science no doubt required just such a double tactic. On the one hand it was necessary to establish the credit, the goodwill, of the new science, to demonstrate that it was a benign pursuit, in no way a threat to powerful and established interests. On the other hand, it was necessary to discredit the older pseudosciences, to draw a sharp line between the scientist and the charlatan. In other words, it was necessary to pacify and befriend the neighbors and at the same time to set the house of science in order.

While cleaning house Bacon naturally tried to chase out the Scholastics first. The overly maligned Schoolmen were the butt of much of Bacon's criticism of the old learning in the *Novum Organum*. His portrait of them is, to say the least, unflattering, and probably quite unfair. Scholastic thinkers, he wrote, having

> sharp and strong wits, and abundance of leisure ... but their wits being shut up in the cells of a few authors (chiefly Aristotle their dictator) as their persons were shut up in the cells of monasteries and colleges, and knowing little history, either of nature or time, did, out of no great quantity of matter, and infinite agitation of wit, spin out into those laborious webs of learning which are extant in their books ....

"Cobwebs of learning," Bacon called them, "admirable for the fineness of thread and work, but of no substance or profit."[6] Their "histories," he said, were altogether unreliable. Their church history was full of deception and of foolish distortion designed to account for miracles and relics. Their natural history was mostly fable, concocted out of imagination, not observation.[7] He addressed the same criticism to the work of the astrologists and alchemists. But the Scholastics were only the worst offenders. People in general, Bacon contended, were prey to a number of illusions—the four *idola* or phantoms of the tribe, the cave, the marketplace, and the theater (the distortions of human fallibility, individual fallibility, received opinion, and different systems of thought).[8] To overcome all these illusions and to reach scientific truth, method was all-important.

In attacking the Scholastics and the larger forces of ignorance and illusion with which he associated them, Bacon took pains to insist that science was not an enemy of true religion. It is said, Bacon observes, "that Knowledge hath in it somewhat of the serpent"[9] and that "experience demonstrates how learned men have been arch-heretics, how learned times have been inclined to atheism, and how the contemplation of second causes derogate from our dependence upon God, who is the first cause." Did not Adam fall because he sought knowledge? Bacon answered by acknowledging that the pursuit of knowledge must be limited to matters outside the province of theology. We must not *"presume by the contemplation of nature to attain to the mysteries of God."*[10] Admittedly, "a little or superficial knowledge of Philosophy may incline the mind of man to Atheism, but a farther proceeding therein doth bring the mind back again to Religion..."[11] Adam's fall came not because he inquired into knowledge but into the knowledge of good and evil. The science of nature, says Bacon, is studiously indifferent to good and evil. To be sure, knowledge must be governed by charity so that it will be referred to the good of man, but in itself the pursuit of natural knowledge must be distinguished from the pursuit of ethical understanding.[12]

Science also had to come to terms with politics. It is alleged, says Bacon, that learning turns men away from military pursuits. It is said that too much learning makes people so curious and incapable of resolution that they are unfit to make political decisions. Supposedly, science leads people to prefer private learning to public business. It is also alleged that science promotes a relaxation of discipline in the state because where science is widely pursued everybody argues and nobody obeys.[13]

Bacon answered that Alexander and Caesar were both learned and yet great soldiers; that philosophers — Seneca, for example — are useful and even necessary to the state; that scholars, far from being lazy, are the hardest working of all because they work for the sake of science and not merely for profit; and, finally, that the state will not suffer but benefit when "duty taught and understood" replaces blind obedience.[14]

But the most emphatic justification of science that Bacon felt he could offer was to say that science was useful. To be sure, Bacon was not blind to the value of knowledge for its own sake. "As the beholding of the light," he wrote,

> is itself a more excellent and a fairer thing than all the uses of it — so assuredly the very contemplation of things as they are, without superstition or imposture, error or confusion, is in itself more worthy than all the fruit of invention... we must from experience of every kind first endeavor to discover true causes and axioms, and seek for experiments of Light, not experiments of Fruit.[15]

But it is not because science is valuable in itself that Bacon argued for it. It is because knowledge is the very root of all power: "Scientia et potentia humanum in idem coincident." [Knowledge and human power come together in one]. Bacon adds: "For where the cause is not known the effect cannot be produced."[16] Science is useful—to the state and to society in general. As Macaulay was to put it, with a mixture of Victorian disdain and civilized tolerance, "To make men perfect was no part of Bacon's plan. His humble aim was to make imperfect man comfortable."[17] "The aim of the Platonic philosopher was to raise us far above vulgar wants."[18] Nevertheless, Bacon's aims were certainly sensible, Macaulay concluded: "The wise man of the Stoics would, no doubt, be a grander object than a steam engine. But there are steam engines. And the wise man of the Stoics is yet to be born." Faced with a man suffering from smallpox, the Stoic can only offer the consolations of philosophy. "The Baconian takes out his lancet and begins to vaccinate."[19]

Bacon would very likely have enjoyed this much of Macaulay's interpretation, for he certainly did wish to give the impression that science posed no radical challenge to the existing state of affairs, whether in religion, politics, culture, or ethics. Since the goal of scientific research was simply to relieve the human estate, science was only a new instrument that would not tread upon sacred ground, would not foster sedition, would not make men morally indifferent. Science, or so Bacon would have had it understood, was harmful to none and beneficial to all.

It is obvious from his writings that Bacon hoped to advance the cause of science by these arguments. Whether he himself actually believed all the justifications he offered is another matter. As careful as he was to present a good case for science—a case he knew would be acceptable—sometimes he hinted at a rather more radical vision. At least some of the time Bacon entertained ideas of what science held in store for society that would have been more disquieting had they been expressed with the same vigor and detail as the other ideas he advanced. Was he being duly respectful or prudent or cynical when he counseled scientists to come to terms with religion? Was there no hint of a conspiracy against divine mystery when he aphorized that "nature to be commanded must be obeyed";[20] or that "the secrets of nature betray themselves more readily when tormented by art than when left to their own course"?[21] These are, to be sure, only deft epigrams, made by a man who cherished the literary flourishes that lend spice to the blandest of nostrums, and yet they have the flavor of heresy in them.

There is somewhat less doubt about the visionary mood Bacon indulged in his description of the scientific utopia in *The New Atlantis* (1624). The story begins with an imaginary voyage, a device which, like the frontispiece of the *Novum Organum* depicting a ship sailing to uncharted lands, reflects the Renaissance spirit of adven-

ture and exploration. Inspired by the discussion of the lost civilization of Atlantis in Plato's *Critias* (and perhaps also in the *Timaeus*),
Bacon imagined a new Atlantis — an island somewhere in the Pacific
inhabited by survivors of the flood which had inundated the original
island. The new civilization that Bacon depicts bears resemblances
to the civilization in *The City of the Sun* (1623) of Thomas Campanella, which he may well have read before composing *The New
Atlantis*. Campanella also gives scientists a prominent place, but his
utopia, like that of Thomas More, is otherwise a conventional
romantic portrait of society as it might be if it were uncorrupted
by the vices of commerce and returned to the supposed bliss of
primitive communism.

In part because the essay was allowed to remain unfinished, it
is difficult to say precisely what Bacon had in mind for the social
system of his ideal commonwealth, but he seems to have conceived
of it somewhat differently than did Campanella or More. In the ideal
Baconian society, not communism but science is the organizing
principle. The accepted religion is Christian, but of a peculiarly
Baconian sort: it is a religion of "light" or science. (The founders
of the community are said to have seen a vision of Christ atop a
pillar of light; the society is dedicated to "God's first creature,
which was light.")[22] This faith is observed in the great scientific
enterprise called "Salomon's House." One of the "fathers" of the
house explains its activities to the foreign visitor in terms familiar
from Bacon's other writings: "The *end* of our *Foundation* is the
Knowledge of *Causes*, and Secret Motions of Things; And the
Enlarging of the bounds of Humane Empire, to the Effecting of
all things possible."[23]

Was Bacon hinting that in the society of the future, scientific
research, rather than military force in being, would provide the
primary instrument of power? Did he think that once Christianity
came to be understood as the pursuit of knowledge and once
society determined to control its natural environment, traditional
political and religious organizations would tend to become largely
ceremonial? There is a monarchy in the New Atlantis, but its
authority is that of a remote and benevolent host. There is also a
priesthood, but it seems to be concerned entirely with works of
social welfare, like the hospitality provided in the community's
hostel, the House of Strangers. Decisions that would appear to be
vital to this ideal society — the decisions involving the pursuit of
knowledge and the application of the results — are apparently entirely
up to the governors of Salomon's House. This authority applies to
the question of whether to make known the information that is
obtained. The father of Salomon's House tells the European visitors:

> *We* haue *Consultations,* which of the *Inuentions* and *Ex-*
> *periences,* which wee haue discouered, shall be Published, and
> which not: And take all an *Oath* of *Secrecy,* for the Concealing
> of those which wee thinke fitt to keepe Secret: Though some
> of those we doe reueale sometimes to the *State,* and some not.[24]

Other internal evidence also suggests that Bacon wished to
draw a sharp contrast between the society guided by a concern
for science and the conventional European style of life. The only
merchants in the New Atlantis are the twelve "Merchants of Light"
who annually go abroad to collect information on scientific activities.
The welfare of families is a proud and vital concern of the community, but there is a total absence of personal acquisitiveness.
Twice the European strangers offer gratuities to different officers of
the society and both times the offer is rejected with the explanation
that since they are already being paid by the state, accepting a tip
would amount to being twice-paid. Status considerations are not
altogether absent, but apart from respect for age, Bacon makes a
special point of describing the honors showered upon the scientists,
no doubt to contrast the comparative neglect of men of genius in
Europe. The rare arrival of a father of Salomon's House is attended
by the pomp and circumstance that in Europe is reserved for royalty:

> He was carried in a rich Chariott, without Wheeles, Litter-
> wise; With two Horses at either end, richly trapped in blew
> Veluett Embroydered; and two Footmen on each side in the
> like Attire. The Chariott was all of Cedar, gilt, and adorned
> with Crystall; Saue that the Fore-End had Pannells of Sapphires,
> set in Borders of Gold; and the Hinder-end the like of Emerauds
> of the *Peru* Colour. There was also a Sunn of Gold, Radiant,
> vpon the Topp, in the Midst; And on the Topp before, a small
> *Cherub* of Gold, with Wings displayed. The Chariott was
> couered with Cloath of Gold tissued vpon Blew. He had before
> him fifty Attendants, young Men all, in white *Satten* loose
> Coates to the Mid Legg.... Next before the Chariott, went two
> Men...Who carried, the one a Crosier, the other a Pastorall
> Staffe like a Sheep hooke.... He sate alone, vpon Cushions,
> of a kinde of excellent Plush, blew...He held up his bare
> Hand, as he went, as blessing the People, but in Silence.[25]

To appreciate the contrast that Bacon intended to draw here we
have only to imagine the same treatment being accorded to the
director of the Royal Society at an earlier time or, for that matter, to
the president of the National Academy of Sciences in our own day.
Clearly, Bacon saw this symbolic difference as a reflection of a
fundamental difference between conventional European society
and the ideal society dedicated to the pursuit of science. In the ideal

society the leading scientist is accorded the honors ordinarily
reserved for royalty and ecclesiastical dignitaries. The crosier of
political rule and the pastoral staff of religious authority sanction his
activities and he is, by virtue of his office, such a figure of eminence
and admiration that a wave of his hand can be thought an act of
blessing.

Is this the sum of Bacon's radicalism or is it only a hint of what
he expected from a society wholly devoted to science? Did he
have in mind a radical alternative to society as he knew it? If the
New Atlantis is a religious society it would not easily have been
recognized as such by his contemporaries. In replacing the monas-
tery with the laboratory and contemplation with experiment Bacon
carried to an extreme the revolt against medieval religiosity that
many of his contemporaries, particularly among the Protestants,
were accustomed to—only in far milder form. Nor is this society, in
its secular aspects, similar in outlook to the European nations, with
their greed for wealth and personal power. Although it is a society
entirely devoted to human needs and wants, it is to be marred by
none of the vices of commercial society—none of the selfishness and
acquisitiveness—and is to be wholly occupied with the advancing
of human welfare. Much of the work of government would presumably either devolve upon the leading scientists or atrophy into
a merely ceremonial function.

Still, these are Bacon's speculations. He advanced them in the
form of an imaginary vision; he might not have expressed them in
any other form. Nor were his more radical views a reflection of a
widespread undercurrent among his contemporaries in the scientific enterprise. Yet they deserve attention if only because Bacon
was a kind of spokesman for early modern science and one of the
very first scholars to recognize that the prospects for science and
those for society were intertwined. In some ways his thoughts are
particularly interesting in the light of more recent experience.
It has been said in criticism of Bacon's scheme that it is over-
organized, that in such an atmosphere no scientist could possibly
be creative or free. Why, for example, should there be three "Inter-
preters of Nature" at the summit of the research apex who are
charged with the major work of analysis? Why not four or a dozen, or
perhaps none at all if the field is not yet ripe for analytical work or if
no one is especially well qualified for the job? Nor does Bacon say
anything about the process whereby decisions are made to allot
scarce resources to alternative courses of research. He apparently
imagined there would be no disagreements or perhaps no scarcity of
resources and personnel. Worse still, he seems not to have had the
least inkling of the likelihood of disagreement over which scientific
theories were valid and which invalid, even though he himself did

not appreciate the contributions of Copernican theory and foolishly rejected the work of Gilbert.

Whatever his shortcomings, however, Bacon must be credited more than any other single individual, both for having recognized the importance of science to society and for having helped to gain acceptance for science from those who might otherwise have reacted to it with fear and hostility. This was, in retrospect, an indispensable and epochal first step. But it was only a beginning. Science, as Bacon understood, had first to win acceptability. More than this would presumably have been too much to expect. In time, however, the partisans of science were no longer satisfied with mere toleration. Science was far too important to be thought of merely as a limited if convenient instrument which might, here and there and now and then, contribute to human welfare. Science, they came to believe, was the indispensable catalyst of all progress, intellectual, moral and social.

## Science and Progress

As Bacon spoke for the era in which modern science fought for no more than a tolerant acceptance, so the Marquis de Condorcet may rightfully be regarded as the spokesman for the cause of science in the eighteenth-century Enlightenment, the man who, better than anyone else in his day, propounded the common conviction that science was the sole hope of humanity. Born in 1743, Condorcet rose to prominence at the age of twenty-two with the publication of a brilliant work on the integral calculus. Hailed by La Grange and d'Alembert, he was elected to the Academy of Sciences and soon became its permanent secretary. The youngest of the *philosophes,* he was one of the few to play an active part in the French Revolution, although, more typically, he was unable to survive its twists and turns. He was among those who composed the Constitution of the Republic and in 1792 he drafted and presented the historic *Report on Public Instruction* to the National Assembly.[26] In 1793, however, proscribed by the Jacobins, he went into hiding and wrote his best-known work, *Sketch for a Historical Picture of the Progress of the Human Mind.* In addition, Condorcet also wrote an arresting commentary on Bacon's *The New Atlantis.* In both works he gave exuberant expression to the widespread belief in the supreme value of science, a belief which, in its intensity and radical implications, makes Bacon's plea for the acceptance of the legitimacy of science a timid predecessor.

Condorcet praised *The New Atlantis* as the daring work of a creative spirit in a time of superstition, but he noted that even in imagination Bacon was limited to the prospects for science under monarchy. *The New Atlantis* had been conceived at a time when "events had not yet pronounced whether the inevitable fall to which reason had condemned kings would be the peaceful work of enlightenment or the sudden result of the indignation of deceived peoples." It is therefore understandable that even a visionary writer should have pinned his hopes for the progress of science on the possibility that "perhaps one day chance would inspire in a monarch a passion for the sciences to the same degree as they have so often had the fever of the chase or a mania for construction."[27] What good would it do, however, if a particular king were struck by a passion for science? Very likely he would choose to support only those projects which piqued his fancy or flattered his vanity. And what guarantee would there be that long-range projects begun under one monarch would be continued and carried to completion by his successors? The great need of the sciences was precisely for comprehensive and long-range support. On neither count could monarchy be trusted to answer the need.[28]

Monarchy, however, was now no longer the only alternative. At last science could expect support for its needs from the one source whose support could possibly be adequate—an enlightened people governing itself in accordance with the precepts of reason. Bacon's ideal of a scientific society, in other words, was about to be realized in history. Thanks to the rapid progress both of society and understanding, it could now be hoped that this vision, so long merely a "philosophic dream," would be realized "by the next generations, and perhaps begun by us."[29] It would take the form, however, not of a single society but of a new stage in civilized history marking the broad advance of reason—reason in the sense of science, reason in the sense of technical know-how, reason in the negative sense of the denial of mystery and superstition, reason, finally, in the sense that every man would, through the use of his natural faculties, come to understand his interest in peace and prosperity. Condorcet's utopia is to come in time as well as in space; it is, moreover, no argument for the withdrawal of the perfect to some remote sectarian Shangri-la. Instead it is a plea, in fact a program, for the elevation of the human race. Nor were scientists to rule society in the place of parliaments or as ceremonial dignitaries. A council of scientists with limited but far-reaching and autonomous power in its own domain was to be elected and held responsible to national electorates and, at the highest level, to the civilized nations of the world. The advance of reason would be one key factor. The other, however, would be the rise of democracy.

Until Condorcet's conjoining of these two ideas they had been isolated components of eighteenth-century thinking. Voltaire was a votary of reason but no believer in democracy. Even Rousseau, who is regarded as the intellectual sponsor of the Revolution, conceived of scientific advance as an unhappy series of accidents that had removed men from their natural simplicity and happiness. In advocating the revolutionary solution put forward in the *Social Contract*, Rousseau had to shut his eyes to his own description of the effects of scientific progress. It was Condorcet's achievement to synthesize the Baconian conception of the utility of science with the Rousseauistic and Lockean vision of a society of freedom and equality. Condorcet believed that the progress of freedom and the progress of science were two sides of the same coin: "Nature has joined together liberty, virtue and respect for the natural rights of man."[30] In order for there to be scientific progress there would have to be freedom—freedom from censorship, dogma, superstition and fanaticism—and in order for there to be freedom on a universal scale the sciences would have to progress to such an extent that the gap between the "haves" and "have nots" would have been overcome. In order for science to make progress, the generality of mankind would have to learn how to recognize the claims of genius. Otherwise science would suffer from lack of patronage, from control by charlatans, and from the tyranny of a new elite, a new priesthood, concerned only with its own privileged position and not with scientific progress.

In Condorcet's formulation, the utopian faith in science received a statement that was more comprehensive, less ambiguous and less tentative than that of Bacon. What had been natural science became reason. What had been an uneasy compromise with religion became a sharp break. What had been an indifference to politics and perhaps to privilege became an advocacy of natural right against the old order. What had been a statement of the utility of science became a manifesto of perfectibility through reason. Where Bacon thought of science primarily as experiment, Condorcet thought of it in terms of Cartesian rationalism. Where Bacon depicted utopia as an imaginary island, Condorcet saw it as the very next stage—the "tenth epoch"—in historical development. Nor was Condorcet's attitude toward religion and politics in the least ambiguous. Science in the form of reason was the enemy of religion and of the old order in everything else as well. Scientific reason would become the basis of a secular religion, a religion of progress, and it would provide the means for creating liberal democracy and ending aristocracy and privilege.

And there are other important contrasts. Whereas Bacon's utopians are isolated from corruption, Condorcet's live in the real world and thrive in the historical process by accumulating experience and profiting from the clash of beliefs. Condorcet's men of the future are not children of light huddling together in expectation of a messianic redemption of the rest of the world. They are the vanguard of this redemption. For Condorcet the advancement of learning is nothing less than the engine of human history. It was obvious that religion must be an enemy of science since religion had always sought to suppress reason in favor of priestly tyranny. The priests preferred to monopolize knowledge and to spread counterfeit truth in the form of dogmas. Religious superstitions, Condorcet believed, could only impede the progress of science.

In politics science was bound to undermine hierarchy and make it finally possible for men to enjoy their natural rights to equality. The French Revolution, Condorcet contended, had finally secured legal equality, but the revolution would only be complete when all would have the same scientific education. Condorcet was not so naive as to think that education would wipe out all differences among men. Like John Locke, he thought it would permit a minimal equality and would prevent any one group from tyrannizing over the others.[31] Instead of a society in which one group, the rulers, would be arrogant and the rest their naive dupes, the mass of men in the scientific age would respect talent and the talented would respect their fellow citizens. Education was absolutely necessary so that citizens would perform functions that would otherwise become the duty of specialists.[32]

For these reasons Condorcet could confidently prophesy that in the future there would be neither an elite with a monopoly of power and prestige, such as the priestly caste, nor a mass held in subjection. This prospect, moreover, did not depend upon any special set of circumstances, but upon the predictable progress of history. Condorcet's utopia, described in the "tenth epoch," is the outcome of the whole of human history and not merely a contrived vision for some separate and peculiarly fortunate sect. Any reasonable man, once enlightened, would be bound to want to further the course of history, to become himself a man of reason, to vote for public education and an end to superstition. An entire society thus enlightened would see the need to promote universal peace and liberty.

With Condorcet then we may say that speculation concerning the role of science in society changed from a utopian secretarianism to utopian historicism, with the addition of an appeal to mankind to speed up the process of emancipation. Condorcet's "ninth epoch," which concludes in his own time, begins with the work of Descartes and ends with the French Revolution. He believed that the political upheaval of the revolution only prepared the ground for the final revolution, the revolution of reason. A political revolution had to come first because until there was freedom of expression there could be no scientific progress; but only another revolution, a revolution of understanding, would permanently free the mass of mankind from erroneous dogma and from want and misery. Only if everyone could acquire education sufficient to enable all to defend themselves against the delusions of prejudice could they be expected to sustain a republican society. Then only could they "confide the care of government to the ablest of their number but . . . not be compelled to yield them absolute power in a spirit of blind confidence."[33] As perpetual secretary of the academy, Condorcet was in touch with the work of the scientists of his day; as a disciple of Turgot, Voltaire and Helvétius, he was a convinced believer in the notion of an indefinite perfectibility; as head of the Committee on Public Instruction in the National Assembly, he undertook a truly farsighted campaign to translate his ideals into reality.

In his commentary on *The New Atlantis* Condorcet considered the problems that might arise from the efforts of enlightened republics to foster science by establishing national and international scientific societies supported by public subvention. He insisted that such societies could only be successful if set up independently of the state. Each society must enjoy sufficient autonomy to regulate its own affairs. The state should be free to supply funds as it sees fit, but the members of the scientific society must be free to accept or reject the offer.[34] Conflicts might well develop among the scientists out of jealousy, out of narrow professional self-interest, and out of the difficulty of distinguishing the true scientist from the charlatan. Condorcet was confident these difficulties would be overcome because the bulk of the membership would be composed of men of integrity from all branches of science whose overriding commitment to the pursuit of truth would enable them to overcome passing squabbles.[35] From the national societies Condorcet hoped would spring a larger and more universal fellowship—"the universal republic of the sciences"[36]—which would serve as an instrument of international peace and enlightenment.

In the short run, the utopian visions of Condorcet, like those of Bacon, worked out in rather unspectacular fashion. *The New Atlantis* had inspired the founding of the Royal Society, but the Royal Society barely had funds enough for a good meal every so often, let alone for the ambitious projects of a Salomon's house. It was not really until well into the eighteenth century that science came to have practical technological application and even then science did not immediately go into the service of social welfare. On the contrary, at first technology became the servant of that very commercial spirit which Bacon had so deplored. Condorcet had, if anything, even worse luck. His *Report on Public Instruction* did not immediately inspire more than a token effort at universal public education. His constitutional projects were ignored by the Jacobins. And his grand vision of a "tenth epoch" in which the right of nature and the science of nature would have joint fulfillment hardly found realization in the immediate aftermath of the French Revolution. A new tyranny succeeded the old as the human and natural resources of Europe were turned to purposes of war. As in Bacon's case, the only vision of Condorcet that found anything approaching immediate fulfillment was his project for a scientific institute. The National Institute of Science and Art was reorganized in 1794, in accordance with the proposals of the philosophers, as a "living Encyclopedia," and the famous École Polytèchnique was founded the same year. In the short run these scientific institutions proved valuable chiefly for purposes of war. Improvements in artillery, signaling, telegraphy and observation balloons were among the benefits France reaped from them.

These were, to be sure, not the revolutionary consequences Condorcet had anticipated. They were easily overshadowed by the social revolution in which science and technology seemed only incidental. The grand controversy that agitated Europe from the French Revolution through the nineteenth century virtually ignored the role of science and technology. No one—not Burke in England or de Maistre in France—sought to blame the French Revolution on Newton or Descartes. When he was made a citizen of the Republic, the chemist Joseph Priestley was forced to flee Birmingham and his home was burned; yet his was hardly a typical case, and in any event it was his sympathies for the Revolution and perhaps his Unitarianism, rather than his chemistry, which was the object of popular hostility. The reactionaries who denounced the Revolution blamed moral philosophers like Rousseau and Voltaire rather than the natural philosophers, and, ignoring their scientific contemporaries, concentrated their fire upon the popularizers and demagogues who whipped the masses into action in the name of some vague belief in "reason." The friends of the Revolution had a different version of what was happening. Paine, Priestley, Price and Mackintosh saw the Revolution as a triumph of justice over injustice, of equality over hereditary privilege, a triumph not without unfortunate side effects, but one which on the whole represented a progressive step. But they did not stress the role of science either.

Out of this controversy between progressives and conservatives, however, there developed another viewpoint that was to have a considerable attraction for many intellectuals. This viewpoint, far from ignoring science and technology, restored them to the center of the stage. Indeed those who developed this line of analysis hoped that, in using such an objective and overriding consideration as the basis of their argument, they might escape the stale conflict between pro- and anti-revolutionary sentiments and bring together what was valid in both opinions in a new and higher unity built upon a platform of scientific and technological change.

The mind with the audacity, the range, and the probity to originate this line of speculation belonged to Henri Saint-Simon. As with other original minds, his was not altogether free from idiosyncrasy—and even worse. Saint-Simon's thoughts were not always orderly and his thinking went through a number of different stages. One preoccupation of all of these stages was a concern for unity in society, a concern he developed first in contemplating the chaos and destruction left by the Revolution. In the first phase of his thought, his search for an alternative to this disunity led him to science. In a loose way, he was acquainted with many of the illustrious scientists associated with the École Polytèchnique; and in his own peculiar way he grasped the importance of their activity. At the same time he was unhappy with what he thought was the irresponsible behavior of the scientists and with the careless neglect of science by society. He belabored the scientists for not leading the way out of the folly of war. In 1813 he addressed a missive to the scientists of Europe in which he admonished them sharply: "All Europe is slaughtering itself—what are you doing to stop the butchery? Nothing. What am I saying! It is you who perfect the means of destruction."[37] The scientists, he claimed, had failed to understand their mission because they had failed to understand the nature of science itself. Bacon had not conceived of the natural sciences as a bundle of specialties in *The New Atlantis*, but as a common tree with many branches. Only if they recognized the unity of the sciences, he felt, would the scientists recognize that in their work lay the design for a reconstruction of the social order.[38]

Saint-Simon believed that the unity of the sciences would best be achieved through a scientific society such as had been proposed by Bacon and Condorcet.[39] After the precedent of Bacon and Condorcet, he was intrigued by the relationship of science to religion, but in his attempt to understand it he sought again to go beyond the choice of acceptance or rejection. Science, he believed, was the only source of our knowledge of the universe; it was therefore the basis of true religion. In an ingenious if audacious argument, well rehearsed by the eighteenth-century philosophers, Saint-Simon explained that Christianity was only a primitive scientific theory. The idea of God, as he put it, had been invented by Christ and elaborated by the priesthood. Now there was a better explanation, provided by science, which deserved to be accepted in place of the one previously developed by the theologians. At first Saint-Simon thought this explanation contained in the principle of gravitation, understood in social terms as the analogous principle of attraction or love. What could be more reasonable than to found a new religion named, appropriately enough, the Religion of Newton? (Had not the old religion also been named for the man who announced it?) Saint-Simon even toyed with the idea of establishing a pope and clergy of the physical sciences, and asserted that it would certainly be wise to recognize the authority of a new priesthood of scientists—natural scientists, social scientists and scientists of culture. This assembly was to be convened in a Supreme Council of Newton to be supported by international subscription. Each subscriber would vote for the election of three leading mathematicians, physicists, chemists, physiologists, writers, painters, and musicians, from whose number a smaller executive council would be chosen to manage the business of the twenty-one men of genius. The leading mission of this august assembly would naturally be to overcome the fragmentation of the sciences, both for the benefit of knowledge and as a step towards the reunification of society under moral auspices.[40] The religion of science, Saint-Simon believed, provided a model for social and political reorganization. Religion, he said, "is the collection of the applications of general science by means of which enlightened men govern ignorant men."[41]

The Council of Newton would serve as the basis of a new society in which science would provide values and understanding and those superior in knowledge would be given an authority commensurate with their ability. Before the scientists, and the people as a whole, Saint-Simon put his case graphically when he asked what would be the reaction if France were suddenly to lose three thousand leading men of ability, including the foremost scientists, craftsmen, industrial producers, artists and men of commerce. Obviously such a loss would be serious and widely felt. But if, on the other hand, thirty thousand others, including the leading members of the nobility, the clergy, and the landed gentry, were suddenly lost, who would mourn their passing except out of sympathy for the survivors?[42]

Saint-Simon realized he would have to sell his conviction of the new importance of scientists not only to scientists themselves but also to others, and chiefly to the two classes who seemed destined to struggle against each other for control of the future—the middle class and the working class. To the *bourgeoisie* he spoke bluntly, saying in effect that they must either ally themselves with the scientific wave of the future or lose power to the proletariat. They had already seen in the days of the Revolution what the savants could do to stir up trouble. It was obvious that the scientists would become increasingly important because of their indispensable role in industry. It was therefore in the best interest of the middle class to support the scientists and to treat them with respect. Only if they courted the scientists would they prevent them from taking the side of disgruntled revolutionaries.[43]

With the workers Saint-Simon took a sterner stand. In England, he declared, where scientists are respected, the workers eat meat every day. In Russia, on the other hand, where scientists are treated with contempt by the czar, the situation is quite different. The Russian peasants are as ignorant as their horses and, worse yet, they are "badly fed, badly clothed, and are soundly beaten with sticks."[44] The moral should have been clear to all. It was in everyone's best interest to honor the scientists and to make authority a function of enlightenment.

After the fall of Napoleon, when monarchy was restored and the middle class grew more powerful, Saint-Simon modified his earlier views. In part the changes were due to his appreciation of the new power of the middle class and in part they were also due to the cold response he had met with from the savants. He had sent urgent letters to the scientific institutions proposing a scientific revolution and in return had received nothing more than curt notes saying that his requests were not within the competence of the institutions.[45] Now Saint-Simon decided to put greater stress on the role of industry in general rather than upon science and to replace the principle of universal gravitation with another bond of morality better suited to the needs of an industrial society. This new principle he called the "positive" morality, by which term he meant to suggest a code that would refer to material interests and that would stand for a concrete alternative to the critical negativism promoted by eighteenth-century liberalism. Industrialism, he believed, stood for concrete, positive ideals, for progress in the full range of reality rather than simply in connection with legal rights, for organic cohesion rather than anarchic disunity.[46]

This conception of industrial society as an alternative both to feudalism and to liberalism led Saint-Simon to try to develop a new science of society. Using the psychological categories of the French physiologist Bichat, Saint-Simon contended that society was composed of three basic types of people, brain, motor, and sensory.[47] The liberal notion of men as naturally equal in rational capacity was to be rejected in favor of this more scientific theory, inasmuch as it was not only more realistic but better suited to the needs of an industrial society. The brain type, he asserted, corresponded to scientists, the motor type to manual laborers and the elite of administrators, the sensory type to artists, poets, and religious leaders, who would provide the emotional cement of the new society. It is important to note that although this is a class system it is one without class antagonism, without domination.

Indeed Saint-Simon envisioned a society in which there would be order, not of the type associated with feudalism or reaction, but an industrial order in which the general welfare, including what he called the interests of the most numerous and poorest classes, would become the chief concern. The organization of this society, however, would depend upon talent and the need for bureaucratic discipline. When Saint-Simon compared the new industrial society with feudal society he drew some sharp contrasts. Under the old system there was exploitation of inferior by superior; now there would be only direction. Whereas before there was antagonism, now there would be cooperation and association. In short the new society would be unified, orderly, peaceful, and productive. The industrial system would provide for all kinds of social planning designed to increase production, to insure full employment without confiscating property, to undertake colonization to take care of surplus population, and to provide amenities and public works.[48]

Saint-Simon was a great author of new schemes and he offered a number of variations on this basic theme. Throughout he retained his preoccupation with industrial society. The only major change came in his attitude toward religion. Saint-Simon spoke in the latest phases of his thought of a new religion of industrialism, or the New Christianity. The nucleus of this new religion would be the academy of science as a modern interpreter of the scriptures. Increasingly he turned the doctrine of the industrial society into a modern version of the religion of love. The enemy is not now idleness but egotism. By combining the religion of love with industrial society, Saint-Simon found a goal that would be preferable, he thought, to all that had gone before. "Political imagination," he said,

> has put the Golden Age in the cradle of the human race amid the ignorance and brutishness of primitive times; it is rather the Iron Age which should be put there. The Golden Age of the human race is not behind us but before us; it lies in the perfection of the social order. Our ancestors never saw it; our children will one day arrive there; it is for us to clear the way.[49]

Saint-Simon may not have been as rigorous a thinker as many lesser minds of his day, but he was certainly original and imaginative. To study his ideas in more systematic form, however, we must turn to the thought of his most eminent disciple, Auguste Comte, the father of the doctrine known as positivism and of the discipline of sociology.

The intellectual reason (there were other, personal reasons) why the disciple broke with the master was that Saint-Simon, according to Comte, was too eager to put his insights into practice before he had elaborated them into soundly based principles. The intellectual situation, Comte thought, was not yet as ripe as his teacher had thought. The main task, he argued, was to establish on firm ground what he called, using Saint-Simon's term, positive science or positive philosophy.[50] Whereas Saint-Simon had used a number of theories to describe the development of the scientific attitude in history, Comte developed a single theory that provided the basis for positivism. This is the theory that there are three stages in civilized history: the theological, the metaphysical, and the scientific or positive phase. In the first stage men look for an absolute final cause that they denote God. In the second, they speak of nature as the final cause. In the third, they are concerned not with absolute causes but with laws — laws governing relations of succession and resemblance.

These three stages, suitably subdivided, would account for the whole of recorded history, but they had a special relevance in a kind of historical microcosm to the contemporary situation.[51] The trouble with European politics, said Comte, was that either one was a reactionary, in which case he wanted to return to the theological stage; or he was a progressive, which meant that he preferred the metaphysical stage. He believed in abstract natural rights, was critical of strong government, wished to overthrow the old central authority, but had nothing positive to offer in its place.

In this seeming deadlock, despair and frustration were endemic. Despite a wealth of evidence, hardly anyone realized that science and industry offered the way out of the dilemma. Why, Comte asked, must humanity choose between order and progress? Why not bring them together within the framework of science and technology? The theological system had done the necessary work of destroying cultic parochialism and magic. The metaphysical system had overturned the obstacles to industrialism put up by feudalism. As yet, however, the only intellectual alternative to feudalism was what Comte decried as a stationary doctrine, rejecting reaction and utopia in favor of things as they were. The positive philosophy, Comte believed, would resolve the contradictions by extending the scientific approach to the study of society. "Social physics" would represent the highest achievement of science, since man and society presented the most complex set of data.[52] From intellectual order would come social order. Scientific calculation would replace political debate; the limited relativism that would necessarily be fostered would cool the tempers of partisan groups; expectations would become more realistic than was the case, for instance, with those who "propose to civilize Tahiti by a wholesale importation of Protestantism and a parliamentary system."[53]

Even more emphatically than Saint-Simon, Comte believed that science and industrialism demonstrated the folly of the liberal belief in equality. Shall every man have an equal voice in the determination of scientific truth? Shall there be no subordination, no rank, in industry? Equality, said Comte, would be absurd in such conditions.

Comte too was bitter toward the scientific class, which, he remarked, might have been expected to lead the renovation of society under the auspices of positive science. Instead, even the scientists were paralyzed by the general anarchistic tendencies of the time and turned away from society in disgust. To combat this irresponsibility, Comte urged a wholly new scientific education designed to overcome the specialization and fragmentation of science.[54]

Comte did not try to describe in precise detail the outcome he envisioned from the advance toward positive society. This society, he wrote, would present the sharpest possible contrast to the military character of previous societies. It would be peacefully engaged in industrial pursuits. It would not be built on egoism, like liberalism, or on the imaginary moral order of theology, but on the real basis of material progress. It would make it obvious that the happiness of the individual is always linked to the expansion of benevolence throughout the whole of society. It would be hierarchical, but not another order of domination; it would be both spiritual and temporal, both theoretical and practical, and it would join labor and capital, town and country.[55]

Marx dismissed Saint-Simon as a utopian. He might well have said the same of his more influential disciple. But Marx was himself in many ways no less utopian. As Raymond Aron has pointed out,[56] both the positivist and the Marxist have awkward ways of accounting for much that mankind has experienced since the middle of the nineteenth century, war in particular. There are many ways, nevertheless, in which the Saint-Simonian–Comtian prophecy has certainly been fulfilled. The degree of organization demanded by advanced industrial society is certainly as great as they thought it would be. The structure of industrial society remains hierarchical, not in any feudal sense, but in the sense of modern industrial bureaucracy. Old ideological debates have been rendered increasingly obsolete because of scientific and technical progress. Scientists and industrialists have acquired greater and greater authority as the impact of their work has ramified throughout every phase of life. The weak point of the theory is surely the assumption that with industrialization the quest for power and personal and group privilege would simply disappear. It is probably this, more than anything else, that accounts for the inability of the theory to explain the continued existence of war or internal social conflict. From a normative standpoint, the positive view has another fundamental shortcoming. Because Comte and Saint-Simon were so anxious to overcome the anarchistic implications of liberalism, they neglected to assure a role for individual freedom. That is why, reading them today, one inevitably has the feeling that already Big Brother is beginning his watch.

It remains true, however, that Saint-Simon and Comte had a better grasp of social reality than many others who became better known as social philosophers. From the seventeenth century until close to the middle of the nineteenth, social theorists were cleanly divided on the importance of advances in science and technology. There were those, like Bacon, Condorcet, Saint-Simon, and Comte, who were ecstatic about the probable consequences of these advances. Most of the better-known theorists, however, were altogether indifferent to them. Hobbes, Locke, Rousseau, Hume, and Burke, for example, may have been influenced by the advance of science but they assigned it no great role in society. Only a few theorists, notably those we have already discussed, were convinced of its revolutionary significance, and these were easily dismissed as visionaries. The economists, the men of practical affairs, were unimpressed. Neither Adam Smith nor Ricardo nor Malthus believed that technological change would have any great effect on productivity and the factors of production. In this they were, in retrospect, remarkably shortsighted.

## Technology and History

It was the great achievement of Karl Marx to have brought together the utopian optimism of the visionary theorists and the naively realistic pessimism of the classical economists. The theory that emerged was not without serious exaggerations, inconsistencies, and oversights, but it had the merit of providing the first really comprehensive theory of the way in which technical and social development were bound together.

With Marx, a new dichotomy arises. Now the question becomes: will the changes to be produced by technological progress be for the better or for the worse? Marx's own point of view is too well known to need detailed elaboration. "The mode of production in material life," he wrote in a famous passage, "determines [conditions?] the general character of the social, political and spiritual processes of life. It is not the consciousness of men that determines their existence but, on the contrary, it is their social existence that determines their consciousness."[57] Marx believed that productive technique was the substratum of the social system, that as it changed society must also change, against resistance from those who profited from the old order and with the assistance of those who could hope to gain from the new one. He foresaw that the development of large-scale, mechanized systems of production would make obsolete the then-prevailing system of small-scale enterprise, with the individualistic relationships it had fostered. In the future, ownership would be concentrated, and all nonowners would be reduced to the status of depressed wage earners. Out of this economic development, induced by the inevitable "laws" of the market economy, would arise waves of revolutionary protest such as had already arisen in the premature instances of proletarian rebellion. Eventually the revolutionaries would wrest control from the capitalist oligarchs and establish a new, collective system of production and ownership.

Marx believed that collectivism, in a form he did not try to discern with exactitude, was the logical culmination of the historical process because of the importance he attached to technological change. All previous social systems were based upon class exploitation because the state of technology had made such exploitation possible and, in a sense, even necessary. Only when technology had advanced to the degree that there would no longer be any need for one class to assure its comfort at the expense of another or, to put the theory on more fundamental terms, only when the advance of technology had made the separation of owners and workers an obsolete mode of productive organization would there be no classes and therefore no possibility of class conflict.

Marx was not altogether without misgivings about the emergence of a higher civilization out of the socialist revolution. He acknowledged that collectivism could conceivably merely result only in "universal envy".[58] In the final stage of history, the mode of production would no longer *determine* the social system; it would only make *possible* the creation of a new society in which egoism would be overcome.

Marx's general theory of historical change, and his generally optimistic confidence in the progressive effects of technological advance were severely tested by the work of Max Weber. It has often been said of much of Weber's work that it is an effort to correct Marx by balancing his overstress on economic determinism with a counterstress on the role of social and psychological attitudes. In this overall respect, however, Weber's theories serve as a modification of Marxian theory but not as a fundamental challenge to it. In the more specific matter of his attitude toward the influence of science and technology upon history, Weber was far more critical of Marxian theory.

"The fate of our times," Weber said in his lecture on *Science as a Vocation*, "is characterized by rationalization and intellectualization, and, above all, by the 'disenchantment of the world.'"[59] This theme of rationalization runs through virtually all of Weber's most important essays and is central to what is novel in his thought. What did he mean by "rationalization"? In the most general sense he meant that civilized societies had outgrown the primitive belief in a world governed by hidden anthropomorphic spirits which might be controlled or appeased through magic. In a technical sense rationalization carried a double meaning, reflecting what Weber saw happening both in social history and in intellectual history. Rationalization in history meant that all social life was being organized and reorganized to suit the demands of an almost passionate desire for efficiency and that all aspects of the social system were coming to resemble the two model institutions of large-scale organization, the factory system and the army. In intellectual history rationalization meant that the theories offered to explain the workings of the natural universe and of society no longer referred to transcendental or metaphysical premises but were restricted to scientific hypotheses supported by empirical evidence.

Wherever he looked Weber found the tendency toward rationalization. When he studied the rise of capitalism he concluded that regardless of the intentions of the Protestant reformers the greatest significance of their revolt in theology and church organization was that their followers were inspired to perform economic functions with diligence and to accumulate wealth. When he examined democracy he saw the same force at work. The American urban boss, he predicted, was doomed to extinction because the demands upon government would become so great and the need for specialists and professionals so widespread that the crude tribal organization of Tammany Hall would prove inadequate. "Where it is large-scale democracy," he asserted, "modern democracy becomes everywhere a bureaucratic democracy."[60] The aristocratic oligarchy of former times is replaced by a new oligarchy of public office-holders, elected and appointed, and the mass of men remain as dependent upon the bureaucracy as they did in earlier times of feudal officialdom.

When he turned his attention to socialism Weber pronounced the same judgment even more forcibly, so as to contradict the propaganda on its behalf from the left. Marx had asserted that under capitalism the worker was separated from the means of production. Weber pointed out that the same was true for everyone in a modern society. The university scholar does not own the books he reads in the library or the instruments he uses in the laboratory, even though he is no proletarian by Marx's definition. The soldier, whether he is an officer or a private, does not own his own weapons as the knight of old owned horse and armor. Judicial and political authorities are paid a salary by governmental authorities rather than left to extract what they can from the jurisdictions they administer.

The separation of ownership and use was inherent in the character of modern society.[61]

Like Marx, Weber believed that behind developments such as these lay the advance of machine technology, which had rendered not only individual ownership but individual labor obsolete. Marx had argued that the very advance of technology had outstripped the social forms, epitomized as capitalism, which had first been developed to accommodate it. The result, he said, was an anarchy of production consisting of a series of contradictions between the capitalist organization of production and the possibilities opened by modern industry, through which the workers were exploited by the owning class. Weber, taking advantage of more recent historical experience than Marx had been able to consider, disputed the Marxian claim that capitalism could not be adapted to technological change. He also disputed the general socialist belief that under nationalization the workers would be emancipated from exploitation. World War I had shown that business and government could work together, not only in the development of cartels and in policies of protection and price stability, but in countless ways designed to meet public needs. Even though this high degree of interdependence might not survive the war, a pattern would have been established for a degree of regulation in the public interest that would, in the future, curb whatever anarchistic and exploitative tendencies capitalist industry might otherwise exhibit. Besides, Weber pointed out, the experience of the Saar coal miners, who were forbidden to strike against the government, indicated that nationalization did not automatically guarantee any improvement in the lot of the workers.[62]

Weber was thus among the earliest to realize that government regulation of industry would affect the Marxian predictions at their major premises. He admitted that there would continue to be business crises, but he argued that they would not be as severe as Marx had anticipated. It was not inevitable that workers be thrown out of work, so long as government took the responsibility for insuring full employment. Nor was it inevitable that ownership be concentrated in the hands of the privileged few, provided that steps were taken to expand the degree of corporate ownership.[63]

Yet, despite his pronounced belief that the Marxian apocalypse need not occur, Weber felt that the tendency toward bureaucratization overshadowed the conflict between capitalism and socialism. The bureaucracy, he believed, would grow at a faster rate than the proletariat and the wave of the future was more likely to install the dictatorship of the official than the dictatorship of the proletariat. Suppose industry were socialized, Weber asked, who would run the factories? Surely not the workers, but the same set of managers who would run the factories under capitalism. The *Communist Manifesto*, said Weber, knows nothing of this. Socialists who had become aware of the dangers of bureaucracy had turned from hope in the state to hope in the trade union. The syndicalists asserted that the political avenue to socialism must be avoided at all costs because it would preserve the repressive bureaucratic state and the professional politicians. Instead they aimed to crush capitalism by the technique of the general strike, thus enabling the labor unions to seize control of industry. In answer Weber could only ask rhetorically, with evident exasperation: Who runs the labor unions if not bureaucrats, and who do the syndicalists think would be capable of running the industries, if not bureaucrats?[64]

Weber did not view the march of rationalization without misgivings. He foresaw a growing tension between rational organizations and the need for personal and emotional expression, between the bureaucrat and the demagogue or "charismatic" leader. And he seems to have been apprehensive lest there would be reactions against the depersonalizing effects of rationalization—eruptions of older, more primitive impulses. The price of increased efficiency, he seems to have felt, might be an increasingly high degree of social control necessary to avoid costly outbursts of irrationality. The danger of the controlled society, rather than the narrower phenomenon of proletarian alienation, struck him as the great spiritual threat of the new industrial society.

Against this spiritual threat rationalization was powerless, because in itself it could offer no new set of values. Plato, Weber noted, had thought that by reaching a universe of ideas higher than than the universe of sensory appearance he would have a standard of values for the ethical man and the good citizen. The Renaissance philosophers believed that scientific reason was the guide to the secrets of nature. The Enlightenment entertained a similar hope. But in modern times, Weber asserted, no one believes that science can reveal anything about the meaning of life or that it can bring happiness.[65] Medicine can preserve life, but it cannot tell us what is a life worth living. Natural science can teach us how to master the technical difficulties of sustaining ourselves and communicating with one another; but it leaves aside, or avoids by making whatever assumptions are necessary for its work, the question of why we should want to master nature technically or whether in the long run what we are doing technically makes any sense in terms of human values.

Did the pursuit of knowledge, *Wissenschaft*, not provide the intellectual with a set of values fundamentally different from the neutral thrust of rationalization toward efficiency? Weber answered that although science does not provide a set of values for ethical conduct it is inseparable from the value of awareness or consciousness. Science could not show anyone the way to happiness but it could enable everyone to see the human condition truly, without illusion. Those who cannot stand to contemplate this truth, he said, can always return to religion. "The arms of the old churches are opened widely and compassionately for him."[66] Weber was not alone in this position. Nietzsche and Freud also argued for consciousness as the sole remaining value, the belief that Weber expressed in the phrase "science as vocation." Science was a vocation, in the deepest sense, in that it was a call to freedom through awareness. The man who accepted this vocation would never be deceived by false hopes or false fears. In rationalized society, which was otherwise without purpose, this freedom was all that could be hoped for. Otherwise the very efficiency and organization of society would enforce conformity and standardization.

## Technocracy in America

In European thought Marx's vision remained the high-water mark of the optimistic appraisal of the effect of technological progress, while Weber's misgivings reflected the growth of a disenchantment with this vision which was to express itself in the work of still more pessimistic spokesmen, like Oswald Spengler. American thought, in this as in so many other contexts, had not yet caught up with the latest turn of the European mind. Just as Europeans were growing uncomfortable over the prospect of a society transformed by modern technology, Americans were beginning to respond to the utopian promises announced earlier by the Europeans. Edward Bellamy was among the first to popularize this utopian view in his widely read novel, *Looking Backward*, published in 1887.

Bellamy imagined that his protagonist had gone to sleep in 1887 and awakened in the year 2000 to find a thoroughly changed society, changed not only in respect to comfort and convenience but also in the degree to which the great innovations of progress were now available to all. How had all this come about? The hero's hosts inform him of what is essentially a literary paraphrase of Marx's predictions. Technological progress—in the form of the steam engine, the telegraph, and the railroad—rendered the old laissez-faire system obsolete. It had become necessary to choose between changing the social order to accommodate these technical advances or suppressing the advances to preserve the system of small-scale private enterprise. Everyone came to recognize that it would be far better for society as a whole to enjoy the economy and efficiency of concentration. It was only necessary, people realized, to allow the process of historical change to "complete its logical evolution to open a golden future to humanity."[67]

To this end, early in the twentieth century all capital was concentrated by social decision in one giant monopoly known as the Great Trust. All industry was entrusted to public authority and removed from the control of irresponsible private corporations. Just as the people had, a century earlier, taken hold of their own government, now they took control of the economy, "organizing now for industrial purposes on precisely the same grounds that they had then organized for political purposes."[68] It was not a matter of hatred and resentment against the great corporations. Everyone came to understand that private corporate enterprise was simply "a transition phase in the evolution of the true industrial system."[69]

Like Marx, Bellamy too foresaw that the state would also undergo a radical change and emerge as a system of administration rather than a system of government, in the old sense of a mediator of social conflict. Instead of a society in which government and industry were separate there would be one industrial army, with ranks ranging from private to general. The officers would be elected from the ten national trade guilds, each embodying a particular type of industrial specialist. The chiefs of the guilds would form a council headed by a general-in-chief, who would also be president of the United States. Not everyone would serve in the industrial army; some, who had nothing to contribute to industry itself, could be exempted for other useful work. But only those in the industrial professions would be eligible to serve in government. Asked whether the members of the liberal professions were eligible for election as president, the spokesman for the new society replies:

> The members of the technical professions, such as engineers and architects, have a ranking with the constructive guilds; but the members of the liberal professions, the doctors and teachers, as well as the artists and men of letters who obtain remissions of industrial service, do not belong to the industrial army. On this ground they vote for the President, but are not eligible to his office. One of its main duties being the control and discipline of the industrial army, it is essential that the President should have passed through all its grades to understand his business.[70]

Bellamy's technocratic socialism, for all its failure to appreciate the noneconomic functions of political leadership and the training requisite to these functions, caught the imagination of a great many Americans, sophisticated and naive alike. It was after reading *Looking Backward* that Thorstein Veblen made up his mind to leave the family farm in Iowa and go east to study economics. Although he was to acquire much erudition and sophistication, Veblen never abandoned the essential beliefs he first found in Bellamy's fictional portrait of the future society.

Like Bellamy, but unlike Marx, Veblen stressed the leadership role of the engineers and did not expect that change would come through the revolutionary activity of the proletariat. Also unlike Marx, Veblen was preoccupied with the mores of social classes, from the habits of the leisure class—as expressed in "pecuniary emulation" and "conspicuous consumption"—to the "instinct of workmanship" motivating the productive classes. In effect Veblen combined Marx's economic analysis with his own psychological and anthropological analysis of capitalist society. This achievement not only provided a badly needed balance to the economic critique of capitalism but also led Veblen to doubt the facile optimism with which Marxists deduced the downfall of capitalism as a necessary consequence of its economic contradictions.

Veblen argued that economic development takes its start from a triad of human drives: the "instinct of workmanship," "the parental bent," and idle curiosity. The first leads men to produce, but to produce only those things that are conducive to sustaining the life of the species and giving expression to benevolent emotions. The second engenders affection not alone for one's progeny but also for others in general. Idle curiosity leads all men to learning and some to science. All three drives combine to make the early stages of social progress a picture of idyllic harmony and achievement. Living close to the soil in small, close-knit groups, their survival hinging upon workmanlike performance by everyone—or so Veblen speculated—the members of the early human communities must have been bound to one another by strong bonds of affection and honesty. All must have had to work unselfishly, and in the effort to survive many must have learned to exercise considerable ingenuity.[71]

The primal paradise, it seemed to Veblen, had been lost for two reasons. Out of a warping of the natural drives, a number of bad habits developed which proved too powerful for the benign natural impulses in conditions of constant adversity. Soon individuals motivated by these perverted impulses took advantage of advances in knowledge to become powerful tyrants. Workmanship was perverted by the belief in magic, the parental bent degenerated into authoritarian patriarchy and then into the absolutist government of elders, priests, and kings, and idle curiosity was entranced by myth and legend.

Following his own powerful "bent" for colorful description, Veblen described the historical change as an advance from savage to barbarian society, distinguishing between two phases of the barbarian era: the predatory and pecuniary. Whereas savage society is devoted to peaceful agriculture, symbolized and organized by the image of motherhood, predatory man is a hunter for whom maleness is everything. Predatory society thrives on war and personal prowess. The chief predominates because he shows the greatest prowess. His followers seek to impress each other by imitating his example and by displaying the trophies of their successes as hunter and warrior: the heads of victims, the skin of the animals they kill, the men and women they enslave and keep as retainers. These possessions are valued by predatory man not because they perform an economic function for him but because they prove that he is an accomplished predator. The same essential set of perverse values survives into the pecuniary phase of barbarian culture, now expressed in new forms made possible by technological progress. The warlike habits of the hunter become the acquisitive habits of the property owner, and property itself becomes the mark of prowess.

One incident of the transition from predatory (feudal) to pecuniary (capitalist) society struck Veblen as particularly important: the loss of the sense of group solidarity. When private property is the measure of achievement, every man pursues his own advantage at the expense of others and at the expense of the community as a whole. What social loyalty remains expresses itself in the image of the war hero or the embattled patriot, and in athletic contests, where the prowess of the hero takes a naked physical form harking back to the hunt. This new and powerful individualism gives rise to the process of social comparison which Veblen aptly named "invidious distinction." It also acts, in the long run, to inhibit production. Although force and fraud are presumably disallowed, and although self-interest at first stimulates people to work harder, the fact that personal gain rather than social utility is the goal of enterprise must from time to time inhibit the adoption of progressive innovations and must also promote a distaste for work. Since the aim of work is possession, the attainment of property exempts people from work. Exemption thus becomes a mark of superiority, a "pecuniary excellence" enjoyed by an entire class of those free to indulge the appetite for leisure. The favored leisure activities are those which reflect the wish to impress others with evidence that work is avoided. The practices of the leisure class, Veblen noted, were in direct contradiction to the instinct of workmanship, embodying the point of view of the consumer rather than the producer, reflecting a concern with profit rather than service, authority rather than authenticity, and promoting habits of deference and mannered politeness rather than the direct honesty of emotions imparted by personal industriousness.[72]

The pecuniary phase, however, is not a wholly corrupt departure from original innocence. Unlike the *rentier,* the businessman is still willing to work. Up to a point the middle class remains concerned with improving productivity. But a cleavage develops between the owners and the producers, between those concerned with selling for profit and those interested only in productive efficiency. The "Captain of Industry" becomes an absentee owner, a shareholder rather than a director. The technological unfitness of this business management of industry becomes evident to all.[73] At the same time the relentless progress of "Machine Industry" enforces regularity and efficiency in whatever areas can be affected by the discipline of the clock and the railway timetable and compels all competitors to adopt new inventions at the risk of being left behind. The result is a deepening contradiction between the requirements of the industrial system and the habits of indolence cultivated by the owning classes.

As a corollary of this economic contradiction there is also a growing contradiction on the level of class attitudes. Machine industry trains the producing class to disbelief in magic and luck and to a preference for impersonal, quantitative attitudes. It is, Veblen thought, a training in "matter-of-fact," in the logic of the machine process.[74] He knew, however, that this training was not altogether successful. Some, especially among the moderately well-to-do, expressed hostility to the machine by joining fantastic cults. Some sought a return to nature, to the simple life, to "get away from the grind." The growing practice of taking a vacation indicated to Veblen that human nature and the machine process were not yet perfectly in harmony, as did the incidence of nervous breakdowns.

These contradictions, he thought, would generate certain potentially corrective adjustments. As business management comes to require greater expertise, the owners tend to withdraw in favor of the technologically competent, the engineers. It was to the engineers, rather than to the proletariat, that Veblen looked for revolutionary leadership. The "Soviet of Technicians," the "General Staff of the Industrial System," as he referred to them, would have to take the lead in adjusting the social conditions of production to the requirements of the machine process. Veblen knew perfectly well how unlikely it was, not to say that it was altogether hopeless, to expect engineers to become revolutionaries. He was, as Max Lerner has said,[75] only a tongue-in-cheek revolutionary, more Mencken than Lenin; he knew that the engineers were "harmless and docile," "well fed on the whole," content with the full dinner pail graciously allotted to them by the "vested interests." The engineers, he said, were as safe and sane, as commercial in their values, as the Captains of Industry who had made them their lieutenants. The owners had therefore nothing to fear "just yet."[76]

Indeed, Veblen was not at all confident of the imminence of utopia. Even though he remained convinced that science must supersede magic and animism; that rational technology and the cultural habits of matter of fact must replace irrational methods and the love of display; that under modern conditions the society with the most advanced productive system would be the strongest; for all this, Veblen was profoundly pessimistic. Human nature seemed to have other, more malevolent features than those accounted for in the instinct of workmanship and the parental bent. Agressiveness was perhaps, after all, more a natural endowment than an accident of history, as indeed was the belief in luck. How explain the survival of irrationality and war alongside the advance of machine industry? Veblen's one major theoretical effort to answer these nagging doubts took the form of his theory of atavistic survival. Warlike behavior was not to be explained, following Lenin, as a necessary outgrowth of capitalism, but, on the contrary, as a survival of older, feudal habits. Germany and Japan could be expected to behave militaristically just because, being relative late-comers to industrialization, they would be compelled to combine advanced technology they could easily borrow from others with social institutions, such as those of Junker and the Samurai, which they could not as easily cast off.

The theory of cultural lag behind technological progress enabled Veblen to account for German militarism, already well demonstrated, and to predict that Japan would behave in a similar way.[77] He held out hope that in both cases this behavior would be temporary, confident that sooner or later industrialism would produce an attitude of live-and-let-live which would replace the fierce predatory impulses lingering from earlier times. Eventually, he believed, people in all modern societies would be compelled to recognize that machine industry made all of their individual and personal marks of prowess puny and foolish. They would come to understand too that the marks of wealth no more connoted superiority than the marks of birth. If anything conferred real superiority—and this to society rather than to individuals—it was the capacity to pursue and apply scientific knowledge. Those who themselves possessed such capacity would not be concerned with honorific distinction or display; they would seek knowledge for its own sake, out of idle curiosity, as workmen striving toward human goals in harmony with their fellows. The rest would be influenced by their example to prize the pursuit of knowledge above all else and to participate in that pursuit to the limit of their ability.

Although Veblen remained ambivalent toward the prospects for progress, other American social theorists who have come after him have shown signs of greater optimism. Notable among these is B. F. Skinner, whose *Walden Two*[78] presents a utopia based upon the predicted achievements of behavioral science. Through the use of the techniques of "positive reinforcement" developed in the study of human and animal learning processes, Skinner's fictional human engineers create a perfectly harmonious community in which the problems of social coercion and freedom are presumably obviated. Although the vision is utopian, the scientific basis for it is at least the professional goal of an organized and reputable school of study. Behaviorists are indeed working toward the development of a science of human behavior which, once fully established, could provide the principles of human engineering. This discipline, or art, has already had notable practitioners, among them the pioneers of "scientific management," Frederick Winslow Taylor and Elton Mayo. In the future it may well aspire to the role in managing society that Bellamy and Veblen envisioned for the technically competent in the management of industry. Such predictions of a scientifically managed society have hardly evoked universal enthusiasm. On the contrary, from the time of Bacon to the present a countertradition has developed which expresses a humanistic reaction against the ominous prospects of social control through science.

## The Humanistic Response

August Comte held out for art what he considered a glorious role in the construction of positive society:

> There is no anticipating what the popular enthusiasm will be when the representations of Art shall be in harmony with the noble instinct of human superiority, and with the collective rational convictions of the human mind. To the philosophical eye it is plain that the universal reorganization will assign to modern Art at once inexhaustible material in the spectacle of human power and achievement, and a noble social destination in illustrating and endearing the final economy of human life. What philosophy elaborates, Art will propagate and adopt for propagation, and will thus fulfill a higher social office than in its most glorious days of old.[79]

Neither Comte's vision of man's future nor the propagandistic role he assigned to art have had much appeal for humanists. Apart from the docile advocates and practitioners of "socialist realism" and their counterparts in other societies, artists and spokesmen for art have had mixed feelings at best about the human implications of progress in science and technology. To some, this progress has seemed more threatening than promising. Human tragedies as well as creature comforts are said to follow in the wake of every advance, as mankind is drawn out of immediate contact with nature and conditioned to standard responses by an environment made artificially uniform and bland. Industrialization, it is said, first ripped human beings from the rural soil in which they had been rooted for centuries, then deposited them without pity on the slag heap of the industrial town, and now leaves them purposeless and trapped in the process of technological change. At first humanists were inclined to scoff at the pretensions of science. Then they were compelled to recognize its power and its significance. Some have sought to come to terms with it, to humanize it by making it synonymous with the general pursuit of learning, and others have denounced it—particularly when it has seemed not just an instrument of change but a dogmatic faith—as a danger to civilization. Now that the importance of science has been recognized in the councils of state, the humanistic response has become more intense than ever, though the direction of the response is by no means uniform.

One initial reaction of the humanistic mind is well illustrated in Jonathan Swift's *Gulliver's Travels*, published in 1726. The Royal Academy of London was then in full flower, its membership a roster of the illustrious figures of the day, its reputation grand even beyond its accomplishments. Dean Swift apparently felt that it was time to prick the balloon. Gulliver describes his voyage to Laputa (whose Spanish name in itself suggests Swift's contempt), which is a flying island in the control of scientists. At the outset of his visit Gulliver is struck by a curious sight. The inhabitants are so preoccupied with their scientific meditations that they require servants to interrupt their thoughts so that they may answer those who wish to talk to them. Gulliver finds himself measured for a suit with a quadrant and a compass and receives a poor fit owing to a mistake in calculation. The houses are also poorly constructed because the instructions of the architects are too refined for simple workmen. The people too are quite peculiar. They lack all imagination and wit, and, surprisingly, are especially interested in politics. They give their opinions freely and often in matters of state and avidly inquire into and dispute all public issues. The same is true, Swift notes, among European mathematicians. "I rather take this quality to spring," says Swift, "from a very common infirmity of human nature, inclining us to be more curious and conceited in matters where we have least concern, and for which we are least adapted either by study or nature."[80]

Gulliver also visits another scientific community, Lagado, which is totally impoverished because of science. Forty years before, a group of Lagadans had gone to Laputa and had been so inspired by its example that they asked for and received a Royal Patent to erect an Academy of Projectors to improve things in their own community. As it turned out, none of the projects could be brought to completion and everyone was in misery because of them. Swift describes the Grand Academy of Lagado with particular relish. Gulliver first meets a sad-faced, ascetic scientist who tells him that he has been working eight years on a project to extract sunbeams from cucumbers and bottle the heat for cold weather. Other scientists are at work building houses from the roof downward, softening marble for pillows, and building linguistic machines with the use of which anyone, without either talent or education, can write poetry and philosophy. A language institute seeks to do away with verbs and participles because, from a scientific point of view, everything is nouns. Even more advanced are those who would abolish words altogether and instead have people carry things around with them that they could simply point to whenever they wished to communicate.

Swift's satire expressed both a humanist's disdain for the pretensions of scientists and also the fear lest science undercut common sense, lest it be turned to purposes dangerous to culture, and lest it make men presumptuous.

A century later there are humanists who are more than willing to concede that science is a benign pursuit, who are indeed so respectful of it that they wish to draw it under the umbrella of humane letters. Ernest Renan, who was to become famous as a critical student of early Christianity, expressed this sentiment in 1848 in a work entitled *The Future of Science*. Renan's position resembles that of the positivists. He favors the development of a new, unified view of science which would end the fruitless controversies among the learned and through which mankind could achieve a common sense of direction absent from each of the scientific specialties. Once science is understood as the pursuit of universal knowledge, it will no longer be seen as the antagonist of art or religion, but rather as the groundwork for a more complete expression of religious sentiment, expressing the most advanced scientific findings rather than primitive mythic suppositions.

Such a science might well be regarded, Renan believed, as a wholesome continuation of the emancipatory aspects of the French Revolution which, it must be recognized, had destroyed the "Gothic order" without replacing it. No new substitute for this old order could possibly be constructed without the help of science. "Science and science alone is capable of restoring to humanity that without which it cannot live—a creed and a law."[81] Science, however, must be understood not as a narrow technical activity but as the sum total of all the intellectual disciplines. In practice, too many scientists refuse to reach out to ponder the moral bearing of their work, contenting themselves with mere technicalities. It is for this reason that science acquires a reputation as a destructive, critical instrument from which the only popular effect that can be expected is doubt and confusion. If science is to become the constructive lever so necessary to a society torn by revolution from all its stable moorings, it must be undertaken as a collective effort, to be underwritten by the state:

> It is the duty of the state to patronize science as it patronized art . . . . Individuals cannot build unto themselves observatories; they cannot create libraries, they cannot found large scientific institutions. The state, therefore, *owes* to science observatories, libraries, scientific institutions. Individuals cannot by themselves undertake to publish certain works. The state *owes* them subsidies . . . . I say that this is a duty of the state.[82]

It must be understood, Renan adds, that public patronage should confer no more right to control science than do subsidies to promote the arts or other activities beneficial to society.

Renan's eagerness to see science embraced into the fold of humane learning was by no means a solution universally agreed upon. Later in the nineteenth century, when science and scientific education became the focus of great public concern, a lively debate broke out in Victorian England in which the leading champion of science, Thomas Henry Huxley, was pitted against the leading champion of literature, Matthew Arnold, in a match that was to be closely duplicated in more recent times by the confrontation of C.P. Snow and F.R. Leavis.

Huxley fired the opening volley in a lecture entitled "Science and Culture" given at the ceremonies marking the opening of a scientific college in Birmingham. Scientific education, he said, was opposed by two quite distinct groups: the practical businessmen who saw no immediate use for science and the "classical scholars, in their capacity of Levites in charge of the ark of culture and monopolists of liberal education."[83] Since enough businessmen had been impressed by the growing usefulness of science in industry to have abandoned the cause to a grumbling but powerless minority, Huxley noted, he would address himself to the objections of the humanists. In doing so he brought into the open what must have rankled partisans of science then and what continues to rankle them now—the accusation that science is not to be considered a part of culture:

> How often have we not been told that the study of physical science is incompetent to confer culture; that it touches none of the higher problems of life; and, what is worse, that the continual devotion to scientific studies tends to generate a narrow and bigoted belief in the applicability of scientific methods to the search after truth of all kinds?[84]

The leading spokesmen of the "Levites," and therefore the all but unavoidable object of Huxley's attack, was Arnold. Huxley freely admitted that Arnold personally had been receptive to science, but he contended that Arnold's arguments lent support to the humanists in their disdain for science and scientific education. If, as Arnold had laid down, culture was "the best that had been said or written," culture was reduced to literature. And yet culture was also supposed to be, in essence, the criticism of life, the pursuit of a "theory of life." Culture was not, as Huxley himself had argued, a matter of acquiring skills or learning, but of developing an attitude toward life in keeping with the highest reaches of human aspiration. And yet it was proposed to attain this theory merely by studying the classics, particularly those in Greek and Latin. To say that such an education would fit a modern man for life, Huxley reflected, would be foolish:

> I should say that an army, without weapons of precision and with no particular base of operations, might more hopefully enter upon a campaign on the Rhine, than a man, devoid of a knowledge of what physical science has done in the last century, upon a criticism of life.[85]

Huxley proceeds to argue that inasmuch as the theory of life is affected by conceptions of the universe, what distinguishes modern times, and therefore modern culture, from what went before is precisely the great changes wrought by the advance of knowledge, not only on a practical level but in the very understanding of life itself. "The distinctive character of our own times lies in the vast and constantly increasing part which is played by natural knowledge."[86] Already science had compelled the abandonment of such previously firmly held tenets as the belief that the world had a known beginning and would have an end, that the earth was the center of the universe and man the earth's prized and unique creature, and that the universe was subject to periodic divine intervention. Science had shaken habits of thought as well by denying to anyone the appeal to authority and compelling everyone to adduce evidence from nature. Can anyone claim that he has an understanding of life if he is ignorant of what science has to contribute to that understanding? The classical scholar is himself a specialist, no less than the scientist, and as to which specialty would best fit a man for life, Huxley would prefer a scientific education; but it is not necessary that the scientist remain ignorant of literature, provided only that he acquires training in modern languages. It is the humanist who, by closing his eyes to all that the natural sciences teach, is condemned to remain a narrow specialist.

Arnold took the occasion of a Rede Lecture and a later address in the United States to make his reply. In an address entitled "Literature and Science" Arnold contended that Huxley had understood too narrowly his definition of literature. Arnold had meant by culture not only *belles lettres* but everything that reaches us through books — the scientific speculations of the Greeks no less than their philosophic and literary speculations.[87] The question to be debated, he contended, was rather how much of an education should be devoted to training in science. Admitting that the habit of dealing with facts is useful, particularly to those who would need to know about natural phenomena in the course of their work,[88] he added that an education in natural science alone would not enable a man to relate the facts he learned to the problems of moral conduct or to the appreciation of beauty. An education in natural science may therefore be adequate for naturalists who are so single-mindedly devoted to their narrow studies that, like Darwin, they profess to have no need for religion or poetry. For most of us, however, such an education would be incomplete and unsatisfactory. The medieval Church may have insisted upon scientifically erroneous conceptions of the natural universe, Arnold admits, but what Huxley failed to appreciate is that it also recognized the need to instruct men in matters relating to moral conduct and beauty. Even "Darwin's hairy quadruped" carried an impulse destined to grow into a desire for humane learning, "nay . . . also, a necessity for Greek."[89] Arnold concluded with a prediction that the humanities would find themselves in competition for a favored place in the curriculum but that they could never be entirely neglected. In a moving passage he warned of an ominous future but expressed confidence in the ultimate survival of humanistic learning:

> What will happen will rather be that there will be crowded into education other matters besides, far too many; there will be, perhaps, a period of unsettlement and confusion and false tendency; but letters will not in the end lose their leading place. If they lose it for a time, they will get it back again. We shall be brought back to them by our wants and aspirations. And a poor humanist may possess his soul in patience, neither strive nor cry, admit the energy and brilliancy of the partisans of physical science, and their present favour with the public, to be far greater than his own, and still have a happy faith that the nature of things works silently on behalf of the studies which he loves, and that, while we shall all have to acquaint ourselves with the great results reached by modern science, and to give ourselves as much training in its disciplines as we can conveniently carry, yet the majority of men will always require humane letters; and so much the more, as they have the more and the greater results of science to relate to the need in man for conduct, and to the need in him for beauty.[90]

Arnold's eloquent statement provides what may well be regarded as a definitive statement of the justification for humanistic studies in the age of science. If it did not still the voices of controversy, the reason may be that later humanists—like the Levisites who succeeded the Levites—could not be satisfied that they could defend the cause of right conduct and beauty by preserving the place of humanistic studies in the academic curriculum. The impact of technology and science seemed to many of them far too wide and deep to be met by an attitude of live-and-let-live. Technology had begun to invade painting and music and even the creation of literature. Changes more indirectly produced by technology were being felt throughout the fabric of the society the humanist was struggling to keep self-conscious and purposive. Typical of this later attitude is the work of Friedrich Georg Juenger, *The Failure of Technology* (1946), which is almost a handbook of twentieth century anti-technological thought. Juenger argues that far from providing improvement, science and its agents, the machines, are the sources of all that is evil in modern society. Industry brings bureauracy, regimentation, and centralized power; technological devices have no purpose but to be operated. The machine, by promoting methodical discipline, promotes moral stagnation. Science and technology promote the waste of resources, darken the air with smoke, poison the water, destroy the plants and animals, subject man and nature to universal exploitation, and cover the earth with junk and scrap from decayed and obsolete machines. According to Juenger, at least, scientific civilization is an unrelieved act of folly.

In the vigor of its criticism, Aldous Huxley's modern classic, *Brave New World*, is in somewhat the same vein. But Huxley adds an important dimension. The brave new world is one in which it is no longer necessary to cope with a separate realm of human needs and values. Science advances to such a point that men can not only control physical nature but human nature as well. It is as if Comte's last reservation were at last removed. Comte had said that utopia would not be achieved until that last, highest achievement of positive sciences—social physics—provided the laws necessary for social engineering. Huxley's utopia becomes possible only on the assumption that just such a science of man has been achieved. Technological progress would first have eliminated the problems of physical insecurity; and the development of a science of man would have made possible the elimination of the problems of psychological and social insecurity. These advances, Huxley feared, would liberate man from the oppression of circumstances only to enslave him to the oppression of deliberate manipulation. The trouble lay in the values promoted and supported by scientific progress. Mass production leads mankind away from truth and beauty toward the pursuit of happiness. The experience of devastation in war leads to the recognition that if there is to be happiness not only the physical environment but man himself must be subjected to scientific control. As Huxley observed, in a later reflection on his work, the nightmare utopia of *Brave New World* takes for granted the advance of the natural sciences. What is unique to it is rather the development of the biological, chemical, physiological, and psychological sciences as they apply to man and as they enable a variety of artificial controls to be imposed upon human nature:

> The theme of *Brave New World* is not the advancement of science as such; it is the advancement of science as it affects human individuals. The triumph of physics, chemistry and engineering are taken for granted. The only scientific advances to be specifically described are those involving the application to human beings of the results of future research in biology, physiology and psychology. It is only by means of the sciences of life that the quality of life can be radically changed. The sciences of matter can be applied in such a way that they will destroy life or make the living of it impossibly complex and uncomfortable; but, unless used as instruments by the biologists and psychologists, they can do nothing to modify the natural forms and expressions of life itself.[91]

Saint-Simon thought that he reached the basis for an orderly society when he found the physiological laws of human character. Even this supposed theoretical discovery pales before Huxley's idea that it may become possible to create people to order, by decanting them out of bottles and rearing them through unconscious suggestion and conditioning, according to plan. In this respect, as in others, Huxley's projection also differs considerably from George Orwell's *1984*. The society of *1984* is founded less upon advanced control over human nature than upon conventional techniques of psychic and physical coercion. The controllers of Orwell's society use the old-fashioned instruments of control familiar to Hitler and Stalin—force, deprivation and physical punishment. They are not practitioners of any science of human nature. Orwell's utopia is far less a discussion of what might be done with a science of behavior than it is a description of what in fact has already happened when the instruments of coercion are concentrated in the hands of a group of revolutionaries who abandon the original goals of their movement for the sake of perpetuating their personal power. Orwell's society rests on a general insecurity, on a need to keep society ready to go to war. The rulers of Huxley's society are not concerned with their own power; they rule a world society in which war has no place.

Indeed, what fundamentally distinguishes Huxley's society from Orwell's is that Huxley's represents a state of history following the period of wars and revolutions. His is the image of mankind after the violence of the dictators and revolutionaries has passed and what is left is a managed society in which no one objects to being managed, but, on the contrary, everyone is happy in his servitude. In this sense Orwell's is the negative utopia of the immediate present, Huxley's of the possible future. Totalitarianism, we may say, is the kind of system that can arise when the physical instruments of control and the instruments of propaganda are developed to an extent sufficient to stamp out opposition. But in Huxley's utopia there are no secret police, there is no Big Brother. Because of the advance of social science and social engineering, there is no need for such control. Control is internalized in every individual. Control rests on satisfying desires implanted in the person by the state, not on the need, by threats or inducements, to get the citizen to sacrifice his interest for the sake of the whole. As Lenina Crowne keeps reminding bashful Bernard Marx, "Everyone belongs to everyone else." In Huxley's society sexual gratification is both natural and altruistic. In Orwell's it is tabu. The keynote of Huxley's utopia is gratification; the keynote of Orwell's is deprivation.

With Huxley's portrait of society we move a long way from the original notions of philosophers contemplating the impact of science and technology upon society. In some respects there is a certain superficial resemblance. Like Comte, Huxley requires a hierarchy rather than democracy. Like Comte he seeks social stability and peace as a replacement for anarchy and war. Like him also he foresees the replacement of individualism and privacy by group solidarity and he postulates the need for a caste system so that all manner of work can be accomplished by willing workers. (Mustapha Mond says that the result of an experiment with a community of Alphas led only to civil war because the Alphas all tried to get out of work they found degrading.) But unlike Comte, Huxley feels that these goals entail others. In the society devoted to happiness there is no room for unhappiness, even if it is discontent which produces creative expression. The new positive society produces not culture but propaganda. It tends also to have a vested interest in everything artificial. It has no patience with back-to-nature movements (as is evidenced on the war against the Simple Lifers) or with partisans of culture (as is evident in the British Museum Massacre). Even science must be controlled because it is also potentially subversive.

Religion is understood as an obsolete cure for the ills of civilized man. Opposition to Christianity is based on the idea that Christianity is a religion of underconsumption no longer appropriate to advanced industrial society. Christianity offers heaven and man makes do temporarily with alcohol and narcotics. But the happiness pill, "soma," has, as Huxley says, all the advantages of Christianity and alcohol with none of the defects. Soma makes the Christian tension between earthly misery and heavenly happiness obsolete. Gratification, not deprivation, happiness, not the passion, the suffering of the Cross, is what is valued.

Since *Brave New World* was written, a number of Huxley's predictions have come remarkably close to realization. The tranquilizer is a staple of the drugstore. The emphasis on developing new consumer wants by planned obsolescence and advertising that whets the appetite for novelty has become a major occupation; and even sleep teaching is being advertised in English weeklies.

Huxley's portrait of the future society stands as a warning against the dangers of a pursuit of science unguided by any concern for humane values. It is also, as a satire, a defense of certain traditional Western values. In short, as relevant to the modern experience as *Brave New World* is, it remains well within the tradition exemplified by Arnold's criticism of the overemphasis on science and his defense of the virtues of humanistic study. A very different, and in a way an even more modern, attitude is reflected in the major work of the brilliant Viennese novelist-of-ideas, Robert Musil. Musil's grand though unfinished novel, *The Man Without Qualities,* is a meditation on the necessity of science to modern man by a gifted writer who was also a trained scientist. Musil earned a doctorate in the philosophy of science and even invented a device for measuring color wavelengths. Unlike Arnold and Aldous Huxley, he believed that the dilemma of the modern intellectual did not consist in a split between science and the humanities but in the divorce between all knowledge and life, or, put in another way, between the pursuit of knowledge and the quest for purpose. In a sense, Musil's problem is more like Max Weber's, but now reformulated to take account of what Musil understood as the overwhelming triumph of science over the speculative and arbitrary claims of ethical humanism.

Musil believed that for the man of intellect, who in modern times is a man necessarily committed to the scientific way of knowing the universe, what is understood by ordinary men as reality is actually unreal, devoid of meaning. The ordinary view of reality takes as ultimate truths just those elements that a man of intellect must find ephemeral phenomena. Ordinary men seek only to come to terms with this presumed reality, while the man of intellect, represented by Musil's protagonist, the mathematician Ulrich, must seek to formulate an alternative that will be meaningful. In this sense Ulrich is an idealist, a man of intellect working to define a possible reality. As yet, however, he is a "man without qualities" (the German is *Eigenschaften,* or "characteristics") because he can neither accept reality as it is understood ordinarily nor adapt himself to it in any particular fashion. Instead he is plunged into a restless pursuit of possible identities, possible alternatives.

Ulrich's pursuit of possibility begins in his disillusionment with two careers, as a cavalry officer and as an engineer. A military school preparation had led him into the cavalry, but he soon realized that he had become involved in nothing more than a system of vain posturing. A brief career in civil engineering proved more educational, inasmuch as it gave him an insight into the great disparity separating the technical conditions of modern life and the lingering habits of the older more naturalistic style of life. All expression, he noticed, mirrors the failure of man to keep pace with the progress of science. We rely on precise slide rules to make our technical calculations, but our way of speaking and thinking is so imprecise that in all other matters we are quite irrational. Despite our giant factories, we still speak a pretechnological language. To be something special, people do not climb a skyscraper but a "high horse" on which they ride "fast as the wind" when their simplest machines go faster. If they have keen sight they are "eagle-eyed," not giant-refractor–eyed. What is true for ordinary language is also true for ordinary values. Despite all that has been learned about the historical and psychological conditioning of behavior, people still talk of good and evil as though they were certain and absolute standards to be applied without regard to circumstances.[92]

Such insights lead Ulrich for a while to think that it would be right for him to be an engineer. He pictures himself conceiving and executing great schemes of construction and striding about, a pipe clamped between his teeth, shod in riding boots. Between bridges he would dispense great ideas concerning the organization of society and the conduct of life. To his dismay he finds that real engineers do not live up to this image. "Why do they seldom talk of anything but their profession? Or if they do, why do they do it in a special, stiff, out-of-touch, extraneous manner of speaking that does not go any deeper down, inside, than the epiglottis?"[93] The ones he met "revealed themselves to be men who were firmly attached to their drawing-boards, who loved their profession and were admirably efficient in it; but to the suggestion that they should apply the audacity of their ideas not to their machines but to themselves they would have reacted much as though they had been asked to use a hammer for the unnatural purpose of murder."[94]

Discouraged, Ulrich leaves civil engineering for the more rarified scientific air of mathematics. Mathematics, he believes, is both the wellspring of scientific civilization and the new religion of scientific man: "a religion whose dogma is permeated and sustained by the hard, courageous, mobile, knife-cold, knife-sharp mode of thought that is mathematics."[95] Ulrich had to admit to himself that the gains of science had their price. He was aware that people held science to blame for the ruin of the soul, for making man lord of the earth but a slave to the machine, for leaving him lonely, in a desert of detail, restless, malicious, callous, greedy, cold. When he became a mathematician Ulrich also knew that there were those who predicted that the doom of Europe would come as a result of scientific progress. But they did not deceive him. "It is significant," he observes, "that these people were all bad at mathematics at school."[96] They were bound to conclude that the natural sciences gave birth only to poison gas and fighter aircraft.

Ulrich would not be one of those mathematicians who pursued the discipline blind to its social implications. He believed that despite its critics, the scientific vocation was the most admirable way of life. If for "scientific attitude" one were to read "attitude to life," for "hypothesis," "attempt," and for "truth," "action,"[97] then one could see just how courageous it was to be a scientist and how science offered the key to life itself. Despite some misgivings he is convinced "that science has developed a conception of hard, sober intellectual strength that makes mankind's old metaphysical and moral notions simply unendurable, although all it can put in their place is the hope that a day, still distant, will come when a race of intellectual conquerors will descend into the valleys of spiritual fruitfulness."[98]

His vocation decided, Ulrich settles down to the role of the promising young man — but not for long. One day he simply stops wanting to be one when he hears the word "genius" being bandied about indiscriminately. (There were, it seemed, geniuses of football, boxing, tennis, and, the last straw, a "race-horse of genius.")[99] It was perhaps understandable that people should have used the word in this way, inasmuch as it recalled the tendency to attribute excellence to greatness of heart, strength, and agility. In truth the craft of the athlete and the craft of the thinker were in a measure identical: what made the horse jump the hedge and the man solve the problem (and the athlete do a bit of both) was at bottom the wish to achieve and excel, disconcerting as it was for the man of intellect to admit the similarity. Ulrich had at first been able to disregard such comparisons because he had persuaded himself that his scientific work was part of humanity's preparation for higher things in the future. He continues to hold the belief, but he can no longer make himself an agent of his convictions because he comes to feel "like a man who has crossed one mountain-range after the other, never getting within sight of a goal."[100] Abruptly he stops work and says to himself, "Good heavens! Surely I can never have meant to spend the whole of my life as a mathematician?"[101]

Unable to work, Ulrich takes an indefinite leave and, through the intervention of his father, a prominent jurist, becomes involved in the planning of a celebration in honor of the Austrian emperor that is being undertaken in order that Austria not be overshadowed when Germany celebrates the thirtieth anniversary of Kaiser Wilhelm's accession to the throne. Among the dignitaries involved in the preparation is Rudolf Arnheim, whom Ulrich labels "a man with qualities." (Arnheim, a German industrialist who is also an essayist and popular philosopher, is in every detail modeled upon the real-life figure of Walter Rathenau.) Arnheim is the perfect opposite of Ulrich—rich, famous, German, Jewish, cultivated, a poet who dictates the price of coal and is the personal friend of Kaiser Wilhelm. "What we all are separately," Ulrich muses, "he is in one person."[102] This synthesis, however, did not represent an active triumph over the disorder of reality but only a passive ingathering of its disparate and contradictory tendencies. To talk of a "fusion of interests between Soul and Business,"[103] to try to bring together the sphere of ideas and the sphere of power, was to make artificial syntheses, to compromise rather than unite. If there was to be a new unity, Ulrich believed, it would have to be won by the hard work of the scientific spirit, and it would have to be based upon the application of exact reason to human concerns no less than to technical specialties.

Instead Ulrich proposes that the Collateral Campaign devote itself to establishing an earthly Secretariat for Precision and the Spirit. What Ulrich has in mind is an agency for applying the scientific attitude to all the affairs of life, and including especially those known as spiritual. The utopian ideal of the possibilist, the very meaning of creativity, he says, is to transfer exactitude from intellect to the passions to such an extent that the passions disappear. And this exact man, he says, "is today in existence! As a man within the man he lives not only in the scientist but in the business man, in the administrator, in the sportsman, in the technician—even if for the present only during those main parts of the day that they call not their life but their profession."[104]

Ulrich is under no illusions about the value of science as a merely technical matter. "Where will it get one, on the Day of Judgment, when mankind's works are weighed in the balance, to come forward with three treatises on formic acid—or thirty, for that matter? On the other hand, what can one know about the Day of Judgment if one does not even know what may have come of formic acid by then?"[105] The point is to use the scientific approach to go beyond science as a merely technical instrument for examining fragments of the natural universe; to forge it into a way of knowing the universe, man, and society. Ulrich proposes to call this attitude essayism or experimentalism—an attitude somewhere between religion and knowledge, intellect and piety, but not to be confused with an aesthetic attitude, which tends to be too concerned with originality and comparison.

As a mathematician Ulrich resents the double standard by which great artists are celebrated and great scientists ignored. "The artistic mind," he says, "claims admiration of the same kind as that accorded to Goethe and Michelangelo, Napoleon and Luther. But scarcely anyone remembers even the name of the man who gave mankind the untold blessing of anaesthetics; nobody probes into the lives of Gauss, Euler or Maxwell in the hope of finding a Frau von Stein; and hardly a soul cares where Lavoisier and Cardanus were born and died."[106] We are all familiar with, and we take for granted, the line "between culture and knowledge, Humanity and Nature."[107]

This gulf between the two cultures, the humanities and the natural sciences, can only be bridged if we recognize that the scientific, experimental attitude should be the standard of all endeavor. But what, one may ask, is to be expected? What, finally, would it mean to be scientific in moral matters? The answer Ulrich gives seems to be that to know ourselves and others is automatically to overcome our separation from others and from things—our egoism, our subjectivity, and therefore our selfishness and hatred. We would not punish a madman as a criminal if we understood him and his deed. We would recognize that in moments of intense activity, whether of love or hate, the personality disappears. We could not remain uneasy in the world if we understood the causes of our anxiety. We would no longer feel the need for some missing goal if we discovered the common ground of all being. We would be transported by this knowledge onto a sea of love. But this sort of ultimate understanding does not come through the easy acquiescence, the desire to assimilate and be popular that guides Arnheim, the new "Superman of Letters," or that has inspired General Stumm, the representative of the military, to wish to impose order on disorder. Feeling wiser than before, Ulrich returns to the Collateral Campaign. He discovers that while he has been drawn to the virtues of passivity and withdrawal, the participants in the campaign have determined that action must be the crowning goal of their efforts. He is therefore thoroughly and radically alienated from the campaign and says he must resign as secretary. But he feels reassured by what he has come to understand. Knowledge and faith, he feels, are bound together; it is only that they have become separated and that the connection must somehow be restored. Faith must take flight from knowledge—though one cannot expect this from the work of a single man. By faith Ulrich means not only the wanting to know or "that credulous not knowing" but "a consciously apprehending insight."[108] But how was this restoration to come about? Surely not by any rational planning, not by setting up a secretariat for precision in matters of the soul—his own idea now seemed preposterous to him. Instead he would now follow the path of withdrawal. Was it entirely a path to passivity and renunciation? No, Ulrich insisted, it was not, for living with his sister Agathe would require tenderness and selflessness, which had been all too lacking in his life. Perhaps this very love for another was the spring of all social feelings. "Perhaps the substance of the Millenium," Ulrich says, "is simply the increase of that force—which at first manifests itself only when two are together—into a sonorous communion of all?"[109] Reflecting on his unsatisfying love affairs, Ulrich recognizes that they at least evoked some compassion in him, and he hopes that now, by living entirely for another, he may experience the highest happiness.

The story continues but it has really reached its end—*"eine art èndung,"* as Musil writes. Clarisse helps the insane criminal, Moosbrugger, escape; Ulrich and Agathe go off to an island in the Adriatic where they realize that their mystical nirvana cannot last. We cannot be sure how Musil would have resolved the story; but perhaps its very incompleteness should be understood as necessary to the answer he found to the questions he posed. For what Musil seems to have concluded is that the separation of intellect from life that he had discerned as the source of the modern dilemma could not be resolved, as he had first thought, simply by the ramification of the scientific attitude into every corner of life. This would indeed be necessary, but it would serve only as a necessary preliminary to the real challenge, which was to elevate science beyond itself, so that it could be understood as a belief in and an instrument for a comprehensive fulfillment of human needs and desires, which, for Ulrich, were concentrated in the desire for love. In still simpler terms, we may say that whereas the humanistic attitude toward science and the scientific society begins with Swift's satiric contempt, it ends in modern times in an attempt to see the scientific enterprise as a vehicle—the only possible vehicle—for humanistic values.

## The Social Scientists and Industrial Society

Unlike humanists, who have had difficulty accepting the claims of science as a way to understanding, social scientists have often been so impressed by the achievements of their colleagues studying nature that they have tried to emulate their methods and adopt their findings. Thomas Hobbes, who was for a while a secretary to Francis Bacon, was inspired by early modern natural science to wish to develop a new "civil science" using the *more geometrico,* or Euclidean geometric method, the inductive principles of Galileo, and at least the imagery of seventeenth-century mechanics. The state, he claimed, could be compared to other vital mechanisms which work by "springs and wheeles, as doth a watch."[110] Later, in the eighteenth century, the prestige of Newtonian physics was such that the traditional understanding of the concept of natural law was drastically changed to accord with what was then understood of the physical universe. Instead of a transcendental normative code of conduct accessible to reason, as well as inborn in the conscience, it became a presumably empirical description of original or primitive human behavior, as demonstrated in the life of primitive man. In the nineteenth century, while overtones of Newtonianism remain, as in Saint-Simon's analogy of universal love and gravitation and in Comte's call for a "social physics," it is the idea of evolution that grips the imagination of the social scientists. In this case, however, the social scientists could claim priority of discovery. The ideas that moved Lyell, and afterward Darwin and Russell, to speculate on the evidence of biology and geology issued originally from social theorists, notably Condorcet and Malthus. Once these ideas received the powerful support of the natural scientists, they become all but irresistible. Marx wished to dedicate *Das Kapital* to Darwin (who declined the honor, saying that he had onus enough from his own work); Herbert Spencer rewrote the liberal theory of society to take account of natural selection and what he designated "the survival of the fittest",[111] and Walter Bagehot devoted his misnamed *Physics and Politics* (1872) to the biologistic study of society as an organism.

Later developments in natural science have had a similar impact. Modern behavioralists in all the subdisciplines of the social sciences seek to extend what began as a theory of physiological psychology to account for the behavior of individuals and groups. An even broader school restricts its studies to matters that can be subjected to quantitative measurement and statistical prediction.[112] Other contemporary social scientists have been drawn to the concepts of communications theory in an effort to develop a model of social structure that corresponds with that of information systems.[113]

Still other contemporary social scientists remain skeptical about the relevance of natural-science methods and models and regard the more conventional study of historical tendencies and problems as still appropriate. Many of these, however, recognize the unique importance of science and technology to modern society. Out of their work has come what may be described as the emerging theory of industrial society. It is an emerging theory in the sense that while it may draw upon the earlier work of theorists like Marx and Weber, it is designed to take account of the developments unique to the twentieth century. These theorists include, among others, labor economists who have been impressed by the passing of the classic opposition of labor and capital into a new form of highly organized cooperation;[114] sociologists who study such aggregate phenomena as social organization and mass culture as functions of industrialization;[115] the economists whose study of economic development requires an understanding of industrialization as a process of growth;[116] historians, political scientists and social theorists whose study of history, international relations, and domestic politics suggests that scientific and technological change must be regarded as a key variable.[117]

While there are many differences among all these theorists, they may be said to share at least a common conviction that the concept of industrial society is one that needs to be developed to accommodate a wide variety of related and important social events. This concept can be said to assume, in the first instance, that virtually all modern nations wish to become and remain advancing industrial societies—societies whose per-capita rate of industrial growth exceeds the rate of population increase, whose output is heaviest in the nonagricultural sectors, whose style of life takes advantage of the most advanced technical methods of communications, construction, processing, and distribution, and whose power to safeguard and advance their interests makes use of, in greater or lesser degree, relatively advanced military systems. To be an industrial nation is to be committed in some degree to all of these preferences, though not necessarily to a single plan of how they are to be attained or to a single set of the ultimate ideals they ought to serve.

Indeed, much of the disagreement among the theorists concerns the question of whether industrialism lays down any fixed parameters within which all industrializing societies must confine their social values and institutions, or whether an extremely wide spectrum of choice is possible. In origin the concept of industrial society grows out of the much more limited concept of the Industrial Revolution, developed largely in the light of European and American experience.[118] Many attempts were made by those who elaborated this theory to isolate the stages of development through which those nations passed, beginning with Great Britain, as they underwent industrialization. They tried to account for a variety of the features of this process, including capital formation; technological change; population shifts and changes in the rate of population growth; the change in values from rural self-sufficiency to urban acquisitiveness; the changes in class power associated with the decline of the aristocracy and the rise of the new *bourgeoisie* and proletariat; the means by which the state fostered industrialization, by direct inducements such as the patent system, and indirectly by suppressing worker discontent; and the development of worldwide industrial empires.

Inevitably they were forced to contend with many variations, especially in connection with the experience of late-comers, who sought by deliberate action to achieve what had happened elsewhere by trial and error. It therefore became more difficult to say whether a stage of small-scale private enterprise was indispensable to the passage from commerce to industry, or whether the state would have the same role to play as it had in England and the United States. The theory of imperialism naturally developed into a classic arena of conflicting interpretations, particularly since political and scholarly considerations often went hand in hand.

The latter-day theory of industrial society is a continuation of these earlier efforts to appreciate the impact and the course of industrialization. Like preceding efforts it seeks to establish certain regularities in the patterns by which societies pass from traditional into industrial modes of organization and to allow for variations.[119] Today there are many more difficulties in such an undertaking. Now that the desire to industrialize has spread from Europe and America to the rest of the world, an ever-larger number of experiences must be considered. The problem of analysis is further complicated by the fact that a number of societies are now well beyond the stage of the initial "revolution." Their problems are connected with the effort to sustain, rather than initiate, industrial growth and to cope with the problems created by industrialization. Other countries are much closer to the stage that was once designated a revolution, but their case is complicated by the fact that often they have not undergone long prior development as nation-states and often find themselves establishing those foundations along with those of an industrial society. A comprehensive theory of industrial society today must therefore take into account a number of historical factors quite absent from the earlier concept of an industrial revolution.

In order to cope with these new elements it has seemed advisable to divide modern experience into that of developing societies and that of advanced societies. Other names will do just as well: backward or underdeveloped countries as distinguished from mature industrial societies. A great deal of attention has lately begun to be paid to developing societies by a host of social scientists, including economists, anthropologists, political scientists, sociologists, and even psychologists.[120] One difficulty in the attempt to formulate a general theory of development has been that in some cases the transition takes place in colonial and sometimes preliterate and tribal societies, and in others in societies with an elaborate civilized history. These societies, moreover, do not operate in political, ideological, or economic isolation. Studies of the developing society must therefore also take account of the international relations in which development takes place. Furthermore since these societies are often in very nebulous states of commitment, either ideologically or in terms of dependence upon other nations, they are often difficult to classify.

Indeed, still another complication is that there are many borderline cases. Countries like Japan are both advanced and developing. For that matter so is the Soviet Union. In some sectors the problems of these societies are clearly those of an advanced nation, in others those of a developing one. Even the most advanced industrial nations such as the United States and Canada, have areas which are relatively backward and whose problems are not entirely those of the advanced states of industrialization. Some distinction nevertheless appears necessary. A sound basis for differentiations may be the state of science in the society.

## Knowledge and Power: The Scientific Society

One major element in the advance of industrial society is of course the change from a dependence on mere applications of scientific knowledge to a situation where basic improvements in scientific understanding are sought in the hope that these will stimulate innovation. In this sense science has indeed become, as Vannevar Bush described it, an "endless frontier" replacing the incentives and opportunities afforded by open spaces and expanding markets. Whereas the old frontier functioned to stimulate investment, to keep up demand for labor, and to dampen social protest, the new indefinite frontier opened by science offers opportunity for the development of new knowledge which can be used to prolong life, curb population growth, increase the supply of food and other consumer articles, speed communication throughout the world and provide weapons of unprecedented destructiveness.

The role of government in the advancement of science has been recognized as crucial. Although privately sponsored industrial research accounts for much of the scientific and technical progress achieved in the last twenty years and much more of the marketable goods, private sources cannot be expected to provide the trained scientific personnel, the facilities, and the projects which are necessary for a full range of scientific activity and which may or may not have immediate dividends. Understanding the relations of government and science has therefore become more important than ever.

Some scientific progress may be of great utility to the developing society, especially in the effort to increase food supply, improve public health, and bring population increase under control. On the whole, however, science of a highly sophisticated order is more of a requisite to the advanced society. It is in the advanced society, for example, that the volume of information required in ordinary business transactions is so high and the rate of flow of such a frequency that computerized systems of storage and retrieval become indispensable. It is in the advanced society where separate avenues of research are so well developed that they overlap and reenforce each other, making possible collaborative advances in industrial products, medicine, and even fundamental knowledge. It is in the advanced society that metropolitan congestion has become so acute that only the imaginative application of engineering and the ecological arts can prevent inconvenience and even paralysis. It is in the advanced society that the industrial waste and pollution of natural resources become a problem requiring a comprehensive effort to understand, to plan, and carry into execution a systematic effort to conserve the natural endowment. It is the advanced society, finally, that finds itself called upon to use its productive and scientific superiority to assist other nations struggling to modernize. Self-interest, no less than idealism, demands that this call be heeded by the commitment of scientific resources as well as by the shipment of relief supplies which, in the long run, do not provide lasting help.

In America the early stages of government involvement with science were almost exclusively centered about military needs. Lately they have been concerned with the broader needs for science as well as with the exploration of outer space. Increasingly they are becoming related to the needs of the economy and the state of social health and welfare. Throughout the phases of this effort, government funding has altered the relationship between public and nonpublic bodies. It is not only that government provides the wherewithal. To some extent government must also determine or influence the pattern of activity by deciding how and where to spend the money. Its spending in effect induces movements of personnel and capital. Its own research activities provide both jobs and training and vital services. In the past two decades government support of science has provided the impetus not only for a breakdown of the traditional separation between public and private but for the development of new intermediate institutions — such as the nonprofit corporation and the university-affiliated research center. It has become necessary for government to solicit advice from those in the scientific professions concerning the allocation of its funds, decisions to approve or disapprove projects for sponsorship, and a broad spectrum of policy issues in which science plays a role, such as proposals in defense policy.

But these developments are only a beginning. They provide only a shadowy outline of the scientific society that is gradually emerging from the industrial society. We can only guess at the shape this new society will take. From what we know now, it would appear that the changeover need not involve the sort of radical transformation in the social structure that many early theorists foresaw. Some changes, however, that are in some sense fundamental, do seem in prospect. It is hard to imagine, for example, that individuals, institutions, or societies will be as independent and as isolated in the future as they have been in the past. Larger units of organization seem inevitable in many areas of social life. Patterns of work and enterprise may well have to be adjusted to an economic system in which none of the components can be permitted great autonomy without endangering the entire system. Much will depend, of course, upon how humanity responds to the complexities and challenges that knowledge brings. Will the nations of the world succeed in securing themselves against the unprecedented dangers posed by modern weapons of mass destruction? Will particular societies appreciate in time the need to make social adjustments to accomodate scientific and technical change?

Questions like these are in the first instance questions of practicality. But they are also, in concrete terms, questions of human values. The answers to them inevitably require an effort to bend both knowledge and power to some conception of social purpose. In the largest sense, this is precisely the challenge that modern science holds for society. The social theorists of earlier times were right to predict that scientific knowledge would become a source of enormous power to society. They also saw that, after the science of nature had begun to make its great contributions, an effort would have to be made to establish a science of man as a complementary source of power. It is by no means certain that this effort can succeed and it may be argued that if it does succeed, it will pose far more of a threat than natural science has ever posed. But there is no escaping the fundamental fact that as knowledge of any kind becomes a source of power, questions of purpose will arise. The test of a great society is surely not simply that it amasses knowledge and turns that knowledge into power, but rather that it does so with a careful and constant attention to the purposes which learning may serve. The test will not be met successfully by reliance on a technocratic elite. In a self-governing society, only the citizenry, guided but not governed by professional specialists, has the right to decide what shall be done with the resources and the human ability which are its inheritance. As Donald F. Hornig, science adviser to President Johnson, has wisely observed, "[I]t will not do for scientists to feel that as experts they are the only ones entitled to answer the broader questions that are posed. Most of these questions need to be answered in concert among scientists, economists, lawyers, political scientists, and citizens at large."[121] The record of

58

the third culture is surely evidence that a concern for the social implications of science is not the preserve of any one group of specialists. What remains to be seen is whether it can become the focus of attention for whole societies and whether these societies can act intelligently to make good use of what their specialists are capable of learning.

## NOTES

1 Snow's essays have been put together in *The Two Cultures: And a Second Look*, New York, 1964. The quotations (pp. 66–67) are from the most recent essay, which first appeared in *The Times Literary Supplement* (Oct. 25, 1963). For a brief critical discussion of this essay see Sanford A. Lakoff, 'The Nth Culture Problem," *Bulletin of the Atomic Scientists* (May 1964), pp. 21–23. For other discussions of the two-cultures controversy see references in the Select Bibliography.

2 See Michael Polanyi's *Personal Knowledge; Towards a Post-Critical Philosophy*, Chicago, 1960.

3 Gertrude Himmelfarb, *Darwin and the Darwinian Revolution*, New York, 1962, p. 55.

4 Charles Singer, *A Short History of Scientific Ideas to 1900*, Oxford, 1959, Chap. VII, pp. 218–287.

5 Quoted by Giorgio de Santillana, *The Crime of Galileo*, Chicago, 1959, p. 310.

6 *Advancement of Learning*, G. W. Kitchin, ed., London & New York, 1950, p. 26.

7 *Ibid.*, pp. 28–29.

8 See *Novum Organum*, Aphorism XXXIX, in Bacon, *The New Organum and Related Writings*, F. H. Anderson, ed., New York, 1960, pp. 47–48 *passim*.

9 *Advancement of Learning*, p. 4.

10 *Ibid.*, p. 6; italics in original.

11 *Ibid.*, p. 8.

12 *Ibid.*

13 *Ibid.*, pp. 13–14.

14 *Ibid.*, p. 14.

15 *Novum Organum*, Aphorism LXX, p. 68.

16 *Ibid.*, Aphorism III, p. 39.

17 Thomas Babington Macaulay, "Lord Bacon," in *Critical and Historical Essays Contributed to the Edinburgh Review*, Vol. II, London, 1903, p. 210.

18 *Ibid.*, p. 213.

19 *Ibid.*, p. 217.

20 *Novum Organum*, Aphorism III, p. 39.

21 *Ibid.*, Aphorism XCVIII, p. 95. The standard translation loses some of the flavor of the Latin: "The secrets of nature reveal themselves more readily under the vexations of art than when they go their own way."

22 Bacon, *The New Atlantis*, A. B. Gough, ed., Oxford, 1924, p. 13.

23 *Ibid.*, p. 35.

24 *Ibid.*, p. 46.

25 *Ibid.*, p. 33.

26 See Condorcet, *Rapport et projet de décret sur l'organisation générale de l'instruction publique*, Paris, 1793.

27 Condorcet, *Fragment sur l'Atlantide, ou efforts combinés de l'espèce humaine pour le progrès des sciences*, in *Oeuvres de Condorcet*, A. C. O'Connor and M. F. Arago, eds., Paris, 1847, Vol. VI, p. 599.

28 *Ibid.*, pp. 599–600.

29 *Ibid.*, pp. 598–599.

30 Condorcet, *Sketch for a Historical Picture of the Progress of the Human Mind* (1795), J. Barraclough, tr., London, 1955, Introduction, p. 10.

31 *Ibid.*, pp. 173–202. See particularly "The Ninth Stage," *Ibid.*, pp. 124–172. For a discussion of Condorcet's and Locke's attitudes toward equality see Sanford A. Lakoff, *Equality in Political Philosophy*, Cambridge Mass., 1964.

32 *Sketch*, pp. 182–183.

33 *Ibid.*, p. 183.

34 *Fragment*, p. 656.

35 *Ibid.*, pp. 604–605, 659–660.

36 *Ibid.*, p. 603.

37 *Memoire sur la science de l'homme*, in *Oeuvres de Saint-Simon et d'Enfantin, précédées de deux notices historiques et publiées par les membres du conseil institué par Enfantin pour l'execution de ses dernières volontés*, Paris, 1865–1878, Vol. XL, p. 40, quoted in Frank E. Manuel, *The New World of Henri Saint-Simon*, Cambridge Mass., 1956, p. 111.

38 *Oeuvres*, Vol. XL, pp. 236–244, quoted in F. M. H. Markham, ed., *Henri Comte de Saint-Simon (1760–1825): Selected Writings*, Oxford, 1952, pp. 23–26.

39 For Saint-Simon's conscious elaboration of Bacon's and Condorcet's belief in the necessity for such a scientific society, see Manuel, *op. cit.*, pp. 73–77 and *The Prophets of Paris*, Cambridge Mass., 1962 Chap.3.

40 Saint-Simon developed this scheme in his *Lettres d'un habitant de Genève* (1803). See Manuel, *op. cit.*, pp. 46–61, 125–138.

41 *Oeuvres choisies de Saint-Simon, sa vie et ses travaux; suivi de fragments des plus célèbres écrits de Saint-Simon*, Paris, 1857, quoted in Manuel, *op. cit.*, p. 126.

42 See *First Extract from the "Organizer"* (1819), *Oeuvres*, Vol. XX, pp. 17–26, quoted in Markham, *op. cit.*, pp. 72–75.

43 See excerpt from *Lettres d'un habitant de Genève...*, in Markham, *op. cit.*, pp. 2–4.

44 *Ibid.*, p. 6.

45 See Manuel, *op. cit.*, p. 83.

46 See *ibid.*, pp. 288–294, pp. 130–138.

47 See *ibid.*, pp. 300–301.

48 See *ibid.*, pp. 243–261.

49 Quoted from "The Reorganization of the European Community," in *Oeuvres*, Vol. XV, p. 248, in Markham, *op. cit.*, p. 68.

50 For a discussion of Comte's break with Saint-Simon see Manuel, *op. cit.*, pp. 332–343.

51 See *The Positive Philosophy of Auguste Comte*, Harriet Martineau, tr., London, 1853, Vol. I, Book I, Chap. 1, pp. 1–16.

52 See *ibid.*, Vol. II, Book VI, Chap. 1–3, pp. 1–110.

53 *Ibid.*, Vol. I, Book II, Chap. 1, p. 45.

54 See *ibid.*, Vol. II, Book VI, Chap. 13, pp. 456–464.

55 See *ibid.*, pp. 434–496.

56 See Aron, *War and Industrial Society*, Oxford, 1958, *passim.*

57 Karl Marx, preface to *The Critique of Political Economy* (1859), in E. Burns, *A Handbook of Marxism (London, 1935)*, p. 371.

58 See the essay on "Private Property and Communism" in the *Economic and Philosophical Manuscripts*, T. B. Bottomore, tr., in E. Fromm, *Marx's Concept of Man*, New York, 1961, p. 125.

59 See the translation of this essay in H. H. Gerth and C. W. Mills, eds. *From Max Weber: Essays in Sociology*, London, 1947, p. 155.

60 See his "Der Sozialismus," an address to Austrian military officers in 1918, in Max Weber, *Gesammelte Aufsätze zur Soziologie und Sozialpolitik,* Tübingen, 1924, p. 497.

61 *Ibid.,* pp. 498–499.

62 *Ibid.,* p. 503.

63 *Ibid.,* p. 504.

64 *Ibid.,* pp. 513–514.

65 "Science as a Vocation," pp. 140–145.

66 *Ibid.,* p. 155.

67 Edward Bellamy, *Looking Backward,* New York, 1917, p. 41.

68 *Ibid.,* pp. 41–42.

69 *Ibid.,* p. 42.

70 *Ibid.,* p. 156.

71 See particularly Veblen's *The Instinct of Workmanship and the State of the Industrial Arts,* New York, 1914, and *The Theory of the Leisure Class* (1895), New York, 1934.

72 See *The Theory of the Leisure Class.*

73 See *The Engineers and the Price System,* New York, 1921, especially Chap. 3, "Finance and the Engineers," pp. 52–83.

74 See *The Theory of Business Enterprise* (1904), New York, 1932, Chap. 9, "The Cultural Incidence of the Machine Process," pp. 302–373.

75 Preface to *The Portable Veblen,* Max Lerner, ed., New York, 1948, p. 16.

76 See *The Engineers and the Price System,* Chap. 6, "A Memorandum on a Practicable Soviet of Technicians," pp. 138–169.

77 See *Imperial Germany and the Industrial Revolution,* New York, 1915.

78 B. F. Skinner, *Walden Two,* New York, 1948.

79 Comte, *The Positive Philosophy,* Vol. II. Chap. 15, p. 560.

80 Jonathan Swift, *Gulliver's Travels,* New York, 1949, Chap. 2, "A Voyage to Laputa," p. 154.

81 Ernest Renan, *The Future of Science,* London, 1891, Chap. 1, p. 24.

82 *Ibid.,* Chap. 14, p. 235.

83 "Science and Culture" (1880), T. H. Huxley, *Science and Education,* New York, 1893, p. 122.

84 *Ibid.,* p. 125.

85 *Ibid.,* p. 128.

86 *Ibid.,* p. 132.

87 "Literature and Science," in M. Arnold, *Discourses in America,* London, 1885, p. 90.

88 *Ibid.,* p. 99.

89 *Ibid.,* p. 135.

90 *Ibid.,* p. 136.

91 Foreword to *Brave New World,* Bantam Edition, New York, 1946, p. ix. See also his *Brave New World Revisited,* New York, 1958.

92 Robert Musil, *The Man Without Qualities,* E. Wilkins and E. Kaiser, trs., New York, 1953, Vol. I, p. 37. For a general study of Musil's life and work see Berton E. Pike, *Robert Musil; An Introduction to his Work,* Ithaca, N.Y., 1961.

93 *Ibid.,* p. 38.

94 *Ibid.,* pp. 38–39.

95 *Ibid.,* p. 40.

96 *Ibid.,* p. 41.

97 *Ibid.*

98 *Ibid.,* p. 48.

99 *Ibid.,* p. 46.

100 *Ibid.,* p. 49.

101 *Ibid.*

102 *Ibid.,* p. 223.

103 *Ibid.,* pp. 93–109.

104 *Ibid.,* p. 293.

105 *Ibid.,* p. 295.

106 *Ibid.,* p. 356.

107 *Ibid.*

108 *Ibid.,* p. 188.

109 *Ibid.,* p. 247.

110 *Leviathan* (1651), W. G. Pogson Smith, ed., Oxford, England, 1947, Introduction, p. 8.

111 For a fuller account of Spencer's revision of traditional liberal

theory see Lakoff, *ibid.*, Chap. 6, pp. 143–155.

112 H. Eulau, *The Behavioral Persuasion in Politics*, New York, 1963, and H. Eulau, S. J. Eldersveld, and M. Janowitz, eds., *Political Behavior: A Reader in Theory and Research*, New York, N.Y., 1956; and Anatol Rapoport, *Science and the Goals of Man; A Study in Semantic Orientation*, New York, 1960; Paul F. Lazarsfeld and M. Rosenberg, eds., *The Language of Social Research; A Reader in the Methodolgy of Social Research*, New York, N.Y., 1955; Paul F. Lazarsfeld, *Mathematical Thinking in the Social Sciences*, Glencoe, Ill. 1954.

113 See particularly Karl W. Deutsch, *The Nerves of Government; Models of Political Communication and Control*, New York, 1963.

114 See particularly Clark Kerr, John Dunlop, Frederick Harbison, and Charles A. Myers, *Industrialism and Industrial Man*, Cambridge Mass., 1960.

115 See particularly William Kornhauser, *The Politics of Mass Society*, Glencoe Ill., 1959 and Daniel Bell, *The End of Ideology*, Glencoe Ill., 1960.

116 See especially W. W. Rostow, *The Stages of Economic Growth*, Cambridge Eng., 1960; Benjamin H. Higgins, *Economic Development; Principles, Problems and Policies*, New York, 1959; W. Arthur Lewis, *The Theory of Economic Growth*, London, 1955; and Paul A. Baran, *The Political Economy of Growth*, New York, 1957.

117 See particularly Herbert Marcuse, *One-Dimensional Man*, Boston, 1964; Raymond Aron, *War and Industrial Society*, London, 1958; François Perroux, *La Coexistence Pacifique*, 3 Vols., Paris, 1958; Barrington Moore, Jr., *Political Power and Social Theory; Six Studies*, Cambridge Mass., 1958.

118 Notably T. S. Ashton, *The Industrial Revolution, 1760–1830*, London & New York, 1948, and Arnold Toynbee, *The Industrial Revolution*, Boston, 1956.

119 See for example G. A. Almond and J. S. Coleman, *The Politics of the Developing Areas*, Princeton N.J., 1960.

120 For a psychological study see David C. McClellan, *The Achieving Society*, New York, 1961.

121 Donald F. Hornig, "The American Scientific Scene," *Transactions, American Geophysical Union*, Vol. XLVI, No. 2, June 1965, p. 379.

# PART I

# Cases and Controversies

EDITOR'S NOTE

In June 1954, after hearings "in the matter of J. Robert Oppenheimer" before the specially constituted Personnel Security Board and after an appeal to the full Atomic Energy Commission, the eminent American theoretical physicist, who had been awarded the Medal of Merit for his scientific direction of the Los Alamos laboratory during World War II, was deprived of his security clearance and barred from access to classified research. Then and since, the proceedings have excited great controversy. It has been charged that they were instigated under the witch-hunting spell of McCarthyism and in an effort to punish Oppenheimer for the advice he had given on a number of matters involving the application of atomic energy to military strategy.[1] It has been pointed out that although Oppenheimer's security clearance was ostensibly reconsidered only because the standards had been changed, the revocation was justified by the Personnel Security Board chaired by Gordon Gray largely on one ground and by the five commissioners largely on an entirely different ground. The board had considered him a security risk for displaying bad judgment in advising against a crash program to develop the hydrogen bomb. The commission rejected this reasoning, holding that it was wrong and a dangerous precedent to punish an adviser for his advice. Instead the revocation of clearance was sustained on the ground that Oppenheimer had displayed "defects of character" in holding back information from security officers and on the ground that he had maintained associations with unreliable people.[2] The essay that follows was written a year after the hearings as a reflection upon the larger implications of this historic episode in the early confrontation between science and government.

# The Trial of Dr. Oppenheimer

SANFORD A. LAKOFF

*That is what novels are about. There is a dramatic moment and the history of the man, what made him act, what he did, and what sort of person he was. That is what you are really doing here. You are writing a man's life.*[3]

Dr. Isadore I. Rabi, testimony to the Gray Board.

## The Trial as Archetype

The great trials in Western history are often revealing indices to the life and troubles of the societies in which they occur. For us the Dreyfus trial is less the trial of an officer for treason than the trial of republicanism in France. In recent times the purge trials of Moscow have provided a vivid portrait of totalitarianism in action in spite of (or perhaps partially on account of) the staged nature of the proceedings. In American history the Salem inquisition, the Scopes trial, the Sacco-Vanzetti case are all memorable as occasions upon which our society was as much on trial as the defendants.

One universal element in all such trials is the participation of articulate men. Yet it is never wholly by the accident of their presence that the trial takes on its importance as a focus for the pressing problems of the day. The trial is an occasion, an historical moment, for which the actors and extras somehow make themselves available. In the great trials the issues run so deep that they inevitably strike capable advocates, if not in the circle of the protagonists, then in the penumbra of lawyers and publicists.

Every trial represents a test of the beliefs of a society, but the great trials stand out because the breach of the law transcends the plane of negative disobedience. In the great trial the crime of the offender is to challenge the very order of society that the law embodies. Consequently the question of the defendant's guilt is overshadowed by the challenge to the society's assumptions of innocence. The zeal of the heresy hunters in the inquisitions of the Middle Ages and the Reformation and the martyrdom accorded their victims are two sides of the same coin. Both attest to the radical nature of the trials and to the equal involvement of pursuers with pursued.

Perhaps the first great trial recorded in Western history was the trial of Socrates. In the grandeur of its pathos and in the relevance it has to all times, it stands as the archetype of all the great trials. It can therefore serve as harmony and counterpoint to the theme of the present composition. That theme, as in all great trials, is a double one, for as the trial of Socrates was equally as much the trial of the Athenian *polis*, so the trial of Dr. Oppenheimer was also the trial of liberal democracy in America.

## THE ENCHANTED VILLAIN

The trial of Socrates was conducted in much the same atmosphere of suspicion and insecurity that pervades contemporary America. Given this atmosphere, it is perhaps not surprising that Dr. Oppenheimer should evoke from his enemies the same imputation of serpentine charisma that was conferred upon Socrates. Socrates begins his defense in the *Apology* by remarking that the strategem of his accusers that most amazed him was their warning to the Athenians to "be on your guard and not allow yourself to be deceived by the force of my eloquence."[4] The testimony of several of Dr. Oppenheimer's accusers bears, implicitly, the same warning. Dr. Luis W. Alvarez testifies:

> ... Every time I have found a person who felt this way (i.e., opposed to H-bomb development) I have seen Dr. Oppenheimer's influence on that person's mind. I don't think there is anything wrong with this. I would certainly try to persuade people of my point of view, and Dr. Oppenheimer is quite free and should try to persuade people of his convictions. I just point out that the facts as I see them, that this reaction has *always* taken place in people that I know have been opposed to the bomb. . . .
> DR. EVANS. Do you think that Dr. Oppenheimer had considerable power with men like Conant, Bush, and Groves?
> THE WITNESS. I don't think power is the right word. Dr. Oppenheimer is certainly *one of the most persuasive men that has ever lived,* and he certainly had influence. They respected his opinions and listened to him.[5]

The theme is repeated by other witnesses called by the review board counsel, Roger Robb. General Roscoe Wilson of the air force—who also testified that his suspicions were aroused because, although Dr. Oppenheimer opposed the attempt to develop nuclear-powered aircraft (on the basis of technical judgment), "at the same time he felt less strongly opposed to the nuclear-powered ships"[6]— explained his reasons for communicating his misgivings to the Director of Intelligence in these terms:

> I would like to say that the fact that I admire Dr. Oppenheimer so much, the fact that he is such a brilliant man, the fact that he has such a command of the English language, has such national prestige, and such power of persuasion, only made me nervous, because I felt that if this was so it would not be to the interest of the United States, in my judgment.[7]

When asked what was the source of opposition he said he encountered to the development of the H-bomb, Dr. Wendell M. Latimer replied:

> A. I judge the source of it was Dr. Oppenheimer.
> Q. Why?
> A. You know, he is one of the most amazing people that this country has ever produced in his ability to influence people. It is just astounding the influence that he has upon a group. It is an amazing thing. His domination of the General Advisory Committee was so complete that he always carried the majority with him, and I don't think any views came out of that committee that weren't essentially his views.[8]

After Dr. Oppenheimer left Los Alamos, Dr. Latimer testified, one of the "whole series of events" which bothered him about Dr. Oppenheimer's conduct was that "many of our boys came back from it [Los Alamos] pacifists. I judged that was due largely to his influence, this tremendous influence he had over those young men."[9] Under cross-examination by defense counsel Samuel Silverman, Dr. Latimer repeated his belief in Dr. Oppenheimer's magical powers: "Not only General Groves, but the other members on the committee, Conant and the other members, they were under the influence of Dr. Oppenheimer, and that is some influence, I assure you." Mr. Silverman persisted:

> Q. Were you under Dr. Oppenheimer's influence?
> A. No. I don't believe I was in close enough contact to be. I might have been if I had been in closer contact.[10]

Pressed to explain the sources of Oppenheimer's mana, Dr. Latimer can only say:

> I had studied this influence that Dr. Oppenheimer had over men. It was a tremendous thing. . . . I have seen him sway

audiences. It was just marvelous, the phraseology and the
influence is just tremendous. I can't analyze it for you, but I
think all of you know the man and recognize what I am talking
about.[11]

In Dr. Latimer's case one possible explanation for his own
particular awe of Oppenheimer comes out in another part of his
testimony. When he was asked by Mr. Silverman why he didn't try
to get the General Advisory Committee behind his drive for an
H-bomb program, he replied: "After all, a chemist does not have
very much influence with theoretical physicists."[12] A sense of
inferiority is not unknown even among academic orders, and it may
be that a certain amount of resentment which chemists have for
nuclear physicists may have worked itself into Dr. Latimer's
opinions. Some such combination of envy and inferiority feeling
might also reasonably account for the awe of the military man,
General Wilson, but it cannot account for Dr. Alvarez' attitude, for
he is himself a nuclear physicist.

The charge of overpowering persuasiveness has a significance
beyond whatever particular motives may be ascribed to the witnesses and certainly beyond any attributes actually possessed by
Dr. Oppenheimer. Socrates recognized in this accusation a strategic
attempt to discredit in advance whatever he might say in his own
defense. He met the maneuver with a stratagem of his own, building
his first argument about a profession of absolute ignorance in an
attempt to give the impression that for the very reason of his ignorance he was incapable of persuading anyone of his doctrine. The
behavior of Socrates in so similar a situation may offer us an insight into one aspect of the trial which is surely puzzling. Dr.
Oppenheimer's friends insisted in their testimony that he has a
superlative ability for crystallizing ideas (hence his value as a committee chairman). Yet it is plain that in the trial he was often vague
and unconvincing in his testimony, especially where something
damaging was at stake. It would appear that without the deliberation
of Socrates, Dr. Oppenheimer was defending himself against the
image of his own power by demonstrating an abject weakness. He
seemed to crave the prosecutor's every trap. When Mr. Robb suggested to him that he told a "tissue of lies" to the security officers
about the Chevalier incident, he made no attempt to refine the
loaded phraseology or to deny the multiple character of his false-
hood, as Dr. Ward Evans was to do in his dissenting opinion.[13]
Instead he made an emphatically affirmative reply: "Right."[14] He
said himself that it was a "cock and bull story."[15]

In a sense the rhetorical exaggerations in the trial were a function of the importance attaching to the men and issues involved. The

great trial has its own archetypical form which stamps the proceedings with special color. Someone had to insinuate that the villain was poisoning the minds of the young—and Dr. Latimer did just that. The reasonableness of Dr. Rabi's position that if the government had qualms about Dr. Oppenheimer it might simply have stopped consulting him without exposing him to public stigma was too pallid to win much favor.[16] The most extreme of the accusers, William L. Borden, went so far as to assert that Dr. Oppenheimer was probably a spy. In a hypothetical question put to the banker, John J. McCloy, Mr. Robb felt no need for qualification in substituting for Dr. Oppenheimer the analogue of a branch manager who associates with thieves and safecrackers.[17] For his part, Dr. Oppenheimer played the role of the hapless innocent with equal exaggeration.

## THE SOPHIST SOLDIER

Socrates would have no difficulty in recognizing another aspect of the trial for what it was. At one point a security officer, Colonel Boris T. Pash, testified to his understanding of Dr. Oppenheimer's motivations in these terms: When Dr. Oppenheimer went to the security officers with the story of the Chevalier incident, Colonel Pash suggested, it was because "he knew or had reason to know that we were investigating....It was my opinion that Dr. Oppenheimer wanted to present this information to us for the purpose of relieving any pressure that may be brought on him for further investigation of his personal situation."[18] This hypothesis has a certain objective logic which might lend it at least a claim on credibility, were the logic not undermined by its psychology. In his recommendations concerning the handling of Dr. Oppenheimer by the army, Captain Peer de Silva worked the same psychological mine for another purpose:

> It is the opinion of this officer that Oppenheimer is deeply concerned with gaining a world-wide reputation as a scientist, and a place in history, as a result of the DSM project. It is also believed that the Army is in the position of being able to allow him to do so or to destroy his name, reputation, and career, if it should choose to do so. Such a possibility, if strongly presented to him, would possibly give him a different view of his position with respect to the Army, which has been, hitherto, one in which he has been dominant due to his supposed essentiality.[19]

The explanations of Dr. Oppenheimer's conduct and concerns tell less about him than about their authors. As his Sophist enemies projected onto Socrates their own pursuit of success in the marketplace, the military mind pictured its antagonist as a man chiefly concerned with personal safety and glory.

## THE SOPHIST LAWYER

But by far the most vigorous exhibition of the sophist temper in the trial was the performance of the counsel for the board, Mr. Robb. Mr. Robb himself gave a most revealing insight into his conduct in an exchange with Colonel John Lansdale, a wartime security officer, not in the regular army but in the reserve, who testified for Dr. Oppenheimer. Mr. Robb is cross-examining:

> Q. Colonel Lansdale, as a lawyer, are you familiar with the legal maxim, "Falsus in uno, falsus in omnibus"?
>
> A. Yes; I am. Like all legal maxims, it is a generalization, and not of particular significance when applied to specifics.
>
> Q. When you are trying a jury case and the veracity of the witness is in question, do you request the court to give an instruction on that subject?
>
> A. Oh, certainly, don't you?
>
> Q. Certainly, I want to know what you do.
>
> A. The instruction usually is that the jury may, but does not have to, take that as an indication, and the judgment is to be exercised in the particular case.
>
> Q. And when you are trying a jury case and you examine a witness on the opposite side and you demonstrate that he has lied, don't you argue to the jury from that that they should disregard his evidence?
>
> A. You are speaking now of what I as an advocate do?
>
> Q. Yes.
>
> A. It depends upon the circumstances; usually I do.
>
> Q. Sure. Any lawyer worth his salt would.
>
> A. Particularly if it is my belief.[20]

At the outset of the hearing Dr. Gordon Gray, the chairman of the Board, made it a point to "remind everyone concerned that this proceeding is an inquiry and not in the nature of a trial. We shall approach our duties in that atmosphere and in that spirit."[21] Yet Mr. Robb found no difficulty pursuing a question premised on the assumption of adversary proceeding. In fact it is quite clear from his questioning generally that he was operating as a prosecutor.[22] The exchange with Colonel Lansdale reflected his effort to impeach Dr. Oppenheimer's character. He made every effort to discredit the testimony of the eminent witnesses for Dr. Oppenheimer which might have been made if he were operating in a courtroom. He concluded a cross-examination of Dr. Hans Bethe as follows:

Q. Doctor, how many divisions were there at Los Alamos?
A. It changed somewhat in the course of time. As far as I could count the other day, there were 7, but there may have been 8 or 9 at some time.
Q. Which division was Klaus Fuchs in?
A. He was in my division which was the Theoretical Division.
MR. ROBB. Thank you. That is all.[23]

Mr. Robb's questioning of David Lilienthal especially roused the ire of Dr. Oppenheimer's counsel. Lilienthal had testified that in 1947 the AEC cleared Dr. Oppenheimer on the charges and information then available. He was presented with a report of a conversation deposited by him in the files of the AEC, and admitted that he had forgotten the conversation. With rather obvious intent to discredit his testimony generally, Mr. Robb proceeded to exacerbate the wound:

Q. Now, Mr. Lilienthal, this was a matter of grave import to you, wasn't it?
A. Yes it was an important matter, one of many important matters, that is right.
Q. It was of sufficient importance, and importance to you, that you took shorthand notes on this conversation, and then dictated a memorandum about it, is that right?
A. That is right.
Q. But it is now your testimony that you had completely forgotten any discussion with Mr. Clifford about a board of review?
A. It is.
Q. And you had completely forgotten that you even considered such a board?
A. It is. I must say it just entirely escaped my mind.[24]

Lloyd Garrison, Dr. Oppenheimer's chief counsel, raised an objection to the procedure under which Mr. Robb, who was in possession of the files, innocently asked the witness to "tell us what happened" in an effort "to make the witnesses look to the board in as unfavorable a light as possible, and to make what is a lapse of memory seem like a deliberate falsification." He observed that such a procedure was perfectly in order in criminal prosecution but questioned its use in an inquiry. Mr. Robb responded indignantly, insisting that his procedure needs no justification. "It is an axiom," he said, "that the greatest invention known to man for the discovery of truth is cross-examination . . ." A discussion ensued in which Mr. Lilienthal and Dr. Oppenheimer's counsel suggested pointedly that the refusal of the board to permit witnesses to consult files to which they had contributed before testifying was not a procedure likely to elicit from a witness his best recollection of what happened. "It seems to me," Mr. Garrison concluded, "more like a criminal trial than it does like an inquiry and I just regret that it has to be done here." Mr. Robb summed up his position by suggesting that "it is demonstrated that the memory of the witness was not infallible" and "since we are depending largely on memory, I think it is a fair test."[25] It was quite clear from Mr. Robb's remarks that he was deliberately pursuing the technique of advocacy which he outlined in his questioning of Colonel Lansdale. If Mr. Lilienthal could have been shown guilty of a falsification *"in uno,"* the presumption of falsity could have been attached to the rest of his testimony. Whether there was falsification or simple lapse of memory without intent to deceive did not concern the lawyer; his job was to cast doubt upon the testimony of witnesses for the other side.

## The Trial of Liberal Democracy

But if the formal parallels marking these two trials are striking, the substantive contrasts are at least as impressive. In the temple of modern democracy, the Periclean altar to Athens has a revered place, even as we recognize that the identity of the new and the old democracy goes not much futher than the level of aspiration. Ours is not a city-state but a nation-state, and the difference in size is important. Aristotle insisted that the *polis* had to be limited in size because he recognized that the peculiar type of democracy which had developed in Athens depended upon the face-to-face relations of a primary group. We have had to recognize that political relations in modern times are inevitably those of the society rather than the community. The verdict in the trial of Dr. Oppenheimer reflects the impact of this development in sharp terms. The reason it was necessary that the size of the *polis* be limited, Aristotle pointed out, was the need for the citizens of the state to "know one another's characters."[26] It was precisely their estimate of his "defects of character" which served as the basis for the majority finding against Dr. Oppenheimer in the final consideration made by the members of the AEC. But the decision as to his character was not made on the basis of their direct knowledge of the man but rather on the basis of reports concerning his conduct. The testimony of so many of his most esteemed associates could not counterbalance the "objective" evidence.

A colloquy between Mr. Robb and Dr. Rabi highlights the difference. When Mr. Robb attempted to elicit from him agreement to the proposition that the members of the board may have had more information about Dr. Oppenheimer's conduct in the matters under consideration than he did, and that this information might warrant a refusal of clearance, Dr. Rabi replied: "It may be. On the other hand, I am in possession of a long experience with this man, going back to 1929, which is 25 years, and there is a kind of seat of the pants feeling on which I myself lay great weight."[27] George F. Kennan attested to Dr. Oppenheimer's character on the basis of personal contact with him "as an associate and neighbor, and a friend at Princeton."[28] The majority opinion of the AEC did not consider such "seat of the pants" evidence. It found defects in his character on the basis of incidents in "the record before the Commission."[29] Since the chief count against him on this score was what came to be known as the Chevalier incident, there is no small irony to this charge. Dr. Oppenheimer was impeached for having failed to reveal immediately the name of Haakon Chevalier to the security officers. At the time he made an explanation of his refusal to name "Professor X" to Colonel Lansdale. Dr. Oppenheimer had said: "What I want to say is this—I'm not kidding you and I'm not trying to weasel out. It's my overwhelming judgment that this guy isn't involved. *That isn't judgment which is based on hope but his character.*"[30]

## THE DEMOCRATIC ELITE

Nor must it be forgotten that Athens was a democracy guided by a leisure class and supported by slaves. Modern democracy is, by comparison, radically egalitarian. In place of a distinct leisure class, our men of power are grouped in a variety of democratic elites, some more open than others, but all subject to the will of a widely enfranchised populace. In the conflict over defense policy, the contours of which the Oppenheimer trial revealed in considerable detail, two of these elite groups, the one military, the other scientific, were the combatants. The decision to shift the focus of defense policy from containment to massive retaliation was made publicly, in full view of the electorate, by Secretary Dulles. But a crucial element in the background of that decision was first exposed in the trial.[31] Long before the policy of massive retaliation was announced, the Air Force, in particular the Strategic Air Command, sought just such a shift in policy, based on increased reliance on strategic air power. When Dr. Teller and his associates approached the Air Force with their plans for the development of the H-bomb, they found warm support. It was the Air Force that enabled them to acquire the second (Livermore) laboratory they believed to be necessary. That Dr. Oppenheimer's views on defense policy were also held by many other major scientists was indicated not only in the decision of the GAC to advise against a crash program when the success of H-bomb research was in doubt, but also in the work of the Lincoln Summer Study Group (1952) and the Vista project (1951). The first was promoted by the Air Force but issued in results far from satisfactory to its sponsors. The Lincoln group recommended increased attention to continental defense, which the Air Force considered would detract from its appropriations. The Vista project recommended increased attention to the development of atomic tactical weapons, which the Air Force likewise saw as a rival to its own policy and interest. Dr. Oppenheimer's position, and that of the scientists generally, was based on the concept of limited war and negotiation, as opposed to the massive retaliation doctrine. Dr. Oppenheimer's major role in the formulation of the Acheson–Lilienthal plan for the international control of atomic energy was an earlier manifestation of that attitude.

The conflict within the ambit of the general policy-making area had as its corollary a conflict over public participation in the making of these highly important decisions. Dr. Oppenheimer, in an article written for *Foreign Affairs* magazine,[32] deplored the bypassing of public opinion in the by-then-successful attempt to shift the focus of defense policy. The military are said to have opposed "Operation Candor" on the ground that only the Russians could benefit from a serious public consideration of such vital matters.[33]

## SCIENCE AND COMMON SENSE

In a sense, therefore, the scientists stood for democracy, while the military men were for settling the matter within the top echelons of the government. But the matter is unfortunately not so simple. For one thing, it was hardly antidemocratic of the military to oppose the publication of scientific information, however necessary that information might be to the formation of sound public opinion, if there were reason to believe the enemy might profit from the disclosure. No less than any other form of government, democracy takes its survival with the utmost seriousness. Inevitably in crisis situations the very self-government through uninhibited discussion upon which democracy rests becomes a dangerous luxury. But even if this dilemma were resolved in favor of free discussion, we would be faced with another problem specific to the nature of modern democracy. That problem is implicit in the title of Dr. Oppenheimer's Reith Lectures, "Science and the Common Understanding."[34] The advance in scientific understanding has taken modern society far beyond the days when the physics of Newton and the biology of Darwin could not only be discussed in popular circles but even adopted analogically by the architects and engineers of political movements. As an acute commentator on the Oppenheimer trial put it, "in a technologically recondite age more and more issues become magical and are considered outside the orbit of public competence. This is a problem of democratic life which no argument for candour can easily turn."[35]

It is not only that the substantive matters with which the scientists deal are beyond the capacity of the public to understand. Even more fundamental is the gap which has developed between the scientists and the public in terms of the mode of understanding itself. A revealing example of this gap offers itself in this part of an exchange between Mr. Robb and Dr. Rabi:

Q. Of course, but as a scientist, Doctor, and evaluating, we will say, an explosion you perhaps would be in a better position to evaluate an explosion having witnessed it and having first-hand knowledge about it than somebody who had not, is that right?

A. ... If you are saying that an eyewitness to something can give a better explanation of it than a historian, that I don't know. Historians would deny it.[36]

This was the same sort of common-sense reasoning as was employed by Oppenheimer's judges when they observed that he was "wrong" in believing, on the basis of his technical judgment, that the H-bomb could not be built. In reality, Dr. Oppenheimer merely felt that given what was known theoretically at the time the expenditure of effort which might otherwise be applied to fission weapons was not warranted. No scientist, least of all one so sophisticated as Dr. Oppenheimer, would ever deny the possibility of new discoveries which might alter radically the conclusions to be drawn from an existing state of knowledge. But the idea that such discoveries would prove the previous conclusions "wrong" is specious popular pragmatism. The scientists are not the only ones who have been victimized by common sense in this way. The identical charge has been used to justify the dismissal of capable foreign-service officers whose "crime" has been to have been "proved wrong" by history.

## BUREAUCRACY IN A LIBERAL DEMOCRACY

At the bottom of this gap between science and the common understanding, in addition to the increasingly recondite nature of scientific knowledge, is the problem of expertise in democracy. As society has become more complex and as the means of dealing with those complexities have become more elaborate, specialization and expertise have tended to become indispensable. At the same time the virtually complete victory of the libertarian-equalitarian aspiration in Western countries has brought into question all semblance of authority and hierarchy, even of a strictly functional nature. There is an inevitable tension between the necessities of highly organized life and the aspirations of modern democracy.

Two crucial aspects of the relation of democracy to bureaucracy came into focus in the trial. One revolved around the limitation of the expert's authority to instrumental functions within his field of competence—a problem inherent in bureaucracy but particularly important in democratic government because policy-making is considered the preserve of the popular will. The other aspect was the conflict between bureaucratic impersonality and the respect for the privacy of human relations to which liberal democracy is committed.

In his concurring opinion against denying clearance, AEC Commissioner Thomas Murray held that Dr. Oppenheimer had a perfect right as a citizen to advance moral reasons for his position on the H-bomb. But, he added, "Dr. Oppenheimer's opinions in the field of morality possess no special authority." Dr. Oppenheimer, said Mr. Murray, "is not an expert in the field of morality."[37] Mr. Murray did not say whether he believed there were experts in the "field" of morality, but it was significant that he could use the expression. His position presupposed the detachment of personality from work upon which modern bureaucracy is based. The specialist, like the ordinary clerk, is expected to take leave of his humanity at the door to his office. He is supposed to be a functionary in the strictest sense of the word, a neutral instrument of the general will. In fairness to Mr. Murray, whose opinion was probably the most considered statement of principle to emerge from the trial, it must be emphasized that he did not question Dr. Oppenheimer's right to advance moral reasons for his opinions. He insisted only that the province of the expert and the rights of the citizen were not identical.

In the trial itself Mr. Murray's opinion on the limitation of the prerogatives of expertise was anticipated by Colonel Lansdale. Although he was the only one of the security officers to testify in favor of Dr. Oppenheimer, Colonel Lansdale made it quite plain that, in his opinion, Dr. Oppenheimer and other of his colleagues at Los Alamos were guilty of believing that "extreme competence in their chosen field" meant that "they were as competent in any other field."[38] They believed, he testified, "that their judgment as to what people needed to know, as to what was security and the like was as good or probably better than others."[39] In contrast to this position was that of George F. Kennan, who alone took the position that a top-level expert was entitled to special consideration. Although he recognized the difficulty the government faced in making exceptions, he pointed out that "exception[al] people are more often apt not to fit into any categories of requirements that it is easy to write into an act or a series of loyalty regulations."[40] Arguing from his own experience, he urged that "people in senior positions in the government" should be "conceded maturity of judgment" enough to know when they should or should not maintain associations with suspect people.[41]

As Mr. Kennan's advocacy of the expert's freedom of association followed logically from his brief for exceptions, so Mr. Murray's denial of this freedom followed from his general defense of impersonal bureaucracy. Dr. Oppenheimer, Mr. Murray contended, "failed the test" of loyalty in his associations and in his relations with the security officers.[42] In both cases he violated the rule that a public functionary must regard his job before his human relations. Indeed Mr. Murray was not alone in this opinion — at least on grounds of broad principle. None of the witnesses and judges in the trial ever went so far as to disagree with the assertion frequently made during the trial that loyalty to country must always come before loyalty to a friend. Even Dr. Evans, dissenting from the majority in the Gray Board findings, was forced to defend Dr. Oppenheimer on the ground that if he still had communistic friends, at least he had fewer of them then than before,[43] and Dr. Henry Smyth, dissenting from the AEC majority, pointed out that he saw his brother Frank only infrequently.[44] These assurances did not placate Mr. Murray; he insisted that the line must be drawn more sharply: "It will not do to plead that Dr. Oppenheimer revealed no secrets to the Communists and fellow travelers with whom he chose to associate. What is incompatible with obedience to the laws of security is *the associations themselves, however innocent in fact.*"[45] Apparently not even love is exempt from official duty. Mr. Murray's principle served as commentary to Mr. Robb's inquest into Dr. Oppenheimer's relations with his onetime fiancée, Jean Tatlock, whom he knew to have been a Communist. Dr. Oppenheimer testified that in response to her request he saw her once in 1943, a year before her death. She was still in love with him, he observed, although he had been married since their previous intimacy. "You spent the night with her, didn't you?" Mr. Robb asked. "Did you think that consistent with good security?"[46] This reduction of the complexity of human relations to the iron distinction between friend and enemy goes beyond the notion of impersonal bureaucracy. It is a subversion of liberal democracy and a taste of totalitarianism.

## SECURITY AND CONFORMITY

Linked to Mr. Kennan's willingness to entertain exceptions to the rigid requirements of security is his belief that total security is impossible. Underlying this belief, in a curious but important sense, is Mr. Kennan's general attack on moralism in our conduct of foreign affairs.[47] The same absolutism which ties our hands in the intricate game of foreign relations is at play in the quest for total security. Indeed, just as it is impossible to understand our conduct of foreign policy without recognizing the role of extrarational factors, so it is impossible to interpret our current preoccupation with security as a purely rational attempt to protect the country from subversion. The evidence to the contrary is all too ample.

The sources of our paramount concern for security include the plain fact of intense international antagonism. But even if this were the sole factor involved, the peculiar character of our reaction to the world crisis could not be accounted for purely in terms of that situation itself. An equally important determinant is the shift in the Western value structure associated with the rise of modern democracy. In the value scheme of Aristotle's ideal *polis*, security was condidered a necessary condition of a higher end. Modern democratic theory in all its variants reflected from the beginning a much more intense concern for security. For Locke, and for Montesquieu as well, liberty was virtually identical with security. Bentham explicitly gave security precedence over equality. Hobbes, who was not given to dissimulation or compromise, put the transvaluation of values in unambiguous terms when he wrote: "To be saved is to be secured . . . ."[48]

The psychological and dogmatic aspects of the current quest for total security are thus hardly alien impositions upon "pure" democracy. In a state of permanent crisis such as we seem to be embarked upon, the danger is ever more pressing that what exists as a tendency under normal conditions for democratic societies to elevate the concern for security to the level of a religious aspiration may be intensified to the point where competing values, such as freedom of speech, opinion, and association, are menaced with extinction. Where security is a dominant consideration, conformity is sure to be its corollary.

Mr. Murray's opinion illustrated the danger all to emphatically. He replaced the traditional "overt act" criterion of liberal democracy by a standard that holds as disloyal "action *or omission*" contrary to the national interest. He required of those within the security system positive "cooperation" with its officers and agents, not merely passive acquiescence. He grounded his notion of loyalty on obedience to positive law, without reference to any standard above positive law such as classical liberalism demands as a safeguard against the tyranny both of a legislative majority and of a despotic executive.[49] For all his obvious concern for the maintenance of our libertarian institutions, Mr. Murray seemed unaware of the tendencies inherent in his position. In this respect he was not unlike a good many of his fellow citizens at this time.

## The Trial of the Scientist

### THE PHILOSOPHER/SCIENTIST AND THE CITY

Perhaps the largest question posed in the trial of Socrates was the relation of the philosopher to the city. Here too Dr. Oppenheimer was not without a forerunner; but again the contrasts were more illuminating than the similarities. By vocation Dr. Oppenheimer is not a philosopher, but a natural scientist. The fragmentation of the intellectual pursuit which permits this distinction would have been foreign to the orbit of classical Greek thought. In a civilization which viewed the cosmos as a single whole uniting and integrating natural, social, and metaphysical phenomena, science could not be detached from philosophy. If in fact this divorce has been made in the course of history, it cannot be said to have been effected without remorse. Nevertheless, it remains true that a terrible abyss in the spiritual history of Western man is marked on one boundary by the identification of knowledge with virtue and on the other by the identification of knowledge with power. As a result the scientist who inherits the prestige of the ancient philosopher is at an initial disadvantage when he and the city come into conflict. Having surrendered all claim to a direct vocational concern with universal purpose and having limited himself to the pursuit of knowledge for the sake of power, he retains no ground of appeal against the city, which guards its monopoly of power with a fierce jealousy. Even the tragic grandeur of Socrates is beyond his reach, for the city's rejection cannot stab him with the pain of unrequited love: the center of his life is not the city but his vocation. He is not the city writ small, nor is the city he writ large. Dr. Oppenheimer was frank to admit that for most of his life he was so absorbed in his vocation that he paid little attention to the problems faced by his society. That he emerged from his laboratory long enough to enlist his name and funds in the cause of the Spanish Republic may indicate at least a sensitivity to moral obligation, but it hardly approximated the deep and abiding relation which the Athenian philosopher could feel with his city, and through the city, with the universe. If there was tragedy in Dr. Oppenheimer's predicament, it stemmed less from his conflict with city than from his internal struggle with the scientific vocation.

SCIENCE AS ADVENTURE

In the picture drawn of this vocation by the parade of eminent scientists who testified in the trial, a recurrent motif—all the more noteworthy because it united Dr. Oppenheimer's friends with his enemies—was the theme of science as adventure.

In the trial transcript the note was sounded first in Dr. Oppenheimer's reply to the Nichols letter setting forth the charges against him. When Arthur Compton asked him to take responsibility for the atomic bomb project in 1942, he felt "sufficiently informed and challenged by the problem to be glad to accept." Of the deliberations of the theoretical study group established soon afterward, he wrote: "We had an adventurous time." The results of this conference led the scientists to realize "how rough, difficult, challenging, and unpredictable this job might turn out to be."[50] "In order to bring responsible scientists to Los Alamos, I had to rely on their sense of the interest, urgency, and feasibility of the Los Alamos mission."[51] That it was interesting, that it was possible, were considerations which were ranked equally with the need for it.

Dr. Hans Bethe, at first opposed to the development of the H-bomb on moral and practical grounds, changed his mind completely when Dr. Edward Teller's momentous scientific advance demonstrated the likelihood of success. The rationale he offers taxes reason to the limit. When first approached to work on the bomb he refused on two grounds: (1) he felt it was a terrible undertaking; (2) it would not solve any problems because what was needed was not increased firepower but increased efforts at negotiating a settlement. Nevertheless in the summer of 1950 he began to work on the project—in the hope that "it might be possible to prove that thermonuclear reactions were not feasible after all." In the spring of 1951, when Dr. Teller made his "brilliant discovery," Dr. Bethe's attitude became unqualifiedly positive: "If thermonuclear weapons were possible, I felt that we should have that first and as soon as possible." Had Dr. Teller made his discovery earlier, he concluded, his attitude might have been different.[52]

General James McCormack, Jr., another witness for Dr. Oppenheimer, testified that the "enthusiasm" of the members of the GAC "fluctuated as the prospects of early technical success fluctuated."[53]

Dr. Teller's discussion of the "psychological reaction" of the Los Alamos scientists to the rejection of the crash program by the GAC paints the image vividly:

First of all people were interested in going on with the thermonuclear device because during the war it had been generally understood that this was one of the things that the laboratory was to find out at some time or other. It was a sort of promise in all of our minds.

Another thing was that the people there were a little bit tired — at least many, particularly of the younger ones — of going ahead with minor improvements and wanted to in sort of an adventurous spirit go into a new field.[54]

The scientific psychology described by Dr. Teller fairly bubbles with a romantic striving after conquest of the unknown. It was against this background that the charge of lack of enthusiasm laid to Dr. Oppenheimer took on its fullest significance. Enthusiasm as a state of mind reflects the scientists' vision of their vocation as an adventure. Within the context of science as adventure even prudence is suspect. Dr. Oppenheimer's chief defense of his opposition to H-bomb development was made on grounds of his technical judgment. Given what was known then, he argued, it was a risky venture compared to the known possibilities of further exploitation of fission weapons. Dr. Teller admitted that Dr. Oppenheimer "warmly supported" the new approach he outlined at a meeting in 1951. He even recalled that he was told at the time that Dr. Oppenheimer had said, in effect, "that if anything of this kind had been suggested right away he would never have opposed it."[55] On the face of things, therefore, Dr. Teller considered Dr. Oppenheimer a security risk for no other reason than his failure to recognize the possibility of success at an early date. In Dr. Teller's words, "If it is a question of wisdom and judgment, as demonstrated by actions since 1945, then I would say one would be wiser not to grant clearance."[56]

What made Dr. Oppenheimer suspect in the eyes of his scientist adversaries, however, was not simply that he was "wrong" in his technical judgment, but rather the inconsistency of his adherence to the code of the vocation. In effect Dr. Oppenheimer called into question the whole notion of science as an adventure in the quest for power, with no other questions asked. This was revealed most strikingly in the final point Dr. Teller made in his discussion, already referred to, of the psychological reaction at Los Alamos.

However, I think the strongest point and the one which was a reaction to this report was this: Not only to me but to very many others who said this to me spontaneously, the report meant this. As long as you people go ahead and make minor improvements and work very hard and diligently at it, you are doing a fine job, but if you succeed in making a really great piece of progress, then you are doing something immoral.[57]

The last sentence quoted is the real index to the source of the antagonism evoked by Dr. Oppenheimer. But real or not, it was apparently impossible for either Dr. Oppenheimer or Dr. Teller to argue directly the place of morality in science. Dr. Oppenheimer had to defend himself on grounds of his sound technical judgment, and Dr. Teller had to attack on precisely the same grounds. The real problem was discussed only incidentally.

## DR. OPPENHEIMER'S APOLOGY

Between the twenty-ninth of June 1954, when the AEC upheld the Gray Board recommendation to deny him clearance, and late November, when he recorded the concluding address in the Columbia University Bicentennial series, Dr. Oppenheimer had occasion to ponder the meaning of his trial. Fortunately he is both articulate and concerned with the meaning of his experience in a way which transcends his own personal involvement. Few men are as well qualified to address themselves to the theme of "Man's Right to Knowledge and the Free Use Thereof." As a scientist, his life has been dedicated to the exercise of that right; as a citizen of a liberal democracy, he inherits a tradition that identifies progress with the ever-advancing exercise of reason; as a sensitive man of his time put to trial by and for the works and aspirations of our society, his conscience is our legitimate critic in history: his apology touches us as that of Socrates attaches to Athens.

The form of his lecture is arresting in itself. The language is poetic, and deliberately so. He sees the world of arts and sciences as a patchwork of quiet villages and speedy superhighways. He fashions his message less by discursive argument than by the instrument of images, symbols, and metaphor. The reason for his choice of an artistic rather than a simply discursive mode of argument is indicated in a comparison of art and science. Both art and science, he argues, have developed out of the matrix of the practical arts. But the language of science and the knowledge it bears have become so esoteric that communication is only possible among initiates. "The frontiers of science are separated now ... by specialized vocabularies, arts, techniques and knowledge from the common heritage even of a most civilized society."[58] Coupled with the difficulty of communication is the absorption of science in essentially nonvital investigations. At its great remove from the life of man, modern science can contribute to the understanding of vital problems only indirectly by means of analogies that scholars in other fields may find helpful. Only the artist retains as the "end of his work" communication with an audience that "must be man, and not a specialized set of experts among his fellows." Only the artist can speak to his fellowman in "intimacy ... directness and ... depth." Only the artist can provide "the illumination, the light and the tenderness and insight of an intelligible interpretation in contemporary terms, of the sorrows and wonders, and gaieties of man's life."

But even as he makes the attempt to gain insight into the problems of modern life and to communicate them in the way of art, Dr. Oppenheimer recognizes that the artist, not less than the scientist—although for different reasons—is bound to fail. If the scientist is barred from insight by his narrow vision and from communication by his specialized vocabulary, the artist is frustrated by an even more tragic barrier—the human condition itself. How can the artist possibly give meaning and beauty to a world from which all meaning has fled? "The community to which he addresses himself is largely not there: the traditions and the history, the myths and the common experience, which it is his function to illuminate and to harmonize and to portray, have dissolved in a changing world." Change itself has been transformed from the predicate to the subject of history. The myths and traditions of the spirit in which the soul of man seeks anchorage and the bonds of political and religious authority which affirm his social existence are all dissolved in the great vortex of change.

At the root of this all-engulfing dissolution, Dr. Oppenheimer finds the "growth in understanding, in skill, in power." If the growth in knowledge bears the responsibility for the present evil, however, it is futile to seek to eradicate what has been learned. Knowledge is irreversible: what is once acquired can never be successfully ignored or suppressed. But Dr. Oppenheimer does not stop at arguing the practical case against the suppression of knowledge. He says it would be "wicked" as well as futile to make such an attempt. Before the advance of knowledge even man is expendable:

> When a friend tells of a new discovery, we may not understand, we may not be able to listen without jeopardizing the work that is ours and closer to us; but we cannot find a book or canon— and we should not seek—grounds for hallowing our ignorance. If a man tells us that he sees differently, or that he finds beautiful what we find ugly, we may have to leave the room, from fatigue or trouble; but that is our weakness and our default.

The terrible quality of these words is weakened only by the pitiable resignation they represent. Whether or not they were intended as a commentary on the trial, they are a concession to Dr. Teller of a significance far beyond whatever verdict he may have won from the jury. It could not have been without deliberation that Dr. Oppenheimer employed the images of "book" and "canon," that he found no grounds for "hallowing" ignorance. Finally, he too takes the position that the scientific vocation is beyond good and evil, a ground even higher than the mount from which the sermons descend. Ignorance is the only adversary; weakness in the face of discovery,. the only sin.

If the scientist is to pursue his vocation most fruitfully he must recognize that his place is not in the larger society, but in the "villages" — in the communities of artists and scientists bound in freedom and cooperation by the common bond of creativity. Even as he recognizes that the artist must write for man, Dr. Oppenheimer is nonetheless thankful that the universities are beginning to provide a home for the artist. For the world served by the superhighways is no place for him: it is "too vast and too disordered." He needs protection from "the tyranny of mass communication and professional promotion." In the village he finds shelter. The same holds for the scientist. For him too meaningful existence is impossible outside the village: "in his relations with a wider society there will be neither the sense of community nor of objective understanding."

The image of the village conveys to Dr. Oppenheimer a sense of meaningful existence. Life in the village is intimate, quiet, creative. It is small in size but its very smallness permits the inhabitant to comprehend it, to know its extent and its limit. The counterimage of the superhighway conveys motion, speed, mechanization, a meaningless infinity. "It begins anywhere and ends anywhere." The superhighways are the arena in which the communities of the arts and sciences come into contact with the general society, but "they do not help." On the contrary they are the media by which the purveyors and promoters distort and destroy the creations of the villages in transmitting them to the general public; and they are the arenas in which the creative man is confronted with "the passivity of the disengaged spectator," a sight in which he sees "the bleak face of unhumanity."

In describing the alienation of the creative man from the larger society, Dr. Oppenheimer was at the same time prescribing a retreat to the village. He does not deny the obligation of the creative man to help "all men," but he argues that this responsibility cannot be executed directly, either by the artist or by the scientist. The place of both is not in the general society but in the universities. The world as a whole, men in general, must attempt to maintain the "precarious, impossible balance between the infinitely open and the intimate." But the special task of the creative man is to work for a "true and world-wide community," for the intimate alone. This mission can be performed only within the universities. There a rival to the superhighway, a simple path, can be opened to the society at large. But the overriding concern of the creative man must rest not with the general society but with the true community, with the maintenance of the village in a "great open windy world." The true community is that of "the man knowing man, the neighbor understanding neighbor, the schoolboy learning a poem, the women dancing, the individual curiosity, the individual sense of beauty . . ." In the world of popular culture, in the larger society, such intimacy, such creativity, are impossible. But by working for the intensification of the life of the village, by extending paths both to other villages and to, the larger society, the creative man may consider that he fulfills his obligation to himself and to his fellows.

## Conscience and Commitment

The overtones of Dr. Oppenheimer's trial in his address are an important background to these reflections. The scientific vocation, the relation of community and society, the creative minority in a mass society, science and morality — these themes of his experience are projected into his dialogue with himself. He seemed to emerge from the trial with a less ambivalent attitude toward his vocation and toward society. His reflections verge on a new edition of the spirit of heresy that has long cast its shadow on Western history. He sees the world as a "total chaos" in which man is an alien. Not God but man makes "partial order out of total chaos." The powers that rule in the world are the forces of darkness. True existence is possible only to the *perfecti*, who are urged to band together in communities united not by power but by love. Yet even as a heretic he feels no enthusiasm, only resignation. The pursuit of knowledge that he advocates is not a "gnosis" which brings salvation, but at best a way of conquest for its own sake, a way of adventure.[59]

The personal dilemma which was his trial, in the deepest sense of the word, remains unresolved. If the pursuit of science is responsible for the evil condition of man, how can the scientist go on working in good conscience? Is it enough that he "leave the room" when he "weakens" or that he retreat from the larger society to the shelter of the academic grove? If the creative minority is to withdraw from the world but continue to work, is there any reason why the creations of the village should not continue to be turned to weapons of destruction? If the wise men depart, who will teach the society the message of the true community?

### NOTES

1 *We Accuse: The Story of the Miscarriage of American Justice in the Case of J. Robert Oppenheimer,* New York, 1954.

2 *In the Matter of J. Robert Oppenheimer; Texts of Principal Documents and Letters of Personnel Security Board, General Mana-*ger, *Commissioners, Washington, D.C., May 27, 1954 through June 29, 1954,* Washington D.C., 1954, hereafter referred to as *Texts.*

3 *In the Matter of J. Robert Oppenheimer; Transcript of Hearing before the Personnel Security*

Board, Washington, D.C., April 12, 1954 through May 6, 1954, Washington D.C., 1954, p. 470. Hereafter this document will be referred to as Trans.

4 The Apology, in The Dialogues of Plato, Benjamin Jowett, ed., New York, 1937, Vol. I, 17, p. 401.

5 Trans., p. 802; emphasis added.

6 Ibid., p. 684.

7 Ibid., p. 685.

8 Ibid., pp. 659–660.

9 Ibid., p. 660.

10 Ibid., p. 663.

11 Ibid., pp. 663–664.

12 Ibid., p. 666.

13 Texts, p. 22.

14 Trans., p. 149.

15 Ibid., p. 153.

16 Ibid., p. 468.

17 Ibid., p. 737.

18 Ibid., p. 816.

19 Ibid., p. 275.

20 Ibid., p. 280.

21 Ibid., p. 20.

22 See Harry Kalven's discussion of the legal aspects of the trial in the Bulletin of the Atomic Scientists, Sept. 1954, pp. 259–269.

23 Trans., p. 331.

24 Ibid., p. 420.

25 Ibid., p. 421.

26 The Politics of Aristotle, Ernest Barker, tr., Oxford, 1950, Vol. VII, iv, 1326 b 13, p. 342.

27 Trans., p. 469.

28 Ibid., p. 469.

29 Texts, p. 51.

30 Trans., p. 875; emphasis added.

31 For a fuller discussion of this aspect of the trial, see Philip Rieff, "The Case of Dr. Oppenheimer," in The Twentieth Century magazine (London), Aug. and Sept. 1953 (two parts).

32 Published in the issue of July 1953.

33 Rieff, loc. cit., p. 219.

34 Published as a book by Simon & Schuster, New York, 1953.

35 Rieff, loc. cit., p. 220.

36 Trans., p. 470.

37 Texts, p. 60.

38 Trans., p. 262.

39 Ibid., p. 263.

40 Ibid., p. 368.

41 Ibid., p. 365.

42 Texts, p. 63.

43 Ibid., p. 22.

44 Ibid., p. 65.

45 Ibid., p. 63; emphasis added.

46 Trans., p. 154.

47 See his American Diplomacy, 1900–1950, Chicago, 1951.

48 The Leviathan, Book III, 38, p. 245.

49 Texts, p. 62.

50 Trans., p. 11.

51 Ibid., p. 12.

52 Ibid., p. 330.

53 Ibid., p. 637.

54 Ibid., p. 716.

55 Ibid., p. 714.

56 Ibid., p. 726.

57 Ibid., p. 716.

58 References to the Columbia address are from the text as published by The New York Times, Dec. 27, 1954, p. 10.

59 See Hans Jonas, "Gnosticism and Modern Nihilism," in Social Research, Dec. 1952, pp. 430–452.

# 3

# Mohole:

## *The Project That Went Awry*

DANIEL S. GREENBERG

I

IN THE PARTNERSHIP between science and government, Project Mohole—a design to drill the earth to unprecedented depths—stands out as an administrative fiasco that deserves earnest scrutiny. For Mohole, while it has its own peculiar characteristics, is a classic case of how not to run a big research program, and those who feel that it is inconceivable that it could happen again might be reminded that it is inconceivable that it could happen at all. Nevertheless, it did, with the result that nearly 6 years after the project was formally initiated, there is no Mohole, and there is not going to be one for a long time. There is, however, a lengthy and unattractive trail of bickering, bitterness, and shortsightedness, involving some of the leading figures of American science and science administration. And there is a record that includes:

1) A burgeoning of costs, from early informal estimates of $5 million to later official estimates of $40 million, and current official estimates of $67.7 million;

2) A running, and still unresolved, dispute over the objectives of the project—specifically, whether Mohole should be narrowly defined as a deepdrilling effort or whether it should be considered part of a comprehensive, multilevel drilling program.

3) An estrangement between the National Academy of Sciences' committee which originated Project Mohole and the National Science Foundation, which is paying for it;

---

DANIEL S. GREENBERG *has been writing a weekly column on science and governmental affairs for the magazine* Science *since 1961; he is currently a research fellow in the Department of History of Science at Johns Hopkins and is at work on a book on science and politics. The present study appeared in* Science *in three installments early in 1964.*

4) The resignation of the committee chairman after the president of the Academy chastised him for publicly discussing the project without first clearing his views with the Academy;

5) The complete dissociation from Mohole of the oceanographic engineer who, to unanimous acclaim, carried out a preliminary phase that set a record for drilling at sea;

6) Congressional charges of political influence and irregularities in the award of the lucrative Mohole engineering contract, with the U.S. Senate voting at one point to withhold further funds;

7) A decision of the Bureau of the Budget virtually freezing Mohole funds until the administrative and financial picture has been clarified.

To trace the events that produced this record it is necessary to go back to the summer day of 1952 that saw the birth of a brilliant, amorphous, and often frivolous group that called itself the American Miscellaneous Society—AMSOC, for short. On that day, at the Office of Naval Research, in Washington, two geophysicists, Gordon Lill and Carl O. Alexis, were sorting research proposals when they concluded that the existing research categories were inadequate for the diversity of the proposals. Everything, it seems, was falling into miscellaneous piles. So, then and there, they decided to establish a miscellaneous society to accommodate diversity; AMSOC was thus born, and in short order many of the outstanding figures of American science spoke proudly of their AMSOC affiliation, though it is clear that if AMSOC were any less of a society it would have been nonexistent. As an organization, its chief function seemed to be to revel in whimsy and in contrasting its freewheeling and witty ways with the ponderous motions of the standing professional societies. AMSOC delighted in its lack of membership rolls, bylaws, officers, publications, and formal meetings. Its only divisions, it noted, were in Etceterology, Phenomenology, Calamitology, Generalogy, and Triviology. It also maintained, it was pleased to point out, relations with the Committee for Cooperation with Visitors from Outer Space, as well as with the Society for Informing Animals of Their Taxonomic Positions. On the serious side, however, AMSOC prided itself on the quality of its "members," its ability to chew over professional matters without fuss or formality, and its abhorrence of stuffiness.

For the first 5 years of its existence it performed no visible function outside of delighting its members, and seemed happily inclined toward promoting the impression that it was a bit on the screwy side (at one meeting, it toyed with a proposal to alleviate Southern California's water problems by towing Antarctic icebergs to Los Angeles). Then, in the spring of 1957, some men sitting around a table came to a conclusion that was to have enormous implications for the earth sciences and, ultimately, to bring AMSOC to world attention.

The scene was the National Science Foundation headquarters, where the earth sciences review panel was feeling a bit discouraged after having reviewed some 65 research proposals. The proposals were sound and well worth while; nevertheless, the panel felt that something was missing. The missing ingredient and the atmosphere of the meeting were later described by Willard N. Bascom, the oceanographer who was soon to be brought in as director of Project Mohole, in his book *A Hole in the Bottom of the Sea:*

> None of these [research proposals] attempted to courageously break through to new ground on any of the most important problems of the earth sciences. While the proposals were by no means trivia, it did not appear likely that any major advance would be produced even if each were carried out to the complete satisfaction of its proponent. Two of the panel members . . . were especially bothered by this. They were geologist Harry Hess [professor of geology at Princeton University] and geophysicist Walter Munk [professor of oceanography at the University of California] and they asked themselves, "How could the earth sciences take a great step forward?" Munk suggested that they consider what project, regardless of cost, would do the most to open up new avenues of thought and research. He thought that the taking of a sample of the earth's mantle would be the most significant.

The idea was indeed a quest for "new ground," for the mantle, which comprises about 85 percent of the earth's interior, lies under 32 to 40 kilometers of crustal covering on the continents, and was far beyond the reach of any available or even dreamed-of drilling equipment. At sea, however, it might be a different story, though at this early stage the thinking had not yet passed to the question of earth versus ocean drilling. At ocean depths of 3000 to 6000 meters there was evidence that the mantle could be reached somewhere around 4500 meters below the ocean floor. It lay there, according to seismic evidence, below the "Mohorovičić discontinuity," named for the Yugoslav geologist Andrija Mohorovičić whose seismic soundings revealed a gap between the crust and the mantle. Clearly the goal of reaching the Moho was about as elusive and as challenging as that of landing a man on the moon, since the deepest land drilling at that date was only 7600 meters, while drilling at sea had been done only in relatively shallow waters. Nevertheless, with the details still to be resolved, the climate was perfect for such a proposal, for the earth scientists had been standing by enviously for several years observing the new-found affluence of the health-related, space, and nuclear sciences, not at all sure how their own disciplines could get in on the expansion of federal support. And there was a series of tantalizing scientific questions that could be answered only by bringing up pieces of the mantle, questions involving the history and composition of the globe's interior. Bascom reports that Munk's proposal evoked the observation, "This [the mantle project] would be the perfect antianalogue of a space probe. Think of the attention it would attract to the earth sciences."

Then Hess suggested that the proposal be referred to the American Miscellaneous Society.

The following month, at a "wine breakfast" at Munk's home in La Jolla, California, AMSOC accepted the challenge, and the attempt to drill to the Moho — later christened Project Mohole by Bascom — began to move along. Lill, the cofounder of AMSOC, became chairman, and a who's who of American geophysics was invited to join AMSOC's first formal subdivision, a deep-drilling committee especially established to promote the nation's venture into inner space. The committee members were Roger Revelle, director of the Scripps Institution of Oceanography; Joshua Tracey and Harry Ladd, of the U.S. Geological Survey; Munk; and Hess, who was head of the National Academy of Sciences — National Research Council earth sciences division. Other members were added later; among them was Maurice Ewing, director of Columbia University's Lamont Geological Observatory. Ewing, it seems, was sitting in the lobby of Washington's Cosmos Club when the newly formed deep-drilling committee passed by en route to its first meeting. He was invited to come along, and thus became a member. (Some persons associated with AMSOC's early days recall that when Ewing protested that he was interested in sedimentary studies — not in boring to the mantle — he was scoffed at and told, "Maurice, you're thinking too small." Two years later, Ewing resigned in disgust, but subsequently was persuaded to return.)

If Ewing was thinking small, he definitely was out of harmony with his colleagues, for AMSOC soon was swept up with the excitement of the Mohole venture, and when the National Science Foundation declared that it could not dispense funds to so ephemeral a group, the once-freewheeling scoffers at institutionalism cheerfully took refuge inside the National Academy of Sciences. It was unprecedented for the Academy to take in an existing committee, but since many of those associated with AMSOC were members, and one — Hess — was an officer of the Academy, goodwill and personal confidence overrode tradition. Thereafter, the quest for the mantle became a project of the AMSOC committee of the Division of Earth Sciences of the National Academy of Sciences. And it was this Academy setting that, quite by accident, brought into the picture Willard N. Bascom, an inventive, restless, cocky oceanographer and mining engineer with long experience and unconventional ideas about deep-water engineering.

Up to this point Bascom had had nothing to do with AMSOC or the deep-drilling venture. Formerly of Scripps, he came to the Academy staff in 1954 to handle a variety of tasks, ranging from studies of civil defense and amphibious warfare to service as science adviser to the Columbia Broadcasting Company. Situated next door to Hess in the Academy building, Bascom became interested in the project and not long afterward was asked by Hess to become AMSOC's executive secretary and to organize and conduct studies on how to carry out the project. Bascom, who doesn't have to be told to run with the ball, interpreted his mandate generously, and, pushed on by his energy and enthusiasm, Mohole proceeded in rapid fashion.

Meanwhile, the fall of 1957 brought Mohole an extraordinary bit of luck when the annual meeting of the International Union of Geodesy and Geophysics adopted a resolution, sponsored by Hess and Revelle, urging nations with experience in deep drilling to study the feasibility of drilling to the mantle. In the course of discussing the resolution, a Soviet scientist arose to announce, "We already have the equipment to drill such a hole; we are now looking for the place." The Soviet boast was money in the bank for AMSOC, and the members knew it, although 6 years later it appears that if the Soviets do have the equipment, they are still "looking for the place."

Now properly housed in the National Academy of Sciences, AMSOC sent over a grant application to NSF, seeking funds for what it referred to as "a courageous attempt to broaden the base on which the most fundamental of earth problems rests." The details of this application are worth noting, for when the fighting broke out several years later, a good deal of it centered around the issue of just what it was that AMSOC had proposed to NSF – was it a narrowly defined effort to drill through to the mantle, or was it a broad-based ocean-drilling program, with the mantle the most ambitious, but by no means the only, objective? In the beginning, when goodwill and enthusiasm were abundant, the documents were fuzzy on this score, and the fuzziness continued for some time, giving rise today to fervent textual analysis in behalf of sharply conflicting positions.

The grant application opened with a request for funds "for support of the study of the feasibility of drilling a hole to the Moho discontinuity." It then went on to itemize the scientific benefits that might result "if an authentic sample of the material *below* the discontinuity were obtained...." But next it proceeded, without great precision or explicit reference to a broad – or, as it later came to be called, an "intermediate" – program, to refer to the value of conducting studies of the "layer immediately *above* the Mohole discontinuity"; and it added that "the sedimentary column from the sea floor to the material mentioned above could be sampled."

Was this a proposal simply to drill to the Mohole, or was it a proposal to conduct a broad and multilevel drilling program? On this very issue a bitter row eventually was to break out (a row, incidentally, which in many respects parallels the controversy over the manned lunar landing; there the camps are roughly divided between those who say getting a man to the moon should take precedence over all else, and those who say the manned landing should be part—but by no means the all-consuming part—of a broadly based space exploration program).

In any case, NSF granted AMSOC $15,000 as a starter, and Project Mohole was officially under way, on the following organizational basis: AMSOC was responsible for supplying the scientific guidance, but since AMSOC was a part-time organization and its executive secretary, Bascom, was full-time, the energetic Bascom pretty much ran the show; at the same time, the Academy provided an institutional base and NSF paid the bills.

This arrangement was a departure from preferred practice for the Academy and NSF, since the Academy, with a few exceptions, is an advisory, rather than an operational organization; and NSF, again with a few exceptions, supports research through standing research institutions. (Not long afterward the Academy was to find itself uncomfortable with its Mohole relationships and was to take steps to disentangle itself, though still remaining associated with the venture.)

At this point in Project Mohole, who was in charge? In the era of goodwill that then prevailed, no one seemed to be particularly concerned. Everyone was pulling together. As for the costs, these would be high, it was acknowledged, in relation to the funds normally available for the earth sciences, but compared to the vast expenditures then pouring into the new-born space age, they were trifling. Collaborating on an article in *Science* in 1959, AMSOC chairman Lill confidently stated:

> The Mohorovičić Discontinuity project probably can be accomplished for $5 million. Earlier and larger estimates were out of bounds. Five million dollars is a lot of money, but compared with the many millions of dollars that are being spent on moon rocketry and the billions being spent on atom bombs, this is not an overly ambitious scientific endeavor.

> The American Miscellaneous Society, with its flair for seeing the lighter side of heavier problems, likes to quote the following proverbs when discussing the "Moho": (i) "When going ahead in space, it is also important to go back in time"; (ii) "The

ocean's bottom is at least as important to us as the moon's behind!"

At about the same time, to help clarify the project for an increasingly interested public, Bascom spelled out its past, and speculated on its future, in an article in *Scientific American*. The article, though not an official statement of the AMSOC committee, unquestionably had its endorsement and stands as the most definitive statement of what AMSOC—the originator of Project Mohole—thought it had in mind when it sought support from NSF. Later statements unfortunately clouded and confused the AMSOC position, but at that early stage Bascom, presumably speaking for AMSOC, stated:

> The principal objectives of drilling to the mantle are ... to obtain samples of the various rocks of the mantle and the deep crust. ... Although reaching the mantle is the ultimate objective of the Mohole project, an intermediate step is likely to yield equally valuable and interesting information. ... No one site or hole will satisfy the requirements of the Mohole project. ...

Bascom then went on to state that "we will have to feel our way along." The first step, he said, would involve drilling in about 3000 meters of water. With this experience, modifications could be made that would permit drilling around depths of 4800 meters. After that "it will be possible to make a sound reappraisal of the kind of equipment needed to go on to the Moho."

And not long afterward, the annual Pick and Hammer Show of the Washington Geological Society presented a review entitled, "Mo-Ho-Ho and a Barrel of Funds."

Now, with surprising speed and a quick success that obscured some of the enormous problems involved in going down all the way to the mantle, AMSOC's professional staff carried out Mohole's phase I, a series of record-setting test drillings in the vicinity of La Jolla, California, and Guadalupe Island, 400 kilometers south of San Diego. Their vessel was *CUSS I*, a modern drilling ship that took its name from its original sponsors, an exploration combine comprising the Continental, Union, Shell, and Superior oil companies. Operated under contract by its owners, the Global Marine Exploration Company, but modified, equipped, and run under Bascom's direction—at a cost to NSF of $1.5 million—it set out from San Diego early in 1961 to test the feasibility of drilling in very deep water, 10 times deeper than any in which oil-drilling attempts had been successful. Of critical importance was Bascom's unique dynamic positioning system, consisting of four 200-horsepower outboard motors, located around the hull and operated by a central joystick which activated them to compensate for shifts caused by wind and current. The purpose of this system, which had aroused considerable skepticism, was virtually to hold motionless the *CUSS I* in winds up to 37 kilometers per hour (20 knots) and surface currents up to 0.55 kilometer per hour (0.3 knot), so that no undue stresses would be introduced into the more than 3 kilometers of drill pipe dangling from its underside. (It worked so well that the 81-meter vessel was generally maintained within a ship's length above the point where the pipe entered the bottom.)

The results were spectacular, and are yet to be matched. Operating in 3300 meters of water, *CUSS I* drilled as far as 180 meters into the bottom. And the AMSOC group pulled off the job within a matter of weeks and within its stated budget. (Once again, all this took place in a period of extreme goodwill when no one was paying very much attention to organizational details. Bascom, though working for the Academy as a member of the AMSOC staff, was designated a technical representative by NSF. As Bascom later explained this setup to a congressional committee: "This method was an administrative makeshift, but it worked, primarily because all of us were anxious to make the tests a success.")

Successful as phase I was, it literally only scratched the surface, for to get to the Mohole it would be necessary to drill in some 4500 meters of water and down through some 4500 to 6000 meters of rock. No rig capable of this was in existence, and now thoughts turned to Mohole's phase II. And it was at this point that the trouble began.

It was the spring of 1961, 9 years after AMSOC's birth, 4 years after Munk had first proposed the mantle project, and a period of stocktaking was at hand. AMSOC's staff triumphantly wrote up its *CUSS I* experiences, "Experimental Drilling in Deep Water," which was issued as an Academy document. (Included was a congratulatory letter from John F. Kennedy, addressed to Academy president Detlev W. Bronk and NSF director Alan T. Waterman. Kennedy extended his congratulations to all associated with Project Mohole "and especially to all those on board the *CUSS I* and attendant vessels who have combined their talents and energies to achieve this major success.")

Thus, on the surface, everything was rosy, but, meanwhile, the organizational relationships underlying the project were beginning to wear badly. Within the AMSOC Committee, the Academy, and NSF there was a feeling that the next phase of Mohole would be so vast, complex, and costly that a new organizational basis would be required. Meeting in late May and mid-June, the AMSOC Committee concluded that it wanted to disengage itself from the actual operations of Project Mohole. Reporting to the Academy on its decision, it stated:

> . . . the administrative demands of continuing work at sea, and the deliberate pace of Committee activities do not mix well.

. . . We decided that the Amsoc Committee should in the future concern itself with matters of scientific policy, engineering review, and budget. . . . We consider that we are responsible to both the National Academy of Sciences – National Research Council and the National Science Foundation. The dual responsibility arises because of our origin and existence in NAS–NRC, and because of our financial support from NSF. In this relationship, we may properly act as the representatives of NAS–NRC in its role of adviser to the National Science Foundation for drilling to the mantle.

The AMSOC Committee then went on to recommend "that the operational and engineering future of Project Mohole be entrusted to a prime contractor," but it urged that Bascom's staff be kept intact and "as part of the terms of the prime contract . . . the contractor must agree to make our staff the nucleus of his endeavor by absorbing them into his organization." Adding a prophecy that was to turn out to be a stunning understatement, the AMSOC Committee noted that "these terms may have inherent difficulties but we may not overlook our responsibility to the staff. . . ."

At about the same time, voices were being raised within the Academy to the effect that the heavy involvement with an operational program such as Mohole was inappropriate for the Academy; that the Academy, in accepting the Mohole project, was veering from its traditional role of aloof and politically uninvolved adviser to government and moving in the direction of the Soviet Academy, which is a heavily operational organization. At the June meeting of the Academy's governing board, these views came to predominate. Several days later, Bronk wrote to Waterman, reporting that the governing board had formally endorsed Project Mohole "as a scientific undertaking of great significance. At the same time," he continued, "the Board urged that the actual operating responsibility for carrying the project to completion be lodged with an organization other than the Academy–Research Council, preferably an organization having experience in the operation of large engineering undertakings. . . ."

Then addressing himself to the question of what was to happen to Bascom's roundly praised and accomplished group, Bronk wrote that in the new fiscal year, which was to start in a week, the Academy would provide support for the AMSOC staff for 90 days "pending completion of the recommended transfer of the staff to whatever prime contractor is selected for operation of the project." Bronk next went on to write:

In connection with the proposed transfer of the staff, I am glad to record my own admiration, and that of our division of earth sciences and our governing board, for the exceptional

performance of Mr. Willard N. Bascom and the staff members
he has assembled in the planning and execution of the experimental drilling phase of the project. . . . In our estimation, this
group has been chiefly responsible for the successful carrying
out of an undertaking that represents not only a scientific advance of unusual significance, but also a distinguished engineering achievement and a major extrapolation of previous practice
and experience.

And thus, with the decision to hire a prime contractor, began
the detachment of Bascom and his group from Project Mohole. It
began slowly at first, but in less than 2 years the much-acclaimed
staff of oceanographers and engineers was completely cut off from
the project whose first stage they had carried out so brilliantly.

Within a few weeks NSF announced that it would hold a briefing
session for prospective contractors for phase II of Project Mohole.
At this point, then, Bascom's group was moving toward a limbo; the
Academy was getting ready to disengage itself from the direct
operations of the project; AMSOC was seeking for itself an advisory
role close enough to be influential but not so close that it would
be in day-to-day touch with the project, and NSF was looking for a
contractor to carry out the venture. Who was in charge? What was
the objective of phase II? It is difficult to say.

## II

In mid-1961, as Project Mohole entered its second phase, the
ingredients for misfortune began to accumulate.

The experienced Bascom group, which had successfully
conducted the West Coast test drillings, was on the way out; the
AMSOC Committee, originator of the project, no longer wanted to
be involved in day-to-day operations and had prescribed a more
remote role for itself; and NSF was shopping for an engineering
organization to design, build, and operate the vessel that would
carry out Project Mohole.

But what was Project Mohole? Was it a quest for no more than a
few lengths of rock core from the depths of the earth? Or was it a
comprehensive drilling program that included the mantle among
several of its goals? Closely tied to these questions was the issue of
technique. Was CUSS I to be followed by the construction of a
so-called "intermediate" ship, a vessel that could go deeper than the
CUSS I but not all the way to the mantle? Or was the ultimate ship
to be built at once? Who was to decide? Was it the part-time AMSOC
Committee, which got together no more than a few times a year; or
was it NSF, which had to foot the bills and account for its activities

to an often-querulous Congress? And, finally, if NSF did take the decision upon itself, would it not be venturing into proscribed territory? The Foundation was established to "initiate and support basic scientific research"; it was not intended to be an operational organization. Traditionally, a standing scientific or educational institution was the operating link between the Foundation and the research programs it supported. But with AMSOC backing away to a lesser role, the Foundation was drawing close to becoming the institutional base for Project Mohole.

A nasty and still unresolved fight was to break out on these issues, but in mid-1961 the success of the *CUSS I* drillings had created an atmosphere of goodwill that obscured the impending difficulties. With the exception of the Bascom group, whose future had curiously been assigned to a still-unselected contractor, everyone involved was feeling quite pleased.

The scientific yield of phase I — previously unobtainable ocean bottom cores — was acclaimed by geophysicists around the world; the engineering achievement was similarly hailed, and in this atmosphere of success the AMSOC Committee sent Academy President Bronk a position paper that has since come to mean all things to all partisans. Hollis Hedberg, (Princeton professor of geology and vice president of Gulf Oil), who was to succeed Gordon Lill as AMSOC chairman — and later to resign in a flurry of rancor — told a congressional committee last spring that the paper clearly supports the position that AMSOC intended an intermediate *program* to be carried out by an intermediate *ship*. Leland Haworth, who was to inherit the Mohole controversy when he succeeded Alan T. Waterman as NSF director, told the same committee that the paper called for an intermediate *program*, but not necessarily for an intermediate *ship* to carry it out.

What the paper actually said was this:

We are agreed that the major scientific objective of Project Mohole is to drill to the earth's mantle, through a deep ocean basin . . . . Our immediate objectives are (*a*) to sample through the second layer and determine its thickness and characteristics; (*b*) to sample the characteristics of the top of the third layer. Also exciting, and of prime scientific importance, is the fact that we now have a new tool, the floating drilling vessel, with which to explore thoroughly the sediments and upper crustal layers of the ocean basins. We find, however, that the major objective of the Committee will entail work enough, and that we must recommend this possible exploration program to you for separate scientific and financial consideration . . . . We agree that an intermediate drilling program is required and should be initiated during fiscal 1962. . . . The budget for fiscal 1962, based upon the utilization of an intermediate ship, is approved by the AMSOC Committee as a minimum budget. It is contingent upon the findings of the [AMSOC] Drilling Techniques Panel, working jointly with the AMSOC staff and eventually with the prime contractor. This group may very well make decisions which will increase the cost of the intermediate program. Specifically, they may decide that an intermediate ship is not needed and that work on the ultimate ship should start at once.... We find that the AMSOC Committee must take as its major responsibility the drilling to and sampling of the earth's mantle. This objective has achieved such worldwide significance that we dare not fail.

Now what did this mean? A reasonable analysis would seem to indicate that the AMSOC Committee was bound for the mantle and wished to share with the prime contractor the decision-making authority on how to get there. But what if—as was eventually to be the case—AMSOC and the contractor were in disagreement? Who was to decide? Apparently quite confident about its role as NSF's scientific adviser on Project Mohole, the AMSOC Committee glossed over the question of authority. So far, things had gone smoothly, and there was no reason to assume that they would go otherwise. Bascom and his staff, in an Academy document, "Design of a Deep Ocean Drilling Ship," written on the basis of the CUSS I experience, had emphatically recommended construction of an intermediate ship as an indispensable step toward acquiring data for design of the ultimate ship. But the Bascom group was being moved out of the picture, and its influence with AMSOC was diminishing.

The AMSOC Committee's recommendations were forwarded to NSF through the Academy, and now, as NSF began its quest for a prime contractor, the tricky problem of conflict of interest seemed to pop up everywhere to reduce the Foundation's maneuvering room. It was not only essential to avoid conflicts of interest, but, with Congress and the press eager to pounce on any real or seeming case of mutual back scratching with federal funds, it was essential to avoid even the *appearance* of conflicts of interest. To do this it was necessary to engage in a delicate juggling act, since much of the competence needed for Mohole was already connected with the project in one way or another. It thus became necessary to make certain that persons associated with the initiation of the project did not benefit financially from its next phase. Because the Bascom group was supposed eventually to work for the prime contractor, it was deemed advisable to keep it out of the selection process, a decision that helped avoid suspicion but did nothing to assist the selection process. And, of course, it was advisable to avoid giving the job to any firm closely associated with the oil industry, since the conflict-of-interest alarmists could easily shout "give-away" on that score.

Thus, with these considerations occupying a prominent place, NSF went looking for a contractor to carry out phase II of Project Mohole.

Now, what was it that NSF wanted the contractor to do? On this point, NSF fell in step with the prevailing imprecision. Up to this time Project Mohole had not occupied very much of the Foundation's attention. Although the project had been under way for 3 years, it was scarcely discussed at NSF's usually exhaustive appropriations hearings until it came up for brief mention at the House hearings in the spring of 1961, about the time *CUSS I* was completing its work. And it was not until nearly a year later that NSF set up its own Mohole Committee — consisting of William E. Benson, head of NSF's earth sciences section; Franklin C. Sheppard, executive assistant to NSF Director Waterman; and Paul A. Scherer, NSF associate director for administration.

The notification to prospective bidders stated:

> The Mohole project will include: (1) The conduct of deep ocean surveys; (2) the design and construction of deep drilling equipment; and (3) the drilling of a series of holes in the deep ocean floor, one of which will completely penetrate the earth's crust.

From here on, NSF was to find itself on the most difficult political terrain of its decade-long existence, charged with having awarded the Mohole contract with an eye more to congressional favor than to engineering competence. Among the critics was Senator Thomas H. Kuchel (R–Calif.), who charged that "politically powerful" and "selfish" interests had dictated the contract award, and Senator Gordon Allott (R–Colo.), who declared that the project "promises to be a $100 million boondoggle."

Twelve single and combined organizations responded to the bidding invitation, and, on the basis of a 1000-point scoring system, a specially appointed NSF selection panel concluded that the Socony Mobil Oil Company (936 points) was the most capable contender. Next was Global-Aerojet-Shell, with 902 points; the Zapata Off-Shore Company, third, with 812; General Electric, fourth, with 811; and Brown & Root Inc., of Houston, Texas, fifth, with 801.

The selection process was described later in a report by the General Accounting Office, Congress's financial investigatory arm, which was asked to study the Mohole contract award by Senator Kuchel, who was obviously outraged at the fate of a constituent firm, which had lost out on the bidding:

> In its evaluation report, the [NSF selection] panel stated that the proposal of Socony Mobil was in a class by itself — outstanding as to every important aspect — and that the proposal

of Global-Aerojet-Shell was in a strong second position. Below these two proposals, the panel found no apparent clearcut order and recommended that preliminary negotiotions toward award of a contract be started first with Socony Mobil and, if unsuccessful, then with Global-Aerojet-Shell. . . .

Following the preliminary evaluation, the [NSF] Director appointed a review panel of four senior officials of the Foundation to make a further evaluation. . . . The review panel also found the Socony Mobil proposal to be the best. . . . In a joint report, the two panels stated that they unanimously selected the proposal of Socony Mobil as their first choice and agreed that the proposals of Brown & Root, General Electric, Global-Aerojet-Shell, and Zapata stood out over the others . . . . Following . . . conferences with the five [above-mentioned] organizations, the preliminary evaluation panel reevaluated the proposals and gave them numerical scores as follows:

1. Global-Aerojet-Shell   .................. 968
2. Socony Mobil Oil Co.   .................. 964
3. Brown & Root, Inc.   ..................... 890
4. Zapata Off-Shore Co.   .................. 890
5. General Electric Co.   .................. 846

As the evaluations proceeded and additional material was submitted by the bidders, the Comptroller General reported that the fourth and fifth entries were eliminated, leaving Global-Aerojet-Shell, Socony Mobil, and Brown & Root in the running. The panel, in a joint report, then notified NSF Director Waterman that "all three organizations were 'competent to effectively complete the Mohole Project' but made no recommendation as to the one which should be selected, because of the panels' inability to reconcile completely varying views of the individual panel members."

The selection process now moved into the final stage, guided by a 14-point set of "competence" and "policy" factors. These included such items as "ability to bring project to a successful conclusion"; "research capability and attitude"; "cost considerations"; "petroleum producer versus engineering construction company"; and "consequences of selection considerations."

As for costs and time, Global-Aerojet-Shell estimated $23 million and 33 to 45 months; Brown & Root, $35 million and 5 years; and Socony Mobil, $44 million and about 5 years. It was clearly stated by NSF, however, that because of the engineeering uncertainties involved in the project, the cost estimates were to be regarded as no more than estimates.

The Comptroller General's report continued:

. . . members of the [NSF] panels, weighing the competence and policy factors in accordance with each member's own views,

were equally divided between the selection of Brown & Root
and one of the oil companies, with Global-Aerojet-Shell favored
if an oil company was to be selected.

The record indicates that the Director of the National
Science Foundation . . . awarded the contract to Brown & Root,
Inc., "as the best qualified, based on (1) Brown & Root's strong
management capabilities, (2) demonstrated capability in successfully completing complex projects, (3) their experience in dealing with the oil industry and other industries with capabilities
that could be used in Mohole, (4) and the conclusion that the
plan it had presented for going ahead with the work will give
the Government the best approach to achieve the scientific and
engineering goals."

In the view of the Comptroller General, was all this cricket?

While the records are not as clear as might be desired . . .
it would appear that any advantage Global-Aerojet-Shell and
Socony Mobil may have held over Brown & Root in the factors
previously considered in the point evaluation was offset by
policy determinations favoring Brown & Root . . . [We] are
unable to conclude that the award to Brown & Root was not in
the public interest.

Having made the decision on a contractor, NSF now drew up a
contract—cost plus a fixed fee of $1.8 million—which made it clear
that regardless of what AMSOC was thinking about, NSF was thinking about Mohole as a program to dredge up a piece of the mantle.
Said the contract:

This project . . . has as its ultimate aim the drilling of a hole
to the Mohorovičić discontinuity. . . . It may prove desirable to
expand this broad scope of work . . . to include other geophysical
surveys, additional shallower holes in other selected oceanic or
continental areas. . . . If such is deemed advisable by the
Foundation . . . it would be accomplished through subsequent
agreement with the contractor.

The decision to award the contract to Brown & Root, Inc., now
brought into the Project Mohole a highly regarded construction
and engineering organization, a multi-billion-dollar outfit that had
handled everything from the construction of 359 combat vessels
during World War II to the construction of a screw-worm eradication
laboratory; from the construction of a 24-mile bridge across Lake
Ponchartrain, near New Orleans, to the fabrication and emplacement of some 240 offshore platforms for major oil companies. However, the decision also brought into Project Mohole the suspicion
that Brown & Root's rise from fifth to first choice (with the accompanying displacement of the firm that was "in a class by itself")
was not altogether dissociated from the fact that Brown & Root's

Houston home is close to the congressional district of Albert Thomas, the Democratic chairman of the House appropriations subcommittee which holds virtually complete sway over NSF's budgetary prospects; and that George Brown, who succeeded to the firm's presidency last year after his brother's death was a close political ally of Albert Thomas.

Whatever the effects of these relationships, the contract with Brown & Root became effective early in 1962. At about the same time Bascom's group resigned from the Academy, incorporated itself as Ocean Science & Engineering (OSE), and shortly afterward became consultants to Brown & Root. From the outset the relationship between Bascom and the proud Brown & Root organization was prickly. (Brown & Root has never shown any disinclination to blow its horn. As its Mohole project manager told a congressional committee, "Our policy is that we will do any job anywhere for anybody. There is nothing that we won't contract, no type of work.") Within 2 months, relations between Bascom's group and Brown & Root had deteriorated to a point where OSE quit and returned to Washington. As one Brown & Root official put it, "They had nothing to teach us." Comments Bascom, "We had everything to teach them. They just didn't want to listen." (Upon its return, OSE was engaged as consultants to NSF, to provide advice on the performance of the contractor from whose service it had just been disengaged. The role with NSF lasted 10 months and was abruptly terminated. With his severance from NSF, Bascom was completely out of Project Mohole.)

Meanwhile, Hollis D. Hedberg had succeeded Gordon Lill as AMSOC chairman, and this change brought into the picture a man who was determined to take the fuzz out of AMSOC's thinking and get it finally settled that Mohole would proceed with two ships. He was also determined to assert AMSOC's leadership of the project, but not to the point of getting the committee more closely involved with the project. Almost from the outset, Hedberg and NSF proceeded to spar.

At about the time NSF was closing the contract with Brown & Root, Geoffrey Keller, NSF's assistant director for mathematical, physical, and engineering sciences, wrote Hedberg that, while it was NSF's "hope and plan that the AMSOC committee will continue to provide major scientific advice for the project," NSF was considering the appointment of a "scientific director" who would be on NSF's staff. Wrote Keller:

> He [the scientific director] would be responsible for making necessary scientific decisions concerning the conduct of the project subject to broad administrative, fiscal, and scientific policies that would be formulated by the Foundation on the

advice of AMSOC and other interested scientific groups and individuals.

This sounded very much as though NSF was moving in to take over the project and downgrade AMSOC's role, and Hedberg's reply did not indulge in obfuscation:

> As Chairman of the AMSOC Committee, which has been responsible for original planning and progress on this project to date, I can only in behalf of the membership of this Committee strongly protest this proposed arrangement and urge on the contrary that whatever posts are necessary for scientific guidance of the project be worked out within the framework of the AMSOC Committee. Moreover, as an individual who has developed a keen sense of interest in this project but has plenty of better things to do than preside over an empty shell, I can only say that unless it can be clearly spelled out that the guidance of scientific objectives remain with AMSOC, I can see no point in continuing as Chairman of AMSOC.

NSF subsequently decided that Project Mohole could do without an NSF scientific director.

In the meantime, Hedberg labored at bringing precision into AMSOC's concepts—and at finally resolving the question of just what the objective of Project Mohole was and how it should be achieved. His answer, in a letter he sent to the AMSOC Committee, was:

> ... the overall ultimate purpose of the project can be simply stated as to contribute to the determination of the nature and characteristics of the as yet unknown portions of the earth's crust and mantle .... The project which AMSOC has launched should in no way be considered merely a stunt in deep drilling. ... And the scope of the project should be such as to take advantage of opportunities ... wherever they may be found—water or land, deep or shallow.

After having proposed enlarging Mohole to extremely broad scope, Hedberg went on to recommend the construction of an intermediate *ship* to carry out the intermediate *program*. The two-ship approach, he said, would permit swift construction of an intermediate vessel that could conduct scientifically useful explorations while accumulating experience for the construction of the ultimate ship. Adding that he had taken up these concepts with NSF and the Academy, he noted that, "without implying any definite commitment on their part, I believe that we of the AMSOC group were impressed with their receptiveness to this proposal."

Now, continuing his efforts to obtain agreement that Mohole was not only deep but broad and multi-level, Hedberg wrote to

Frederick Seitz, who had succeeded Detlev Bronk as president of
the Academy, AMSOC's institutional base.

> It is certainly my own strong feeling that this experimental-
> exploratory state (sometimes called intermediate stage) must be
> carried out as an integral part of the AMSOC project . . . since in
> my opinion the achievements to be expected from this stage
> are necessary to the justification of the whole project. I do not
> think, however, that as a part of the AMSOC project it neces-
> sarily has to be carried out under the same contractor as the
> Mohole itself, since the contract signed by NSF with Brown &
> Root, Inc., refers only to "a hole through the crust of the earth."

Seitz, in turn, forwarded the letter to Waterman, adding:

> From my acquaintance with the extensive discussions of the
> scope and execution of the Mohole Project, I am convinced that
> the recommendations of the Executive Group of our [AMSOC]
> Committee are sound, and I am glad to transmit them to you
> herewith.

At this point, then, Hedberg, as chairman of the group which
had originated Mohole, regarded the project as a broad and un-
restricted two-ship drilling program, a program which seemingly
had the endorsement of the National Academy of Sciences. Brown
& Root, on the other hand, was working under a contract which
directed it to devise a means for drilling to the mantle—and no
more. And NSF, as author of the contract, presumably shared this
conception, although, in theory, AMSOC was NSF's scientific
adviser on the project. Meanwhile, as this confusion of purposes
was building up, members of the Senate, egged on by disappointed
constituent firms, were blasting away at NSF for the manner in
which it had awarded the contract. Clearly, the engineering problems of Mohole were formidable, but they were beginning to pale
alongside the organizational and political problems.

## III

By the spring of 1963, Project Mohole was so beset with controversy that the Bureau of the Budget directed NSF to withhold
further expenditures "until the situation is clarified."

Presumably, satisfactory clarification was then provided for
in January 1964 NSF received authority to proceed with Mohole
along compromise lines worked out by NSF's new director, Leland
J. Haworth. But in the intervening months, the Bureau—which is
the White House's chief agent for controlling federal expenditures—
could hardly be blamed for concluding that wisdom called for at
least temporarily bringing everything to a halt. Around the time of

the cutoff edict, the divergence in thinking between Brown & Root and a majority AMSOC Committee was becoming unbridgeable; AMSOC itself had developed a split on the issue of an intermediate versus an ultimate ship; NSF was being attacked on Capitol Hill for its award of the contract; and Bascom, while employed as an NSF consultant, had taken to public sniping at the performance of Brown & Root, NSF's choice for the Mohole contract. (Speaking at U.C.L.A. 2 weeks before NSF suddenly terminated his contract, Bascom declared that phase I, which he had directed, "was a tremendously successful first step . . . . But for two years, nothing more has come of it [Mohole]. It's anybody's guess when it will get off the ground.")

As for Brown & Root, its performance at the start was no spring of joy for the beseiged NSF. Clearly, the technical problems of moving from phase I (180 meters into the ocean bottom, while operating in 3300 meters of water) were trivial compared with the ultimate goal (4500 to 6000 meters into the bottom through some 4500 meters of water). In terms of the evolution of equipment and technique, it was not unlike a jump from airborne to space flight, and a quick start was out of the question, regardless of which firm or combine took on the job. In addition to the general fray over scope, technique, and objectives, skirmishes now broke out on the question of Brown & Root's competence. Senator Kuchel took to the floor to express his skepticism, and Brown & Root's public relations director retorted that it was Brown & Root's conviction that the Foundation "showed great wisdom" in awarding the contract to Brown & Root. He added, "Certainly our project manager, Bowman Thomas, has had more experience in drilling off-shore than any other human being. I presume the Foundation considered this in its decision to give us the contract." (Whether it did or not, Thomas departed Brown & Root about 3 months later to tend to his own off-shore drilling interests.)

Eventually Brown & Root put together a Mohole team that is generally considered to be a fine assemblage of engineering talent, but, as Haworth delicately phrased it when a congressional committee asked him last November to comment on Brown & Root's progress, "This was before my time, but it is my impression that the Foundation, at least individual members of the Foundation staff, probably at one time had somewhat the feeling that . . . maybe the start was a little slow."

In any case, in April of 1963, 13 months after it received the contract, Brown & Root unveiled its recommendations for carrying out the Mohole's phase II. The plan was spectacular, and so was AMSOC's reaction.

Theoretically, Brown & Root was offering no more than informed recommendations on various engineering possibilities for carrying out its contractual obligations to bore a hole to the mantle. But Brown & Root made it abundantly clear that its preference — and the bulk of its effort — had gone into designs for a floating platform, 70 by 75 meters, resting on six huge columns. The columns, in turn, rested on two submarine-shaped hulls, 112 meters long and $10\frac{1}{2}$ meters in diameter. Propelled by screws on the stern of each submarine hull, the platform could travel to the drilling site under its own power. Once there the platform would be partially submerged by flooding; propellers located in each column would operate to keep the platform stabilized above the drill pipe, in much the fashion that the outboard motors had stabilized *CUSS I*. The positioning system would be designed to maintain the craft within a 150-meter radius in 5500 meters of water, even in gale winds of 60 kilometers per hour. Construction cost was estimated at $40 million. It would cost about $9 million a year to operate; drilling time to the mantle was estimated at $2\frac{1}{2}$ to 3 years.

The conclusion of Brown & Root was that the drilling art had advanced to the point where the platform could be built without going through AMSOC's proposed intermediate step. Plainly, Brown & Root was living up to its end of the bargain. It had been hired by NSF to chart a plan for drilling through the crust of the earth — the contract stated explicitly that any other objective would be separately negotiated — and the firm had come up with a proposal to drill through the crust of the earth.

However, with Brown & Root proposing to bypass AMSOC's intermediate ambitions, Hedberg lost no time in getting his committee's opposition emphatically on the record.

Having hammered away at the need for an intermediate *ship* and *program* ever since he succeeded Lill in 1962, Hedberg now presented the issue to his 19-man committee in blunt terms. Would the committee prefer, he asked in a poll, "(a) to get the intermediate-size vessel built now and take its chances on getting the ultimate vessel later, or (b) to get the ultimate vessel built now and take its chances on getting the intermediate-size vessel later." Twelve members voted for an intermediate vessel now; five favored going to the ultimate vessel at once; two did not return their ballots.

A majority of AMSOC was willing to stake the project's future on the intermediate program, and Hedberg now drew attention to an Academy-Foundation agreement, concluded a few months before, which stated that, while NSF retained final decision-making authority, "the Project should be aimed to attain as far as possible the scientific objectives conceived for it by AMSOC . . . with whom the Project originated."

Mohole had now turned into a seemingly interminable war for NSF. With considerable justification, NSF could contend that it had come into Mohole with the understanding that it was footing the bill for a program to drill to the mantle, not for a general program of deep ocean drilling. At least five of AMSOC's own members seemed to share this conception of the project, and AMSOC's own deep-drilling panel had concluded, 1 month after the Brown & Root presentation:

> It is our opinion that a properly designed floating drilling platform . . . offers the best solution of the requirements for both the intermediate and ultimate objectives of the Mohole project.

On the other hand, AMSOC's naval architecture panel had come to precisely the opposite conclusion. And Bascom's group, now on the brink of success as general oceanographic consultants, was ready and, in fact, eager to supply details for anyone looking into the hypothesis that all was not well with Mohole.

Meanwhile, the congressional critics, amply supplied with information from whatever source, kept up a barrage at NSF. And to the general dismay of the Academy and NSF, numerous snickering articles about Mohole began to break out in the popular prints. *Newsweek*, for example, came up with a piece titled "Project No Hole?" which asserted that "many top-ranking scientists have lost faith with Project Mohole." And *Fortune* came out with an article, "How NSF Got Lost in Mohole." Politicians would ordinarily shrug off such remarks as a standard occupational hazard (didn't Harry Truman once say, "If you can't stand the heat, get out of the kitchen"?). But for the leaders of the scientific community, with their traditional concern for maintaining an appearance of dignity and keeping spats out of public view, Mohole was becoming an egregiously painful sore. What they did not realize was that things would get worse.

Three AMSOC members, while retaining membership on the committee had gone off and formed a private consortium, Oceanic Research and Exploration, Inc., to promote sedimentary and intermediate exploration. Today, nearly a year later, nothing has come of their efforts, but their move did nothing to contribute to an appearance of unanimity within AMSOC. And a month after the establishment of the consortium the Bureau of the Budget took a long-expected step when it curtly advised NSF that the situation called for putting a brake on further expenditures. Writing to NSF Director Waterman, the head of the Bureau stated:

> You will recall that when this [post *CUSS I*] phase of the project was brought initially to our attention, total costs of $15 to $20 million were anticipated. Last fall, when a request for $15 million was included in the budget for further funding, a total

cost in the neighborhood of $50 million was discussed. Since then your [latest] congressional presentation... states that the Foundation regards $50 million as a minimum figure and that the ultimate total may be considerably higher.

Given the financial as well as the technical uncertainties, together with the unique administrative problems involved in a project of this magnitude... I believe the Foundation should withhold its approval of further financial commitments... until the situation is clarified.

(In August, shortly after Haworth became head of the Foundation, the Bureau of the Budget, upon his request, released an additional $2 million to prevent Brown & Root's design efforts from coming to a complete halt. But no funds were allowed for construction, leaving total Mohole expenditures, from the very beginning until the present, at slightly over $7 million.)

In the meantime, NSF itself was seeking a way out through a special study convened by its senior advisory body, the National Science Board.

Such was the state of affairs in the fall of 1963 when both the House subcommittee on oceanography and NSF's Senate appropriations subcommittee decided to take a long look at Project Mohole. The House committee, which does not have specific jurisdiction over NSF, apparently was just looking into the affair to find out what it was all about, but the Senate committee, with direct money authority over NSF, was keenly interested, and especially so was one of its members, Senator Allott, the Colorado Republican who had been blasting NSF ever since it passed by one of his constituents and awarded the contract to Brown & Root. The effect of these inquiries was to disabuse anyone of the notion that things were so bad that they could only improve.

A star witness at both proceedings was AMSOC Chairman Hedberg, who came on like a rock-eating drill. Informing the committee that "personally I would far rather see this project killed where it now stands than to see it carried out in a manner not worthy of its potentialities," Hedberg warned that "there must be insistence that it not be allowed to degenerate into merely another publicity stunt." Continuing, Hedberg declared:

... this project can readily be one of the greatest and most rewarding scientific ventures ever carried out. I must say also that it can just as readily become instead only a foolish and unjustifiably expensive fiasco if there is not an insistence that it be carried out within a proper concept and in a well-planned, rigorously logical, and scientific manner....

It is my opinion that there is a steadily growing ground swell of informed public opinion against the thought of a poorly planned, foolish, and extremely costly attempt to unnecessarily "shoot the works" by trying to drill an ultradeep hole to the mantle before we have anywhere near enough information on the rocks above the mantle.... The initial false glamor of the Mohole idea is wearing off in the face of realities, and I am sure that the informed public now finds a much greater appeal in a broad sensible program of crustal investigation carried on at a moderate rate rather than in a crash Mohole stunt.

Mixed into his emotionally stated position, however, were some extremely compelling arguments for the intermediate-ship approach.

The Brown & Root platform, he pointed out, could not transit the Panama Canal. It could go the long way around, but, clearly, its mobility was limited. Furthermore, Hedberg said, alluding to the argument that the mantle was the agreed-upon and only objective, "even supposing the project had been mistakenly presented in such a shortsighted or misleading way, nothing has happened to date which would preclude its being adequately redefined now...."

The case for the intermediate ship, he asserted, rested not only on the need to accumulate data for design of the ultimate vessel, but also on the need to develop an orderly and long-term program.

...we should be thinking of a continuing program in subocean-bottom drilling research which will inevitably be a long process, but which need go no faster than its early results justify. If we get encouraging results from early intermediate-depth drilling, this may constitute adequate justification to make everyone glad to go ahead with the preparation of an ultimate Mohole vessel. On the other hand, it is not at all inconceivable that early results may indicate that there is either no need or no possibility of drilling to supposed Mohole depths, in which case it would have been a reckless disregard of taxpayers' money to have prematurely or needlessly built the huge vessel now proposed....

Whatever the technical merit of Hedberg's argument, the impact was enormous. Academy President Seitz promptly reprimanded him for presenting "such formal testimony to the Congress without first clearing your proposed testimony with me...." Seitz added that unless Hedberg would agree to consult him on communications with "any organization or agency outside the Academy ... so that I can decide whether your communication merits the attention of the [Academy] Council... I will have no choice but to request the Council to permit me to reconsider your own status as chairman of AMSOC."

Hedberg promptly submitted his resignation in a characteristically tart letter that concluded with the hope that "some of the hysteria which seems to be surrounding this Mohole Project will soon be dispelled under wise leadership by you [Seitz] and Dr. Haworth." He also pointed out that he had attempted to discuss his forthcoming testimony with Seitz, but the Academy president was tied up at the time with preparations for the Academy's centennial celebration, and he added that in testifying he had made it clear that he spoke for himself and not for the Academy. And thus, Hollis Hedberg, who had headed AMSOC for nearly 2 years, stepped out of the picture.

His testimony, however, seems to have hit home with the Senate Appropriations Committee, for it was soon to issue a report stating that "Such a diversity of scientific and engineering opinion has been presented ... that it is obvious that construction of a large drilling platform at this time would be unwise." The committee accordingly directed that further expenditures on the platform be withheld, but later retreated from this position when, in conference with Rep. Albert Thomas's committee, it was decreed that funds would be provided for NSF and the Bureau of the Budget to "use good judgment and work out a sensible proposition."

A proposition, however sensible, has now been worked out on terms devised by Haworth, who, in his first half-year as NSF director, has devoted more time to Project Mohole than to any other Foundation activity. As proposed by Haworth, Brown & Root will be given authority to build the *ultimate* platform, but the platform will initially be equipped with an *intermediate* drilling rig. By following this course, he testified, the Foundation was recognizing the mantle as the ultimate objective, but, while minimizing the costs, would benefit from the experience gathered in intermediate drilling.

Haworth went on to say that he favored a "supplementary drilling program," not directly associated with Project Mohole, that would presumably carry out the upper-level exploration advocated by members of AMSOC. And, he added, "with the advantage of hindsight, I regret that the work of Brown & Root was not paralleled by a continuous drilling program directed both at the development of equipment and techniques." Haworth also pointed out that it was his hope eventually to turn over Mohole's management to a university or an oceanographic research institution, and thus to have it run on what has come to be the standard basis for handling big projects financed by the Foundation.

The Haworth proposal was, in effect, an attempt to find some common ground among the parties that had for so long been enmeshed in the Mohole controversy, and, apparently it has succeeded. The Bureau of the Budget has given the Foundation authority to go ahead with an ultimate platform rigged for intermediate drilling. In this tight budget year, however, the supplementary ship had been put aside; but it is understood that the Bureau accepts it in principle. And an effort is now being made to bring an outside institution into the project, though nothing definite has yet been arranged.

As for AMSOC, it's going out of business. At a meeting this past weekend in Washington, Mohole's originators are reported to have agreed that it would now be wise to dissolve the committee and reconstitute it into a group that would be concerned only with the scientific aspects of Mohole. A separate Academy group to provide engineering advice may also be established. Just what this means remains to be seen, since it would seem to be a difficult matter to dissociate Mohole's science from its engineering. But with Haworth firmly taking charge, AMSOC was in no position to promote any new squabbles. Nor was the Academy willing to tolerate a continuing source of dissension on its premises. (Academy officials have long felt that AMSOC, beginning with its whimsical title, was an inappropriate body to be housed under the Academy's prestigious roof.)

One final development is that NSF, in its determination to keep tight control over the project, has engaged Gordon Lill, AMSOC's first chairman, to join the Foundation staff as Mohole director. Lill, who is now with Lockheed, is expected to take up his duties about mid-February.

The sentiment at the Foundation, as expressed by one official long associated with Mohole, is that "everyone made lots of mistakes." At this point, everyone involved is eager for peace and progress, and it would therefore appear the Mohole now has reasonable prospects for proceeding, with nothing but technical difficulties to occupy its time and energies. However, on the basis of past performance, even the most thorough-going optimist could not be blamed for witholding judgment.

# 4

# Scientific Advice and the Nuclear Test Ban Treaty

CECIL H. UYEHARA

WHEN John F. Kennedy became President in January 1961, nuclear test ban negotiations took on a new complexion, a new purpose, and a new drive. President Kennedy was not merely intuitively or emotionally committed to a test ban; he believed in the value of a test ban on grounds of policy, and he was determined to do his best to try to break the deadlock in the negotiations. During the presidential campaign, Kennedy assured former Atomic Energy Commissioner Thomas E. Murray that if elected he would "exhaust all reasonable opportunities to conclude an effective international agreement banning all tests – with effective international inspection and control – before ordering a resumption of tests." (Geneva Conference, p. 125)* In office, the depth and seriousness of the President's desire for a nuclear test ban may be gauged by his observation that the failure to reach an agreement with the Soviet Union on this problem had been the greatest disappointment of the first year of his administration. This determination was underscored by an *aide-mémoire* of June 17, 1961, from the United States to the Soviet government just after the Kennedy-Khrushchev summit meeting declaring that "an agreement for the discontinuance of nuclear weapons testing is and will continue to be a prime objective of the U.S. Government." (Hearings-2, p. 272) This presidential deter-

---

* See list of publications and documents, p. 160.

CECIL H. UYEHARA, *formerly on the staff of the Bureau of the Budget, is currently Chief of Special Operations, Office of Vietnam Affairs, Agency for International Development. This essay was originally prepared for the Science and Public Policy Seminar (Harvard) in 1964. As indicated in the text, some of the information derives from interviews with government officials and advisers. The interpretations and conclusions, however, do not necessarily reflect the views of any government officials or agencies.*

mination permeated all discussions within the government, as well as those with allies and with the U.S.S.R. Kennedy's sense of dedication was so strong that, as an associate put it, one could practically "taste his commitment." When he said that it was imperative to "get the genie back in the bottle," he was expressing a feeling that was also a concern of the highest priority to his administration.

The Kennedy administration's approach to the nuclear test ban problem was based on a number of stated and unstated assumptions of a political, military, and technical character. Subsequent proposals, particularly those made in the summer of 1962, were built upon these propositions:

1. The first and perhaps basic assumption was an eminently political judgment that an uncontrolled and accelerated arms race would not provide the world with permanent security. Instead, each nation would find that its sense of insecurity would be heightened. Secretary of State Rusk declared that "war has devoured itself because it can devour the world... No responsible man will deny that we live in a world of vast and incalculable risks." (Hearings–6, p. 67) President Kennedy, in an address to the nation on July 25, 1962, said unequivocally that the risks in a test ban "pale in comparison to those of the spiralling arms race and a collision course toward war."

2. The development of ICBM and nuclear warheads since 1957 and the likely future proliferation of nuclear weapons to possibly less responsible nations created a situation in which it was unlikely that any nation could achieve an overwhelming military position. (Wiesner, p. 922)

3. Nuclear weapons developments had reached such a point of sophistication that during the implementation period of an arms control system, warheads would be available for any military needs. Further developments were therefore unnecessary.

4. The absolute growth of Soviet capability to inflict damage on the United States had narrowed the range of contingencies in which the American nuclear deterrent was still credible. (Hearings–6, p. 109; statement by Secretary McNamara)

5. Not only had the Soviets narrowed the range of our deterrent credibility, but they were also narrowing our technological superiority as each year passed. Ultimately, near-parity would be achieved, possibly at the level of a mature nuclear weapons technology.

6. The third generation nuclear weapon—the all-fusion "clean" weapon—was not a military requirement of the utmost importance, although it was then reportedly in the planning stage and had been regarded as a necessary next step in weapons development. Otherwise, no further spectacular breakthroughs in nuclear weapons were expected or thought militarily necessary.

7. The dilemma of steadily increasing military power and steadily decreasing national security was thought to have no technical solution. As Dr. Herbert York, Director of Defense Research and Engineering under President Eisenhower, said in the 1963 treaty hearings, if we continued to look for solutions in the area of science and technology only, "the result will be a steady and inexorable worsening of this situation." (Hearings–6, p. 762)

Given these assumptions, the policy problem required an assessment and weighing of risks. Simply put, the question that had to be decided was whether the vast and incalculable risks of continuing an unlimited arms race, including a full-scale nuclear weapons testing program, outweighed the risk of a nuclear test ban with its possible violations and technical breakthroughs, clandestine testing, and sudden abrogation. This balancing of risks precluded the attainment of a mythic absolute security. The goal of a nuclear test ban was regarded as the most attractive and most feasible first step, which hopefully would lead to still larger and more significant steps in arms control and disarmament. The Kennedy administration was committed to the view that meaningful policy guidance for a nuclear test ban treaty with "adequate control" could be created within the context of this balance of risks.

Soon after Kennedy was elected President, Walt W. Rostow, who later became chairman of the Policy Planning Council in the State Department, and Jerome B. Wiesner, later the President's science adviser, attended a Pugwash Conference in Moscow on disarmament. The Soviet representatives gave them the impression that a nuclear test ban could be worked out, given the right combination of conditions. Upon taking office Kennedy appointed Arthur Dean as United States representative to the Geneva Conference on Disarmament, John J. McCloy as presidential adviser on disarmament, and James B. Fisk as chairman of a special study panel on technical problems. With British support, the administration proposed a new approach containing substantial moves toward the position of the Soviet Union on many major questions. This included a number of specific changes from previous American positions:

1. LENGTH OF MORATORIUM   Since it was now estimated that the joint research program proposed by the United States to the Soviets in May 1960 would take longer than the original estimate of two years, a three-year program and corresponding three-year moratorium on small nuclear explosions below 4.75 magnitude was proposed.

2. INSPECTION OF NUCLEAR DEVICES   The West would accept, on a reciprocal basis, Soviet-proposed safeguards for nuclear devices used in the research program and in any peaceful nuclear detonations. The President would seek legislative approval allowing

Soviet inspection of internal mechanisms of nuclear devices. Representative Chet Holifield, chairman of the Joint Congressional Committee on Atomic Energy (JCAE), said his committee would be willing to recommend to Congress such a change in the Atomic Energy Act, if the other terms of the treaty were accepted. (Hearings–2, p. 266)

3. HIGH ALTITUDE TESTS   The West would consent to a total ban on high altitude tests and adoption of the main recommendations made by Technical Working Group–I (a group of experts from East and West) in June–July 1959.

4. CONTROL POSTS   The West would agree to move two control posts from Soviet Asia into adjoining territories; control posts in the United States would be reduced by one. The Soviet Union would then have two in Europe, one on a Soviet island, and sixteen in Soviet Asia, a total of nineteen. The Soviets wanted only fifteen.

5. ON-SITE INSPECTIONS   The West continued to favor inspection of an agreed percentage of either located or unidentified events. If a realistic element of deterrence was to be built into the system, the annual number of on-site inspections would have to bear a reasonable scientific relationship to the anticipated number of unidentified events in each country. On this basis, the West proposed twenty on-site inspections in the Soviet Union. The Soviets would be allowed to have twenty inspections in the United States and twenty on British territory. The Soviets continued to insist on a maximum of three inspections.

Concerning the qualifications for on-site inspections, the West wanted an area of 200 square kilometers (77 sq. miles) if regional travel times of seismic waves were known for control posts surrounding the epicenter and 500 square kilometers (193 sq. miles) if the travel times were not known or the control posts did not surround the epicenter, to be eligible for inspection. The Soviets would not accept this stipulation and instead insisted that an event should be looked upon "as suspicious and subject to inspection" only if it was located in an area of 200 square kilometers. The West, using data from the Hardtack II nuclear test, believed that under Soviet criteria too many unidentified events would slip through the inspection net.

This was the first time, as Earl H. Voss, author of *Nuclear Ambush*, and a severe critic of the nuclear test ban, correctly observed, that a United States administration had agreed within its own house on a complete program for ending nuclear tests. (Voss, p. 459) But this unity of purpose had no immediate results. On April 16, 1961, the United States proposed a complete treaty, including these revisions, that would ban further nuclear tests underground above 4.75 seismic magnitude, in the sensible atmosphere, underwater, and in outer space, and that would establish a moratorium on tests below the treaty threshold of 4.75. This proposal by the Kennedy administration was essentially the same as that proposed by its predecessor on February 11, 1960. It too was rejected by the Soviet Union.

In another attempt to break the impasse, the West on May 29 proposed a sliding scale of inspections ranging from a minimum of twelve to a maximum of twenty. If there were as few as sixty unidentified events, then there would be twelve inspections; if the number was a hundred, then there would be twenty inspections. This calculation was based on the Soviet claim that there were never more than sixty unidentified events a year—a change from the figure of twenty used in earlier years. On scientific grounds, there was no basis for any annual limit on the number of inspections, but as a practical matter it was recognized that "twelve or so" *complete* inspections were the most one could expect to mount in a year. (Geneva Conference, pp. 154, 537–538; Hearings-2, pp. 275–276) As Ambassador Dean put it, "I think all of our scientists were generally in agreement that somewhere between twelve and twenty was a reasonable number." (Hearings-2, p. 276) The Soviets summarily rejected the West's offer of a sliding scale and called again for a political decision on the basis of a few on-site inspections.

The annual appraisal of developments in detecting and identifying nuclear explosions conducted by the JCAE in July 1961 provided another glimpse, though murky, into the relationship between scientists, scientific advice, and United States treaty proposals. The overall review of technical progress was pessimistic. Yet, according to Dr. Richard Latter, a skeptical Rand Corporation scientist, the so-called Geneva System, the basis of Western proposals in 1961, appeared to have a "good probability" of detecting, but not always identifying and locating accurately, nuclear explosions in the atmosphere, underwater, in space, and underground. The link between technical pessimism and policy optimism was not clear. The committee was told that some of the scientists called to testify had helped the Arms Control and Disarmament Agency (ACDA) draft the proposed treaty. (Hearings-2, p. 262) Dean even said, though without elaboration, that "contrary to some of the testimony [meaning pessimistic testimony] you heard here, our scientific advice, both British and American, was that the control system set forth in our treaty would provide reasonably adequate control over those regions which the treaty purported to control." (Hearings-2, p. 280)

In retrospect, during its first year in office, the Kennedy administration did not move as dramatically in the test ban negotiations as Kennedy's preelection commitment may have suggested. Essentially, his administration continued the policy of the previous administration with some refinements. Kennedy had made an equally strong—if not stronger—promise to right the "missile gap." As an immediate security problem, this issue probably took precedence over the test ban negotiations. This is not to discount in any way the President's strong conviction that something had to be done to control the arms race. He also had to consider the military needs of the country, especially in view of his sobering experience at the summit with Khrushchev in June, the subsequent Berlin crisis in the summer of 1961, and the sudden resumption of nuclear testing by the Soviets in October 1961. These external forces and events were hardly conducive to the success of any test ban negotiations, even though, at the same time, the very crises they precipitated underscored the urgency of coming to some kind of an agreement before it was too late.

Domestically, the situation was no more favorable to a test ban. The United States Air Force doubted whether the Soviets were abiding by the voluntary moratorium. At congressional hearings on a test ban in 1963, Air Force Chief of Staff General Curtis LeMay continued to voice these doubts. The clamor and pressure within the administration for resumption of United States nuclear testing and concern over possible Soviet cheating eventually persuaded the President to appoint a panel of scientists to "thoroughly study the possibility of Soviet cheating and to assess the relative effect on the comparative status of the two countries in weapons development." (Report-1, p. 39) The skeptics' contention that the Russians were probably already cheating was proved false in the fall of 1961 when the Russians vigorously resumed nuclear testing. Furthermore, the results of the Vela research program, which were to affect test ban policy and proposals, had not yet come to light by the end of 1961.

## The International Effort to Arrange a Treaty

Between the April 1961 treaty proposal and its amendment in March 1962, the international situation had been dangerously heated up by Khruschev's threats over the Berlin situation. A pall had been thrown over the test ban negotiations when the Soviets broke the moratorium and resumed testing in September 1961. While Kennedy and Prime Minister Macmillan condemned the Soviet betrayal of the moratorium, they offered on September 3 to conclude an immediate agreement "not to conduct nuclear tests which take place in the atmosphere and produce radioactive fallout" and to rely on existing means of detection which were believed to be adequate without additional controls. Khrushchev formally rejected this offer on September 9. On September 5, Kennedy ordered resumption of nuclear tests in the laboratory and underground. The sense of gloom was compounded by the Soviet insistence on setting off a 60-megaton explosion despite appeals from the United States and the United Nations to refrain from testing such a mammoth device.

Pressure for a nuclear test ban was maintained, if not increased, by the nations of the world meeting in the United Nations General Assembly in the fall of 1961. On November 8, the United Nations adopted an Anglo-American resolution calling for the conclusion of a test ban treaty as quickly as possible and stipulating:

    1. Cessation of tests in all environments under inspection and control of machinery adequate to ensure compliance.

    2. International control machinery that would be representative of all parties and "staffed and operated to guarantee its objectivity and effectiveness, avoiding self-inspection."

    3. Executive action not obstructed by veto, and administrative responsibility in one person supervised by a commission.

When the Geneva Conference was resumed in mid-November 1961, the Soviets proposed a new agreement to ban tests in the atmosphere, underwater, and in outer space. The proposal maintained that national systems of detection and identification were adequate to monitor an agreement in these three environments, thus making international controls unnecessary. It claimed that control in these areas was not "fraught with any serious technical difficulties." The Soviets added an unacceptable additional condition: the nuclear powers were to refrain from underground tests until a control system for such tests could be agreed upon. This amounted to an unpoliced, unlimited, and unverifiable test ban.

Kennedy and Macmillan had implied in their earlier suggestion of September 3 that "existing systems" without additional controls — meaning presumably national detection and identifications systems — were adequate to detect atmospheric tests, but they continued to insist that international controls were needed for all three environments and underground tests. The Soviets were accused of "repudiating every previous agreement for international inspection and control undertaken by the U.S.S.R. during three years of patient and laborious negotiations at Geneva." (International Negotiations, p. 38) To expect each party to the proposed Soviet agreement to monitor its own performance in fulfilling the treaty, the West contended, "would be both technically and politically inadequate." (Ibid., p. 40)

On March 2, 1962, Kennedy authorized a new series of atmospheric nuclear tests. In an address to the nation he stressed four points: (1) that no single decision of his administration had been more thoroughly or more thoughtfully weighed; (2) that Soviet tests in the fall of 1961 had emphasized development of new weapons and reduced significantly the yield-to-weight ratios of nuclear weapons; (3) that the Soviets apparently did not possess missiles able to carry 100-megaton bombs, and that although much information had been gathered about the antiballistic missile (ABM) problem, a successful antimissile defense system had not been developed; and (4) that although these tests had not given the Soviets nuclear superiority, any further Soviet series, in the absence of further Western progress, could well provide the Soviet Union with a nuclear attack and defense capability so powerful as to encourage aggressive designs.

The President urged the Soviets to sign an agreement by the latter part of April, when the United States was scheduled to resume testing. Khrushchev retorted the next day that this was tantamount to "atomic blackmail."

It was in this gloomy atmosphere that preparations for the conference of the Eighteen Nation Committee on Disarmament* which was to meet on March 14, 1962, in Geneva went forward in Washington. While the United States and the United Kingdom proposed to eliminate the 4.75 seismic magnitude threshold on underground tests suggested by both the Eisenhower and Kennedy administrations, the ACDA was investigating the results of the Vela program to see how the West's negotiating position might be affected by the new data.

The new Western proposals represented a considerable effort to draw closer to the Soviet position. Elimination of the threshold would have made the treaty a comprehensive test ban agreement. Furthermore, the United States and United Kingdom were not requesting additional control posts on Soviet territory or additional on-site inspections. There appeared to be no scientific basis for this change. It was essentially a politically determined shift and a logical conclusion to the earlier threshold proposal. While the West could legitimately call for inspections of unidentified events above the 4.75 threshold, it could not justify a demand for an on-site inspection of any shot it might have detected but not identified as of natural origin under this threshold, since these would have been covered by the proposed moratorium. Since detection capabilities would not suddenly vanish under the somewhat arbitrary 4.75 magnitude, but actually traverse a spectrum from good to bad, it was not logical to accept a particular threshold as limiting when there was always the possibility of detecting seismic events below the 4.75 threshold.

---

*The Ten-Nation Committee (five NATO and five Warsaw Pact nations) had been enlarged in the United Nations by adding eight neutral nations.

In addition, the possibility of a limited test ban treaty seemed remote; if anything appeared within the realm of possibility, it was a comprehensive treaty. Moreover, such a treaty proposal would, if signed, slow down nuclear weapon development, allay the world's near-hysteria about radioactive fallout from continued nuclear tests, and provide a constructive response to the universal appeal for peace.

The Soviet Union rejected these proposals and even retracted an earlier concession, claiming that not even underground tests required international controls. Khrushchev adamantly maintained that Western claims of the inadequacy of national means of detection contradicted "universally known facts." He pointed out as proof of this contention the detection by the United States of an underground Soviet nuclear shot, conveniently ignoring the fact that it was well above the threshold of underground detectability. In a plenary meeting of the conference on March 23, 1962, Rusk replied that contrary to Soviet claims "there was little new evidence to justify any far-reaching changes in the control system recommended by the 1950 experts." (International Negotiations, p. 58) Notwithstanding appeals by the neutral nations for a new moratorium, summit correspondence, and suggestions by neutrals of a mixture of national and international control systems, the deadlock continued, and the United States remained determined to carry out its nuclear tests, which had been delayed only because of lengthy preparations.

At the same time, nevertheless, the Eight Neutral Nations' Proposal of April 17 appears to have been a catalyst which ultimately led to the drafting of two treaties proposed by the United States and the United Kingdom to the world later that year at Geneva. In their unflagging attempts to discover a formula for a permanent test ban, the neutrals believed that possibilities existed of establishing by agreement a system for continuous observation and effective control on a purely scientific and nonpolitical basis. They suggested such a system might be based on already existing national networks of observation posts and other new posts established by agreement. They suggested the creation of an International Commission of Scientists, possibly from unaligned countries, with an appropriate staff. And they proposed that the commission consult with the party on whose territory an unidentified event occurred about measures of classification including verification *in loco*. After the commission informed the parties of its assessment of the event each country would be free to determine its own action.

By the time the conference recessed in mid-June 1962, the United States and the U.S.S.R. had agreed to use the joint eight-nation memorandum as one of the possible bases for reaching agreement on a test ban. But their respective interpretations of this acceptance and of the memorandum differed widely. The United States recognized, in a summation to the conference on May 29, that "national networks would play a genuine role under the scheme of supervision envisaged by the joint memorandum." (International Negotiations, p. 246) The Soviet Union merely praised the neutral nations for their constructive proposals and suggested that they constituted a useful basis for reaching agreement. More specific Soviet interpretation of these proposals came later in the summer of 1962.

## The Changing "Guidelines" in the Kennedy Administration

Well before the United States put forward its new proposals at the Geneva Conference in 1962, important changes of emphasis and conception had gained wide acceptance among the policy makers in the Kennedy administration. It is not known when these ideas "jelled," but they are generally described as coming to the fore in 1961. The authorship of these "guidelines" is not clear. Very likely they were not the creation of any single individual but of a pooling of ideas, hopes, and evaluations by a small group intimately involved in constructing a technically more acceptable and more negotiable position. It must be emphasized that these guidelines were never, as far as is known, written in a memo and circulated from the White House or the ACDA to other governmental agencies. They were instead the result of the collective thinking of this small group; they were probably more implicitly understood than explicitly agreed upon. These guidelines, furthermore, did not contradict or supercede the assumptions discussed earlier.

The major change in emphasis concerned the issue of verification. The number of inspections had always been the crux of the nuclear test ban problem in the past. Whereas a relatively "fool-proof" system to check every suspicious event had been demanded, policy advisers to President Kennedy now urged the idea of using detection (and identification) as a primary deterrent to cheating. This was almost, but not quite, a radical change in policy. On-site inspections were not to be dispensed with; instead of relying so heavily on the "inspection" leg, the weight was to be shifted to the other leg, the "detection" leg, as the main element of deterrence. Even so, the two legs were recognized to be absolutely necessary for a viable test ban agreement, on technical and political grounds.

This change of view had an immediate impact on the acceptability of detection ranges, on the type of evasion to be feared, and on the role and number of inspections to be insisted upon. A new degree of flexibility, glaringly absent in earlier negotiations, entered the picture on the Western side. The West would not, of course, want to allow even one clandestine shot to escape detection, but it was not going to look upon one or even several successful clandestine shots as an immediate indication that the strategic balance of power had collapsed or was about to collapse in the near future. It had made a political-military-technical judgment that the probability of a major advance or even a breakthrough resulting from a single or several successful clandestine tests in space, the atmosphere, underwater, or underground would be very low; that no breakthrough would occur could not be categorically claimed. It was estimated, somewhat arbitrarily, that a change of any order of magnitude, or even a less substantial improvement, would have to depend on about twenty shots. While single-shot evasion was technically possible, the adminstration believed that a system which would provide a low probability that a series of clandestine shots could slip by undetected would be acceptable. The President was perhaps more stringent than his advisers when he said in a press conference that "we would not accept a test ban which did not give us every assurance that we could detect a series of tests underground. This is the Administration position. We would not submit to the U.S. Senate a treaty which did not provide that assurance nor would the Senate approve it." (Hearings-1, p. 234) It was hoped, of course, that the technical state of the art would improve sufficiently to provide strong support for reliance on remote detection. This change was explicitly pushed within the administration and technical developments which would endorse it were vigorously pursued.

The change of emphasis was not unanimously accepted. Dr. Jack Ruina, the Director of the Defense Department's Advanced Research Projects Agency (ARPA), indicated his agreement when he stated that "we are dealing not so much with detection of a single event but rather a series of events, as many as 20." (Hearings-1, p. 82) On the other hand, Admiral George W. Anderson, as Chief of Naval Operations, testified that he thought that "great progress can be made in individual tests conducted clandestinely." (Hearings-5, p. 335) It could not be assumed, he claimed, that Soviet progress would depend on a series of tests, rather than a single test. "After all," he said, "we in our own Trinity test made a significant proof by just one test." (Hearings-5, p. 324) He was supported by General Curtis LeMay, Air Force Chief of Staff, who also claimed that single shots had produced "substantial results" but conceded that "generally you need a series of tests." He was especially concerned because the Soviets had carried out two comprehensive series of tests, and could therefore presumably hope to gain much from further testing of small explosions which might go undetected. (Hearings-5, p. 381)

When the Joint Chiefs of Staff sent their evaluation of the March 1963 version of the comprehensive test ban treaty to the Secretary of Defense, the Secretary suggested, among other things, that the Joint Chiefs' wording be changed to include a significant qualification: "We also recognize that the possibility of detection through inspection increases in proportion to the number of tests in the series, and that any militarily significant advance in nuclear technology would probably require many tests." (Hearings–5, p. 324) The Joint Chiefs did not agree with the changed emphasis and did not include it in their evaluation.

These evaluations were fundamentally technical or scientific in nature. They had to be based upon a thorough knowledge of the possibilities of future developments and the mode of past improvements and breakthroughs in particular fields. Though the opposing position came from two military officers, their judgments were no doubt based, in part at least, on advice from their scientific advisers. Political ideology, basic attitudes, and a pinch of justifiable military conservatism undoubtedly colored their evaluations of technical data. The political decision makers were in no better position. They could accept anywhere from perhaps three to twenty tests, depending upon the degree of stringency and risk they found tolerable. But in making the choice they would be mixing one part scientific advice—reflecting the extent to which progress in the past had depended upon single or series of tests—and one or more parts political judgment.

A second major change in emphasis was the switch from international teams to bilateral or national teams. The experience with international teams in Laos, Korea, and other places did not exactly offer models of close cooperation. Control over these teams was complicated, diluted, and strained. Bilateral teams, it was thought, would allow more direct control over movements, personnel, and judgments.

In addition to these changes, the Kennedy administration made an effort to identify the type and degree of risks about which a judgment would have to be rendered before any test ban treaty could be considered acceptable. As a result, the factors in a balance sheet of risks were more clearly recognized than in earlier years, particularly by the nontechnical political leadership. It was understood more clearly that science had limitations beyond which a political judgment would be necessary. The risks could be divided into two groups: technical and politico-military.

In the purely technical group were such questions as the acceptability of the technical means of verifying a violation, judgments as to what the Soviets might do in attempting evasion, and calculations of the marginal advantages that might accrue to the

Soviets from a few shots a year in the low kiloton range. It was recognized that there was no scientific basis for a particular number of inspections, twenty, twelve, ten, eight, or seven. The selection of any number involved uncertainty; but which one was tolerable had to be a matter for political judgment. At most, the degree of "reasonableness" in the selection of a particular number might be increased or decreased by the results of technical and scientific studies. It was noted that all of the technical steps—detection, identification, location, and inspection—were not necessary to deter cheating. Since a complex of psychological and technical factors constitute deterrence, the optional combinations of technical steps would require political decision. The administration chose to emphasize detection and identification.

On the politico-military level, a number of factors were considered: (1) the relative military posture of the nations concerned, either in the absence of an agreement, or under an agreement obeyed by all sides, or under an agreement evaded to the extent permitted by the agreed control mechanism; (2) the capability of unilateral intelligence, both by clandestine and technical means, to detect a violation; (3) the degree of incentive for violating a specific agreement, since even if evasion proved possible, the effort might not be worth the gain in military weapons development; (4) the effect of the agreement on world opinion and on the prospects for further arms limitation measures; (5) the effect of any control measures agreed on in decreasing secrecy barriers; (6) the effect of any control measures agreed on in precipitating disputes or incidents; (7) the cost of the control measure in relation to the value of detecting the violation; and (8) the economic effects of an arms limitation step. (Derived from a talk by Professor Wolfgang Panofsky at Tufts University, March 7, 1964.)

## Test Ban Policy Reformulation and Vela Program Results

In the spring of 1962, the Science and Technology Bureau in the ACDA began looking over and analyzing the results of the Vela research program. Because the ACDA was preoccupied with other disarmament considerations, this small group of experts was largely on its own in studying the technical and nontechnical implications of the Vela data. New facts, new clues, new techniques, and a collection of symptoms were coming to light. By themselves, they were of no great value, but when combined they provided the basis for a possible new approach. When the political implications of the newly "uncovered" data were fully realized, the climate and conditions for a test ban changed. Perhaps prompted by the initial survey of the Vela results, the ACDA apparently decided to evaluate seriously the possibilities of the neutral nations' proposal of April 16, 1962.

Since the ACDA was still a very young organization, and organizationally diverse and "hard to pull together," a special *ad hoc* interagency committee was created by the ACDA; it was chaired either by Adrian Fisher, Deputy Director of the ACDA, or by Dr. Franklin Long, appointed Assistant Director for Science and Technology of the ACDA in February 1962. This interagency committee, with representatives from the ACDA, the State Department, the Department of Defense (DOD), the Joint Chiefs of Staff (JCS), the Central Intelligence Agency (CIA), and the White House, met periodically from late April through July 3, 1962.

When the ACDA began this review, it asked the DOD for "a reassessment of the development of the Vela Program and of the monitoring system now operated by the Defense Department to detect and identify nuclear weapons tests." (Hearings-4, p. 5) The DOD reply was particularly significant in two respects: it noted that the establishment of a better capability of long-distance detection of earth tremors caused by nuclear explosions or earthquakes was now possible (Hearings-4, p. 5) because consistent data to detect seismic events at long ranges at magnitudes 4 (2 KT) in tuff (or 19 KT in alluvium) or .5 KT in salt could now be obtained. Secondly, the reply noted that earlier estimates of the number of tremors from earthquakes in the Soviet Union which might be confused with tremors from nuclear explosions were shown by actual observation and research to be several times larger than previously estimated. (Hearings-4, pp. 5-6; Hearings-5, p. 13; International Negotiations, p. 262)

Dr. Ruina of ARPA nevertheless cautioned, in the March 1963 JCAE hearings evaluating the Vela effort, that "important as some of the new results have been and however significant the change in the whole technical picture has been, in no technical sense can any of the individual developments be considered a scientific breakthrough." He meant that there had been no dramatic improvement increasing a capability ten times or more or any discovery of a new principle or approach. But the test results were nevertheless significant. The Western proposals outstanding at that time were mainly based on data available in 1958. The technology and techniques available at that time required reliance on a large number of control stations near expected sites of seismic events. This requirement was compounded by the Western desire to cover both the northern and southern hemispheres. Sheer numbers therefore resulted in a large, cumbersome organization that would take many years to construct and cost up to $5 billion to create and operate. In addition, an international organization would have to recruit, train, and support an elaborate personnel system.

The Vela program provided the basis for a more practical approach. In ascertaining the number of earthquakes and analyzing the relationship between the earthquakes and explosions, the Vela program concentrated on underground nuclear explosions. The research program emphasized analysis of seismic waves as the only promising physical technique for relatively distant detection and identification. These seismic waves, however, constitute only a small portion (about 4 percent) of the total energy released by a nuclear explosion. Contrary to extrapolated estimates used in the 1958 count of earthquakes in the world, the latest figures were measured or counted down to about the equivalent of 2KT. The number of earthquakes below 2KT was extrapolated, but it must be borne in mind that the detectability threshold of the seismometers is not a clear line but a gray area. Degree of confidence decreases as the earth tremors decrease in size. This is compounded, of course, by the fact that nature is not consistent from year to year; the number of earthquakes may change by a factor of two each year. It was learned that *the total count for world earthquakes did not substantially change between 1958 and 1962–1963 — except for the vagaries of nature — but the distribution of the earthquakes among the various kiloton equivalents was radically rearranged.* (Hearings-1, p. 48) Eighty percent of earthquake energy is estimated to be released in the vicinity of the Aleutian Islands, the Philippines, New Zealand, and the western part of the Americas.

It was estimated that there were about 170 seismic events in the Soviet Union above 2 to 6KT in tuff with Rainier coupling in comparison with 600 estimated in 1958. Twenty of these could be identified "with high probability" (Hearings–1, p. 104) as of natural origin, leaving 150, according to Dr. Carl Romney, Assistant Technical Director, Air Force Technical Applications Center. One-half of these could be recorded with sufficient clarity so that there would be features in waveforms that would help identification, not as absolutely positive, but with "varying degrees of positiveness." (*Ibid.*) Then there would be the remaining half (75) where the seismic signals would be so weak that on-site inspection might be necessary.

Dr. Long analyzed these 170 events in a slightly different manner. He felt that 55 percent, or 95 of these events, would have seismic indications of natural origin. Of the remaining 75, 30 would occur in areas where clandestine tests were unlikely, for example, those where the focus or epicenter lay more than 10 km across the borders of adjoining countries or more than 10 km from the Soviet coastline. Another 15 of the remaining 45 would occur in places where it is conceivable for testing to take place but that either would be so close to the outside world or so remote as to make the technical problems of clandestine underground testing difficult—places like the Kurils or the east coast of Kamchatka. The majority of the final 30 seismic events might be expected to occur in central Kamchatka or the Pamirs Mountains near Afghanistan or Pakistan. (Hearings–1, pp. 404–405)

If one were to be able to distinguish between tremors from earthquakes and those from explosions, a comparison of their magnitudes would be essential. This had not been done in any definitive sense in the past. Furthermore, statistics on the number of earthquakes in the Soviet Union were reliably known only for the major ones. The total number of earthquakes was obtained by extrapolating in a regular proportion as the earthquake magnitude decreased. The Vela project collocated the long-period (10 sec) seismographs for seismic surface waves and short-period (less than 1 sec) seismographs to measure the body waves of explosions. In addition, a standard worldwide seismological network and 40 mobile seismographic stations in the United States were established. Data came flowing in from these sources in late spring and early summer of 1962. By the end of June, tentative conclusions were reached, and by late July, a new relationship between the estimated numbers of seismic events in the U.S.S.R. and their equivalence in terms of underground nuclear explosions had been established "beyond a reasonable doubt." (Hearings–1, p. 89)

*The upshot of this discovery was that the number of earthquakes in the Soviet Union equivalent to a given explosion in tuff was reduced by a factor of about two and a half. (Ibid.)* Whereas it had been estimated that in 1960 there were about 450 earthquakes in the Soviet Union of 2KT equivalent in tuff, the new data lowered the estimate to about 170 events. These empirical results were, in general, "authenticated" by a book published in 1961 by the Commission on Seismology of the Soviet Academy of Sciences called *Earthquakes in the U.S.S.R.* and which became available in the United States after the new estimate had been calculated. It should be pointed out that there was no change in the total number of detectable earthquakes in the Soviet Union. The number of earthquakes in a given seismic magnitude had been decreased in each category. There were, as a result of the revised method of equating natural earthquakes and man-made explosions, fewer earthquakes in the U.S.S.R. equivalent in size to the type of underground explosions under Hardtack II coupling than previously estimated.

The West's capability to detect underground seismic events had also improved substantially. (Hearings–4, p. 53) Detection ranges were divided into three zones: 0–1100 km, 1100–2500 km, and 2500–10,000 km. The Vela investigators were interested in the possibility of detecting seismic events ranging from hundreds of

### TABLE 1–1960 ESTIMATES
*Annual Numbers of Earthquakes in U.S.S.R.*
*Territory (Focal Depth Less Than 60 km)*

| Yield (kiloton) explosions in tuff | Numbers of earthquakes larger than given explosion | | |
|---|---|---|---|
| | Estimated minimum | Best estimate | Estimated maximum |
| 2 | 225 | (450) | 900 |
| 5 | 110 | (216) | 430 |
| 19 | 50 | (97) | 195 |
| 40 | 25 | (55) | 110 |
| 80 | 20 | (36) | 70 |

(Based on Rand Corp. Study; estimates of the Air Force Technical Applications Center (AFTAC) were 25% higher; (*Source:* Hearings–1, p. 90.)

tons to 100-KT yields because this was believed to be the spectrum most significant for military and technical developments. It was now estimated that by available methods shots down to 7KT or 10 to 20KT in dry alluvium could be detected. A potential violator could conduct clandestine shots up to 2 to 3KT with some confidence that he would not be caught. According to Dr. Ruina, the United States could build "with a high degree of confidence," a system which would detect magnitude 4 events—that is events of 1 and 2 KT in tuff with Rainier coupling—in the Soviet Union. Below this magnitude "the performance is rather sporadic." In some cases below magnitude 4 one may obtain excellent signals, but generally performance drops significantly at this level. (Hearings–1, p. 71)

In long-range seismic detection, it was found that signals from a seismic event dropped off steeply from 100 to 1,000 km, but did not continue to drop off. Instead, the signal amplitude between 1500 and 2500 km actually rose slightly and then diminished only very gradually out to 5,000 km. (Hearings–1, pp. 485–486) The importance of choosing seismically "quiet areas" cannot be overemphasized if a sufficiently high signal-to-noise ratio is to be obtained in order to detect a 1-KT shot in granite several thousand kilometers away. Thus it was now feasible "to design a detection system based entirely outside the Soviet Union . . . capable of detecting explosions of about 1KT in granite, 2 to 6KT in tuff, and 10 to 20KT in alluvium. This requires no new research." (Hearings–1, p. 99) This new approach envisioned a system of fifteen seismic detection stations

## TABLE 2–1962 ESTIMATES

*Annual Numbers of Earthquakes in U.S.S.R. Territory (Focal Depth Less Than 60 km)*

| Approximate yield (kiloton) | | |
|---|---|---|
| *Explosions in granite* | *Explosions in tuff* | *Explosions in alluvium* |
| 0.3 | 0.7-2 | 2-4 |
| 1 | 2-6 | 10-20 |
| 2 | 5-15 | 35-70 |
| 10 | 19-? | 70-150 |
| 20 | 40-? | 200 |
| 40 | 80-? | 400 |

| Numbers of earthquakes larger than given explosion | | |
|---|---|---|
| *Estimated minimum* | *Best estimate* | *Estimated maximum* |
| 280 | (400) | 630 |
| 125 | (170) | 250 |
| 55 | (78) | 110 |
| 25 | (39) | 55 |
| 17 | (24) | 35 |
| 11 | (16) | 22 |

(*Source:* Hearings–1, p. 90.)

located in quiet areas outside the Soviet Union where the noise level is low. Choosing these sites would be critical. Careful choice would be worth high investment costs, since it was expected that not more than about twenty internationally run seismic stations could be obtained. Each of these stations would be equipped with arrays of ten to twenty seismographs similar to the research stations in the Vela program.

The research program had produced a somewhat unusual result: the 1962 detection system was more capable than the controversial Geneva System above the 4.75 magnitude level whereas below that level it was less capable. (Hearings–1, p. 101) There would not be 70 unidentified events, not even 70 events, but only 40, some of which could be identified. For events between 4.0 and 4.75 magnitude the numbers had also been lowered. Formerly it was estimated that there would be 600 unidentified events above 4 magnitude. Now, it was estimated that there would be only 170, of which 150 would be of varying degrees of uncertainty. This was a substantial improvement. The 1962 system proposed to apply inspections to the many small earthquakes above 4 magnitude, so there would be more unidentified events per inspection. But in the 1960 system these unidentified events could be ignored because they were included in the voluntary moratorium area. Under the 1962 proposal, shots below 1 KT in granite, 2-6 KT in tuff, and below 10-20 KT in alluvium would not be detected. Of course, detection capabilities do not drop to zero at this point; the capability gradually diminishes from good to not too reliable. It was not expected that *all* seismic events would be detected, even with considerable technical advances in the foreseeable future. It was certainly true that some events would always escape detection.

In addition to these major developments, there were several others which impinged in one way or another on Western thinking about test ban proposals. It was found, for example, that there was a high degree of variability in picking up seismic signals in different locations. While this variability "perturbs our ability to detect and identify" seismic events, it also significantly complicates the problem of the potential violator. (Hearings–1, p. 403) He cannot reliably make calculations based on averages. Identification remained the most intractable problem in detecting, identifying, locating and inspecting possible nuclear explosions. At the reliable threshold of 10 to 20 KT, it was estimated that less than one-third of all detected events would have features that would help in an identification analysis; two-thirds would have so little information that essentially nothing could be said about them. Many underground nuclear events would be so identified because they could not be identified as earthquakes. Decoupling, which had been a problem in earlier years as a probable concealment method, was no longer a problem in 1963. While the principle was correct, the costs of digging gigantic holes in the bowels of the earth—a hole 45 to 55 feet in radius 3,000 feet below the surface of the earth to muffle a 10 KT explosion down to 3 KT—and especially in scarce, dry alluvium, which is like sand and gravel, appeared prohibitive and all but completely impractical. The likelihood of success in on-site inspections had been ridiculed in earlier hearings and used by test ban opponents to flay treaty supporters. Now it was admitted that while a probability number could not be assigned to the effectiveness of a single inspection, on the other hand the system would give "some probability" which could not be precisely evaluated. As a result, a violator would find it difficult to satisfy himself that all his evasive techniques, covering a wide spectrum, and not just a single phenomenon, could be effectively covered at once. Neither side could prove conclusively that either concealment or detection could be absolute. But the difficulties of evasion were obviously considerable. While it was recognized that on-site inspections might not succeed against a determined cheater, they could be used as a powerful psychological deterrent. In this way, they might have a stabilizing effect on the operation of a comprehensive test ban treaty. The test ban was technically acceptable without on-site inspection, but it would not have been politically acceptable, particularly for the Senate. Inspections were therefore essential. Thus, again, science and engineering provided the techniques and know-how but only up to a point. Beyond that point a judgment of risk and of political requirements had to be made—and made in a more or less arbitrary manner.

It had long been recognized that both the United States and the U.S.S.R. could perform militarily useful nuclear tests in space, and that if these tests were conducted far enough into outer space they would not be detected. There have never been any known nuclear tests far out in space. (Hearings–1, p. 402) It has long been acknowledged that such tests would be extremely lengthy and uneconomical. Although no means of detecting such tests have actually been developed into hardware, American scientists were certain that effective means were within the state of the art. A foolproof detection system to cover the area within the earth's orbit around the sun could not be promised. But the detection system, once created, would complicate the concealment tactics of a potential violator. Any such attempt was described as extremely difficult, a waste of scientific manpower and very costly, requiring a large operation and many people.

While detection of nuclear test explosions from 10 km to outer space was good, there could be no positive verification since the detector could not know for sure that some natural phenomenon might not have produced the same signal. The ACDA, in a statement to the Senate Armed Services Committee in September 1962, had divided space into three regions and evaluated the identification probability in each:

1. *Stratosphere test 10 to 100 km:* fair degree of probability.
2. *100 to 1000 km:* fairly good identification.
3. *Beyond 1,000 km:* ground-based detection systems would be able to detect yields from 1KT out to perhaps 100,000 km. Scientific judgment, at these heights, devolved into a statement of mutual uncertainty on the part of the detector and potential violator.

The final evaluation by Secretary Rusk of the possibility of testing in space was that it "seemed so remote that this would yield results, experimentally or as part of a testing program, that this was a remote risk, and did not raise the question of a testing arms race uninspected in the usual sense." (Hearings–4, pp. 27, 64, 100–101; Hearings–1, pp. 324, 356, and 374) Since underwater testing had not been regarded as important in the past, not too much technical attention had been focused on this aspect of test detection and identification. The total number of seismic signals underwater as of March 1963 had been less than ten. If an underwater detection system were to be installed, a network of hydrophones would need to be created. As of March 1963 no hardware had been produced for this purpose. Underwater surveillance serves less to police underwater tests than to augment other methods of long-distance detection, identification, and epicenter location. The underwater detection network could be placed in areas twenty or more miles off the east coast of the Soviet Union where perhaps 60 percent of Soviet earthquake activity occurs. Without this underwater detection opportunity these areas would be inaccessible. Because these stations can be unilaterally operated, unilaterally placed, and unilaterally maintained by each nation, a potential violator would not know the real capability of the underwater detection system. A worldwide installation of an underwater detection system would provide a method of detecting seismic events well below 1KT. It was not expected that this system would provide any new criteria for the identification of seismic events, but only that it would contribute data of the greatest value bearing on established criteria. (Hearings–6, p. 319; Hearings–4, p. 62; Hearings–1, pp. 114, 124, and 425)

In gathering data and reformulating policy, the ACDA drew on many sources of advice and appraisal, including the technical and scientific capabilities of the AEC, CIA, JCS, Defense Atomic Support Agency, Air Force Technical Applications Center, ARPA, and the President's science adviser. The ACDA was given briefings by Dr. John Foster, Director of the Lawrence Radiation Laboratory at Livermore and Dr. Carson Mark, Director of the Theoretical Division of Los Alamos Scientific Laboratory, on the current state of nuclear weapons technology and the prospects for development with further testing. Dr. Foster played a major role in briefing other agencies of the executive and congressional committee on similar subjects in relation to the test ban. Nongovernmental consultants were also used by the ACDA in obtaining the latest information and interpretations of all data related to test ban problems. Many of these experts came from universities, research institutes, private and governmental, and industry. The corporation known as Mathematica, Inc., for example, contributed to a clearer understanding of the effects of different quotas of on-site inspections through the use of statistical methods and game theory. At times, panels of experts from government, industry, and universities were convened by the ACDA to study such problems as the usefulness of unmanned seismic stations or the utility of oil exploration in on-site inspections. (Hearings–5, pp. 50–51)

## The Uses of the New Data: The 1962 Treaty Proposals

The new data from the Vela program could have been used either to bolster the West's earlier proposals or to open previously closed avenues of negotiation. A political decision was made to explore the possibility of a more "negotiable" system. It was the position of the ACDA that if a test ban treaty was still in the national interest, then the new technical data should be used to devise a control system which would (1) cost less to construct and operate, (2) be simpler to manage, (3) be in operation sooner and (4) have an estimated detection threshold comparable to that estimated in 1961 for the more elaborate system detailed at that time. (Hearings–4, p. 50)

The Vela data allowed the West to move away from dead center. The positions of both sides had been allowed to become frozen during the three-year stalemate. The "Third Zone" detection capability, ranging from 2500 to 10,000 km, now allowed the United States to reconsider completely the cumbersome and overblown international control systems to be located on Soviet and Western territory. This resulted in the proposed system of "internationally supervised national stations" rather than of internationally operated stations proposed by the United States in April 1961 and earlier drafts. Substantially fewer stations in the Soviet Union would be required. The technical reassessment also made it possible to decrease the number of on-site inspections required for verification. This substantial change in the American position did not imply that identification of detected seismic events would be possible by seismic means only; a system of effective, reliable, objective on-site inspections of unidentified seismic events was still necessary. "Indeed, to the extent that there is greater reliance on seismic data from distant stations, the problem of identification becomes more difficult; and the need for on-site inspections—within the agreed number—is intensified rather than diminished." (International Negotiations, p. 262)

When the interagency committee completed its tasks, subsequent staff work was accomplished on both the technical and the political levels with some overlapping in personnel. The technical group met informally to study the interrelations between technical progress and a possible treaty. It consisted of the Director of Defense Research and Engineering in DOD, the science advisers to the President, the CIA, and the ACDA, an Atomic Energy Commissioner, the Director of ARPA, the Deputy Special Assistant to the President for National Security Affairs, and the General Counsel, DOD. Except for the last two, all the members were scientists from such disciplines as nuclear physics, physical chemistry, and electrical engineering. The technical group was informally representative of the Committee of Deputies on which it was probably a majority. Although the group had two representatives from the defense establishment they were both civilians. Furthermore, the group consisted only of political appointees in very high positions. As a "floating group" it would be convened by one of its members on an informal basis to "settle" technical problems arising in the effort to formulate the American position. It is significant that this group could meet and dispose of business without the participation of military representation—a notable advantage in the light of the skeptical position taken by the JCS toward the idea of a comprehensive test ban treaty.

The political staff work was done by the Committee of Deputies —the actual working body of the Committee of Principals. The membership of the Committee of Deputies overlapped to a large extent with that of the informal technical group. This committee was of a more formal nature than its technical counterpart and consisted of a somewhat larger membership. The deputies considered the various treaty drafts prepared by the ACDA interagency committee. Since it was this committee that more or less created the treaty policy for "ratification" by the Committee of Principals and the President, the dominant scientific group among the deputies played an extraordinary and critical role on the scientific and, more importantly, on the political policy-making level. It met formally many times for this purpose between July 20 and July 27, 1962, when the treaties were submitted to the Committee of Principals. It was the deputies who urged the adoption of a simple limited test ban treaty, which was eventually signed and ratified in the summer of 1963.

The Committee of Principals was originally created by Eisenhower to prevent the best ban problem from becoming enmeshed in the cumbersome National Security Council structure. When Kennedy downgraded the National Security Council, the Committee of Principals was in effect taken over by the President as a means of reaching a consensus within the executive concerning the nuclear test ban treaty and other disarmament problems.

The Committee of Principals consisted of the President, the Secretary of State, the Director of the CIA, the President's Science Adviser, the Chairman of the AEC, the Secretary of Defense (usually accompanied by the Chairman of the JCS).* There were only two scientists on this body, although each member was "backed up" by working scientists in the Committee of Deputies and the Technical Group.

The workings of the Committee of Principals are not well known; the use of this method in the decision-making process, however, was an unusual departure from the norm. As an operating organ it has been described by a participant as a "curious body" that was generally poorly prepared and ineffective except when the issue was clear cut and the President keenly interested in the topic at hand. At its best it functioned as a kind of "debating society" where disagreements and agreements were made clear before the problem was presented to the President for choice or approval. Certain individuals, as is to be expected, played a more influential role than others.

Secretary McNamara took a very strong personal interest in thoroughly understanding the technical and scientific problems. At one point he summoned the scientists to a seminar over which he presided, the purpose of which was not only to examine the technical intricacies of a test ban, but also to "persuade" the scientists to agree to the use of a common set of figures. The Committee of Principals reportedly did not discuss the nuclear test ban problem substantively but merely acted as a ratifying body.

---

*Under President Kennedy, the Committee of Principals consisted of Secretary of State Rusk, Secretary of Defense McNamara, CIA Director John A. McCone, AEC Chairman Dr. Glenn T. Seaborg, and Dr. Wiesner. The JCS chairman was added "formally and officially" to the committee on May 22, 1963. This was more a formal move than one of substance, since he had always attended with the Secretary of Defense. (Hearings–6, p. 119) According to another source, the Director of the U.S. Arms Control and Disarmament Agency was also formally added at that time. (Hearings –5, p. 302) The Special Assistant to the President for National Security Affairs, McGeorge Bundy, Edward R. Murrow, the Director of the U.S. Information Agency, and the President's press secretary, Pierre Salinger, served as advisers to the Committee of Principals. (Hearings–5, p. 302)

The Committee of Principals met without the President on July 26, and then, on July 27, July 30, and August   with the President. It gave unanimous support to the proposed treaties, which the President later approved. When McNamara was asked at the Senate hearings on the limited test ban treaty whether he could suggest names of opponents to this treaty in the DOD, he said he could not and mentioned Dr. Edward Teller as the only opponent of sufficient scientific stature. Dr. Teller at that time was out of the government teaching at the University of California but was a consultant to the Ballistic Missile Division of the Air Force. Whereas in the Eisenhower administration, opposition was clearly surfaced even in the Committee of Principals, where the Secretary of Defense and the Chairman of the AEC were known to oppose the test ban, the opposition in the Kennedy administration was much more quiescent and submerged. According to one participant, a supporter of the treaty, there was a certain amount of "arm-twisting" in the effort to obtain unanimity. In the end, whatever the process, general agreement was reached.

On August 6, the Soviets were informally notified of American intentions to submit a new treaty proposal. On August 9, Ambassador Dean described the significance of the Vela research results to the Subcommittee on a Treaty for the Discontinuance of Nuclear Weapons Tests.* Earlier, the President, Rusk, and the DOD had announced that important findings had come from the Vela program suggesting that instrumentation could do a better job than was earlier supposed in regard to detection and identification.

On August 27, the West tabled two treaty proposals, a comprehensive test ban in all environments and a limited test ban in three environments, outer space, atmosphere, and underwater. The allies made it clear in a joint statement issued by Kennedy and Macmillan that while they strongly preferred a comprehensive treaty they would also be willing to sign a limited treaty "if this represents the widest area of agreement possible at this time." (International Negotiations, p. 285) The essence of the comprehensive treaty lay in the continued acceptance of the obligatory nature of on-site inspections, an unspecified reduction in the number of on-site inspections, and a network of detection stations smaller than previously proposed but nationally manned and internationally supervised, inspected, and monitored. These stations would be completely outside the Soviet Union rather than both inside and out.

---

*The subcommittee was established by the Conference of the Eighteen-Nation Committee on Disarmament on March 21, 1962 and was composed of the representatives of the United States, the United Kingdom, and the Soviet Union.

It was anticipated that no international detection system would be necessary to enforce the limited treaty. Both treaties permitted explosions for peaceful purposes if the United States, the United Kindgom, and the Soviet Union unanimously agreed to them.

The Soviets turned down these proposals, claiming that there had been no substantial changes in the Western stand and that the proposals were not in line with the eight-nation memorandum. Soviet representative Kuznetsov insisted that the memorandum called for "invitational" rather than "obligatory" on-site inspections, and that national stations rather than international control posts were supposed to be used for detection of nuclear explosions. He rejected the partial test ban, arguing that this would preserve the possibility of underground testing, leading to unlimited testing and the "legalizing of the nuclear weapon." (International Negotiations, p. 108) But this was only a prelude to more serious consideration by the Soviets and more concessions by the United States.

## The 1963 Proposal: An Attempt to Break the Deadlock

Despite the Cuban crisis – perhaps because of it* – a series of letters was exchanged between Kennedy and Khruschev on the test ban issue. In December 1962, Khruschev suggested that "black boxes" be located in remote parts of Russia, and to satisfy political conditions and requirements in the United States he would agree to two to three inspections. Soviet willingness to accept inspections was applauded by the United States but the low figure of two to three inspections was not deemed acceptable. Black boxes too were satisfactory but not in remote areas. The next letter exchange resulted in the abortive New York talks in January 1963 at which the United States lowered its required number of inspections to seven. The Soviets insisted on talking only of the number of on-site inspections and black boxes and persistently refused to discuss how inspections would be carried out.

The failure of the New York talks has been laid to difficulties of communication. In retrospect, the Soviets apparently genuinely desired a treaty but misread United States insistence on the technical importance of inspections as paying public obeisance to the on-site inspection principle. The West, on the other hand, misjudged the Soviet offer of three inspections as propaganda, as it had been in the past, while the Soviets believed they had made a major concession.

---

*Secretary Rusk, testifying in favor of the partial test ban treaty in August 1963, suggested that the Cuban crisis had played a positive role in emphasizing the urgency of the test ban treaty.

Kennedy and Macmillan again appealed to Khrushchev to reconsider his position before it was too late. At a press conference Khrushchev, in a surly mood, withdrew his on-site inspection offer but called for two East-West delegations to meet in Moscow on July 15. The West felt that such a meeting might be only a pawn in the Sino-Soviet dispute since a major conference on the split was scheduled for July 1. A sense of hopelessness hung over proponents of the test ban in Washington. "I am certainly pessimistic for the immediate future," ACDA Director Foster told the JCAE in March 1963. (Hearings–1, p. 440) But "major shifts of position have often come unexpectedly," he said, alluding to the Austrian Peace Treaty. (*Ibid.*) While the Soviets had steadfastly refused even to recognize the principle of on-site inspection in the fall of 1962 they had suddenly changed their minds, as evidenced in Khrushchev's letter to Kennedy of December 19, 1962, in which he returned to the position he had held in November 1961. Foster believed the Soviets had reversed themselves because of American insistence on the need for on-site inspections. (Hearings–1, p. 441).

The ACDA continued to consider possible ways of "refining" the two treaty proposals put forth in August 1962. As one scientist-participant put it, "it was unfortunate that we did not thoroughly think through the logical extensions of the August 1962 proposals before they were tabled at Geneva." (Interview) The result was what is known as the "March 23, 1963 draft treaty" for a comprehensive test ban. This draft seems never to have been made public, although it was circulated among various governmental agencies and triggered congressional hearings on the nuclear test ban. It was never tabled in Geneva; instead the United States and the United Kingdom negotiated with the Soviets on the basis of an April 1, 1963, memorandum laying out the general principles, on-site inspection arrangements, and the use of automatic seismic stations. (Hearings–5, pp. 36–39) A number of topics, such as black boxes and the quality and quantity of on-site inspections, which figured in summit correspondence and other negotiations in 1962 –1963, became part of the new proposal.

The nature of this new treaty proposal can best be described by outlining the key changes that were made in comparison with the August 1962 draft treaty:

1. The nuclear powers would rely on their own national detection stations for the collection of seismic data, supplemented by the use of automatic seismic stations. The nuclear powers would be responsible for the design of their own detection systems and their operation and supervision. Each country could maximize the control it had over its control stations; it could build in as much flexibility as it liked, and incorporate the newest and most useful equipment as it

wished. It could change the location of control stations at will, without the consent of others. The system could be adjusted to political conditions and directed toward the Soviet Union, Communist China, or others, as required. The exact capabilities of the national systems did not need to be disclosed, thus adding to deterrent force. This system had its disadvantages. Control stations could not easily be introduced into another country and information produced by one country might not be accepted by an international commission. (Hearings–1, p. 395)

2. The monitoring stations would not be internationally supervised or composed of one-third Soviet nationals as in the earlier draft. Under this system, therefore, haggling over the number of stations could be avoided, since the number would depend on the felt needs of the member nations and not on an agreement.

3. Inspection would be reciprocal. The United States and the United Kingdom could designate fourteen out of twenty members of an inspection team to visit the Soviet Union; the team leader would be either American or British. There would be no Soviet nationals on the team. The same principle would hold, of course, for an inspection team coming to the United States. The August 1962 draft allowed the executive officer of an international commission to select team members with no explicit requirement to include American or British nationals on a team going to the Soviet Union.

4. This new proposal emphasized the importance of the arrangements concerning the conduct of on-site inspections. Depending on what arrangements were agreed upon, the West was willing to lower its on-site inspection quota to seven. This reduction emphasized the need to maximize the deterrent effect of each on-site inspection. This reduction, in turn, was expected to enhance the feeling of confidence each side would have in the verification system and in the observation of the treaty.

5. To locate the epicenter of seismic events the side requesting an on-site inspection would use its own data, which would provide four clearly measurable and mutually consistent arrival times based on location criteria listed in the treaty. This was in contrast to the Geneva System where the executive office of an international organization made the determination based on data from all stations, including data obtained from the country where the unidentified event was supposed to have occurred. The boundaries and location of the suspected area would have to be located within an area no greater than 500 sq. km or an ellipse with a semimajor axis no larger than 15 km.

6. The April memo envisioned the creation of an international commission with greatly reduced powers and activities compared to earlier concepts. For the nuclear powers, it would serve as "a means

of communication and as a coordinating organization for detection stations operated by various nations, particularly nations other than the three principal nuclear powers." (Hearings–5, pp. 14–15, 36–39, 82–84)

The changing American and British positions from 1958 to 1963 can be succinctly summarized in a chart:

|                       | 1958–1962                | August 1962                          | 1963        |
|-----------------------|--------------------------|--------------------------------------|-------------|
| Type of system        | International ("Geneva")  | Internationally super- vised national | National     |
| Number of stations    | 170 plus 10              | Not definite but fewer               | U.S. choice |
| Supervision           | International            | International                        | National    |
| Manning               | International            | National                             | National    |
| Collocation           | Complete                 | Largely U.S. choice                  | U.S. choice |

(*Source:* Hearings–1, p. 394)

These alterations resulted from a determination on the part of the West to try to find a more negotiable comprehensive test ban treaty which would not compromise its security. The method used was in effect a combination of political adaptations of technical knowledge and the application of statistical analysis. The disagreement between the Communists and the West centered less on the number of on-site inspections than on the acceptability of the principle. While the West was always insistent on the necessity for inspections, the Soviets only recognized the principle occasionally, and then grudgingly. When they did recognize it, they never followed this "concession" with a willingness to accept more than two or three inspections per year. This small number had always been unacceptable to the West, which had begun with a request for twenty. In its attempt to find a more satisfactory formula, the West gradually lowered its requirements to seven, with hints that even this figure was negotiable depending upon certain other conditions.

The constant and seemingly one-sided lowering without any Soviet response was criticized as an unwarranted concession and aroused the consternation of the Senate Preparedness Investigating Subcommittee during its hearings on the test ban in 1963. It would, therefore, be a useful digression at this point to study the historical developments in this seemingly one-sided numbers game, and its interaction with technology, the laws of probability, and the dilemmas of political choice.

The United States draft annex of December 16, 1958, provided for the inspection of all unidentified seismic events above an equivalent yield of 5KT, of 20 percent of unidentified events with lower yields, and of any events below that yield that had an "unusually high probability of being of nuclear origin." The Hardtack II tests in the fall of 1958 seemed to indicate that this request was too optimistic. The Geneva System might detect many times the number of events anticipated by the United States in 1958 but it would be unable to identify enough of them. In a letter to Khrushchev on May 9, 1959, Eisenhower maintained that the United States did not demand an unlimited number of inspections but insisted that the number should be "in appropriate relationship to scientific facts and the detection capabilities."

The February 1960 treaty advanced by the United States proposed two formulas for calculating the number of unidentified events above the 4.75 magnitude threshold which should be inspected: (1) 20 percent of all events above the threshold located by the system, (2) 30 percent of all such events still unidentified after application of American criteria, or (3) a flat 20 inspections on the assumption that there would be about 100 unidentified seismic events above the threshold in the Soviet Union. In 1961, the United States proposed a sliding scale of twelve to twenty inspections depending on the numbers of unidentified events in a given year. The Soviets proposed three veto-free inspections a year, but the two sides could not agree on the criteria to be used in selecting the unidentified events. When the United States decided to drop the 4.75 threshold in March 1962, it did not increase the number of on-site inspections and suggested that these be restricted in the main to the seismic areas of the Soviet Union. When the Vela program verified the Soviet claim that there were fewer earthquakes of a given magnitude, the United States lowered its request for inspections to eight to ten per year in October 1962. This was lowered again on February 19, 1963, to seven in informal discussions with the Soviets in Geneva. According to ACDA Director Foster,

> [E]ach case has been the result of adjustments which have come about because of better knowledge of the circumstances, better equipment with which to examine, better methods of carrying out the inspections, a greater knowledge of what we had to look for and what we can find.... [A]s we come down we have also changed other elements of the inspection system. The proposal, when we made it, of seven on-site inspections must be associated with a different makeup of the team, a different ability to look at what we were looking for, a management of those teams by our side; in effect an adversary proceeding and a somewhat more diluted international system. (Hearings–1, p. 433; for details see Hearings–5, pp. 24–27)

The March 1963 proposal emphasized the quality of the on-site inspection. The number is "not really the most important element of the system," said Dr. Foster (Hearings–5, p. 39) Dr. Haworth, then

AEC Commissioner, said that "the exact number of inspections within one or two or something like that is not nearly so important as being sure that those inspections can be conducted effectively." (Hearings–5, p. 272) The number chosen must be "large enough to deter possible violations of a test ban treaty by confronting a potential violator with a real probability of discovery if he chose to conduct secret underground tests." (Hearings–5, p. 26)

Dr. Foster maintained that the number chosen has "a mathematical relationship to the number of suspicious events which are otherwise unidentifiable. But the exact mathematical relationship certainly is not precise." (Hearings–5, p. 40) He explained that there was a close connection between the number of inspections and the laws of probability. This idea was adapted from industrial quality control techniques where only a fraction of a number of products going through a production line is checked to assure that specifications are being adhered to. Using this method, Dr. Foster asserted, it was possible to attain a 98 to 99 percent assurance against cheating. (Hearings–5, p. 43)

But what number would constitute a satisfactory deterrent? The lowest official figure proposed by the Kennedy administration was seven inspections. From the viewpoint of the laws of probability this was "somewhat more than is needed," according to Dr. Foster. (Hearings–5, p. 43) This figure, he maintained, would certainly have a strong deterrent effect on the evader. There was "no magic" in choosing a number, he claimed, no precise mathematical technique, except that it was somehow related to the general order of magnitude of unidentified events.

That one, two, or three inspections would be wholly unacceptable, was the unanimous position of the President's technical advisers. One inspection would probably be used at the beginning and one at the end of the year, leaving only one to cover eight to ten months. Each inspection, it was estimated, would take about six weeks, allowing seven to be undertaken in a year. Seven times was believed to be as frequently as inspections could be accomplished and frequent enough so that no one could test any "substantial series" without fear of being challenged. (Hearings–5, p. 62) According to this reasoning, five inspections were felt to be the minimum acceptable. Dr. Brown conceded that what constitutes an acceptable risk in regard to numbers of inspections is a "difference of judgment" – a difference reflected in the disagreement between the administration and the opponents of a test ban treaty. (Hearings–5, p. 48) Dr. Brown said he would not be happy with four inspections, "somewhat unhappy" with five. (Hearings–5, p. 48) Dr. Foster was equally "somewhat unhappy" with five, but added, "I would certainly believe that this is not unreasonable, especially if one could carry over unused inspections to the next year on a limited basis, or overuse one's quota a little in a given year." (Hearings–5, p. 43) While Dr. Foster said he would be unhappy with six, Dr. Brown claimed he could live with six or seven, providing inspection procedures were accepted and the decision on inspection was not subject to negotiation. (Hearings–5, pp. 43, 48) Dr. Long said five inspections would be "an absolute minimum no matter how well the modalities were handled and how well the provisions for carry-over." (Hearings–5, p. 100)

Elaborate "clearance" procedures were reportedly followed in order to obtain a firm consensus if and when the administration would have to obtain the consent of the Senate. It is not at all clear, however, to what degree the comprehensive and limited test ban draft treaties of August 1962 and the comprehensive treaty of March 1963 were evaluated in depth from the military, political, technical, economic, and strategic point of view *before* they were discussed with the Soviets. Much of this part of the record is shrouded in executive privilege. Hearings on the test ban treaty provide a glimpse and interviews provided some implicit elaboration.

## THE MILITARY ESTABLISHMENT

Like all other interested agencies, the military was represented on the interagency technical group and Committees of Deputies and Principals. But the participation of the military, and even its approval or disapproval, did not necessarily imply a full-fledged evaluation. The Senate Preparedness Investigating Subcommittee implied that it had prompted the first searching analysis by a number of the executive agencies, particularly the services. Testimony on the treaty and acknowledgments during interviews seem to indicate that the draft treaties were considered and evaluated on the highest echelons, horizontally speaking; but a vertical in-depth analysis by the several services appears not to have taken place until the possibility of a real treaty was imminent.

The JCS and DOD participated in all arms control talks and had representatives at the Geneva and United Nations conferences. They analyzed reports from Geneva, participated in the Department of State's instructions to the field, and, together with the ACDA, initiated arms control research studies.

The Secretary of Defense and Chairman of the JCS participated in the Committee of Principals, commented on drafts and instructions, and reported directly to the President. The JCS therefore had every opportunity to press its opinions in the highest forums. According to General LeMay the JCS was instructed by the new administration early in its tenure to consider all aspects of the problem, from a political as well as a military point of view. (Hearings–5, pp. 733, 750)

The attitude of the JCS toward the August 1962 comprehensive test ban treaty proposal may be surmised from the stand it took on the March 23, 1963, draft treaty in hearings held by the Senate Preparedness Investigating Subcommittee. Although the JCS claimed that its views were forwarded to the ACDA, Dr. Foster of the ACDA said he received recommendations from the Secretary of Defense who approved the comprehensive treaty, rather than the views of the JCS collectively or individually. (Hearings–5, pp. 57–58) Except for a few quite important changes, the JCS appears to have been a passive partner in "creating" the treaty, although it commented actively on ACDA drafts. The chief reason was that the JCS considered the comprehensive test ban treaty inconsistent with national security. (Hearings–5, p. 305) Admiral George W. Anderson, representing the JCS at the Preparedness Subcommittee hearings in June 1963, while admitting that "this is a matter of judgment," disagreed with Dr. Haworth's contention that "the risk of working out a treaty with the Soviets was less than the risk of going ahead with unlimited testing." (Hearings–5, p. 310) The Admiral's views were contrary to the working assumptions of the political civilian leadership in the Kennedy administration. It is not clear whether this skeptical feeling pervaded the meetings of the JCS, but it would not be unreasonable to assume that it did. The Joint Chiefs declared that an effective test ban could be supported only if at the time such a treaty was signed the Soviets did not have an advantage over the United States in nuclear weapons technology and that the treaty met additional conditions. The draft treaty, the JCS felt, contained a number of deficiencies, the most critical of which was the "absence of a threshold." The treaty would offer the Soviets too great an incentive to conduct clandestine tests. The JCS had always insisted that the treaty should permit tests where they are not detectable, particularly underground. They also opposed the seven on-site inspections as inadequate in relation to the annual number of suspicious events in the Soviet Union. The other objections concerned requirements and areas for on-site inspections, the authority of the international commission, "undue reliance" on the state being inspected for logistic support, and too long a delay for withdrawal from the treaty. They felt that clandestine tests underground, in the atmosphere at low yields, and in deep space, would lead to Soviet advantages in offensive, defensive, and tactical weapons where the United States was presumably ahead. The problem of testing an antiballistic missile was one of the major considerations which influenced General Wheeler, Army Chief of Staff, to pronounce the treaty unacceptable. (Hearings–5, p. 660) McNamara did not accept the necessity for a threshold on prohibited tests. This was the principal difference between him and the JCS.

In anticipation of a possible Soviet policy reversal, General Taylor, Chairman of the JCS, said that he ordered a review of the limited test ban proposal by the JCS in mid-June 1963, even though no specific proposal was then "technically" available (a draft treaty had been made public one year earlier). (Hearings–6, p. 280) This action was prompted by the conversations between Harold Wilson and Khrushechev on June 10.

In reaching an overall evaluation of the limited test ban treaty, the Joint Chiefs were obviously put in an uncomfortable position, since they had so recently opposed the administration's comprehensive test ban proposal. The new evaluation began with the remark: "In this review they [the JCS] deliberately set aside all considerations of former positions taken on other occasions on the subject of a test ban treaty and focused their attention on this particular treaty at this particular point in time." (Hearings–6, p. 272; Hearings–5, p. 587) Plainly, the JCS were bending over backward to accommodate the administration. While pointing to about five technical-military disadvantages in the treaty, the JCS admitted that if the treaty would contribute to "further division of the Sino-Soviet Bloc, this would be a major political achievement with important and favorable military implications." (Hearings–6, p. 275) It was also acknowledged that if the treaty would restrain further proliferation of nuclear weapons, technical-military disadvantages would be further offset. The JCS therefore gave the treaty their support provided certain safeguards were accepted by the administration. General Taylor later testified that no one asked him directly whether he approved or disapproved the treaty. But when the Joint Chiefs were asked whether they would recommend adoption of the limited test ban treaty if it had not already been signed, only General LeMay replied, "I think I would have been against it." (Hearings–6, p. 373) The others said they would have supported it. (Hearings–6, pp. 374–375) There were differences, said General Taylor, in the scientific and technical communities on the interpretation of some facts. But the differences, he claimed, were not serious and "they did not create any real problem for the Chiefs in reaching their final decision." (Hearings–6, p. 282) The differences were a matter of emphasis and they centered on the antiballistic missile problem and systems testing limitations, which was "the hardest one for the Chiefs." (Hearings–6, p. 303) Of the four Joint Chiefs, General LeMay obviously had the hardest time giving his consent: "I haven't spent as much time on any other subject that has ever come before the JCS." (Hearings–6, p. 395)

LeMay claimed that "all [meaning presumably the JCS] were caught a little bit by surprise at the seriousness of the administration in trying to get a treaty." He went on to say: "It wasn't until we saw the instructions to Mr. Harriman that it dawned on me anyway that we were really serious about trying to negotiate a treaty." (Hearings—5, p. 732) On the surface this appears to be an amazing admission. The policy intentions of the administration, which had by then been in office for two-and-a-half years, had been clearly and often set forth, and the President had repeatedly declared his determination to secure a test ban.

In formulating their judgments about the various test ban proposals, the JCS and the Secretary of Defense had the entire scientific community to call upon, as well as their own very extensive research and development organizations. It is not wholly clear how these resources were organized and how and to what extent their judgments influenced the final outcome. But there are a few indications of how it was accomplished.

In the technical hearings sponsored by the JCAE, scientists and engineers tended to use slightly different sets of figures for their respective purposes. This made comparison very difficult for policy-making purposes. The administration, therefore, tried to persuade the scientists to agree to a common set of figures which could be used as a base. This set of figures, known as "the Bible," was essentially a correlation of earthquakes measured in kiloton yields for detection and was not concerned with identification and location. "The Bible," it was hoped, would be the foundation from which a more rational political interpretation, hence policy recommendation, might be derived and upon which a consensus could be built. The government found it very difficult even to get agreement on this first set of figures. When the administration attempted to revise "the Bible" to include detection by *all* means in the atmosphere, space, and underwater, as a basis for a decision on the limited test ban treaty, agreement was impossible; "the Bible" was never revised before the treaty was signed.

The JCS invited such scientists as Drs. John Foster, Norris Bradbury, and Teller to brief them on the nuclear test ban treaty and its scientific implications. They then questioned these scientists closely on their interpretations in a kind of congressional hearing in the JCS "tank" in the Pentagon. It was significant that a small group of scientists were constantly called upon to testify for the services to various governmental groups and congressional committees.

Only a little information is available on the manner in which the Air Force took a position on the treaty. General LeMay appointed General Nathan Twining, former Air Force Chief of Staff, to chair a committee to assess the validity of three premises which, it was claimed, were stressed in official statements to support the desirability of a test ban. They were: (1) that the United States held a nuclear lead and was most likely to maintain it if there were a test ban treaty; (2) that nuclear technology had reached a point of diminishing returns, and under a test ban no developments were likely to occur that could upset the balance of power; (3) that the risk of surprise abrogation could be reduced to an acceptable level by a national policy of maintaining strong weapons laboratories and test facility readiness.

The contents of the report and committee membership were not made public except that the committee concluded that the above premises were not valid—another example of judgments contrary to a number of the Kennedy administration's basic assumptions. The report was submitted to the Secretaries of Defense and the Air Force in addition to the Air Force Chief of Staff. Only one member's name was disclosed: Dr. John Foster, who was against the treaty. Dr. Bradbury, who was for the treaty, was apparently not on the committee. The leanings of the membership can be further gleaned from Twining's remark that his skepticism and distaste for the treaty "would be agreed to by this group, except the statement of overall position on the test ban. And I think most of them would agree with that." (Hearings–5, pp. 311, 532, 979–980)


## THE PRESIDENT'S SCIENCE ADVISER AND SCIENCE ADVISORY COMMITTEE.

Dr. Jerome B. Wiesner, the President's Science Adviser, was convinced of the value and urgency of arms control and disarmament. He had played an influential role in arms control prior to 1961. He had already been a member of the President's Science Advisory Committee (PSAC) under Eisenhower and had served on the PSAC Panel on Arms Limitation. He had been staff director of the United States delegation to the conference to prevent surprise attack in late 1958. Just before the Kennedy administration took over, Dr. Wiesner and Walt Rostow attended a Pugwash Conference in Moscow in late 1960. Dr. Wiesner's commitment to arms control strongly complemented Kennedy's conviction of the need to decelerate the arms race.

The influence of successive presidential science advisers has grown steadily in the nuclear test ban field. Dr. Wiesner's role in "educating" the President in the technical details of the test ban contributed greatly, perhaps critically, in making Kennedy possibly the best-informed layman on the subject at the time.

In contrast to the widening influence of the special assistant, PSAC's role seems to have diminished. While it was a driving force within the government after being elevated to the White House in late 1957, it gradually receded in national security and test ban affairs under the Kennedy administration. The reasons for this shift can only be surmised. The forceful role taken by the science adviser himself may have preempted the role of PSAC. The test ban problem may have been thought to transcend PSAC responsibilities. There was no longer any great controversy among scientists over the value of a test ban as a first step. The creation of the ACDA in 1962 may have been thought to have removed the necessity for PSAC participation. Drs. York and Brown, both former PSAC members, were a scientific arm, so to speak, as successive Directors of Defense Research and Engineering in the DOD. It may also have been thought that McNamara's decisive management of the military establishment not only obviated the need for PSAC's intervention but made it politically undesirable for PSAC to concern itself too deeply with military affairs, as it had done in the past. Such a consideration may well have been reinforced by the probability that, unlike Eisenhower, Kennedy would be likely to support his Secretary of Defense in vital matters of national defense.

## DEPARTMENT OF STATE

It is not clear what role the Department of State played in the nuclear test ban. The chief of the United States delegation to Moscow was the department's undersecretary. Secretary Rusk unequivocally stated that he gave more personal time to the ACDA than to any other bureau, except the Bureau of European Affairs during the Berlin crisis, and in his personal consultations with McNamara the work of the ACDA would be "on any list of the top three items in terms of time spent." (Hearings–6, pp. 83–84) Of course, time spent is not necessarily a measure of importance, and the ACDA was responsible for more than the nuclear test ban, but Rusk's testimony indicates the seriousness with which the test ban was viewed in the Kennedy administration. The department's science adviser was not known to have played an active part in the nuclear test ban arrangements. This may have been due to the active role played by the science adviser of ACDA.

## ATOMIC ENERGY COMMISSION

The Chairman of the AEC, Dr. Seaborg, reported unanimous support by the commissioners of the limited test ban treaty to the

Foreign Relations Committee (Hearings–6, p. 221) Dr. Haworth, who became an AEC commissioner in April 1961 and was formerly Director of the Brookhaven National Laboratory was described as a "pillar of strength" in the AEC for the pro-test ban group. Despite the influential role played by Dr. Haworth, however, the AEC as a whole was, according to one critic, "by-passed" in the power structure that determined the direction of nuclear test ban policy. The commission had participated in the extensive research studies which were the foundation of the treaty proposals, but it merely commented on these proposals. The AEC was represented in the Committee of Principals, but it did not insist on representation at the Moscow negotiations, where the Plowshare Clause of the partial treaty was deleted. The AEC did not participate in this deletion except through the Committee of Principals, which probably approved the final treaty.

## THE ROLE OF THE SCIENTISTS

Scientists played a highly constructive role in the formulation of the test ban proposals. Indeed there could scarcely be a better example of what McGeorge Bundy had in mind when he tried to define the relevance of scientific advice. Science, he said,

> has to be present not simply at the moment of crucial decision one-minute before zero-hour. Science has to be present in the process of consideration ... [T]here is no way of making progress effectively if there is not an intimate connection with the kind of knowledge, the kind of perception, the kind of awareness of possibility and impossibility which we associate with the scientist. ... the scientist should be *there* through time, one way or another. (Bundy, pp. 422, 423.)

In the test ban negotiations, scientists were in fact very much on the scene from the beginning of serious negotiations until the conclusion of the agreement. At the start, in 1958, they merely provided the President with an alternative source of advice. In time they outgrew this role and became a factor in the decision-making process. The important changes of policy that derived from the interpretation of technical data were made at the instigation of scientists —notably Brown, Wiesner, Haworth, Ruina, and Long. They were the principal architects of the shift of emphasis away from inspection as a deterrent toward detection (or identification) as a deterrent.

Was the advice of the scientists colored by nonscientific assumptions or ideological bias? The record indicates clearly that in this instance the scientists were hardly apolitical. Two scientists who agreed on the same set of facts could nevertheless draw diametri-

cally opposite policy conclusions from the data. It is not at all clear
from this experience that "scientists are often in a position to exercise their political and ethical judgments as citizens in a more
realistic and balanced manner than other citizens." (Brooks, p. 80)
Indeed, as Conant has pointed out, "emotional attachment to one's
point of view is particularly insidious in science because it is so
easy for the proponent of a project to clothe his convictions in technical language." (Conant, pp. 114–115) The fury of the argument
over the test ban treaty is surely evidence for Conant's argument,
but it should also be pointed out, in fairness, that Dr. Teller, the
most outspoken critic of the treaty proposals, was at one time a proponent of a test ban and that Dr. Brown, one of the principal defenders of the treaty in 1963, had been one of the most intense skeptics
in earlier years. Don K. Price's observation that a scientist who
contributes to policy-making "often tends to lose sight of the limitations of his expertise" to the extent that "his judgments become unscientific and perhaps as nearly personal and prejudiced as any
laymen's" comes closest to describing what really happened.
(Price, pp. 132–133)

And what of C. P. Snow's suggestion that scientists are uniquely
gifted with foresight that is invaluable to society? (Snow, pp. 81–83)
There is little evidence in the record of scientific advice in the test
ban negotiations that would substantiate this assertion. It is probably
more accurate to say that the scientists' sudden rise to prominence
has been due more to the usefulness to society of their specialties
than to the usefulness of their personal faculties. The technical
knowledge of scientists was quite indispensable, but it did not provide any reliable predictions of the all-important political and military consequences of a test ban treaty. The scientists' "foresight"
was at most a limited technical foresight which had to be integrated
with other estimates. The decision as to what proposals to put
forward remained "non-scientific."

## The Achievement of a Limited Treaty

On June 10, 1963, President Kennedy made a major foreign
policy address at the commencement exercises of American University in Washington D.C. As part of his strategy of peace, the theme of
his speech, he declared that the United States would refrain from
further nuclear testing in the atmosphere so long as others would
also refrain. He looked forward to an agreement on a comprehensive
test ban treaty at the forthcoming July meeting in Moscow.

The administration's hopes for a comprehensive treaty were so
great that it was ready to regard a partial test ban treaty as a welcome step in the right direction rather than as an unsatisfactory

alternative. His speech was made against the background of the recent adoption by the Senate of a resolution put forward by Senators Dodd and Humphrey concerning the desirability of a nuclear test ban. Kennedy felt that although a test ban was in sight, a breakthrough of some sort was needed. Kennedy and Macmillan tried to impress on Khrushchev the urgency of the situation in a message to him at his Black Sea resort on May 31. Khrushchev's reply reached Washington on June 6. The diplomatic tempo was nudged a little when Khrushchev suggested the possibility of a partial test ban treaty in a speech July second in East Berlin. This suggestion was made in the midst of a successful European tour by Kennedy and was in itself a startling proposal in the light of past Soviet rejections. It had been foreshadowed to some extent by Harold Wilson's comment after his conference with Khrushchev in Moscow on June 10 — the day of Kennedy's speech — that a limited test ban "seems to offer more hope of an agreement" and that Khrushchev had withdrawn his earlier offer of two to three inspections a year. From now on "the tide of time and events" gathered momentum day by day, racing toward a peaceful and constructive, if limited, climax after five years of exasperating negotiations.

Although a reconstitution of the American mission to Moscow now became imperative, the United States still apparently operated on the assumption or the hope that a comprehensive treaty could be concluded despite Khrushchev's retraction of the inspection offer. This was indicated by the inclusion of an American and British seismologist on the negotiating teams. After Khrushchev met with the delegations in Moscow it became clear that there would be no on-site inspections. The probability that a comprehensive treaty would be initialed slipped to zero, although the United States delegation, it appears, would probably have accepted a compromise of five inspections per year despite its anxiety lest the Senate withhold consent. The prospects for a partial test ban treaty suddenly became very encouraging. The Soviets proposed a nonaggression treaty coupled with the test ban, but did not press the issue. They also produced their own treaty draft which was mainly a translation of the West's proposal. Differences existed but they were plainly negotiable. Only two technical points remained: the definition of an underground test and deletion of the clause concerning atomic explosions for peaceful purposes. The first was defined by indirection in the prohibition of explosions whose radioactive fallout would spill over the territorial limits of the country where the explosion occurred. (Article I, 1. b) The second was deleted. After about ten days of negotiations, the limited test ban treaty was signed on July 24 in Moscow between the United States, the Soviet Union, and the United Kingdom.

Intensive hearings were then held by two competitive congressional committees in the spring and summer of 1963. Most members of the Senate Foreign Relations Committee were receptive, while most members of the Preparedness Investigating Subcommittee of the Committee on Armed Services were generally hostile. Scientists testified extensively at both sets of hearings. Half of the witnesses called by the Foreign Relations Committee were scientists, as were a third of those testifying before the Preparedness Investigating Subcommittee. For purposes of senatorial consent, the administration's case was presented to the Foreign Relations Committee in the main by the Secretaries of State and Defense and the Director of Defense Research and Engineering, a nuclear physicist. The government significantly did not rest its case for the treaty on technical or military grounds but on the assertion by the Director of Defense Research and Engineering, Dr. Brown, that "unless we get some kind of arms limitation as well as maintaining our own military capability the next ten years are going to see further degradation in everyone's security as other nations obtain nuclear weapons, less responsible ones than have them now, I think that will make everyone less secure...*I believe that the treaty should be approved for these broader reasons.*" (Hearings–6, p. 562; emphasis added) If the committee had waded into the technical aspects of the treaty, an interminable wrangle might have resulted between friendly and hostile scientists, and Senate divergences would have been accentuated. The executive was well aware that defense of the treaty on narrow technical grounds would come under heavy fire as any cursory study of the several hearings held by the JCAE in 1960 and 1961 would reveal. Technical details of the detection and identification systems were not stressed; nor were the possible advances in weapon systems through clandestine testing much discussed. The treaty was presented as the best available alternative to the specter of an unlimited arms race. Assuming reasonable safeguard measures were adopted, it was contended that the Soviets would be unable to alter the balance of power in any serious manner. This "broader approach" was quite deliberately taken by the government to obtain speedy consent to the treaty.

Of the twelve scientists who testified before the Foreign Relations Committee, only four were connected with the government at the time, but others had been closely associated with the administration. Of the twelve, only two opposed the treaty. One was the director of the AEC's Livermore Laboratory and the other, also a former director of the same laboratory, was now with the University of California. The committee was also informed that in a poll of Nobel-Prize-winning scientists, there had been no opposed views recorded. The positive role of the scientific community in urging the Senate to give its consent was indeed overwhelming. Yet it must be stressed that the issues critical in evaluating the limited test ban treaty were primarily political rather than scientific in nature. Nevertheless, the role of science and scientists was pushed to the fore in justifying the treaty. As one scientist very closely associated with the formulation of the treaty put it, science was "utilized" – in a constructive way in this case – for an explicitly political purpose. After hearing from the scientists and debating the issues, the Senate gave its overwhelming consent on September 24, 1963.

## Science and Policy: Concluding Observations

The scientists who participated in the formulation of the policy could never be sure when they were expected to confine themselves to technical estimates and when it was understood that they would have to take nontechnical factors into account. In the congressional hearings, legislators often seem to have been looking to scientists for an answer, a decision, or a recommendation upon which they could rely in making up their minds. At the same time, the scientists were under a certain intangible pressure from the executive to "do their best" to create a climate of acceptability for the proposals. Inevitably, the scientists were compelled to give advice that was comprehensive rather than simply technical, in the sense Robert Oppenheimer had in mind when he stated his conviction that a scientific adviser had "one overriding obligation. It is his principal one in which he is delinquent if he fails and that is to give the best fruits of *his knowledge, his experience and his judgments* to those who have to make the decisions." (Oppenheimer Hearings, p. 66; emphasis added.) Oppenheimer's "directive" might well be modified by Bundy's note of caution. The scientific adviser, Bundy points out, "should carefully limit the occasions upon which he should speak *ex cathedra* in order not to lose his infallibility." (Bundy, p. 807) But this is not a problem for the scientists alone. It is up to the decision maker, whether in the executive or the legislature, to learn to cut through scientific advice so as to separate the technical from the political without putting an inordinate burden upon the scientific adviser.

It may even be argued that, in this case, the major importance of scientific advice lay not so much in that it provided the basis of decision as that it helped create a political consensus in favor of the decision. In the process of acquiring scientific advice, the prestige and presumed objectivity of scientists were mobilized to ascribe to the treaty a certain aura of technical legitimacy. A similarly questionable use of scientific advice is easier to identify and has come in

for much criticism. When the work of the 1958 Conference of
Experts is examined, it is clear that no great effort was made to
separate political and technical issues. The result was that scientists
were sent to negotiate political questions. The resulting difficulties
ought to serve as a warning against an overreliance on science and
scientists for decisions that are only partly technical in character.

That science can be used for partisan purposes has been
well demonstrated by the test ban controversy. The key reason is
of course that science has its limitations. Panofsky has suggested
that scientists can more easily agree about what to work on, where
to start, and when to stop, than upon projections of the data they
obtain. (Panofsky Address, cited *supra.*) A good example is the
JCAE report on the technical aspects of a test ban in 1960 enumer-
ating five points on which there was general agreement and three on
which there was disagreement. The areas of disagreement were
those on which the data were insufficient to provide a basis for firm
conclusions—the degree and practicability of decoupling by means
of large cavities, the extent of future improvement in detection
networks and devices, and the significance of further weapons
development in clandestine tests. (Report–2, p. 4) Similar disagreements often cropped up between scientists representing the
two sides in the cold war.

The threshold problem, which plagued the negotiations all
along, is another case in point—and one which cannot be eradicated
by scientific data at all. Additional information may shift the numerical factors, but some tests or natural seismic events will always go
undetected below a certain point. The data, moreover, must be
handled with care. The erroneous estimate in 1958 of the number of
earthquakes in the Soviet Union was incorporated in policy-planning
even though it was said to contain a certain "probable error."
The "probable error" fluctuated substantially in the subsequent
reevaluation and in the actual count and extrapolation in the Vela
program in 1962.

Such qualitative terms as good probability, adequate control,
and negligible risk are not susceptible to quantitative analysis.
Scientifically speaking, therefore, they are meaningless. As Robert
Gilpin has written, "one cannot depend upon the methods of
science to validate or invalidate the conflicting cases of the scientists;
instead he must turn to an examination and evaluation of nontechnical assumptions which really divide the scientists and the
policy-maker." (Gilpin, p. 267) Generally speaking, the scientific
or technical aspects of a problem, such as the actual capabilities of a
detection or identification system, are not overriding, but the
possibility of substantiating or refuting the value judgments through
an acceptable scientific procedure appears distinctly remote.

Closely related to the limitations of science is the understanding of the recipient of scientific advice, be he policy maker or legislator, of the limited powers of science, the limited nature of known facts, and the limits of scientific objectivity. The scientist may himself be partly responsible for the notion that scientists are coldly factual, capable of analyzing seemingly insoluble problems with scientific objectivity, and able to provide a precise and ready-made scientific solution for practically any question. The policy maker may tend to accept this stereotype too easily. This can be particularly unfortunate when what is at stake is the special role science and technology play in international relations. Senator Henry M. Jackson noted the danger well:

> I think we seem to have assumed in connection with our efforts to try to reach an agreement with the Soviets that in one way or another science can solve Soviet ideological obstructionism. I am confident, Mr. Chairman, there are a lot of people who feel that the scientists somehow will overcome the difficulties that we have, that are inherent in the Soviet system of refusing to open their borders to inspection, that the scientists are going to solve that for us. And I think this is one of the real dangers in trying to reach an agreement based on current scientific information. (Hearings–4, p. 26)

These expectations are closely linked with the lack of understanding about the diversity of scientific opinion. Senator Fulbright declared with astonishment:

> One of the most unexpected developments, at least from my point of view, has been the wide divergence of views among the acknowledged experts, particularly in the basic scientific areas ... I thought that these intellectual giants would arrive at some sort of common conclusion ... This has been very puzzling to me ... [It is] very difficult to evaluate the quality of each scientist who has testified. (Hearings–6, pp. 639, 642)

Senator Symington asked Dr. Teller why, after he had worked with Dr. Brown for so many years, they both held such opposite views. "I don't know," was Teller's simple answer. He might have said that intertwined with their common professional commitment to science were different political commitments which undoubtedly influenced their judgments and that, as Dr. William C. Foster noted, it was "impossible to spell out in terms of cold scientific facts" the advantages of the nuclear test treaty. (Hearings–5, p. 772) As Dr. Foster candidly acknowledged: "I think you can get almost any statement you want from a range of scientists ... It is a matter of judgment." (Hearings–1, p. 462)

Even where there is no such extreme disagreement, scientific advice may nevertheless provide only a range of options in lieu of absolute certainty. In the case of on-site inspections, the decision maker had an option of a spectrum of five through twenty inspections which he could use in negotiating with the Soviets. With regard to the necessity for atmospheric tests in developing the antiballistic missile, on the other hand, an adviser could only note that it might be produced with perhaps 70 to 80 percent reliability without further tests. The option facing the decision maker was either to accept this figure and negotiate for an atmospheric test ban or to eliminate that environment from the negotiations. Since there was no spectrum of choice, the technical adviser's counsel was tantamount to policy. The policy maker's dependence on the scientist in cases such as this is very great. But it can never be complete. Senator Mansfield accurately summarized the mission of the legislator when he concluded: "We have had military opinions, we have had scientific opinions ... The Committee must now combine all of these opinions into some kind of a sensible whole." (Hearings–6, p. 492)

The nuclear test ban has shown once again, but more starkly perhaps than in earlier instances, the delicate balance between scientific fact and advice and political judgment; the limitations of science; and the absolute urgency for the scientists and the political leadership to appreciate this relationship in formulating national security policy. It has also raised the delicate issue of freedom and control in the direction of scientific research. When the West proposed a comprehensive test ban treaty, it was implying, among other things, that it was willing to place a lid on the future development of a particular aspect of science. Such a treaty would in effect "freeze the technical *status quo*." This is probably the first time in history that any group of nations has recognized the desirability of an agreement among the leading military powers, and ultimately the other nations of the world, to curtail almost to the vanishing point that part of their technology that could lead to the development of new weapons. But just what advances might be foregone? On this there was no general agreement.

Dr. William C. Foster contended that there was nothing very important to be gained from further research:

> [W]e are approaching theoretical maximums ... We are talking about certain aspects of the science in which the nuclear physicists state that the theoretical limits of scientific advances are fixed and that neither of us [has] yet reached those theoretical limits. But that since we have come nearer to them than the other side with continued laboratory work or testing, the ultimate results will be that we both come as near to those theoretical limits as it is possible for human beings to get. (Hearings–4, p. 450)

President Kennedy, on the other hand, in his speech to the nation justifying the resumption of nuclear tests made the claim that

> we must test in the atmosphere to permit the development of those more advanced concepts and more effective, efficient weapons which, in the light of Soviet tests, are deemed essential to our security. *Nuclear weapon technology is still a constantly changing field.* If our weapons are to be more secure, more flexible in their use and more selective in their impact—if we are to be alert to new breakthroughs, to experiment with new designs—if we are to maintain our scientific momentum and leadership—then our weapons progress must not be limited to theory or to the confines of laboratories and caves. (Emphasis added.)

Dr. John Foster took a similar view:

> Even from the technical, strictly technical point of view, looking ahead, I think we just always, each of us, underestimate—we certainly have in the past—the technical potential of nuclear weapons and their effects.
>
> For example, read the Fisk report made up some 3 or 4 years ago, and compare it with the latest report assessing the government's position and notice the sharp difference in emphasis of what is important in the nuclear effects field in just three years ... Now how can we look ahead in the next 3, 4 or 10 years and say ... that on balance we can assess the advantages one way or the other ...? We are involved in a field of technology that is not fully understood, nor its applications, and hence, new experiments frequently bring surprises. (Hearings–5, pp. 411, 465)

General LeMay also disagreed with the idea of a technological freeze:

> I am one who believes that we are just at the beginning of our investigations into the nuclear weapons field. I don't believe we will reach the end. There is much more left to be discovered. I think that we are just scratching the surface. I think the greatest advances will come in the yield-to-weight ratios, and probably secondarily in cost of producing the weapons. (Hearings–6, p. 389) I don't assume that we are going to come to an end of any research and development programs. For there is always something to be learned in the future subject. I don't think we are going to come to an end or grind to a halt in the nuclear field having discovered everything we could about it. (Hearings–6, p. 361)

Indeed, attitudes toward "nuclear maturity" are inseparable from attitudes toward the pursuit of knowledge in relation to the prevention of war. The same problem arose in connection with the consideration of whether to develop the hydrogen bomb. In 1949 the majority opinion of the General Advisory Committee of the AEC recommended against a crash program in the belief that it would be "wrong at the present moment." The minority went further, calling the development of the H-bomb an evil thing and arguing that it would be wrong, on fundamental ethical principles, to initiate its development. Later, however, the GAC chairman, Robert Oppenheimer, admitted to misgivings about the committee's recommendation:

> [W]hat was not clear to us then and what is clearer to me now [1953] is that it probably lay wholly beyond our power to prevent the Russians somehow from getting ahead with it. I think if we could have taken any action at that time which would have precluded their development of this weapon it would have been a very good bet to take that, I am sure. . . . [I]t is my judgment in these things that when you see something that is technically sweet, you go ahead and do it and you argue about what to do about it only after you have had your technical success. That is the way it was with the atomic bomb... I cannot very well imagine if we had known in late 1949 what we got to know by early 1951 that the tone of our report would have been the same... In the spring of 1951, there were some inventions made... and from then on it became clear that this was a program which was bound to succeed... [I]nvention is a somewhat erratic thing... [I]f we had had at that time the technical insight that I now have, we would have concluded that it was almost hopeless to keep this resource out of the enemy hands and maybe we would have given up even suggesting that it be tried. I think if we had had that technical knowledge, then we should have recommended that we go ahead full steam, and then or in 1948 or 1946 or 1945. (Oppenheimer Hearings, pp. 80–87)

Fourteen years later, Dr. Teller, styling himself a "lobbyist for unborn ideas" (Hearings–5, p. 555), opposed a test ban on the ground that it would "prohibit future science, future progress [and was] directed against knowledge, our knowledge . . . [W]e are not trying to predict the future, and when some of the best and most outstanding people contradict each other, they do so because the future is necessarily uncertain." (Hearings–6, pp. 418, 423, and 427) Dr. Brown, on the other hand, while conceding that the test ban would place inhibitions on some part of nuclear science, contended that one must also consider the purpose for which knowledge is pursued:

> While we are in an arms race it behooves us to get all the knowledge that we can get, and, of course, we have been doing that. We are carrying out an enormous research and develop-

ment program in the military which has the purpose of improving our security but our relative security depends on the knowledge which the other side has too and... preventing a war is far more important than any knowledge that you might get. [Furthermore] what we are talking about here is certainly not pure science. It is engineering application which can also be applied to peaceful or to military pursuits. But what engineering applications get done, it seems to me, are always determined and should always be determined by the need of society and not necessarily by the desires of scientific investigators. Scientific investigators should have freedom in science, but this isn't science. (Hearings–6, p. 547)

At least one PSAC member admitted that the acceptance of a total nuclear test ban was based less on scientific reasoning than on a "guess that no terribly new knowledge was likely to come out of a mature technology, or that this knowledge would be potentially militarily decisive." (Interview) In 1962–1963, when the treaties were advanced, there was no technological concept on the horizon comparable to the idea for an H-bomb. Nothing like this was "in the cards or being proposed." The all-fusion weapon, which is sometimes mentioned as a third-generation weapon, was declared to be not militarily significant, although in earlier years it was said to be a major object of American nuclear research, with distinct and important military significance. (Interview)

The issue of mature technology could not be decided empirically. It was conceded by the decision makers that technological improvements might be possible or even probable, but they also held that a major breakthrough was improbable and that any military value which might derive from such innovations would not constitute a menace. Nevertheless, since new technological developments have seldom looked attractive, and since military technology has had such a dynamic career during the past quarter-century, a sense of uneasiness is bound to linger when an essentially arbitrary lid is placed on any branch of technology, even though only on a particular and highly specialized section of technology, nuclear weapons technology. Since the comprehensive test ban has not yet materialized, these deliberations prove academic for the time being. They will play an important role, however, in any future negotiations.

Certain aspects of the H-bomb controversy and the resultant Oppenheimer "trial" in 1953 bear uncomfortable similarities with the test ban controversy. The first ended with the development of the H-bomb, the disgrace of Dr. Oppenheimer, and an almost irreconcilable split in the scientific community. The nuclear test ban controversy is replete with the sort of ammunition that was used

in the attack on Oppenheimer. One can at least imagine circumstances in which the proponents of a test ban might be accused of
trying to weaken the national defense, very much as Oppenheimer
was accused for opposing the crash program to develop the H-bomb.
So far there is no inkling of any resurgence of the acrimonious
atmosphere created by the controversy over the H-bomb and the
Oppenheimer trial. It may be that the scars of that lamentable affair
will prevent a new outbreak. The statement of one of Dr. Oppenheimer's opponents is worth repeating in this context for the sake
of the warning it contains and by way of a concluding thought:

> I was on the opposite side of pretty violent controversy from
> Dr. Oppenheimer in at least two cases . . . [I]t is a fair general
> observation that when you get involved in a hot enough contro-
> versy, it is awfully hard not to question the motives of people
> who oppose. This, I am sure, could not but have colored my
> views on the subject . . . If it ever comes to the day when we can't
> disagree and disagree violently in public and on national
> policy, then of course I feel that it will be a calamity for our
> democracy. (Oppenheimer Hearings, p. 768)

## PUBLICATIONS CITED

### Books and Articles

Brooks, Harvey. "The Scientific Adviser," in Robert Gilpin and Christopher
    Wright, eds., *Scientists and National Policy Making*, New York, 1963,
    pp. 73–96.
Bundy, McGeorge. "The Scientist and National Policy," this volume,
    Chap. 13.
Conant, James. B. *Modern Science and Modern Man*, New York, 1957.
Gilpin, Robert. *American Scientists and Nuclear Weapons Policy*, Princeton
    N.J., 1962.
Price, Don K. *Government and Science: Their Dynamic Relation in Ameri-
    can Democracy*, New York, 1954.
Snow, C. P. *Science and Government*, Cambridge Mass., 1961.
Voss, Earl H. *Nuclear Ambush: The Test-Ban Trap*, Chicago, 1963.
Wiesner, Jerome B. "Comprehensive Arms-Limitation System," *Daedalus*,
    Fall 1960, pp. 915–950.

### Documents

(Geneva Conference) U.S. Department of State, U.S. Disarmament Admin-
    istration. *Geneva Conference on the Discontinuance of Nuclear
    Weapons Tests, History and Analysis of Negotiations* (1961).
(Hearings–1) U.S. Congress, Joint Committee on Atomic Energy. *Develop-
    ments in Technical Capabilities for Detecting and Identifying Nuclear
    Weapons Tests* (88th Cong. 1st Sess., 1963).
(Hearings–2) U.S. Congress, Joint Committee on Atomic Energy. *Develop-
    ments in the Field of Detection and Identification of Nuclear Explo-
    sions (Project Vela) and Relationship to Test Ban Negotiations,
    Hearings* (87th Cong. 1st Sess., 1961).

(Hearings–3) U.S. Congress, Joint Committee on Atomic Energy, Special Subcommittee on Radiation and Subcommittee on Research and Development. *Technical Aspects of Detection and Inspection Controls of a Nuclear Weapons Test Ban, Hearings,* Parts 1 & 2 (86th Cong. 2nd Sess., 1960).

(Hearings–4) U.S. Congress, Senate Committee on Armed Services. Preparedness Investigating Subcommittee. *Arms Control and Disarmament, Hearings* (87th Cong. 2nd Sess., 1962).

(Hearings–5) U.S. Congress, Senate Committee on Armed Services, Preparedness Investigating Subcommittee. *Military Aspects and Implications of Nuclear Test Ban Proposals and Related Matters, Hearings,* Parts 1 and 2 (88th Cong. 1st Sess., 1963).

(Hearings–6) U.S. Congress, Senate Committee on Foreign Relations. *Nuclear Test Ban Treaty: Hearings* (88th Cong. 1st Sess., 1963).

(International Negotiations) U.S. Arms Control and Disarmament Agency. *International Negotiations on Ending Nuclear Weapon Tests, September 1961–September 1962* (1962).

(Oppenheimer Hearings) U.S. Atomic Energy Commission. *In the Matter of J. Robert Oppenheimer: Transcript of Hearing before Personnel Security Board,* Washington, D.C., Apr. 12–May 6, 1954.

(Report–1) U.S. Congress, Joint Committee on Atomic Energy. *Developments in the Field of Detection and Identification of Nuclear Explosions (Project Vela) and Relationship to Test Ban Negotiations, Summary Analysis of Hearings* (87th Cong. 1st Sess., 1962).

(Report–2) U.S. Congress, Joint Committee on Atomic Energy. Special Subcommittee on Radiation and Subcommittee on Research and Development. *Technical Aspects of Detection and Inspection Controls of a Nuclear Weapons Test Ban, Summary Analysis of Hearings* (86th Cong. 2nd Sess., 1960).

# 5

# The Establishment of NASA

ENID CURTIS BOK SCHOETTLE

MOST AMERICANS engaged in the research and development activities concerned with outer space work under public auspices. Professionally they may be members of university staffs or employees of private industry, but their particular projects are almost always publicly authorized and publicly supported. Since October 1, 1958, the overall direction of the American space effort has been lodged in the National Aeronautics and Space Agency (NASA), an independent civilian agency within the executive branch of the federal government. That agency, directed by a single administrator responsible to the President, was provided in the fiscal year 1966 with 5.17 billion dollars for the formal legal purpose of seeking "the solution of problems of flight within and outside the earth's atmosphere and problems for the development, testing and operation for research purposes of aircraft, missiles, satellites and other space vehicles."

The object of this study is to explain why such organizational and financial arrangements exist. Why is the space program a public endeavor? Why is it directed by a civilian rather than a military agency? Why is that agency under a single executive? Why is it financially supported at such a scale and with relatively few congressional or budgetary constraints compared with other publicly supported enterprises?

In a broad sense these policy choices reflect a national response to the challenge of Sputnik. The launching of the first Soviet

ENID CURTIS BOK SCHOETTLE *is currently Lecturer in Political Science at Swarthmore College. This study was done under the auspices of the Organization Research Project at MIT under NASA sponsorship. It is part of a doctoral dissertation on policy-making in the space program now in preparation under the direction of Professor Robert C. Wood of MIT, presently Under Secretary, Department of Housing and Urban Development.*

satellite on October 4, 1957, represented a Russian achievement in particular scientific and engineering fields which dramatically surpassed that of the United States. The American public and American political leaders viewed this achievement as signaling a dangerous and adverse shift in the balance of military power between the two nations. In the interests of national security, they made a reallocation of national resources to redress the balance. Since previous space research and development activities had been carried out by combined private and military efforts and found wanting, new organizational structures were devised. These changes in resource allocation and management, it was expected, would enable the United States to exhibit in the near future technological superiority in the space field.

Yet on closer examination this broad explanation is not satisfactory. It fails, first, on the grounds of precision and specificity. It does not account for the initial failure of the nation—as a nation—to anticipate Sputnik I. It does not differentiate among those segments of the public and the political leadership which responded with great intensity and great concern and those which did not. It does not explain why, among several organizational alternatives and several possible levels of support, particular choices were made. It establishes no basis for estimating the probabilities that the newly established arrangements and programs would enable America to take the lead in space exploration.

Second, this explanation fails to illuminate the process by which the transformation of our space effort from a small, privately oriented one to a large, publicly oriented one took place. Its gross characterizations of public alarm and official response do not describe how our political system functions in resolving an issue of this magnitude; what considerations motivated influential persons and groups within the system; or what actions they took with what results to account for the successive decisions which in one year led to the establishment of NASA. Thus, it neither identifies the prime components of the system and their interaction nor makes clear what units of political influence are in fact responsible for the present particular pattern and scale of operations. Yet knowledge of these factors is essential if we are to distinguish between the consequences of public and private management of the space effort, account for the objectives and character of the present program, and arrive at some judgment of how it might be directed for more efficient achievement of certain goals in the future.

To achieve greater precision and more explanatory value, this study selects and organizes facts according to a contemporary model of how political influence is distributed and applied in national politics. The success of the Soviet launching is treated as generating a conflict (or issue) within the national political system. More accurately, the launching expanded the scope and intensity of a conflict which had been previously confined to relatively few activists within the system. After Sputnik, other activists with different motivations, political resources and intensities of interest, operating under different informational and structural constraints, became engaged in the issue. Although all the activists could be said to be motivated by common considerations of national security, their perception of these considerations, their place within the system, and the impact of the conflict upon their political resources established a second order of objectives which differentiated their preferences for possible solutions to the conflict.

In a new and larger structural context, the activists devised strategies by which they sought to have their preferences for successive policy choices prevail. To assure the success of their strategies, they sought to make coalitions with other activists by discovering identities of interest, by persuasion, by bargaining, or by the exercise of superior formal authority (coercion). Finally, the space agency emerged: a product of the combined strategies of the most influential and interested participants.

Obviously, an analysis which screens data by these criteria does not identify all the relevant forces which help account for the structure and magnitude of our space effort. Neither does it exhaustively characterize the properties of the forces which it chooses to emphasize. Highly relevant traits of personality, undocumented or undisclosed actions of major participants, and unconscious motivations probably escape detection. Rather than providing an exhaustive historical treatment, this study primarily attempts to identify the structure of political power and the functioning of the political system which together inaugurated—and indeed still largely sustain—the nation's greatest technological venture.

## Space Before Sputnik

The technological success of Sputnik I surprised most American citizens, and the political reaction which followed caught many American political leaders unaware. Yet not every segment of the public nor every public official had failed to anticipate the Soviet accomplishment or its political repercussions. There was a United States space program in being prior to October 4, 1957. But it was an effort with which few citizens were familiar, with limited support by figures of national prominence, carried forward in the lower echelons of the national bureaucracy. Those who anticipated that the launching of an earth satellite would be a political event of first magnitude lacked the resources, motivations, or skills to arouse the nation or persuade its leaders to take action.

The origins of the American program were in the defense establishment. In 1946, the Department of the Navy recommended to the Joint Research and Development Board that a project to place a small satellite in orbit around the earth be initiated. The Committee on Guided Missiles of the board rejected the proposal as "not having sufficient military requirement."[1] There the matter rested until 1954, when a confluence of interests from within the DOD and a portion of the scientific community then engaged in planning the International Geophysical Year occurred. As to the first, in September of that year, Dr. Werner von Braun of the Army Ballistic Missile Agency published a classified paper, "The Minimum Satellite Vehicle Based upon Components Available from Missile Developments of the Army Ordanance Corps."[2] After discussions within the Ordnance Corps and with civilian scientists, von Braun made his first efforts to initiate the project. In December, a joint voluntary Group of the Army and Navy undertook design-planning and christened their effort Project Orbiter.

So far as the civilian scientists were concerned, their interest in a satellite project derived from America's forthcoming participation in the IGY. This "year," like its predecessors, the First Polar Year of 1882 and the Second Polar Year of 1932, was designed to accomplish a world-wide program of geophysical observations and research in a limited span of time. The IGY, lasting from July 1, 1957, to December 31, 1958, was sponsored by the International Council of Scientific Unions (ICSU), a nongovernmental organization of constituent national scientific academies, among them the American National Academy of Sciences, and the Soviet Academy of Science. In the fall of 1951, the ICSU decided to convene a special committee, consisting of representatives from thirteen general or technical scientific unions in the geophysical disciplines, to work on plans for a year of geophysical research. In early 1952, the ICSU Executive Bureau called upon individual nations to establish national committees for the IGY, which would plan and direct each country's research efforts. Finally, in October 1952 the ICSU constituted the Comité Spécial de l'Année Geophysique Internationale (CSAGI) to coordinate the programs of the IGY.

In response to the ICSU directive, the National Academy of Sciences, as the American affiliate, called on the government to authorize its participation in the IGY. At an early stage, the National Academy persuaded the government to do so. Sometime before the May 1954 deadline for the submission of detailed national research programs, the National Security Council (NSC) decided that the United States "should make a major effort during the IGY." The NSC requested the National Academy's National Research Council,

established in 1916 to coordinate governmental and nongovernmental scientific efforts, to direct and plan the scientific research.
This agreed, the Council established a special US National Committee for the IGY. The NSC also ordered the Department of
Defense (DOD) "to furnish whatever support was necessary to
place the scientists and their instruments in remote locations."[3]
Finally the NSC charged the National Science Foundation (NSF)
with providing governmental support for the IGY and serving as the
channel through which official funds were requested and administered. Thus, in October 1954, when the CSAGI decided to advocate
earth satellite projects as part of the IGY program, the American
IGY effort was already firmly tied to the major governmental
scientific agencies of the NSF and DOD and, through the quasi-
governmental National Academy, to the necessary pools of disciplinary expertise in the private scientific community.*

Although the IGY initiated the policy decision to go into space,
the American space program originated much earlier in the scientific bureaus of the military services. And even within the military
establishment, tension between the scientific and military missions
of a space program characterized its history. In 1945 the Bureau of
Aeronautics in the Navy established a Committee for Evaluating the
Feasibility of Space Rocketry. In November of that year, the Committee recommended that high priority be given satellite development. In 1946 the Bureau, through the newly established Office of
Naval Research (ONR), developed a satellite proposal. In 1947 the
Air Force's Project Rand also found that earth satellites were
technically feasible. In March 1948, the Technical Evaluation Group
of the Committee on Guided Missiles of the Research and Development Board in the DOD reviewed these two proposals. It decided
that neither the Navy nor the Air Force had "as yet established
either a military or a scientific utility commensurate with the
presently expected cost of a satellite vehicle. However, the question
of utility [deserved] further study and examination." At the end of
1948, Secretary of Defense James Forrestal revealed that the earth
satellite program, previously carried out independently by the
services, was to be assigned to the Committee on Guided Missiles
for coordination.[4]

The satellite program remained at this study stage within each
service for several years. Then, in June 1954, a group of rocket
specialists including Frederick C. Durant III, president of the

---

*On the two subcommittees of the US National Committee for the IGY
most directly concerned with the space program—the Rocketry Technical Panel and the Earth Satellite Program Technical Panel—there
were representatives of relevant Government research agencies and
private scientific specialists.

International Astronautical Federation; Dr. Werner von Braun, of the Army Ballistic Missile Agency (ABMA) and previously of the Third *Reich's* Rocket Development Center at Peenemünde; Fred L. Whipple and Fred Singer, professors of astronomy and physics, respectively; and ONR-Air Branch Chief George Hoover, met at the ONR. These men all believed that some specific satellite program should be put into development. Von Braun suggested the possibility of using the Army's Redstone missile, based on the German V–2, and the Loki rocket configuration to launch a satellite. This combination, he claimed, would not need major development work. All agreed that a satellite should go up as soon as possible, for military and prestige reasons, despite the fact that it would initially permit only a small payload with a minimum of scientific instrumentation. Two months later, the ABMA and the ONR were authorized by the Chief of Army Ordnance and the Chief of Naval Operations to proceed with development of a joint Army-Navy satellite program, using the Redstone booster, to be designated Project Orbiter.

Meanwhile, during the early fifties, the Naval Research Laboratory (NRL) in the ONR was working on a high-altitude research vehicle, the Viking rocket. With Aerobee-Hi rockets as a second stage, the NRL believed this configuration could launch a satellite for sustained atmospheric research. It conceived of the project as a purely scientific experiment. The Air Force also had its satellite proposal, using the Atlas ICBM motor as a booster.

By late 1954, all the service labs involved in space research were encouraged by news of the CSAGI proposal for including satellite launchings in the IGY research program. Thus spurred to action, they submitted the three satellite proposals to the Office of the Secretary of Defense (OSD). At this point, on March 28, 1955, Secretary of Defense Charles Wilson ordered Donald Quarles, Assistant Secretary of Defense for Research and Development, to coordinate the various satellite proposals. He also ordered the three services not to commit funds for satellite R & D without prior approval from Quarles.[5]

While these developments took place within the military establishment, satellite proposals emerged from private scientific sources as well. As early as 1948, James Van Allen of the University of Iowa had proposed a satellite experiment at the meetings of the International Union of Geodesy and Geophysics. Later, in 1954, various international scientific unions such as the International Scientific Radio Union passed resolutions emphasizing the utility of satellite observations which could expand upon the isolated findings of research rockets. Finally, as a result of pressures from its constituent unions, the CSAGI in October 1954 proposed that

satellite launchings be attempted as part of the IGY research effort.*
It then called upon the Academies of the two countries capable of
undertaking such a mission—the United States and the Soviet Union
—to seek authorization for the satellite mission.

In America there had been scientific support for a satellite
mission for some time. In 1954, the Space Flight Committee of the
American Rocket Society (ARS)—the private professional association
of atmospheric scientists and aeronautical engineers—filed a report
with the NSF about the utility of earth satellites for scientific research. This report culminated several years of effort to interest the
government in a scientific venture into space and, in the opinion
of some observers, "was the spark plug that ignited the space
satellite idea. [The ARS's] work had a tremendous influence on the
NSF when that institution had to decide whether artificial satellites
were to be recommended."[6]

The NSF was soon charged with this responsibility. In March
1955 the US National Committee for the IGY, in response to the
CSAGI's directive, completed a feasibility study and endorsed
an American earth satellite project in a report to the National
Academy and to the NSF. The NSF, as the governmental agency
responsible for expediting the IGY, and as the major advocate in
government for scientific affairs, approved the National Committee's
proposal for an instrumented, scientific satellite and forwarded the
proposal to the President.

In April 1955, upon the recommendation of the NSC, Eisenhower ordered the Secretary of Defense to "develop the capability
of launching a small scientific satellite by 1958 under the auspices of
the IGY." He also instructed the DOD to review various satellite
proposals and to recommend "an equipment program and operating
structure" by August 1, 1955. At this time the NSC issued one
significant reservation: that the satellite project was not to interfere with the development of military rocketry—then so critical
in the "balance of terror."[7]

Assistant Secretary Quarles was responsible for executing the
President's order. In April or May, Quarles convened the Advisory
Group on Special Capabilities, or Stewart Committee, a civilian
body of eight members chaired by Dr. Homer Stewart, Professor
of Physics at UCLA. The services and Secretary Quarles each proposed two members. The Committee reviewed the three proposals:

---

*The CSAGI proposal declared that "in view of the advanced state of
present rocket techniques, consideration should be given to the launching
of small satellite vehicles, to their scientific instrumentation, and to the
new problems associated with satellite experiments." Sullivan, *IGY*,
p. 276.

the Air Force plan utilizing the Atlas ICBM motor; the Navy proposal based upon an improved Viking rocket with two additional stages; and the Army plan based on the Redstone booster with three additional stages. The Stewart Committee considered the three in the light of the primary question: "What program will be the most certain of placing the most useful satellite vehicle in orbit, . . . within the IGY and with the minimum interference to priority military programs."[8] The three basic criteria were, therefore: reliability; scientific utility; and non-interference with military programs.

On this basis, the Committee eliminated the Air Force bid as interfering with the development of ICBMs. Then, by a 5–2 vote, the Committee supported the Navy proposal as superior to the Army's on all three grounds. First, the Viking seemed more reliable and needed only two additional stages. Second, the engine for the Viking could be made available without interfering with weapons projects, while the Redstone was itself a military rocket. Third, the NRL had had extensive scientific experience with the Viking, the rocket's second stage, and upper atmospheric research equipment in general. Moreover, the Viking project had been declassified and thus security problems were smaller and the amount of technical data which might be released greater than in the case of the Redstone. There were also indications that the Viking "promised to carry the largest payload with the smallest and lightest rocket vehicle," thus offering the most economical investment.[9]

The majority had among its ranks Dr. Joseph Kaplan, the chairman of the National Committee for the IGY, and Richard Porter, chairman of the National Academy's Technical Panel on Earth Satellites for the IGY. It can be assumed then, that these men thought the Navy proposal had the greatest scientific potential. The two dissenters from the majority view—besides Dr. Stewart himself, who did not vote—were Dr. Clifford C. Furnas, Chancellor of the University of Buffalo, who was soon to replace Quarles as the Assistant Secretary R & D, and Dr. William Pickering who, like Dr. Stewart, was from the Jet Propulsion Laboratory, a contractor to the Army. These men all favored the Army's Project Orbiter as offering "greater flexibility as a launcher for a satellite"—which they deemed crucial in a program as short as the IGY period.[10]

Public dissents from the Army followed the release of this report on August 4. On August 14, Chief of Army Ordnance Leslie Simons issued a memo claiming that the Redstone was available and could perform the first orbital flight by August 1957. He also argued that the satellite mission would not interfere with the Redstone missile program, since the missile would already be under production. Finally he cited the Navy's admission that it would be necessary to develop a new Vanguard rocket, rather than depend on an improved Viking. He claimed that the Redstone would be far more reliable than a new rocket developed within the unusually short period of two years.[11]

Despite this submission, the Advisory Group stuck to its previous decision, and the proposal went up to Quarles' R & D Policy Council, consisting of eight assistant secretaries and service R & D officers. Again, over Army dissent, the Navy project was recommended. On the basis of these findings Deputy Secretary of Defense Reuben Robertson authorized on September 9, 1955, what came to be called Project Vanguard.[12]

The separation of the scientific satellite mission from the development of military hardware and the Administration's general economy drive tended to relegate Project Vanguard to low priority status within the DOD. Dr. John P. Hagen, director of the Vanguard Project in the Naval Research Laboratory, found that his requests for top priority transmitted through Navy channels to the DOD were "not granted in the form in which [he] asked for them."[13] On April 2, 1956, the Navy requested that the Vanguard be included in the "S" category of the Master Urgency List of the DOD, the Department's hightest priority category for urgent military items such as ballistic missiles. On May 29, the DOD directed, instead, its inclusion as Item #1 in Category "1", outranked by the items in Category "S". Hagen made a subsequent request for Category "S" status in October 1957, which was approved on November 7, four days after the launching of Sputnik II. Furthermore, the Office of the Secretary of Defense funded the project from its emergency fund, with frequent delays and penurious oversight until August 1957, when Congress appropriated $34.2 million to complete the project. At various times back-up programs for the Vanguard were suggested, in case the NRL failed to meet the IGY schedule. As early as August 24, 1955, the R & D Policy Council unanimously recommended that the time-risk factor in Project Vanguard be brought to Secretary Wilson's attention to determine whether the Redstone should be established as a back-up. In 1956, the ONR requested an additional launching pad and six additional satellite launching vehicles. Finally, the National Committee for the IGY suggested to the DOD that six more satellite launching vehicles be scheduled. The Pentagon, however, was already disquieted by the increasing costs of the project and refused these additional requests on economy grounds.[14]

While the Navy struggled with its new assignment, the Army continued to push Project Orbiter—and continued to meet with OSD resistance. In April 1956, Dr. Furnas, now Assistant Secretary of Defense for R & D, an early supporter of Project Orbiter on the Stewart Committee, requested the Army to explore the possibility of using the Redstone (Jupiter-C) missile as a back-up to the Vanguard. The Army immediately did so, and found that with some development and retooling, the Jupiter-C could fire a satellite in January 1957, several months before the Vanguard's scheduled deadline. On May 15, however, Lt. Gen. James M. Gavin, Deputy Chief of the Army Office of Research and Development, received a directive from William Holaday, Special Assistant to the Secretary for Guided Missiles, that "without any indications of serious difficulties in the Vanguard program, no plans or presentations should be initiated for using any part of the Jupiter or Redstone programs for scientific satellites."[15]

Nevertheless, the Army Ballistic Missile Agency was proceeding to develop the Jupiter IRBM with a recoverable nosecone, based upon the same engine design and preliminary hardware work done on Project Orbiter. In September 1956 the Army launched a Jupiter-C missile with its solid fuel upper stages in satellite configuration, and with sand in its fourth stage in order to test nosecone recovery. The test missile was a brilliant success, flying 3300 miles and 600 miles up into outer space. According to Maj. Gen. J. B. Medaris, Commander, ABMA, USA, "We had on hand a back-up missile for that one still in the original (Orbiter) satellite configuration, and at varying times during this period we suggested informally and verbally that if they really wanted a satellite we could use that back-up missile as a satellite. In various languages, our fingers were slapped and we were told to mind our own business, that the Vanguard was going to take care of the satellite problem."

Again, in November 1956, Medaris sent a proposal through Brucker to the OSD, suggesting that the Jupiter-C's proven and available hardware could be spared from its military mission, and should be used to launch a satellite. In June 1957, the OSD sent back to the ABMA a reminder of the May 15, 1956 directive which had instructed the Army to stay out of the satellite business. Indeed, by this time the ABMA campaign for the satellite mission was thoroughly irritating to the OSD. It was in this context that Secretary of the Army Brucker had to state publicly that same month that "the Army did not covet any part of the Navy's mission" and that the Army considered the satellite program to be in capable hands. Furthermore, Brucker sternly added, an Army satellite would be "gross interference in and duplication of" the Navy's mission and the Department of the Army was "embarrassed" at renewal of the request by the ABMA.[16]

Faced with this official opposition, the ABMA and Army R & D personnel fell silent. Gavin, Medaris and von Braun watched through the summer as the Vanguard met more delays and as the Soviets moved closer to launching. Gavin testified that he met with a group of civilian scientists in the Army on September 12 and after "worrying for two weeks" prepared another proposal for the DOD to authorize an Army satellite program on a crash basis. "We did not send that out and, of course, on the fourth of October they launched."[17]

In retrospect Medaris found the experience "somewhat incredible." Gavin termed it "very frustrating—and that is an understatement." Politically, however, it was consistent with all the administration's stated positions: its determination to separate the development of the satellite launching vehicle from that of any military missile program; the fact that the administration conceived the satellite program not as a prestige race with the Soviet Union but as a purely scientific endeavor; and finally, the relatively low level of financial and administrative support which the Administration and particularly the highest echelons in the DOD gave to the satellite program.[18]

The limited nature of the space program prior to Sputnik was not due to a lack of information about Soviet advances in the field. Both the military R & D groups involved in space and civilian participants in the IGY knew by late 1954 that the Soviets had established an Interdepartmental Commission on Interplanetary Communication in the Soviet Academy of Sciences. It was known that Soviet programs utilized military ICBMs and that the Soviets were placing hightest priority on the space mission. In January 1955, Radio Moscow announced that the launching of earth satellites would be possible in the near future. In August 1955, in response to the White House announcement of the American Satellite program, Leonid I. Sedov, Chairman of the Interdepartmental Commission on Interplanetary Communication, announced that the launching of satellites larger than those proposed by the US would be possible within two years. In June 1957, *The New York Times* reported Russian assertions that rockets and instrumentation for a satellite project were prepared and that a satellite would be launched in a few months. In July, the Soviet magazine *Radio* requested amateur radio operators to watch for signals from Sputniks. September 18 brought a Moscow Radio report of an imminent launching. The disinterest expressed by the public at large at this news only mirrored the limited dimensions of official concern.[19]

It was in this atmosphere of public unconcern, service competition, and the administration's interpretation of the satellite program as a research venture essentially unrelated to matters of high policy, that A. N. Blagonravov, the chief Soviet delegate to the International Conference on Rockets and Satellites of the IGY, left Moscow for the Washington meetings on September 30. At the airport, he remarked to American reporters, "We will not cackle

until we have laid our egg."[20] He undoubtedly expected, however,
that he would not have to wait very long.

## The Launching of the Sputniks and the Spread of Political Conflict: October 4–November 4, 1957

On October 4, 1957, the Soviet Embassy in Washington held
a reception in honor of members of the International Conference on
Rockets and Satellites. Shortly after five p.m., Walter Sullivan,
veteran science reporter of *The New York Times*, was called to the
telephone. It was the *Times'* Washington Bureau with the news that
Radio Moscow had just reported the launching of a Russian satellite.
Sullivan relayed the news to Dr. Lloyd Berkner, chairman of the
International Council of Scientific Unions, who then interrupted the
festivities to announce:

> I've just been informed by *The New York Times* that a Russian
> satellite is in orbit at an elevation of 900 kilometers. I wish to
> congratulate our Soviet colleagues on their achievement.[21]

Despite the scientific acclaim which greeted Sputnik I, as the
news went out over the wires the event was soon drowned in its
political implications. The impact of Sputnik upon the American
public was intense. Six months after its launching, 91 percent of a
sample population polled by the Survey Research Center at the
University of Michigan had heard of the satellite. Of the 64 percent
who attributed some purpose to the American satellite program,
almost 33 percent believed it to be in direct competition with the
Russians'. While the fear and astonishment noted in the populace
just after the Russian launching abated as American satellites went
up, two major implications of the Sputnik continued to disturb
groups polled. First, the launching had revealed that the Russians
possessed a significant rocket and missile capability, with obvious
military implications. Second, and more generally, American public
opinion was startled by a Russian achievement in what Americans
believed to be their own special province: scientific and technological capabilities.

In addition to this shock and dismay, Sputnik also engendered
in the American public willingness to make sacrifices in order to
match Soviet space achievements. This national reaction brought
with it a shift in American public opinion. In the immediate post-
Sputnik period, there was a significant decline in confidence in the
Republicans as the party best equipped to deal with national problems. In most foreign policy and national security decisions, the
American polity is content to follow the leads of the administration.
Sputnik, however, in Gabriel Almond's terms, "sprung opinion
loose from executive support and dependence for a brief interval".[22]

From a limited conflict within a small segment of the military and scientific elites, space suddenly grew into a major national conflict embroiling the administration, the entire military establishment, the scientific community, Congress, and the public at large in a political issue which was to ramify through many facets of American life. The reactions of nationally known political figures to Sputnik now created a broad arena of national debate which brought into question America's political leadership, scientific and technological capabilities, educational system, defense policy, and, indeed, her very potential for national survival. The year of the Sputnik had begun, and with it the birth of NASA.

## THE ADMINISTRATION

At the outset of the new debate it was plain that the administration had miscalculated the political significance of Soviet technological virtuosity. This miscalculation can ultimately be attributed to the President, the apex of the American political system. It had been Eisenhower's choice, among contending advisory opinions and organizational biases, that determined the scientific nature of Project Vanguard. Thus, after Sputnik, the President's responses in the new conflict became the focal point for other actors' reactions in the now enlarged political arena.

Of necessity, Eisenhower had to evaluate the launching of Sputnik I in terms of its implications for national security, partisan politics, the power of the executive branch, and the program of his own administration. With immediate evidence that a strong, perhaps even hysterical, public reaction was setting in, the President faced prospects of a radical realignment of his previous bases of support.

In this posture of political defensiveness, Eisenhower's first reaction was, not unnaturally, to attempt to contain the scope of the conflict. Thus, the initial White House communiques minimized the significance of the launching and tried to suppress the rising political storm.[23] In his news conference on October 9 Eisenhower emphasized that ballistic missiles had consistently and properly received more priority than satellites; that the only Soviet victory was in political propaganda; and that his scientific and military advisers assured him there was no need to accelerate defense programs. After discounting the military significance of Sputnik, he sought to calm the nation by relating that his apprehension about national security had not been raised "one iota."[24] Moving to the scientific argument, he asserted that the satellite program had "never been considered as a race," merely as "an engagement on our part" and that "in view of the real scientific character of our development, there didn't seem to be a reason for trying to grow hysterical about it."

> From the beginning, the whole American purpose . . . has been to produce the maximum in scientific information. The project was sold to me on that basis . . . . I don't know of any reason why the scientists should have come in and urged that we do this before anybody else could.

When queried about what America could have done to avert what at least some newsmen were interpreting as a crisis, Eisenhower responded that he had done "everything I can think of . . . and I don't know what we could have done more." Finally, in a personal conclusion he would later regret, he sought to find out what all the fuss was about. After all, "the Russians have only put one small ball in the air."

Others interpreted Sputnik somewhat differently, and as shock, criticism, and positive suggestions appeared in all quarters, the President began turning to those of his institutional supporters whose interests would be served in allaying, if possible, or retrieving, if necessary, a rapidly deteriorating political situation. The President's "official family", his staff, the Vice-President, the heads of executive departments, and the Republican leaders in Congress, moved initially to his defense. In the month following Sputnik, Special Assistant Sherman Adams, Secretary of Defense Charles Wilson, Clarence R. Randall (a special assistant to the President for international economic affairs), Secretary of State John Foster Dulles, Senate Minority Leader William Knowland, and Vice-President Richard Nixon all sought to sustain the tenor of the President's position. Alternatively, it was this group which Eisenhower selected to voice the guarded concern of the White House and its intention to "do something" about Sputnik. These men, whose political futures were more or less dependent upon the President himself, thus attempted to remove the onus of the crisis from Eisenhower's shoulders in order both to defend him from personal political attack and to preserve his freedom of action.

Randall and Adams, both personal assistants who had no bases of influence except those derived from the President, and Wilson, the outgoing Secretary of Defense, were the most outspoken belittlers of the Russian achievement. Randall, in an off moment, dismissed the satellite as a "silly bauble . . . a bubble in the sky."[25] Adams, in the same vein, asserted that the American satellite program sought to "serve science, not high score in an outer space basketball game."[26] Wilson merely repeated what he had said all along: that the Sputnik had nothing to do with military preparedness or relative missile capabilities. These men had nothing to lose from such uncritical assertions. Moreover, their statements, while not reflecting the growing political concern within the administration, served definite purposes. It was important that defense of the administration be voiced so that its moves to correct the situation would appear to be starting from the highest possible threshold.

Other spokesmen for the President, notably Dulles, Knowland, and Nixon, had to voice support of their chief within the limits imposed by their other political obligations. Although enjoying the complete confidence of the President, Dulles was still forced to consider the concerns of his department and the views of his critics. Thus, it was in his interest both to support the President and to minimize damage to his own special province by pursuing foreign policy moves in the space arena at once appealing to the President and to his own critics.

The Soviets had been making extraordinary mileage out of their achievement, and editorial comment from both neutralist and allied countries showed that Sputnik was one of the most stimulating events of the recent past. In response to this barrage of successful propaganda, Dulles took two tacks. Sharing in part the immunity from political pressures of the President's personal advisers, he belittled the Sputnik and emphasized the contributions of German scientists to the Soviet satellite program.[27] On the other hand, he did embark on two new policy ventures. First, he initiated moves toward cooperation with NATO allies in scientific and technological efforts, and asked for an amendment of the Atomic Energy Act of 1954 to permit such cooperation.[28] Second, he used outer space to untie the "inseparable" package of disarmament proposals which the West had offered in London, thereby proclaiming America's interest in the use of outer space for peaceful purposes.[29] Thus Dulles could claim for Eisenhower that the United States had initiated definite new policies in the international politices of outer space.

On another political front, Senate Minority Leader William Knowland represented the President in a congressional arena that was becoming increasingly involved in the missile and satellite issue. Knowland, as the leader of the President's party in the upper house, was obligated to defend the administration's posture. At the same time, Knowland was obliged to protect his own role in a legislative branch constitutionally divorced from the executive. Moreover, Knowland at this time harbored presidential ambitions. Thus he, more than Eisenhower's personal advisers or even Dulles, had to maintain a degree of distance from the President's own position.

Knowland appeared to compromise his various political obligations. By calling for a "bipartisan review" of the entire defense effort, he fulfilled his senatorial role; by arguing that politics should be ignored in assessing past responsibility and future plans, he defended the administration as best he could.[30] His position that the national security program needed regular review "from time to time" was designed both to make the congressional action seem like business as usual and to put any future policy shifts of the administration in a favorable light.[31]

Finally, Richard Nixon served as the spokesman for the policy shifts which were to occupy the administration in the subsequent months. His own strategic position could be characterized as complex. As a presidential aspirant, Nixon logically could not afford to identify himself too closely with the mistake of the President. At the same time, as heir apparent of Modern Republicanism, Nixon was dependent upon the sustained reputation and prestige of Eisenhower. Thus, Nixon both advocated effective responses to the Sputnik within the administration and announced those which the President chose.

In a speech on October 15, Nixon first indicated that some action would be forthcoming in response to the Sputnik by stating that the nation must place its security before a tax cut. Given the administration's previous advocation of governmental economy, this linkage of high spending and national security was a necessary move in order to win credibility for any future plans to bolster the national defense. Although making no direct reference to the connection between past government economy and the pace of the Vanguard project, Nixon did argue that America "must react . . . strongly and intelligently to [Sputnik's] implications." He did not abrogate the basic tenets of his chief: "Militarily," he assured his audience, "the Soviet Union is not one bit stronger today than it was before the satellite was launched." Yet he did reflect the forthcoming shift in the administration's emphasis when he added, "we could, however, make no greater mistake than to brush off this event as a scientific stunt."[32]

The President not only sought to limit the conflict by enlisting his supporters in a public attempt to downgrade Sputnik. He also attempted to enlarge current programs and to initiate, within the executive branch, new efforts which might speed America's space effort, thereby preempting his critics. His immediate policy moves were in three major directions: increased emphasis upon the missile program; high-level consultation with representatives of the scientific community; and a personal appeal to the people.

In the defense field, the administration reacted to the apparent Soviet lead in rocket thrust capability by ordering a stepped-up missile program. Although this would entail no major increase of funds, rumors became current that the President would permit the DOD to spend above its $38 billion ceiling if such action were necessary to expedite the missile program. In effect, the administration removed certain financial bottlenecks on research and development work.[33] Even more important, government officials were shifting from the initial administration position of minimizing Soviet missile claims to "expressions of guarded concern about the status of the United States' missile program in comparison to the Soviet's."[34] Thus the administration conceded that Sputnik did indeed carry implications for America's strategic missile capability.

More notable than any early policy shifts were the mode and character of the administration's new concern. In the two weeks following Sputnik, *The New York Times* observed, more scientists visited the President than in the previous ten months. Dr. Detlev Bronk, President of the National Academy of Sciences, Dr. Alan Waterman, Director of the National Science Foundation, and Dr. John Hagen, Director of Project Vanguard, were all present at the NSC meeting on October 10 that first grappled with the implications of the launching. Later in the month, Eisenhower met with his Science Advisory Committee in the Office of Defense Mobilization to discuss the pursuit of basic research in the federal government and its role in any technological competition with the Russians.[35] Indeed, this new access of scientists to the highest echelons of policy-making was the most obvious change in the administration's style in the immediate post-Sputnik weeks.

Finally, Eisenhower decided to discuss defense, space, the need for an enlarged scientific effort, and problems of government spending in a series of nationwide speeches during the winter. He used these speeches as forums for assuring the country that America did not face an immediately dangerous crisis. At the same time, he stressed the policy changes he had chosen to meet the Soviet challenge. Significantly, he exposed himself to some Americans who expected an integrated program to meet a critical situation. If he did not feel a new national security program was necessary, he was at least prepared to answer the various political actors who thought it was.

## THE DEPARTMENT OF DEFENSE

In contrast to the President's desire to contain the conflict engendered by Sputnik, leaders within the Department of Defense wished to capitalize upon it. Within the constraints imposed by being part of the executive branch, DOD officials—particularly military officers not politically dependent upon the commander-in-chief—sought to enlarge their own roles, missions, and budget in the space field. Like other actors in the political system both responsible to the President and enjoying bases of influence apart from him, the DOD simultaneously supported Eisenhower and attempted to direct his choices toward departmental goals.

By an ironical twist of fate, Secretary of Defense–designate Neil H. McElroy was visiting the ABMA arsenal at Huntsville when Sputnik went up. Back in Washington four days later, the Secretary gave no evidence that what must have been a roaring good conversation over lunch had produced any policy shifts in the satellite program. Together with other DOD spokesmen, his public support of the President was unequivocal.

In replying to their civilian and Army critics, DOD officials emphasized the separate nature of Project Vanguard and looked back to the fateful 1955 decision to account for America's comparative position vis-a-vis the Russians. Holaday further observed that the Sputnik "was not evidence of Soviet technological superiority in missiles and rocket development"[36] and SHAPE headquarters assured reporters that there were no military potentialities of earth satellites of which it was aware.

The Defense Department bore the brunt of such public debate, since it was charged with operational control over a satellite program which administration policy had failed to exploit. In addition, the Soviet ICBM capability directed attention to American missile efforts. While such attention intensified the department's effort to fend off critical attack, it simultaneously enabled the military establishment to pursue the new mission openly. The DOD stood to gain from an American space program if this program were primarily military in emphasis, and the department capitalized upon the absence of clear-cut space policy to assert its own claim.

McElroy revealed the department's new concern by a series of immediate policy decisions, all of them contributing to a space effort. In the field of military support for scientific research and development, the Secretary revoked former Secretary Wilson's August 17 directive reducing service test and evaluation expenditures.[37] He returned basic research funding, which had been reduced to compensate for overexpenditure earlier in fiscal year 1958 to its original appropriations level, thus augmenting available funds by $9 million.[38] Further, the Secretary lifted certain overtime restrictions on missile development work.

In the ballistic-missile field, McElroy announced that he would assume personal direction of the program, ordering weekly service progress reports and declaring himself constantly available to discuss any problems. Like the President, he believed the program basically sound, and emphasized that removal of technical and administrative bottlenecks would suffice to speed it on its way. His heightened interest, however, attested to both the administration's increased evaluation of the Soviet ICBM capability, and its willingness to consider a larger American effort.

Finally, in the space field the DOD gradually shifted to a new emphasis upon prestige and military objectives. The services' reactions varied with the level and success of their respective space roles. The service directly responsible for the ongoing satellite program echoed the DOD's initial reaction to Sputnik. Rear Admiral Rawson Bennett, Chief of Naval Research, depicted Sputnik as "a hunk of iron almost anybody could launch."[39] His commanding officer, Admiral Arleigh Burke, Chief of Naval Operations, supported this contention by arguing that America had rocket power sufficient to launch a satellite of Sputnik's weight. There was some internal opposition to this official sanguinity. Rear Admiral John T. Hayward, Assistant Chief of Naval Operations, Research and Development, later indicated that there had been some reappraisal of Project Vanguard within the Navy at this time. "When Sputnik went up and everything was confused I made the same proposals that you gentlemen have gotten legislation for now. And I was slapped down pretty hard."[40] Like the President, however, the DOD and Navy officials publicly dismissed the existence of a space race in which the United States had not yet crossed the starting line.

Army spokesmen took a more parochial tack. Civilian scientists within the Department of the Army and the Huntsville team immediately reminded the news media that the Army could have launched a satellite in 1956. Indeed, four days after Sputnik at the Eighth International Astronautics Federation Congress in Barcelona, Major General Holgar N. Toftoy, Commander of the Redstone Arsenal, and Brigadier General John A. Barclay, Department Commander, ABMA said an army satellite could have been up in 1955. To this Barclay cryptically added that the wisdom of the Vanguard decision "remains to be evaluated."[41]

A small stir ensued within the department. The next day the Office of the Secretary of the Army issued an order to Army personnel that any public statements about the Army's satellite or ballistic-missile capabilities were inappropriate and therefore banned.[42] Shortly thereafter, both the Navy and the Air Force issued similar directives since, as the Air Force explained, "any comments are almost certain to be misunderstood."[43]

Indeed, comments were guaranteed to be misunderstood, since the DOD's public position at this juncture was an uncomfortably composite one. Nonetheless, the department was moving into the space field. The Air Force immediately accelerated its high-altitude research rocket firings, Project Farside, in an attempt to offset the impact of Sputnik. The first news of these firings was of reported failures and the Air Force refused to comment on the project.[44] The acceleration was significant, however, since only a few months before the DOD and the Air Force had curtailed the mission. In the ill-starred Vanguard program there was no order to accelerate. Such a course was considered, but further evaluation revealed that it would be a sufficient technological feat to keep the project on schedule. Furthermore, a crash effort would seem like "me-tooism." Instead, for the first time, the DOD turned to serious consideration of long-term, large military space projects. In the days following Sputnik, the Air Force received a sympathetic hearing on its reconnaissance satellite program, and von Braun was invited to present an Army proposal for a circumlunar space platform.[45] Although these proposals would not become operational for several years, their review by the DOD revealed a new interest in space efforts which might outstrip the Russians. No longer were such futuristic projects considered science fiction; no longer was outdoing the Russians for prestige purposes considered beyond the mission of the DOD.

## THE SCIENTISTS

Perhaps the most significant impact of Sputnik was that it focused upon scientific and technological prowess as both a major factor in cold war competition and as a major component of national preparedness. In the months following the launching, national interest in scientific affairs and in the state of American science and technology increased markedly. Libraries reported increased circulation of scientific literature; department stores reported increased sales of binoculars; local government officials reported increased attempts at amateur rocketry; and newspapers devoted more space to scientific news.

In October 1957 the American scientific community had no clearly defined role in the highest echelons of public policy-making. A number of distinguished scientists and engineers had been alienated from government work in the McCarthy era, and their outlook reached its peak of disaffection in the years after the Oppenheimer security hearings. The military services and some other executive departments had established scientific advisory committees, but the highest level of formal scientific participation in the Executive Branch was in the Office of Defense Mobilization.

Sputnik signaled the reappearance of the scientists as important members of the national political system, but with uncertain objectives. From their earlier participation in Project Vanguard, the scientists bore a certain responsibility for the American position.

As scientists, however, they appreciated the Russian accomplishment. Hence, a strong flavor of ambivalence characterized the immediate reactions of the scientists to the launching. Some expressed admiration for a significant scientific feat; others were critical of the low priority given Project Vanguard and of the rejection of Project Orbiter. Underlying both attitudes was a general concern that American scientific progress and educational standards were rapidly being surpassed by the Soviet Union.[46] Moreover, many scientists cited Sputnik as evidence of Soviet ICBM capacity and suggested that America undertake a vast program of scientific research and development to match it. Their suggestions had impact. Torn between traditional respect for the international achievements of science and concern for America's welfare and security, the scientists suddenly had substantial opportunities for influence.

In the first days after Sputnik it seemed clear the scientists intended to use their opportunities. The administration was prepared to give careful attention to their views. And as private and public debate intensified many scientists sought to broaden the agenda of subjects for high-level consultation beyond the obvious fact that the scientific satellite program needed increased support. Instead, they called for — and secured — a general review of all government scientific policies by Eisenhower's new-found official scientific advisers.

Their voices, in turn, were heard. On November 3 John Finney reported that "for the first time, in the past weeks top government officials have been heeding the advice of scientists and educators."[47] Although the scientists did not at this time offer a clear policy of what they wanted in space, they had gained access to the President and a right to be consulted by him in future space policy.


## THE CONGRESS

After Sputnik, the key institution which determined whether or not and, if so, how far the political conflict would be broadened, was the United States Congress. With the administration following a policy of reassurance, continued high political visibility of the satellite program seemed possible only if powerful congressional leaders chose to maintain it. Such was the character of the issue that it almost guaranteed an initial reaction — for it served many purposes of many legislative members.

The immediate and predictable response of virtually all congressmen to Sputnik was a rash of public statements commenting gravely upon the seriousness of the situation. Quite beyond the chance for general publicity, however, there were other gains to be achieved for the parties and subparties within Congress, key leaders, and important committees.

On a party basis, reactions to the launching divided, as might be expected, four ways. The liberal Republicans had to defend Eisenhower and at the same time push him into policy decisions which would maintain his, and hence their, prestige. Accordingly, they were most anxious to limit the conflict engendered by Sputnik. Conservative Republicans, less loyal to the President, were cross-pressured by concern with the Russian advance and their long-time advocation of the balanced budget. Their reactions were more critical of the President than those of their liberal brethren, and thus less designed to contain political conflict. Predictably, liberal Democrats were the chief opponents of the administration, anxious to evaluate the space program in a partisan context. But the group most interested in expanding the conflict engendered by Sputnik were the moderate Democrats, particularly the two Texans who then, in concert, led the legislative branch of the government.

Lyndon Johnson, Sam Rayburn, and their followers had in their own view more to gain from the crisis and more influence by which to achieve their ends than any other segment of Congress. Their ability to shape congressional policy and their decision to capitalize upon the issue became the crucial factors in determining the scope and intensity of the conflict.

Both segments of the Republicans were on the defensive. Moderate Republicans, in order to maintain their own and their party's standing with an aroused public, sought to save the President, even if in their view he would not save himself. Senators Javits and Case and Representative Keating all called for greater co-ordination of the missile and satellite program and greater defense expenditures, maintaining that government economy must be subordinated in times of crisis. Their simultaneous appeal was that partisan criticism should be avoided lest it impede the defense effort; keeping politics under the rug was a condition of their strategy's success.

These spokesmen were joined by Senators Bridges, Saltonstall, and Flanders, all senior Republican members of the Armed Services Committee with relatively safe Senate seats. However, they placed more emphasis on program needs and less on party interests. Bridges, who led his party in the defense debate, was the most outspoken. He joined the Democrats in demanding a full-scale Senate inquiry into the defense effort and attacked "ostensibly responsible spokesmen for the Administration for grossly misleading statements belittling Sputnik," an obvious reference to Randall and Adams.[48] He called for less concern "with the depth of the pile on the new broadloom rug or the length of the tailfin on the new car, and [greater readiness] to shed blood, sweat and tears if this country and the free world are to survive."[49] Like the liberal Republicans, Bridges abjured partisanship, not because he feared its use against himself, but because it might place limits upon his Senatorial autonomy as a rather swashbuckling critic of the administration.

Few orthodox Republicans were this immune to the political risks of protesting too much about the administration's defense posture. As conservatives, some were legitimately concerned about the expenditures which a stepped-up space program would require. Others, faced with hard campaigning in the fall, needed presidential and party prestige for their own career purposes. Thus, some conservative Republicans discounted the Soviet achievement in the same way Eisenhower's close advisers had done. Homer Capehart evaluated the launch as "psychologically bad, but practically it doesn't mean much."[50] Alexander Wiley saw it as nothing to worry about, but rather as "something to keep us on our toes."[51] Logically, it was this group which consistently accused the Democrats of playing politics with national defense.

Senator Knowland stood midway between the two Republican positions. Harboring strong political ambitions and a high regard for his own autonomous power as leader of the Senate's Republicans, the Minority Leader vacillated between support of an inquiry into defense policy and castigation of Democratic partisanship. His behavior reflected a thorough realization that the forthcoming session of Congress could bode no good for the Republicans, and that it was in the majority party that the congressional response to Sputnik would ultimately be fashioned.

As the majority party, the Democrats initially responded to the challenge of Sputnik with an attack led by their liberal wing. On the evening of October 4, Senators Symington, Jackson, Mansfield, Smathers, Anderson, Humphrey, and Kefauver were already placing responsibility for the Soviet space advantage on Eisenhower's lack of leadership and program of economy-above-all. They demanded that the missile and scientific space programs be accelerated and coordinated, and called for investigations and a special session of Congress. They scored "the soothing platitudes of the Administration spokesmen"; termed Sputnik a "devastating blow to the prestige of the United States as a leader in the scientific and technological world"; and called upon the President "to assume personal responsibility for speeding the missile program."[52]

Similar sentiments were voiced by ranking leaders of the national party, Truman, Stevenson, Harriman, Butler, and Benton. On October 11 the Democratic Advisory Council of the Democratic National Committee issued a statement charging that "the Russian achievement is visible proof that the administration has failed to understand the amount of effort which is needed by our country in basic research and in applied engineering if we are not to become inferior to the Russians."[53] In rapid-fire order the council charged that the administration valued economy above security; claimed that, had Truman's missile program been sustained since 1953, the United States would never have been surpassed; and called upon the President to be a leader. Former President Truman chose to attack both Republicans in general and the Republican administration in particular, announcing that in the 1958 elections "we'll rub Ike's halo out altogether."[54] At the least, there were obviously some Democrats who were gleefully preparing to try.

Despite the sound and fury, Senator Lyndon Johnson was the chief architect of the Democrats' ultimate strategy. He was equipped with the formidable political resources of a Majority Leader. He was a moderate capable of pulling the disparate elements of the Democratic party into effective voting coalitions; a powerful member of the Senate Armed Services Committee; a man of political flamboyance sufficient to gain the public's attention; and had political ability sufficient to gain almost anything he set out to get. Although master of only one-half of Congress, Speaker Rayburn was his devoted friend, mentor, and supporter. Johnson had a deep loyalty to and faith in the Democratic party and firmly believed in the congruence between what was good for the Democrats and good for the nation. He was vitally concerned with the nation's security. And, finally, he wanted to become president of the United States.

To Johnson it seemed that he and his party could reap the greatest political rewards from Sputnik by working with, but consistently ahead of, the administration. In this posture, the Democratic leadership in Congress, with the aid of liberal Republicans and the more partisan Democrats, could appear as the defenders, indeed the architects, of national preparedness. Johnson feared that a partisan attack upon the administration might backfire into countercharges of Democratic politicking with national survival. Yet he had no intention of declaring that politics stopped at the atmosphere's edge. (Von Braun was later to comment that "space was bigger than Texas." This did not necessarily make it any different.) Thus Johnson's statement shortly after Sputnik that the Soviets were first in space "due to the lack of intelligent, united effort in the United States" appeared as an appeal to united effort on behalf of his own prospectus for military preparedness.[55]

Johnson worked swiftly to establish his position.[56] Senator Symington, a long-time critic of the administration's defense effort, had greeted Sputnik with pleas for both a special session of Congress and an investigation of the national defense effort by the Senate

Armed Services Committee. Upon reaching Chairman Richard
Russell he was informed that Johnson had already set an investigation in motion, although diluting its partisan flavor by calling it an
"inquiry." On the day after Sputnik, the staff of the Senate committee
and members of Johnson's personal staff were already collecting
data. Chairman Russell waited to call the inquiry until he could contact Senator Styles Bridges, the ranking Republican on the committee. When he did so, he found that Johnson had already arranged
matters in agreeably bipartisan fashion. Thus Johnson initiated the
Senate Armed Services Committee's Preparedness Subcommittee's
"Inquiry into Satellite and Missile Programs." The inquiry would
serve as an arena in which the whole defense posture of the
Eisenhower administration would be examined and found, under
the aegis of Johnson, most seriously wanting. It would also serve as
a vehicle by which the Democratic Party in Congress, again under
Johnson, would offer the nation a program for enhancing its security.
Finally, it would put Johnson himself, and his statesmanlike concern
for the nation's preparedness, in the headlines of every newspaper
in the land.

The Majority Leader was clearly able and anxious to take the
initiative in policy-making for national security affairs, including
space. His choice to do so, more than perhaps any other factor,
guaranteed that the resolution of the space issue would take place
in a broad political arena.

## THE TAKE-OFF INTO SELF-SUSTAINED STRATEGY

The immediate response of the major political participants to
the launching of Sputnik was in all cases a cursory examination of
the profits and losses which might accrue to each from the event.
The administration and the Congress, representing general political
interests within the system, had to place the onset of the space age
within the broader context of national security and political climate.
They viewed the space program as a channel for the advancement
of political values and moved, either defensively or offensively, into
the new arena. They recognized that space was becoming a focal
point for the generalized concern voiced by their constituent
groups.

On the other hand, the military establishment and the scientific
community were specifically qualified to assess the potential role
of space in the national effort. Although each had other, and at this
time more pressing, missions, each possessed technical skills
necessary to promote a space program. Moreover, they both recog-

nized that the markedly increased interest of the political generalists in the field was the means through which they could transform their specialized influence into broad public policy.

In the first month after Sputnik, then, the immediate reactions of the involved political activists determined that space policy would become a genuine political conflict spreading throughout the political system. Once the existence of the space issue had been established, the activists moved to assess their self-interest and strategic choices in regard to it. Questions of who wanted what and how emerged as soon as the arena of competition was recognized. Out of the ensuing conflict would rise the power structure that would establish the new space agency.

## Everybody Has a Space Capability: November 1957– April 1958

In early November, while the administration struggled unsuccessfully to contain the controversy generated by Sputnik I, the half-ton dog-carrying Sputnik II intensified public and political concern.

The new satellite was a sobering reminder that the space race was not a one-shot affair, but an urgent, long-term scientific and technological challenge. Immediately after its launching the administration, building upon initiatives of the previous month, began to take actions committing the United States to a space effort. As its intentions became clear, competition for a role in either the technical-scientific or political exploitation of space became clear as well.

The administration spent the five months after Sputnik II evolving its space policy, for the most part behind closed doors. During this period, its posture was to proclaim its intention to build a new space effort but to avoid specific choices. Given this hiatus, other political participants were free to press their own claims while the administration debated its choice, and to make clear their respective positions and policy preferences. The administration's delaying action—necessary in any process of policy formulation— provided the perfect backdrop for the sustained competition of the interested activists.

These other participants set to work first to build strategic positions which might serve them best in procuring a greater role in space. It would be from these positions that the administration's ultimate proposal to establish NASA, submitted on April 2, would be evaluated. For the moment, however, each political participant sought to convince the administration of its own special capability in space by calling loudly for recognition of its skills and resources. It was a veritable "Anvil Chorus."

## THE ADMINISTRATION

Although the broad outlines of the nation's space program remained undetermined in the period between November 1957 and April 1958, the administration did make certain interim organizational and budgetary decisions to speed up the present effort. But these limited steps did not suffice to stave off the critics — throughout this period the administration remained on the political defensive. Its behavior was due in part to a continuing desire to contain the conflict as far as possible. It was also dictated by the special requirements of the executive office in the American political process.

The nature of these requirements demands a brief explanation. The heart of the administration's problem was that, while critics could call for an all-out space effort, the administration itself could treat space only as one part of a broad national security effort. Necessarily responsible for the entire policy spectrum of the government, the administration's ability to focus upon and exploit the space effort was more limited than that of its critics. Thus, no matter what the magnitude of the official effort, critics could always complain.

Yet at the same time any administration can more easily establish the magnitude of national security policy, including space, than any other field of national policy. The "arena of decision-making"[57] for national security lies primarily in the executive branch; without enormous effort, neither the public nor the Congress can significantly alter the strategic choices of the administration, once they are made. Thus the administration could, within limits dictated by its desire for political survival, afford to accept criticism of its space effort, expecting that, once questions of character and magnitude were resolved within the administration itself, it would regain its traditional initiative.

Thus the administration was neither able nor impelled to outshout its critics. Instead it acted to preserve its own freedom of choice, so that it could later exploit the relative congressional acquiescence and latent public support which exists for national security policy. As events were to disclose, this was a politically viable posture. Moreover, because it was a relatively conservative choice, it fitted the administration's fiscal and partisan philosophy.

So far as public statements were concerned, Eisenhower's attitude toward the space challenge during this period was one of serious calm. He reassured the nation that it was not in severe danger. His State of the Union message stressed that the present American deterrent capability was sufficient to wreak annihiliation on the

Soviet Union, thus discounting any "real and present danger" to the United States. He also reiterated the theme that economic wisdom was the ultimate defense and that America could not have "both what we must have and what we would like to have."[58] Throughout the interim period the President constantly plied these two themes: inviting national consensus in support of his program; disparaging partisans and alarmists; and urging Americans to "throw back their shoulders, thrust out their chins and say 'America is strong and will grow ever stronger.' "[59]

However inherently strong the administration's power position, it still suffered political damage. Eisenhower's popularity had declined ten percent since the 1956 election and the Sputniks accelerated the trend.[60] In January, therefore, he was confronted with the most skeptical Congress he had known, one which openly intended to fill the "vacuum" of executive leadership.

As in the first days of immediate reaction to Sputnik I, Eisenhower's advisers joined in public defense of their chief. Predictably, Dulles and Adams emphasized only the positive side of the administration's achievement. After Explorer I, America's first satellite, went up on January 31 Dulles observed that "if we put our mind to it, we can do almost anything that can be done."[61] Adams went further and claimed that not only was the administration doing fine, but that any missile lag which might have inadvertently occurred during the present administration was the Truman administration's responsibility.[62] Alternatively, it was Nixon who presented both aspects of the administration posture. After the Explorer was launched, for example, he both boasted that the U.S.S.R. had no monopoly on scientific achievement and warned against excessive optimism.[63] In all cases these spokesmen were speaking for the President; in all cases, too, they implicitly or explicitly asked the nation to trust Eisenhower in defense matters.

Finally, White House tactics sought both to disassociate the President from current difficulties and to associate him with the successes of America's early venture into space. After the Vanguard failure, Hagerty claimed that the White House had in no way been involved in the excessive publicity which surrounded the attempt and which was subsequently widely criticized. He also referred all questions concerning the failure to the DOD.[64] Yet the announcement of the successful launchings came first from Eisenhower's office. In essence the emergent information policy concerning the satellite program was a simple one. Hagerty revealed it when he remarked to reporters that if Explorer II went into orbit the White House would announce it; if not, the newsmen could get their news from the Army and the National Science Foundation.[65]

The administration did more than talk, however; it made certain preliminary moves to expand the future space effort. These actions were on three fronts: higher priority for science as a national resource; an expansion of the ballistic-missile and satellite effort; and a more liberal attitude toward the omnipresent pressure to allocate more resources to space activities.

One major step to raise the prestige of science after the Sputniks was the formal recruitment of scientists into the ranks of the policy makers. The presidential conferences of October with scientists and educators began to bear fruit: in a nationwide television speech on November 7, Eisenhower announced the appointment of Dr. James R. Killian, President of the Massachusetts Institute of Technology, as his new Special Assistant for Science and Technology. On November 29 the President transferred the President's Science Advisory Committee from the Office of Defense Mobilization to the White House, thus buttressing Killian with a broadly gauged advisory structure. These moves were intended to "give science an impressive new voice in the inner circle of Government."[66]

At the same time the President sought to put some of the earlier suggestions of scientists and educators into effect: specifically in the areas of scientific education, basic research, and scientific cooperation with NATO allies. In a speech televised in Oklahoma City on November 13, he echoed the scientists' claim that scientific education was the most critical problem facing the nation, and offered initial suggestions which were to become his first legislative proposal in the new national security effort. The administration bill, finally approved as the National Defense Education Act, provided $1 billion over a four-year period for grants to colleges and technical schools, and graduate fellowships.

To further scientific cooperation with the allies, Eisenhower announced in December a preliminary agreement with Prime Minister Macmillan on joint British and American research activities, contingent upon amendment of the Atomic Energy Act. In support of such cooperation, the White House announced in late December the appointment of Wallace R. Brode, Associate Director of the National Bureau of Standards, as Special Assistant to the Secretary of State for Scientific Affairs.[67]

In the field of basic research, the new fiscal year 1959 budget included a request for $150 million for the National Science Foundation, three times as much as the actual appropriation of the previous year. The request for the National Advisory Committee for Aeronautics (NACA) was increased more than 50 percent to permit advanced research in space flight. Finally, the DOD requested 50 percent more than in the previous year for basic research applicable to military research and development, including space.

Eisenhower also provided increased funds for national security including space research and exploration, although in relatively marginal amounts. While promising a "very considerable" increase in defense spending, Eisenhower later reversed himself and indicated that the 1959 budget would be only moderately higher than the current one.[68] (Predicted defense spending in 1959 was to be between $38 and $40 billion, as compared with $38.4 in 1958). This ambiguous posture stemmed from conflict between Eisenhower's public rejection of price tags for defense and his commitment to fiscal responsibility. As late as December he still hoped to maintain a balanced budget and to avoid raising the debt limit.[69] By January 15, however, he was asking Congress to raise the ceiling by $5 billion.[70]

So far as interim organizational steps for space were concerned, Eisenhower concentrated upon the DOD. He announced on November 7 that Mr. William M. Holaday, former Special Assistant to the Secretary of Defense, would become the Director of Guided Missiles vested with the full authority of the Secretary to supervise and coordinate the missile program. Holaday was also granted temporary control over the satellite program. The next day the DOD authorized the Army's satellite program as a backup for Project Vanguard. And, most significantly for our purposes, on November 15 McElroy announced that he would subsequently appoint a new director for advanced weapons development, including guided missiles in early stages of research, anti-missile missiles, satellites, and space platforms. Such weaponry, according to McElroy, would be developed by a single manager and subsequently assigned to the services for use. The President also began to make clear his long-range conception of the structure of the space program. As early as his Oklahoma City speech Eisenhower suggested that the distinction between civilian and military exploitation of space upon which the Vanguard decision had been based would remain a primary criterion for assigning the space program. He then stated, in discussing the satellite program:

> If the project is designed for scientific purposes, its size and cost must be tailored to the scientific job it is going to do.... If the project has some ultimate defense value, its urgency for the purpose is to be judged in comparison with the probable value of competing defense projects.[71]

By early February there were indications from the White House that this distinction would be institutionalized in arrangements separating military and nonmilitary space programs. On the fourth, Eisenhower ordered Killian to draw up a timetable for scientific objectives in space, with the special charge of matching these with an organizational structure for research and exploration in space.

The following day in his news conference, Eisenhower indicated that he was sympathetic to a division of responsibility: the emplacement of space weaponry in the DOD, and overall responsibility for space sciences in a civilian agency. The President thus distinguished between "what is in the realm of probability in the whole scientific area [and] . . . the defense aspects of this business."[72]

It is clear that the principle of divided control of the space mission between military and civilian operating agencies had been established when Killian was instructed to draw up his report.[73] After this time White House spokesmen substantiated this principle in increasingly forceful terms. On February 17 Nixon stated in a speech at the Jet Propulsion Laboratory that the exploration of space was a civilian task for two basic reasons: first, "research as well as operations in this field [should] not be established by military need and military opinion," since such military limitations would, in Nixon's view, put unnecessary and destructive limits upon scientific investigation. Second, he considered it "vitally important that we continue to emphasize that our efforts [in the space and research fields] are for peaceful purposes."[74]

In late March Eisenhower made his first explicit commitment to civilian control of space: "I expect to send up shortly recommended legislation providing for civilian control and direction of governmental activities incident to a civilian space program."[75] On the same day he released "An Introduction to Outer Space," the space primer prepared by Killian and his committee, under the direction of Dr. Edward Purcell. This primer outlined a projected program for scientific exploration of space under civilian direction. Finally, on April 2, Eisenhower sent to Congress his message proposing the National Aeronautics and Space Agency with expanded authority and mission to direct all American projects in space, "except for those projects primarily associated with military requirements."[76] Thus the administration, exercising its crucial role as initiator of the legislative process, chose to formulate the space mission around the key concept that scientific-civilian dimensions of space would be distinguished and separated out from the military dimension.

## THE DEPARTMENT OF DEFENSE

The Department of Defense is both a part of the administration and a military establishment vested with the monopolistic mission of defending by force the national security of the United States. This mission requires such vast resources and specialized personnel that the department can exercise a significant degree of independence apart from the political control of its commander in chief. Moreover, within the department the services have analogous independent power positions. While outlining the separate space policy positions of the department vis-a-vis the administration and, in turn, of the services within the department, overturns the organization charts, it acknowledges political reality.

The civilian officials in the Office of the Secretary of Defense as members of the administration publicly supported Eisenhower's level of commitment to the space effort. As military officials, however, it was also their duty to impress upon the President the potential military significance of space exploitation. Moreover, each service sought to protect and extend its mission in space in opposition to each other's claims, while together pressing a broad program of space activity upon the civilian officials in the OSD. Thus the DOD was at once an extension of the administration, a single military agent making peculiar strategic demands upon the administration, and a multiple actor expressing divergent service claims of space capabilities. This Janus-faced quality of the DOD makes the task of interpreting its claim upon America's potential space capability a peculiarly complex but equally important one.

## The Office of the Secretary of Defense

Throughout the period from November until April, the OSD officials argued consistently that the Sputniks did not reflect an operational Soviet military advantage. However, they did admit the military significance of the powerful rocket thrust which had launched the satellites. Thus, given the department's primary mission to promote the national security, its major reaction to the Sputnik crisis was to accelerate the missile program. To this end, McElroy authorized the production of both the Jupiter and the Thor IRBMs on November 26, speeded development of the Atlas ICBM in December, and authorized research and development on the Minuteman ICBM early in 1958.

In general, the OSD sustained the official position which had led to the Vanguard decision: that the exploitation of space should not hamper the major task of developing America's ballistic-missile capability. On November 11 Undersecretary of Defense Donald Quarles indicated that the United States had rockets capable of lifting satellites as heavy as the Sputniks, but that the DOD did not consider this a proper military use of the vehicles.[77] In a speech to the American Rocket Society, Holaday repeated this argument, saying:

> We will be able to have large satellites whenever we want them. . . . When we are assured of an adequate IRBM capability

and an ICBM system with the necessary support equipment and
stockpile of missiles, then we intend to jump into space. To do
so beforehand would be like trying to lock the front door and
let [sic] the back door stay open. This does not mean that we
will discontinue space work. We will have an effective and
continuing program. But missiles will be our Number One job.[78]

The exploitation of space, insofar as it contributed to a stronger
defense posture, was included within the DOD's overall mission.
Its significance, however, would be evaluated relative to the utility
of other defense programs.

     Despite this formal doctrine the OSD did, however, specifically
accelerate the space program in response to the Sputniks. Politically, the Sputniks had proven a disaster. The DOD, while denying
responsibility for the initial Vanguard decision, acknowledged that,
had the political effects of the Soviet's preemption in space been
foreseen, the decision might have been made differently.[79]

     The DOD thus assumed increased responsibility for the politi-
cal dimension of space. On November 8, four days after Sputnik II
went up, the DOD authorized the Army's Project Explorer as a
supplement to Project Vanguard. As McElroy later explained:

In consultation with my associates, [it was my belief] that there
was some doubt... as to the success that would be attendant
upon the launching of a satellite by the selected... Navy Vanguard method. We felt that there had been *some evidence that
our major competitor in the world was able to do this.* We felt
that in the general interest of this country, both nationally and
internationally, we should make certain that we would be able
to launch satellites for our IGY commitment which went
through the year 1958.[80]

The DOD's information policy concerning IGY satellite launchings
also reflected this new political concern. The extreme publicity
surrounding the Vanguard's first test failure produced extremely
adverse domestic and international reactions—in Britain the
Vanguard was variously termed the Puffnik, Flopnik, Phutnik,
Kaputnik, and Stayputnik. Thereafter, the DOD adopted extremely
secretive policies. There were no further press releases concerning
preparations for firings, and public announcements were made only
after launching attempts.[81]

     Furthermore, the DOD expressed an immediate substantive
interest in military space projects after the Soviet launchings and
requested the services to submit proposals for projects consistent
with their missions. McElroy indicated that the DOD would undertake an active program in various fields of space exploitation.

We have felt the responsibility, and do feel the responsibility
for any kind of military weapon development, no matter in what
field it may reach . . . . (It is necessary) to recognize early in the
game the importance of some very novel kinds of weapons
which some people are likely to brush off as Buck Rogers
stuff.[82]

Soon this recognition of the political and substantive implications
of space for military activities led to organizational changes and
research and development programing of considerable significance.
Despite its early emphasis upon missiles it became clear that
the Pentagon wanted a major role in whatever space program
appeared.

The first evidence of this policy choice was the organization of
existing military space programs. The OSD seized the initiative
from the services. On November 15 McElroy announced that he
would appoint a new director for the development of advanced
research projects: in effect, a single manager for space and other
advanced missions. Until this agency could be set up, space would
be under the jurisdiction of Holaday, the Director of Guided
Missiles.[83] McElroy was intent upon this mission being organized
within the OSD—precluding the possibility of a service taking overall control over the incipient space program.[84]

In keeping with OSD's thinking, when the Air Force set up a
new Directorate of Astronautics on December 10 to manage advanced space programs within the service, Acting Secretary Quarles
announced that he had asked the Air Force to delay such action
until the new Advanced Research Projects Agency was organized.
Quarles claimed that the DOD, while not opposed to the Air Force
plan, considered it "premature."[85] The issue was closed when
Secretary of the Air Force William H. Douglas suspended the order
on December 13 under OSD instructions. Department officials
felt that "apparently the Air Force wishes to show its ability in
this field and see if it can grab the limelight and establish a position."[86] They took quick action to quash this attempt to usurp the
military space mission.

The OSD intent was "an immediate one: to pull under a single
manager . . . the first time this has been done in the DOD—actual
operating units for the Research and Development work that goes
on in the anti-missile missile field and in the satellite and space
applications field."[87] The ARPA was to have authority to develop
such weapons and to turn them over to services for deployment and
use. McElroy testified that after consultation with all the services
the entire DOD was agreed that the new agency should control all
activities of any service in these areas.

In December, however, the OSD modified McElroy's announced plan for a single-manager, inhouse-capability agency. Holaday testified that

> if this group took off and developed its own engines and everything... it would be wasteful. The planning and thinking... is that we will be a cooperative group, not fighting, and will use the available material [the services] have to help out in [the agency's] program.[88]

This change reflected a serious struggle within the DOD. In competing for particular space missions the services had adopted strong positions for or against the prospect of an all-powerful operating agency for advanced research and development.[89] Moreover, some outside contractors were criticizing the potential disruption that such an agency would introduce into the contracting procedures of the services.[90] These arguments respecting the establishment of the ARPA continued for months while McElroy sought a director for the agency.

Thus, as ARPA came into existence, the exact extent of the new agency's potential authority remained unclear. Nonetheless, McElroy's general position had Eisenhower's support. On January 7 the President sent a message to Congress requesting transfer of $10 million from various military appropriations to the ARPA in the Supplemental Defense Appropriations Bill for fiscal year 1958. This sum would cover the expenses of establishing the agency, including "acquisition and construction of such research, development and test facilities and equipment as may be authorized by the Secretary of Defense."[91] Shortly thereafter, in the State of the Union message, Eisenhower argued that

> some of the important new weapons which technology has produced do not fit into any existing Service pattern. They cut across all Services, involve all Services and transcend all Services at every stage from development to operation, In some instances they defy classification according to branch of Service.... In recognition of the need for single control in some of our most advanced development projects, the Secretary of Defense has already decided to concentrate into one organization all anti-missile and satellite technology undertaken by the DOD.[92]

The administration clearly believed that the establishment of the ARPA was well within the broad powers of the Secretary granted under the National Security Act of 1947, as amended, permitting him to transfer, reassign, abolish, or consolidate noncombatant functions.

The Congress, however, claimed that the administration had

usurped a legislative function by altering the roles and missions of the services without its approval. Consequently, Congress adopted the attitude that the ARPA was largely a stopgap measure, pending further congressional consideration of space organization. The conference committee on the Supplemental Appropriations Bill directed the Secretary of Defense to engage in research and development on advanced weapons systems, either through the department or one of the services, and permitted the department to undertake for one year such nonmilitary space projects as the President designated. The committee, however, deleted all specific reference to the ARPA, providing at best a shaky legislative history for the new agency.

On February 7, ignoring service and congressional opposition, the OSD announced the formation of ARPA and the appointment of its director, Mr. Roy W. Johnson. The relevant directive[93] provided "within the DOD, an agency for the direction and performance of certain advanced Research and Development projects," including the nation's space research and the development of space weapons. ARPA was authorized to contract out research and development work with other agencies of the government and outside contractors, or to acquire such facilities as it might need. Thus the DOD had established what was on paper a powerful operating agency, the only organization in government with the explicit mission of developing advanced space projects.

With ARPA established, the OSD moved to add substance to the newly invigorated military space program. It requested proposals from the services for military space projects in an effort to avoid interservice rivalry.

Against stiff service opposition, Holaday and later ARPA reviewed a number of projects, although most decisions were postponed pending refinement of the organization. Among those decisions which were made in order to carry out the DOD's temporary responsibility for space programs were the November 8 authorization of the Army's Project Explorer and the March 23 directive ordering one or two lunar probes under Army auspices, three under Air Force direction, and the development of mechanical ground-scanning systems by the Navy. Military space projects were highly classified, but we know that one of these, the Air Force reconnaissance satellite Pied Piper, was funded during this period. Major decisions about the man-in-space program, the one-million-pound thrust engine, and weather and navigational satellite programs were not made, although relatively small investments were ordered for component development, preliminary engineering, and design work on these programs, pending final decisions.

Conflict concerning responsibility in the space field both

between the various services and ARPA and between the future civilian-military allocation of the space mission contributed to the relative inaction of the ARPA programmers.[94] Yet the level of support ARPA enjoyed was also the result of conscious policy choices in the OSD. John Finney, of *The New York Times*, one of the best-informed observers of ARPA's efforts during this early period, suggests that the "deliberate" pace of the agency's activities reflected the apathy toward space development permeating the highest echelons of the OSD and the administration. Although this relative inaction was in part due to unsettled organizational questions, it also reflects the priorities which DOD officials assigned to the space mission. While holding that the military establishment should be empowered to define those areas of space development which might contribute to the military mission, the OSD had to weigh military space efforts against more immediate claims upon the defense budget. The resultant assessment embodied in the military space budget for fiscal year 1959 indicated that the OSD was not pressing an urgent, top priority effort in the military exploitation of space.*

The OSD's effort to assert control over the total space program on a low-priority basis conflicted, of course, with the embryonic administration policy. Two days before the OSD established the ARPA, Eisenhower announced that the Killian Committee would investigate organizational alternatives for the nation's future space effort.

By implication the administration contradicted the OSD's reforms. As early as November McElroy suggested that the DOD take responsibility for developing the civilian uses of space if requested by a civilian agency to do so. "Our responsibility," the Secretary maintained, "on the civilian aspects of satellites involves whatever decision another agency of Government wishes to make in respect to using us. In that case we are glad to offer our services if we can be helpful but we do not consider that it is a responsibility of ours to initiate in that field."[95] He agreed that the government should pursue basic research and exploit civilian potentialities in the space field and that the National Science Foundation, AEC, and NACA all had responsibilities in the area. Since, however, the only capability for exploring space lay in the military, he conceived of a

---

* The FY 1959 budget request for ARPA was $520 million, of which $72 million were for nonmilitary lunar and scientific satellites to be later transferred to the civilian agency; $310 million for an anti-missile missile system and for the Pied Piper; and the remaining $138 million for all other space programs. These included projects that were both clearly military and those whose civilian or military nature was under discussion: the man-in-space program, the million-pound engine, weather and navigational satellites, satellite-tracking systems, instrumentation projects, the development of power sources. (See *Hearings on H. R. 11881*, p. 1164, and also *The New York Times*, May 25, Section IV, article by John Finney).

civilian space program as one of collaboration between the military developer and the civilian user. The model uppermost in his mind was apparently that of the IGY, in which a civilian agency designed a scientific mission in space which the DOD performed. To implement this relationship his sole suggestion was that Killian should study "whether there cannot be some improved coordination of the research activities in these various parts of the Government, [since] I think that it is possible to make improvements."[96]

During the months of policy hiatus, the DOD's opposition to a civilian space agency was almost axiomatic. Holaday testified on December 13 that the establishment of an independent civilian commission to control the satellite and space program would "radically upset the program in all areas." In response to further questioning, he stated that it would indeed be a "disaster" to place space development outside the military, since "you cannot do development work in this area without being related to and with the military people in all this."[97] He argued that all scientific aspects of space likely to produce civilian applications would be useful for military purposes as well, and thus properly belonged within ARPA. The OSD view persisted until the administration chose to place nonmilitary space exploitation in a civilian agency. As members of the administration, OSD officials then had to support this choice. Their support, however, was conditional upon the assurance that the military establishment's freedom to pursue its own interests in space would not be restricted by any formal commitment to overriding civilian control.

## The Services

For each of the services, as for the OSD, the introduction of space into the military mission implied a possible change in its roles and missions. Each was involved in part of the embryonic space program; conversely, each would profit from benefits accruing from a military space program. The services provided not only the resources by which the DOD could exploit space, but also one of the strongest stimuli for this development. Moreover, in the period of policy-making from November until April, the services were peculiarly free to emphasize, in congressional hearings and through public media, their own particular space capabilities. Thus, with the initial spasm of reaction over, the services became independent political actors in the struggle for space.

THE NAVY The Navy was the least involved of the three services in the contest for space. It did not view space as a natural outgrowth of its mission, although it did express interest in exploiting certain navigational, communications, and meteorological aspects of space. Furthermore, the Navy did have to carry on with Project Vanguard.

That project seemed rapidly to lose its charm for the service. After the first two Sputniks the Navy maintained a decorous posture, merely reiterating that the Vanguard was on schedule. This entailed four test-vehicle launchings, some of which might carry six-pound test satellites, between December and March, and six fully equipped twenty-pound scientific satellite launchings to fulfill IGY commitments by the end of December 1958. When the DOD announced authorization of Project Explorer to supplement the Vanguard on November 8, the Navy publicly welcomed the Army aboard the scientific venture. It continued to stress that neither Soviet nor Army competition would alter its plans. Unofficially, however, the Navy attempted to accelerate the program, indicating that, if initial tests were successful, a fully equipped satellite might be launched in January.[98] With the failure of the first test on December 6, in the full glare of national and international publicity, the Navy fell silent and concentrated upon keeping the project on schedule. Subsequent postponements and still another failure before the first successful test launch on March 17, in addition to the successful Army launching in January, downgraded the project still further. Indeed, the OSD seriously considered eliminating Vanguard and utilizing some of its components in Army and Air Force satellite vehicles.[99]

Under the cloud of failure, the Navy continued to emphasize that Project Vanguard was a purely scientific endeavor unrelated to either naval capabilities for military research and development or to the Navy's mission. Garrison Norton, Assistant Secretary for Air, testified that the Navy was not a competitor with the other services for the production of space vehicles. Although the Navy had requirements in space, it had no desire to develop its own capabilities for these. On the other hand, it was willing to put its own research facilities at the disposal of whatever agency or service was designated by the OSD to develop a space capability, just as it had for the National Science Foundation and the National Academy of Sciences in Project Vanguard.[100]

In general, the civilian Navy officials and the officers in the Pentagon discounted the military significance of space exploration. Secretary Norton warned in December against "Buck Rogers" thinking, terming the development of operational ballistic missiles the DOD's primary task and urging that nothing dilute this effort. These officials also resisted any reorganization of the space program within the DOD. Admiral Arleigh Burke, Chief of Naval Operations, stated flatly: "[I]t appears to me that this pressure toward reorganization is an illogical reaction to our not having an operational ballistic missile or satellite in the sky."[101] Norton agreed, arguing that each service should have its own research and development organization with the DOD merely providing a monitoring organization to prevent duplication and facilitate communication between the services. In part, this skein of attitudes reflects the Navy's traditional fear of DOD centralization, which gravely threatens to limit the roles and missions of the service. Specifically, however, it reveals that the Navy, although relatively disinterested in space, preferred to retain its option to pursue this mission rather than to lose it irrevocably to a centralized agency or to one of the other services.

Navy research and development people, however, dissented from these views. Dr. John Hagen, Director of Project Vanguard, emphasized both the military and political significance of space, and recounted his dissatisfaction with the low priority placed upon the Vanguard. Hagen particularly stressed the need for scientific research in military development and complained that the DOD gave basic research virtually no priority.[102] As far as organizational alternatives were concerned, he argued that

> what is needed — and the precise location of the organization is perhaps debatable — is a single organization devoted to this type of work [space investigation and flight]. Whether that organization would be better placed in the DOD or whether it is better in a separate agency is the question to which I do not have the answer, but I know it would work within the DOD. There should be, however, this single agency into which policy decisions would be passed and then both the authority and the responsibility for action would be given to the agency.[103]

This reflection of professional scientific rather than service bias introduces yet another set of particular interests and missions existing within the DOD. The research and development scientists, both civilian and military, shared many attitudes with their scientific colleagues and yet were among the most outspoken advocates within government for a high priority program of great magnitude in space exploitation. They were also to be the most sympathetic individuals within the DOD to the concept of a civilian space program.

THE ARMY    In sharp contrast to the Navy, for the Army space exploitation was a matter of profound significance. Unequivocally, service spokesmen favored the establishment of a centralized military agency to conduct space research and development.

The reasons were not obscure. The Army had already proved that its research teams and facilities at the ABMA and the Jet Propulsion Laboratory were capable of undertaking advanced space research projects. Yet the Army labored under a restrictive mission assignment in ballistic missiles. In an organizational shake-up the Army, specifically its research and development elements, was convinced that its teams could be preeminent in a military space effort. But, if space were to remain divided among the respective services, it seemed likely that the Air Force would assume an increasing portion of the mission. The immediate tasks as Army leaders defined them in the months after Sputnik were therefore to impress the DOD officials with the service's capability in space, and to support the establishment and decision-making powers of the ARPA.

Four days after the launching of Sputnik II, the Army received its chance to prove itself. McElroy authorized the launching of Jupiter-C test vehicles carrying an eighteen-pound Explorer scientific satellite to supplement Project Vanguard in the IGY. Determined to avoid an Army-Navy satellite race, however, the Secretary declared that the OSD would retain authority over the launching schedules of the two projects. Although the Army had sought the mission vigorously for three years, now it was apparently caught off guard. It was also disappointed because it was required to work within the framework of the IGY and therefore had only a limited satellite mission. Medaris and von Braun announced that the DOD directive failed to provide precise information about the number of satellites to be launched and the schedule to be met, and continued: "Until we are sure that we fully understand the participation that is expected of us we will have no comment."[104] Thereupon, the OSD directed the Army to proceed immediately with modifications of the guidance system for the Jupiter-C, ordered the Navy and National Science Foundation to provide the satellite instrumentation, and specified that the Army was to undertake two launchings, the first around February 1. At this point the Army plunged full speed ahead, convinced that it could beat the Navy in launching a full-scale satellite.[105]

In Medaris' words:

> I have language from the Army that says in good old-fashioned military terminology 'you will on or about such and such a date do so and so' . . . the directive I now have is in words of one syllable and leaves nothing to the imagination. It just delights my soul.[106]

He and his team were justifiably confident. The Jupiter-C, previously prepared as a satellite launching vehicle for Project Orbiter in 1956, was almost ready, requiring only a modification on the nose-cone and the addition of some minor components to return it to its original form as a satellite carrier. When the first Vanguard exploded on December 6, Army preparations speeded up. And on January 26, when the second Vanguard shot was postponed, the Army was officially authorized to make the next attempt.[107]

At 10:48 P.M. on January 31, 1958, America's first earth satellite the Army's Explorer I, was launched into orbit. The research and development team under von Braun and ABMA officials immediately issued abrupt, forthright statements that the Explorer had proved the "capability of the Army's scientific and industrial team in the realm of outer space exploration."[108] Lieutenant General Arthur G. Trudeau, the new Army chief of research and development, mentioned the entire service in his boast: "The Army has never let the people down yet; ...any time they give us the ball we know what to do with it."[109] On a more parochial level, the Explorer's home town of Huntsville celebrated New Year's Eve all over again. Fire engines and police cars unloosed their sirens and ten thousand shrieking citizens roamed through the streets, carrying placards with such messages as "move over Sputnik, space is ours" and "our missiles never miss."[110] Only one breach appeared in the convivial spirit. After the tracking station in the Azores had picked up the satellite's signal, an aide asked Medaris whether he should contact Washington. The General is reported to have responded, "Not yet; let them sweat a little."

The Army's jubilation stemmed not only from the successful launch but also from the prospects it raised for the Army's subsequent role in space. All echelons expressed the opinion that the space mission was as important as any mission in the military establishment, if not more so. Given the restrictions upon the conventional manpower capability of the Army and the two-hundred-mile limitation placed upon missiles under Army operational control by Secretary Wilson in November 1956, space offered the Army a new lease on life. Hence its spokesmen's emphasis on the significance of space for military purposes was never divorced from outspoken assertion that Army teams were well qualified to go into space.

Secretary Brucker argued that it was imperative to demonstrate capabilities in the satellite field, adding that "the Army has a unique capability to make significant and early contributions to this conquest of space."[111] General Gavin flatly stated that unquestionably space exploration was "the most important thing confronting the country today."[112] He viewed the military satellite as a development of "tremendous significance, perhaps the most significant thing in our times,"[113] and gave it higher priority than the development of ballistic missiles. Although emphasizing the political and scientific significance of space exploration, his major concern was with achieving military control of space before the Russians did.

You have got to get out there and get out there first and be able to sit down in international councils and determine as to who is going to be out there and who is to do what out there.[114]

In Gavin's view the control of space would dictate control of earth, and while he could not predict the changes space would introduce into the daily lives of human beings, he predicted "tremendous things will happen and we must get out there."[115]

Medaris echoed Gavin's view that military satellites should have greater priority than ballistic missiles by identifying the coupling between the two.

I feel that the priority should always be on the furthest thing out that you can conceive as a possibility. The priority today should be on the attainment of a space capability by the U.S. at the earliest possible date. Now you get all the ballistic missiles if you do that. They will come out just as an outfall of a properly developed forward-looking program that has as its aim the development of at the least parity, and hopefully control in the space area.[116]

In the same vein, von Braun outlined the nation's need for large, powerful single engines of at least one-million-pound thrust and for immediate financial support in the order of $1 to 1.5 billion annually, if the country was to avoid the mortal danger of Russian space domination.[117] Such a program, he predicted, would be the determinant factor in the military balance of power within fifteen years.

With their views on the significance of space underlined, Army spokesmen moved on to sketch the program and organizational arrangements best suited to the interests of their service. After Sputnik II the Army formally proposed to the OSD the immediate Army launching of several 200 to 300 pound reconnaissance satellites during 1958; development of more powerful rockets by the Army and Air Force, including initial work upon a single million-pound thrust engine; lunar, solar, and planetary probes; manned satellites, including lunar voyages; satellite developments in mapping, geodesy, meteorology, and communications, which would all offer civilian applications; the development of an anti-satellite capability; and work upon advanced propulsion techniques, including nuclear, ion, and photon power.[118] In forwarding the program through Army and OSD channels, Medaris termed it a national rather than an Army plan, emphasizing that it sought to build from existing hardware in all services, avoid interference with ongoing weapons programs, and utilize whatever teams and facilities had proven capabilities in space research.[119] Finally, Medaris depicted the Army as fully qualified to participate with other service research and development teams in such an effort.

With such interests, it is not surprising that the Army gave strong support to the establishment of the ARPA. Brucker indicated that he preferred a centralized space mission within the OSD, adding that he sought no disagreement with the Air Force but that centralized direction could best utilize the capabilities distributed among the various services. Gavin, who argued strongly for a competent military staff directly responsible to the OSD, concurred. Medaris, the commander who would be directly under the supervision of such an agency, were it established, also favored a single decision maker (although he opposed an operational agency within the DOD which would remove the space mission from "experienced teams").

> I believe sincerely that the best method for achieving it is that there must be someone responsible only to the Secretary of Defense; that is, right at his right hand, who is assigned by the Secretary and the President the power of decision in the things that were outlined in (the Army program) which do not exist, the authority to say yes, and the courage to do so, who through the medium of a very small staff can carry out the necessary job of assigning these projects, approving the total plan, assigning the resources, and monitoring the total competency to see that they do not fall backward.[120]

Such an agency, in the minds of these Army officials, would properly protect the interests of their service. Yet while the Army sought centralized direction for the space mission, it was intent upon maintaining military control. Medaris reflected this Army position in his adamant opposition to an independent civilian space agency.

> I believe that that individual [decision-maker] should properly be within the DOD, since otherwise you will have great collision of resources throughout the whole system by his being, by there being unfamiliarity with the current state of other things which affect the availability of resources and manpower in the different areas required to carry these things out, whereas, if he is working as a direct subordinate of the Secretary of Defense, he will normally and naturally be fully informed all the time with respect to the current status of other demands and will therefore place his requirements on people who are most able to carry them out.[121]

According to Army officials, a civilian agency divorced from the DOD would cause total confusion and seriously hinder the nation's venture into space.

As in the case of the Navy, however, service scientists differed from their military colleagues. Von Braun's proposal for a new space organization envisaged a broad, expensive national space program under what he termed a "national space agency" either in the OSD or as an independent, civilian agency, and armed with both inhouse facilities and contracting authority. His major thrust was that "this kind of thing obviously does not belong in the Navy or the Air Force or the Army. It is a development of an entirely new technology...."[122] He noted that at the moment the services were jockeying for position in the space contest and urged that no single one be permitted to gain control of such a crucial mission.

Although the elimination of service rivalries seemed his major concern, von Braun indicated that the scientists and the military differed in their views of the proper locus for the space mission. Hesitating initially to state his own choice, under Senator Johnson's close questioning he conceded that he ultimately would prefer to organize the space program in a way comparable to atomic energy. For the short run, however, he settled for assigning the space mission to the OSD with service research and development and missile capabilities utilized as that office chose.[123]

Thus the Army presented a coherent posture of favoring a broad military and scientific space effort under centralized direction by an agency within the OSD. Such a position favored the Army's participation in space, for, were one service to receive the mission, it seemed likely to be the Air Force. If the OSD were in charge of allocating space projects, however, Army leaders believed that its proved capabilities in scientific and military exploitation of space could secure a very respectable slice of the pie.

To a limited extent the DOD did permit the Army to exercise its space capability. In February it authorized a third Explorer shot and gave informal approval for two fifty-pound satellite launchings with the Jupiter-C rocket vehicle. In March it directed the Army to use these two satellites for lunar probes in the IGY program. And, according to Medaris, the OSD requested a firm schedule and budget proposal for Army space projects through December 1958. Medaris indicated that he anticipated the Army would "get the go-ahead on at least the first twelve months of this program."[124]

Yet at the same time there were indications that the Army would not win the long-range space mission it so avidly sought. In January, the retirement of Lieutenant General James M. Gavin, Army Chief of Research and Development, was an ominous sign that the service could not expect OSD support for the reorientation of service and military structures necessary to exploit a massive new program. Gavin indicated to the Senate Preparedness Subcommittee on January 6 that his vigorous advocacy of an urgent space effort hurt his chances for promotion. Implicitly he suggested that the DOD's evaluation of the Army's special space role and appropriate program was far from his own view. Announcing his resignation he explained:

I don't want to defend next year's budget because I don't believe in next year's budget, the Research and Development budget, of the Department of the Army. I don't want to be put in the position of coming before Congress and saying that I approve of certain things that I don't.[125]

Confirming Gavin's fears, John Finney of *The New York Times* reported on March 6 that authorities within the OSD were predicting that though scientific or "prestige" assignments would still be made to the Army, the Air Force would be charged with developing military applications of outer space.[126] McElroy, according to Finney, considered space exploitation consistent with the Air Force's overall function. Such an assignment was precisely the opposite of the Army's goals.

THE AIR FORCE    The Air Force position stemmed from an earlier allocation of missile responsibilities. The Air Force had operational control over much of America's potential booster capability: the Thor IRBM, and the Atlas, Titan, and Minuteman ICBMs. Moreover, it had been working in space research since the end of the World War II. This program was almost entirely military, and hence classified, but throughout the months after Sputnik, ongoing projects received enough public attention to indicate that the Air Force was more deeply involved in military exploitation of space than any other service. Buttressing these advantages was the service's claim that the space mission was a natural outgrowth of its military responsibility in the earth's atmosphere. Accordingly, the Air Force saw its interest to be that of resisting, or at least downgrading, the centralization of the space mission within the OSD. Its rule of thumb was that the less control granted to the OSD, the greater the portion of the space mission that might fall to the Air Force.

The Air Force's evaluation rested on an interpretation of space exploitation as a natural extension of the ballistic missile program. Although ardently contending for the space mission, the Air Force sought above all to protect the status of its ongoing aircraft and ballistic-missile programs. Hence, top officials in the service, like officials in the OSD, concentrated on the need to maintain control of the air with ballistic missiles. Under pressure, Secretary Douglas stressed that space developments and ballistic missiles should be given equal priority, but added: "I would like to leave the priority with the ballistic missile program to the extent that the two might conflict."[127] Similarly, Richard E. Horner, Assistant Secretary for Research and Development, argued it would be "utter folly to reduce the sense of urgency on the ballistic missile program at this time"[128] and agreed with Douglas that, if ballistic missiles and space operations were competing for resources, the missiles should be given top priority. Such competition could, of course, be avoided if the pace of both missions were determined concomitantly by the Air Force.

Only General Bernard Schriever, Commander of the Air Force Ballistic Missile Agency, specifically stated that in long-run terms, national security would depend upon space superiority.[129] Yet he, too, argued consistently that 90 percent of the developments in the missile program could be applied to space and that the two must move together.

> The entire astronautical development program which I have touched upon can be initiated at once, with no dilution in diversion of our ballistic missile programs. As I analyze the future, if we are to meet the challenging requirements of either ballistic missile acceleration or of astronautics, we must recognize where our strongest capabilities lie today and make certain decisions now.[130]

In short, all the Air Force witnesses who testified before the Preparedness Subcommittee argued that space was important, even crucial, but not so important as to divert resources from ongoing missions. Hence, Air Force spokesmen did not argue, as the Army had, that space was the most significant arena of potential military activity. Instead, they evaluated the significance of space for national security and sought to pace space exploitation in terms of the development of Air Force roles and missions.

The Air Force had a strong case, both logically and empirically. Its ballistic-missile capability provided a fine basis upon which to build an astronautics program, and Air Force officials constantly repeated this refrain. General Schriever argued that "our present studies have shown that by using our presently existing rocket engines and missiles, we can provide both at the earliest date and at the greatest economy, not only unmanned reconnaissance of the moon, but also a basic vehicle for manned space flight."[131] Indeed, he stated that current Atlas, Titan, and Thor programs would provide booster capacity for all the space missions of interest to the DOD for the next ten years. Moreover, the Air Force had ongoing space programs in a broad range of fields. It had engaged in high altitude research to study cosmic rays, thermal characteristics and effects upon human beings launched in balloons. The School of Aviation Medicine at Randolph Air Force Base had been investigating medical aspects of outer space, and research and development groups in the AFBMA had been working on guidance and propulsion problems of space flight. Air Force witnesses argued that this comprised a broad, comprehensive program in which the service was making real progress.

Specifically, two Air Force space projects were in the final stages of development in the early months of 1958. The X-15 research aircraft, developed with NACA cooperation, was scheduled to fly in early 1959. If successful, this model would permit man to fly at speeds above one mile per second and at altitudes above one hundred miles, at the boundaries of outer space.[132] Hence the aircraft presented many of the reentry problems confronting manned satellite flight. Second, the 117-L reconnaissance satellite, or Pied Piper, was closer to operational deployment than any other military satellite program. The OSD had authorized the Air Force to move into the systems development stage shortly before Sputnik I and subsequently accelerated the program.[133] The Air Force hoped to launch a test vehicle by October 1958 and to launch the first actual satellite by spring 1959. The test vehicle, incorporating certain components of the final satellite, would use the Thor booster; the satellite itself would eventually utilize the Atlas, thereby gaining a significantly heavier payload.[134] Both programs called attention to the Air Force's capability for scientific and military exploitation of outer space, and the service used them to bolster its claim for operational responsibility in this field.

Organizationally as well, the Air Force undertook to preempt the space mission. On December 10 it established a short-lived Directorate of Astronautics with Brigadier General Homer Boushey, Deputy Chief of Staff for Research,[135] as its director. According to the Air Force, the new directorate would be an internal management organization to pursue and coordinate advanced research projects within the service under the overall guidance of ARPA. As indicated earlier, the OSD interpreted this move as a clear Air Force attempt to establish hegemony in the military space program and to undermine the ARPA. But the announcement of these plans by Donald Putt, Deputy Chief of Staff for Development, was a measure of the enthusiasm with which Air Force officers, particularly those in research and development, viewed the space mission as an extension of service responsibilities.

Like the Army, the Air Force presented a plan for future space exploration to the OSD which would further the service's long-run interest in space. Unlike the Army's national plan, however, the Air Force offered proposals which were primarily to be executed by Air Force facilities. The most significant divergence from the Army's plan was the Air Force's disbelief in the necessity of developing a single, million-pound thrust engine. The Air Force preferred to rely on combinations of its existing rocketry.[136]

General Thomas D. White, Chairman of the Joint Chiefs of Staff and Lieutenant General Clarence S. Irvine, Air Force Deputy Chief of Staff for Materiel, had predicted already that the next war would be fought by space weapon systems.[137] The Air Force space plan now reflected this prediction by providing an evolutionary shift from present ballistic missiles to future space weaponry. The present Thor booster, with second-stage hardware from the Vanguard, could reputedly lift 3000 pounds into orbit by late 1958.[138] With additional third-stage hardware, the Thor could undertake unmanned reconnaissance of the moon, impacting a small instrumented package upon it by the end of 1959. A slightly modified Thor with a high-energy fueled upper stage already under development could put a larger payload in orbit, make initial unmanned reconnaissance of Mars and Venus, or send an instrumented recoverable package around the moon. Later the Atlas could make soft lunar landings, and the Titan, with high-energy second and third stages, could put even greater weights into orbit, support extended manned satellite missions, deliver larger payloads to Mars and Venus, or launch manned circumlunar flights. In addition to building the required booster capacity for these programs, the Air Force emphasized that it was currently working on the guidance systems, payloads, and manned experiments to be used in the projects. "In other words," Schriever concluded, "we are not just groping around. We can actually specify things."[139]

It was obvious, however, that what they had specified was a program to be undertaken primarily by the Air Force. To men like General White, this was utterly logical, since the Air Force was "synonymous with air warfare" and space was merely a natural extension of air.[140] Hence, contrary to its typical support for greater centralization within the DOD, the Air Force was bitterly opposed to the establishment of ARPA. In the words of General Irvine:

> What we don't need down in Washington is more commissions, more czars and more organizations. We have a President, a Congress, an Administration, and a Secretary of Defense. I said and I say again, we don't need any more czars or any more institutions. We need decisions by the Secretary of Defense and we need less people in the OSD. We need the delegation to the three military departments of the jobs that belong to them, and somebody with guts enough to hit them over the head if they don't do it that way.[141]

The chief impediment to progress in space, according to all Air Force witnesses, lay in separating research and development of weapons systems from their military user. In General White's words, "I would naturally prefer to have it (space) in the Air Force because I think we have done more in that respect than anybody else, by a very great margin, and naturally I would like to go on with it." Believing that space was within its mission, the service was therefore determined to keep space research and development in its own laboratories.[142]

So, in addition to pressing its own claims in space, the Air Force disparaged the concept of a strong operational space agency within the OSD. Schriever argued that "any program to establish a separate astronautics management agency would result in duplication of capabilities already existing in the Air Force ballistic missile programs at a cost in funds and time similar to that already expended on these programs."[143] Schriever admitted under close questioning that he did support a central decision-making agency.

> If that is the way it is set up, I am all 100% for it. But if attempts are made to set up a procurement staff and do the contracting out of the Pentagon and set up a big technical staff there and make all the technical decisions, I say you are not going to set up a very good thing. The draft of ARPA that I have seen to date . . . does go to the point where they would set up their own labs, perhaps; they would set up their own procurement organization. This kind of an agency is what I am against. Now they may set it up.[144]

But a low-powered ARPA was only acceptable to the Air Force, not its preferred choice. White indicated a willingness to go along with the establishment of the ARPA with the proviso that "no matter who develops these things, the service that is going to use the end products should be cut in from the beginning."[145] And, he immediately added, the Air Force would be the primary user of such end products, since it utilized "everything that fits into our roles and missions, and in my opinion, almost everything in space does."[146] Once assured of major operating responsibility for military space exploitation, the Air Force came to accept the existence of a downgraded ARPA. Unlike the Army, the Air Force's future in space depended on a narrow definition of ARPA's functions. In its view, the agency ought to be limited to high-level decision-making, duly respectful of the Air Force's responsibility and capability for pursuing its roles and missions out into space.

Thus each of the services added its own evaluation of the space effort and organization which the DOD should adopt to that of the OSD. By the end of March, however, problems raised by the ambiguous powers of ARPA were further complicated by the President's advocacy of a civilian space agency to share responsibility with ARPA for the exploitation of space. The attitudes which the OSD and the individual services took toward the proposed NASA were derived from those which they had adopted toward the ARPA. Their new strategies, however, were more similar than the earlier ones. While disagreeing among themselves as to the organizational and budgetary support necessary for military exploitation of space, they were at least agreed upon the need for exploitation by the military establishment. Confronted with a civilian challenge to their freedom to determine what programs were to be considered militarily significant, the services closed ranks with the OSD. As the stalwart defender of the popular faith of national security, the military establishment used its substantial resources of power and influence to meet head on other political actors who doubted either the wisdom or the utility of turning space over to the generals.

### The Scientists

Sputnik both popularized and politicized science in America. The political generalists responsible for national policy-making had recognized in the scientific specialists the technical skills necessary to meet the current crisis and had called upon them to be the "saviors" of the nation. The scientists responded with uncertainty and ambivalence, and, unlike other political activists, remained essentially unsure of their strategy in space policy-making throughout the subsequent months. This conflict arose, in essence, because the scientists continued to be uncertain of their objectives even while their new political influence was on the rise.

Three important attributes characterize the scientists' political behavior throughout the months of policy hiatus. First, they were entering the political arena as only newly prestigious and relatively inexperienced participants. Second, they faced many unresolved questions in their relations with the federal government that they considered more fundamental than space. And, last, in contrast to their own view of the Sputnik crisis as a vehicle for the overall reconstruction of scientific relationships with government, their political hosts expected them to engage actively in policy-making for space. While these characteristics were common to the entire scientific community, as months passed shades of difference and of emphasis emerged among the scientists outside and within the federal government. These differences in turn did contribute to the policy product.

THE NONGOVERNMENTAL SCIENTISTS The scientists outside of government felt these pressures most acutely. During the period from November until April they displayed little urgent concern with the national space effort. This relative disengagement from the issue had two roots: the traditional insulation of the community from the political arena, only slowly modifying after Sputnik, and greater interest in other public policy issues concerning science. For these reasons the scientific community outside government assigned a relatively low priority to the immediate exploitation of space and displayed a marked reluctance to offer specific recommendations upon the organization of the space effort.

The first cause of the scientists' disassociation from policy-making for space lay in their reluctance to see science politicized. The weekly journal *Science* set the tone for most scientific journals when it editorialized in late November:

> Current emphasis on science in the thinking of... public leaders illustrates both a good trend and a bad habit. To have greater attention given to the welfare of science is good, but to have attitudes change so quickly and radically is a part of the inconsistent, on and off support that interferes seriously with steady scientific progress.[147]

In short, the scientists feared that the political weight attributed to space might drive the country into programs more massive than what they might consider professionally warranted.

Second, the scientists were more interested in other national scientific efforts than they were in space. The public statements of civilian, nongovernmental scientists in the months after Sputnik give a composite picture of this interest.[148] All expressed the basic conviction that the status of science and technology was a measure of social progress in the modern world; urged America to recognize Soviet scientific achievements; reiterated the crucial need for scientific breakthroughs and risk-taking if America were to gain in the cold war; and finally, entered a plea for American society to upgrade the status of the scientist. To these ends they urged basic reforms along a variety of fronts. They called for federal support of the educational system, both to make it more challenging in general and to increase the amount of scientific instruction in particular. They sought increased government support for basic research; greater recognition by the federal government of the scientific input in weapons development; better organization of military research and development programs; and greater mobilization of the nation's scientific capabilities for the national security effort. They recommended better working conditions for scientists in federally supported projects or government agencies, including more translation facilities, less restrictive contracting procedures, freer exchange of information with other scientists, and less stringent security measures.[149]

On these broad issues, the voices of the scientific community were loud and strong. There was, however, only passing reference to space and markedly little precise opinion in the public record concerning either the significance or the potential organization of the space effort—with the exception of a few proposals by particularly space-oriented scientific fraternities or organizations. When these did appear, furthermore, they supported the IGY view that the space effort should be directed toward what might be scientifically valuable.

In testimony before the Senate Preparedness Subcommittee, the star scientific attractions, Dr. Edward Teller and Dr. Vannevar Bush only mentioned in passing that space should be a specific arena of activity in an expanded scientific effort.[150] In two public speeches in January and February 1958, Dr. Isidor Rabi, the chairman of PSAC, while referring to the satellites as "an accomplishment...of utility,"[151] urged America not to allay its sense of urgency in general scientific progress because of the successful Explorer flight.[152] In discussing the organization of the scientific effort, various scientists such as Dr. Arthur Compton and Dr. Lee duBridge praised the Killian appointment, but did not assign him any particular role in organizing the space effort.[153] The major general scientific association to meet in the months following Sputnik II, the American Association for the Advancement of Science, made no mention of a space program in the report of its Parliament of Science, although most of its discussion was devoted to "science and public policy."[154]

In facing the specific problem of designing the nation's future space effort, proposals predominantly sprang from space-oriented professional organizations. There were five such public, unsolicited proposals for the organization and exploitation of space. These statements included a proposal for an Astronautics Research and Development Agency to control outer space development, presented to the president by the American Rocket Society on October 14, 1957; a petition in *The New York Times* on November 7 from the editors of *Missiles and Rockets* suggesting a National Advisory Committee on Astronautics; a proposal for the organization of a National Space Establishment submitted to Dr. Killian on November 21 by the Rocket and Satellite Research Panel of the National Academy of Sciences; a joint summary proposal of the American Rocket Society and Rocket and Satellite Research Panel issued on January 4, 1958; a statement by the National Society of Professional Engineers on February 13, recommending the establishment of a federal Space Exploration Commission; and finally, a statement by the Council of the Federation of American Scientists suggesting control of outer space by the AEC along the lines of a bill, S. 3117, currently sponsored by Senator Clinton Anderson.[155] Although varied in scope and organizational detail, each of these proposals suggested an independent, federal space agency or commission outside the DOD using either the NACA or the AEC as organizational models.

Both the American Rocket Society and the Rocket and Satellite Research Panel had initiated work on their proposals before October 4, and their combined proposal, supported as well by the National Academy of Science, is perhaps the most authoritative and specific of these markedly similar proposals. It argued "on the assumption that it is imperative that the U.S. establish and maintain scientific and technical leadership in outer space research in the interests of human progress and national survival," that there be created a national space flight program and a unified national space establishment to undertake the scientific exploration of space.[156] Its functions would be "to unify and greatly expand the national effort in outer space research and in the practical utilization of space capabilities specifically excluding space weapon development and military operations in space which are considered to be the responsibility of the DOD."[157] It was considered "strongly desirable that the National Space Establishment be given statutory status as an independent agency in order that its work ... be freely directed toward broad cultural, scientific, and commercial objectives ... [which] transcend the short-term, though vitally important military rocket missions of the DOD." The drafters emphasized that the NSE would not have defense missions, and that in the immediate future, DOD facilities and missile technology would be required to execute the mission of the NSE. It was specifically mentioned that the NSE be set up "in such a way that it enjoys the unqualified support of all three services ... Such a situation is believed to be possible only if the NSE is an independent agency from the outset—or if it is directly responsible only to the Secretary of Defense during its early years— with the clear prospect of independence at the earliest possible date."[158]

Thereafter, the proposal listed a timetable of space projects to be pursued in the subsequent decade, and outlined relatively explicitly the distinction between the missions of the NSE and the DOD in space. The only reference to future coordination between the two agencies was that there should be "clear channels for mutual cooperation ... in order to assure no jeopardy of short-term, vital military need on the one hand, and in order to assure maximum rate of advance of space research on the other."[159] Finally, the proposal concluded with emphasis upon the potential educational, cultural, and intellectual contribution of space research to the United States and the world. Space was depicted as an "endless frontier," offering meteorological, agricultural, communications, commercial, navigational, medical, and biological aids to man's life. Many would be of military value, but the sponsors argued that "their greater value [would] be to the civilian community at large."[160] "To use a homely example," it concluded, "the telephone is certainly a valuable military device, but its importance to the civilian population is vastly greater."

This proposal seems based upon two major assumptions: that the peaceful, civilian exploitation of space was of greater ultimate significance than military operations in the same area; and that military uses of outer space could be demarcated with relative clarity, thereby permitting streamlined civil-military liaison. The scientists definitely envisaged the NSE as the single agency in charge of overall planning and basic research for the national space effort, as well as being responsible for the development and operation of civilian missions in space.[161] On the other hand, the military was to develop space vehicles only for specific military requirements that would be proved feasible by the prior research efforts of the NSE. The proposal urged effective liaison between the military and the civilian agencies but offered no specific suggestions as to how this should be accomplished. By implication, a correct division of military and civilian functions in space would be based upon agreements between military and civilian scientists concerning what constituted military requirements.

This proposal had widespread support from the nongovernmental scientists who were interested in space. Of the thirteen scientists who specifically submitted their views on the organization of space to the Preparedness Subcommittee, ten of these either explicitly supported the NSE proposal or recommended that aspects of the missile as well as the space program be placed under such civilian control.[162] Nine of these ten, not surprisingly, were members of the Rocket and Satellite Research Panel.* The other three, Dr. Clark Millikan, George H. Clement, and Simon Ramo—all closely connected with the Air Force—recommended vesting control of space in a central organization within the DOD, or in one of the services, presumably the Air Force.

A second specific proposal on space came from the IGY. On February 14, 1958, the Technical Panel on the Earth Satellite program of the U.S. National Committee for the IGY submitted to the administration a plan for future American space efforts entitled "Basic Objectives of a Continuing Program of Scientific Research in Outer Space."[163] It focused exclusively upon the scientific returns to accrue from outer space and stressed the scientific dimension of space as the basic motivation for exploring this new frontier.

The IGY marks the beginning of man's exploration of outer space... The interests of human progress and our national wel-

---

*Among them Drs. William G. Dow, Krafft Ehricke, Leslie M. Jones, W. W. Kellogg, Myron H. Nicols, Marcus D. O'Day, William H. Pickering, N. W. Spender, and J. H. Allen.

fare now demand that a long-term program of space exploration be formulated and pursued by the U.S. with the utmost energy. Although there will inevitably be benefits from such a program of a very practical nature, *the basic goal must be the quest of knowledge about our solar system and the universe beyond.*[164]

The proposal suggested future projects in the fields of sounding rockets, earth satellites, lightweight satellite experiments, advanced satellite developments, lunar investigations, planetary and interplanetary investigations, and finally manned space flight. This effort was to be supported with due awareness that space technology would develop gradually; that initial payloads, distances, and scientific observations would be modest; and that manned space flight would be in the relatively distant future since it could "not now be very clearly justified on purely rational grounds."[165]

As participants in an unofficial, apolitical, international scientific alliance and common effort, the IGY Committee was perhaps obliged to discount the political repercussions of the space race—indeed, to discount the very existence of such a race. Yet more general principles were evident in its proposal. First—and most basically—scientific value judgments were to determine whether space projects rather than other scientific endeavors would be undertaken. Second, within the space program itself the maximization of scientific achievement would serve as the basis for selecting among possible projects. No other considerations were explicitly introduced as criteria for initiating either a space program or any specific project. And throughout the proposal there is no reference whatsoever to military uses of space, prestige purposes of space exploitation, or any specific treatment of commercial or civilian advantages to be gained from space exploration. This IGY model represented in the extreme the shared emphasis of the private scientific community upon the scientific nature of space exploration, rather than its political or military aspects.[166]

THE GOVERNMENT SCIENTISTS Like the scientific community at large, the great majority of government-employed scientists and those working in close advisory capacities, ranked space exploitation below other scientific activities and urged broad civilian control of whatever space effort was undertaken. The most notable dissenters from the assignment of a low priority to space were some, but by no means all, scientists in military employ and the German rocket scientists, whose zeal for space exploration had remained constant under Hitler, Truman, and Eisenhower alike. In general, however, these government officials, both out of professional bias and need to protect the overall scientific mission of the government, downgraded the space mission and attempted to dissuade other political actors within government from precipitating a crash program in space.

In the first few months of his tenancy in the White House, Dr. Killian made no specific public references to the space program. His mission was, in the short run, to unscramble the missile program, and in the longer run to "help the President follow through on the program of scientific improvement of our defenses" and to encourage proper government support for science and technology.[167] As the job evolved, his duties included overseeing various scientific panels of the PSAC, and presiding over a scientific board of review for planning decisions confronting the President.[168] Killian and the PSAC were to advise upon, coordinate, and expedite "problems of national policy involving science and technology" which ranged over a spectrum from federal support of scientific education to organization of military research and development policies. Charged with the task of presenting to the government the overall interests of science, space was only one of their major concerns.

Of the government scientists outside the White House, those within the military services were, not unnaturally, the most concerned with the space program. These men presented an interesting combination of service and military loyalties and professional scientific commitments in viewing the significance of the space effort and its potential organizational structure. In the cases of eleven scientists employed by the military services who answered specific questions before the Preparedness Subcommittee about possible organization of space, all favored centralized research and development efforts perceptibly more than the military spokesmen of their respective services.[169] Predictably, however, the Air Force scientists were less enthusiastic about centralized direction of the space effort than were scientists in the other services.

Like other members of the DOD, these eleven military scientists stressed the need to integrate scientific and military exploitation of space. They repeatedly cited Project Vanguard as an example of inefficient use of resources, stemming from an arbitrary divorce of military and scientific missions. At the same time, however, six of them argued that scientific exploitation of space was an urgent and necessary mission of government that would be best organized within the civilian branch of the government along the lines of the Rocket and Satellite Research Panel's proposal. Two of the six believed that such an organization should be first established within the DOD and later moved out into an independent agency, an alternative considered in the Rocket and Satellite Research Panel proposal and also supported by Drs. Hagen and von Braun.[170] In either case it seems that the scientists within the military establishment—more clearly than almost any other specialist group concerned with space—foresaw the necessity for an organizational solution which would structure space around interdependent but still distinct military and scientific missions.

Among the civilian agencies of government the AEC, NSF, and the NACA all professed interest in space. Immediately after Sputnik, some elements within the AEC considered that space might fall within the Commission's province since nuclear energy would be important in future rocket propulsion. In general, however, the AEC and the NSF were more concerned with the enhanced overall status of science within government, from which they would profit, than with acquiring the new space mission. They neither argued for a major government program in space nor publicly expressed views as to how a space program might be organized within the executive branch. The NACA, however, did see new agency programs arising from the space mission. The aerospace concept of a continuum of inter-related research had been operative in the Committee's planning for several years. At the point of diminishing returns in purely aeronautical research, NACA needed an expanded mission for organizational survival. Thus, through internal reorganization and by public advertisement, the committee sought to promote its own capabilities for the government's space effort.

On November 12 General James H. Doolittle, the chairman of NACA, announced the creation of a new Special Committee on Space Technology within NACA. With the appointment of this committee's chairman, Dr. H. Guyford Stever, Associate Dean of Engineering at MIT, on January 12, NACA's promotional campaign began in earnest. On January 16 NACA adopted a resolution "on the subject of space flight," asserting that NACA had within its broad original authority "investigation of problems *relating to flight in all its aspects outside of or within the earth's atmosphere,*" thereby including missiles, satellites, and outer space projectiles and vehicles as well as aircraft.[171] After outlining its work in space research since 1945, including the X-15 research airplane, and stressing that "the urgency of an adequate national program of research and development leading to manned satellites, lunar and interplanetary flight is now apparent," the resolution proposed that the national space effort could be "most rapidly, effectively, and efficiently implemented by the cooperative effort of the DOD, the NACA, the National Academy of Sciences, and the NSF."[172] The proposal vested research, development, and operational control of military missiles, satellites, and space vehicles in the DOD; authorized NACA to develop technical devices and conduct flights of additional vehicles and other operations for scientific research in space; and granted overall planning functions and assessment of research priorities to the NAS and the NSF.

On January 26 Dr. Hugh Dryden, the Director of NACA, expanded upon this proposal in a policy statement before the Institute for Aeronautical Sciences. After citing the alternative proposals for space organization, both civilian and military, he concluded:

> There is another solution to the problem of how best to administer the national space technology program, one which clearly recognizes the essential duality of our goals—the prompt and full exploitation of the potentials of flight into space for both scientific and military purposes. Actually this solution is old and well-tested. It is explicitly stated in the 1915 legislation that established the NACA with responsibility to "supervise and direct a scientific study of the problems of flight, with a view to their practical solution".... The Committee structure of the NACA embraces both the non-military and the military elements of aeronautics. The research of the NACA [is] designed to be useful to both the non-military and the military segments of aeronautics. The entire operation of the NACA is based upon the premise that coordinated teamwork effort by all parties concerned provides the surest guarantee of progress in aeronautics."[173]

If Dryden viewed NACA as eminently suited for the new space mission, he still believed that a major revamping of the agency was in order. He stressed the need for new research facilities, a larger staff, and expanded contracting authority. And, based upon years of experience in doing work with military services in aeronautics, he also was impressed with the need for military exploitation of space. The NACA proposal thus approached the position of civilian scientists in the military establishment in its recognition of the dualism involved in any space effort and its conviction that the military program should be well coordinated with the civilian. It also offered many of the features which the nongovernment scientists had valued in their various proposals: broad civilian control of the space effort, and an established channel through which scientific criteria could be used in determining the amount of resources allocated to space. As such, NACA was an obvious nucleus for a new space agency.

### The Congress

Like the administration, the Congress had a general responsibility for space policy. Within Congress, as within the executive branch, certain key partisan groups, committees, and individuals chose to view space policy from particular perspectives, aligning themselves with similar-minded elements within the executive branch or among the public. These coalitions emerged during the period of space policy hiatus with special strategies evolving out of the shared interests of the coalition members.

Nonetheless, in its general role Congress displayed a greater institutional interest in the establishment of NASA than the modern Congress conventionally reveals in policy initiation. As time passed, a congressional, as distinct from an administration, policy for space emerged, different in philosophy and tone, which overrode the more limited aims of the internal cliques and confronted the executive directly on many points. All major congressional leaders came to share in a process of heightened deliberation and creative program-building not typically found in contemporary legislating.

PRESESSION SPACE POLITICS    The initial efforts at semi-independent congressional policy-making occurred shortly after Sputnik II. The moderate Democrats led by Johnson and Rayburn, although lacking a comprehensive legislative program of their own, saw themselves as the protectors of national security. Believing the administration slow and cautious, they were prepared upon almost any aspect of the space issue to go beyond the administration proposal.

While the administration worked on its legislative proposal, Johnson gradually built a congressional coalition both willing and able to engage in at least quasi-independent policy-making. To do so, Johnson fought a determined battle against the partisan Democrats' strategy of unrestrained criticism and sought instead to push the administration into greater action.[174] The two Texans' major point was that the country lacked leadership and that the Democrats would provide it, whether or not the administration went along.[175] It was this theme that dominated the conduct of the Preparedness Subcommittee hearings and motivated Johnson's frequent proposals for improving the nation's national security posture. By concentrating upon such a forward-looking strategy, Johnson alternatively ignored and disparaged the arrant partisanship of both liberal Democrats and conservative Republicans. Although unable to divest the space issue of all partisan overtones, it was he more than anyone else in government who raised the space issue to a level of truly national debate, a level at which the Eisenhower administration remained implicitly, if not explicitly, on the defensive.

By contrast, the more moderate Republicans and Republicans interested in military affairs took the tack that the entire country must support Eisenhower in a national program to meet the Soviet challenge in space. This strategy, however, was complementary to that of the moderate Democrats: it required both prodding the administration into more decisive action and cooperation with the Johnson-Rayburn branch of the Democratic party in Congress. Like Nixon, this group called for a bipartisan review of defense policy, expressing concern with the rate of scientific and technological progress and emphasizing the need for coordination in the satellite and missile programs. Senator Styles Bridges, emerging as the major spokesman for this group, voiced the opinion that Congress would appropriate whatever was necessary for the defense effort, and that missiles and satellites deserved the highest priority effort the government could provide.[176]

Thus both their congressional and partisan roles impelled these Republicans to take their critical stance. When the strategy of the moderate Democrats emerged as the dominant strategy of the session, it was in the interest of moderate Republicans to go along in order to limit as much as possible the freedom with which Johnson could appear as the defender of national security.

This coalition chose the Preparedness Subcommittee Hearings as the specific instrument by which Congress initially joined the space policy-making process. The "Inquiry into Missiles and Satellites" was itself a broad examination of the defense posture of the United States, not directly focused upon the space program. Yet in reviewing past and ongoing space projects, the Preparedness Subcommittee (hereinafter referred to as the committee) came to certain conclusions that would later enjoy broad congressional support and that had important impact on the organization and magnitude of the future program. The issues on which the committee concentrated its criticisms of the then-current administration program became guidelines for the emerging congressional position.

From the outset, the committee fulfilled its constitutional function as overseer of the administration, with stress upon institutional rather than partisan criticism. "It is," Johnson explained, "not important what kind of a record we make for an election if circumstances are such that we do not have any more elections. That could easily happen if we spend our time eating each other up."[177] Throughout the proceedings Chairman Johnson sought and eventually attained unanimous findings to comprise a truly bipartisan report in the face of what the committee considered a genuine national peril.

United in this evaluation, the members were determined to "find the facts and see what the Senate can do to help out."[178] Johnson's opening statement on November 25 set the tone of the deliberations:

> Our country is disturbed over the tremendous military and scientific achievements of Russia. Our people have believed that in the field of scientific weapons and in technology and science that we were well ahead of Russia .... It would appear we have slipped dangerously behind ... in some very important fields. But the Committee is not rendering any final judgments

in advance of the evidence on why we slipped or what should be done about it. Our goal is to find out what is to be done.[179]

Given its oversight function, pessimism characterized the committee's basic assumptions. Questions and comments in open testimony indicate the Senators believed that the Soviet Union was close to an operational ICBM capability. They believed, too, that America was behind the Russians in the development of space weapon systems, and that America would need to undertake a vigorous program to regain a balance of power in space.

In the course of a thorough inquiry, these beliefs seemed to find expert substantiation. From November 25 until January 23 approximately seventy witnesses appeared before the committee in both public and executive sessions; questionnaires were circulated to almost two hundred individual organizations, scientists, engineers, educators, and industrialists; and the total printed testimony ran to more than seven thousand pages.[180] Inevitably, in this broad effort, the space program came under scrutiny.

One set of problems which the committee considered was the overall coordination of the missile and satellite program. Johnson, Stennis, and Bridges were especially concerned with this issue; Stennis inquired repeatedly whether there should not be some single individual who could make binding decisions upon the DOD and the Budget Bureau in the satellite and missile field. The committee found the chain of command in the missile program confusing and Killian's role ambiguous. When informed that Killian was primarily an adviser, it expressed disappointment that he did not have control over the entire satellite and missile effort.[181] Although it did not favor either military or civilian organization in its January report, the committee did urge a centralized locus of responsibility for space. Senator Kefauver was perhaps most articulate on the organizational issue, arguing that the DOD's dominance in space development would, in effect, exclude substantial scientific research—an activity he considered exceedingly valuable. In the hearings, Kefauver favored a Secretary of Science to coordinate such nonmilitary applications of space. Although this alternative never won wide support, it did identify the need for a coordinating mechanism to mesh military and nonmilitary space projects—a problem which neither the scientists nor important members of the administration had yet directly faced.

These deliberations about space were always set, however, in the broader context of national defense policy. In the hearings, the Senators concentrated chiefly on the DOD's effort. As the inquiry wore on, they became critical of the Department's competence in scientific research and development. In this context, the committee criticized the department's organizational arrangements for the missile and satellite programs; its estimates of the existing military situation; and its failure to anticipate the space challenge. It dealt with particular harshness with Quarles and Holaday, responsible officials before the Sputnik crisis. Chief Counsel Edward Weisl and Senator Johnson were brusque in their questioning of both men and emphatic in their belief that the officials lacked a real sense of urgency. After a particularly acid review of Quarles' speech to the U.S. Conference of Mayors, in which Quarles argued that the Soviet Union did not have an operational ICBM capability and that its satellites had not been of military significance, Johnson remarked:

> If that is your idea of a speech that is calculated to arouse people ... to spur them to expedite the existing program, to chart new courses, to outline new goals, to regain a superiority that has been lost ... then your evaluation of the effect of the speech is different from mine .... There is a great feeling, I think, in the committee and in the country that there has been nobody in a real hurry about this whole situation and there has been a lot of public officials who have been making statements which are calculated to laugh the whole thing off.[182]

Never losing this suspicion of the DOD, the subcommittee came to feel that the OSD was less concerned about space than the Congress, some scientists, some service representatives, and the public.* Nor did the committee conclude that the department had sufficient appreciation of the value of scientific research. It exhaustively reviewed the present satellite program; then expressed shock, consternation, and incredulity about the whole affair. In particular, it disapproved of the department's refusal to recognize the propaganda value of satellites by failing to authorize Project Explorer after September 1956.[183] To the Senators, the current satellite effort seemed "relatively small ... relatively unsuccessful, and certainly late."[184] To the committee, the Vanguard decision and its dismal aftermath underscored the danger of assigning low priority to scientific, in contrast to military, research and development, and of making decisions on the basis of service rivalries. To the members, the need for new arrangements for advanced research and development was clear.

---

*Indeed, this conviction led to a game of "can you top this" between Weisl and Quarles:

WEISL:    I know that the members of the Committee, after hearing the evidence that we have heard, are tremendously aroused over the potential threat.

QUARLES:  I doubt that any member of the Committee is any more aroused about the threat than I am, Mr. Counsel.

WEISL:    And we feel that the public must be aroused ... so that they will make the sacrifice ... necessary to meet that danger.

As a consequence of committee skepticism of the civilian OSD leadership, its members gave special weight to the opinions of representatives of the scientific and military communities who favored a more urgent effort. These witnesses possessed the expertise necessary to meet the crisis and they seemed natural partners for the congressmen. The committee displayed marked deference to the scientific witnesses. It praised the loyalty and contributions of Teller, Bush, von Braun, and Van Allen and reiterated the legislative intent to expand research facilities and resources.[185] The committee also paid its respects to military men who might oppose the official OSD posture.

Halfway into the hearings the retirement of General Gavin seemed to provide a dramatic substantiation of the committee's fears. Gavin was popular with the committee, which openly admired his tenacity in pushing Project Explorer in the face of OSD opposition and his general espousal of scientific research and development as a crucial factor in military preparedness. After his initial testimony on December 13, Johnson commented, "You talk like the kind of fellow that I have been looking for ever since we started these hearings, and that is a fellow who thinks that things can be done perhaps a little bit faster and perhaps a little bit better.... [I am not convinced that] the higher echelons are what I call can-do fellows."[186] At the end of the day, after Gavin had recounted rather vividly the fate of Project Explorer, the need for drastic reorganization of the DOD, and his own fear of the consequences if America continued to ignore space, Johnson and the other members were clearly impressed.

Accordingly, Gavin's announced retirement in late December gravely disturbed committee members, who suspected "administration rubber-hose tactics" might have forced him to resign. When Gavin reappeared before the committee on January 6, he reiterated that he could not support the Army research and development budget and intimated that his chances for assuming a choice command had been denied because of his earlier outspoken testimony. When he bluntly acknowledged that he preferred to retire rather than mislead Congress, Johnson exploded.

General, I just think this is a horrible situation. I am surprised that it exists.... I do not think there has been a time in the 26 years that I have been in Congress when we needed men of your capacity, your experience, and your foresight as much as

QUARLES:   I have just stated that I was at least as aroused as any member
                     of the Committee, Mr. Counsel...
WEISL:   I can assure you that the Committee is—
QUARLES:   Pretty aroused.
WEISL:   Very aroused.

we need them now. We are trying to get to the bottom of this thing. . . . We are concerned; the people are concerned. We want leaders whom we can trust and who will speak frankly, and whose only language is the language of candor. We think you are one of them . . . I hope, General, that you will reconsider because I do not want an Army or a Navy that is made up of just a group of yes men. I think that that is just what we will get if you come up here and put it on the line as you see it and then resign.[187]

Clearly the Gavin resignation further persuaded the Senators that the Administration underestimated the crisis, and made them even more determined to correct the situation.

When the unanimous report was issued, three important themes appeared to form the basis for future Congressional action. First, the Senators were clearly convinced space exploration was an important national objective. Second, they were prepared to consider radical organizational changes, urging that the administration "accelerate and expand Research and Development programs, providing funding on a long-term basis, and improve control and administration within the DOD or through the establishment of an independent agency."[188] Finally, by emphasizing how critical was the situation and the administration's apparent inability to meet it, the Preparedness Subcommittee declared Congress' willingness to embark upon an independent course to assure a greater space effort.


THE LEADERSHIP OF SENATOR JOHNSON   As the Preparedness Subcommittee's hearings ended, it was apparent that Lyndon Johnson's early strategies were bearing fruit. Partisan controversy had been minimized and semiautonomous Congressional participation in the policy-making process secured. As the new Congressional session opened in January, Johnson maintained his bipartisan coalition and urged the administration to work closely and informally with a Democratic-led Congress.

That Johnson believed this course of bi-partisan prodding would lead to the best attainable defense posture is unquestionable. In addition, however, he had tremendous personal investment in such statesmanlike behavior. His recognition of the significance of space for him had, if anything, increased since October 4, and he was determined to pursue the course of action he had embarked upon in the Preparedness Subcommittee hearings. In tours across the country he outlined a massive civil and military space program under a new independent space agency; called for increased missile production of such magnitude as to delight the Army and the Air Force and appall the comptroller general of the DOD; and advocated a space effort under the United Nations to conquer the new frontier for purely peaceful purposes.[189]

The Majority Leader also delivered his own "private State of the Union Message" to the Democratic Party caucus two days before the President's. It was no ordinary review of a committee's findings by its chairman nor an ordinary catalog of problems delivered off the cuff by the Majority Leader to his party. Rather, it was a careful, solemn and eloquent document—widely distributed to the press before its presentation—outlining a long list of popular objectives befitting—as reporters were quick to note—a presidential candidate. It was, in short, Johnson's move to the center of the political arena— a warning, in James Reston's view, that the governments of the Soviet Union and the United States would now have to prepare themselves to deal with Texas.[190]

This document—an extraordinary one in American political annals—reveals much of the future character of the legislative process affecting space. That Johnson made such a speech at all indicates the degree of congressional initiative he intended to extract from his colleagues. The contents further suggest the great significance which Johnson, and the Congress which he led, attached to space. Finally, the speech was dramatic confirmation of the individual leadership of the Senator in this area.

Johnson's substantive argument was a simple one. In his mind the exploitation of space by selfish men, e.g., the Soviet Union, was the gravest threat facing the world. By contrast, its exploitation by those devoted to freedom, e.g., the United States or its allies, could both alter the face of the earth and liberate it from all potential enemies. Thus, the major task of the session was to devise an organizational structure and a substantive program which would assure American superiority in space: an incomparable opportunity to save the nation and the world.

Charged with such a task, Johnson recommended several lines of attack. First, he urged that the United States revise its previously low estimation of the significance of space. Second, he made the expansion of America's scientific capability a first aim of national policy—by aid to education, support of basic research, and increased military investment in advanced research and development. Third, he urged that scientists manage the space program, since "from the evidence accumulated, we do know the evaluation of the importance of control of outer space made by the United States has not been based upon the judgment of men most qualified to make such an appraisal."[191] Fourth, he wanted the United States in a position of unquestioned domination of space. "There is something more important," he argued, "than any ultimate weapon; that is, the ultimate position . . . of total control over earth [which] lies somewhere out in space."[192] This effort would entail development of a missile capability, but would extend far beyond it. More significant, however, was that such military domination would provide, for the first time in history, an alternative to war, and make total security possible. Finally, Johnson called for a new advanced weapons and space agency outside the DOD, on the model of the AEC. Only such a structure, under a President who recognized the significance of outer space for America, could coordinate and maintain a top-priority space program.

The political repercussions of this "message" were immediate and far-reaching. It was clear that Johnson, for his own and his country's welfare, would press for a major space effort. How far he would pursue this goal within his self-imposed confines of positive cooperation with the administration remained an open question. Two facts were certain: he would await the initial suggestions of the administration in order to build upon them according to his evaluation of their merit. And he would be a potent ally for any other official or group who wished a greatly expanded program in scientific and military exploitation of outer space.

There was nothing parochial in Johnson's position. Unlike military spokesmen or scientists, he was vitally concerned with both aspects of space exploitation. He delved deeply into the substance of the program as he sought to shape its future form. The result of his effort was to establish his own interests and those of the Congress at a level of importance rarely seen in the process of policy-making in a modern state.

Johnson was not the only congressional figure with a role to play in the space issue. House Majority Leader John McCormack emerged as a secondary power in the legislative process. His concern with space stemmed from a long-time personal interest in scientific progress and in science-based industry such as that surrounding his home district in Boston. He had been involved with governmental scientific development since he served as a Congressional watch-dog for the Manhattan Project in World War II. He felt close personally to MIT and to its former President, Dr. Killian. He thus was instinctively sympathetic to the efforts of the President's new special assistant. McCormack's behavior in the legislative process concerning space was more conventionally bipartisan than Johnson's. While perhaps as interested in space as the Senator, he acted more to expedite policy than to initiate it, and was in general willing to accept administration leads.

Finally, although no other members of Congress were so crucially concerned with space as Johnson and McCormack, a variety of proposals for space policy were introduced during the initial months of the session. The most significant of these supported federal aid for education, new governmental organization of the scientific effort, and reorganization of the DOD. Others specifically dealt with space. Prior to the submission of the administration's space bill, the bills reflected particular authors' interests, whims, and loyalties. Senator Anderson and Representatives Holifield and Durham, for example, all members of the Joint Committee on Atomic Energy, introduced similar bills amending the Atomic Energy Act of 1954 to develop outer space through the peaceful application of atomic energy.[193] Other Democratic congressmen suggested that independent commissions be established to organize the space effort.[194] Three bills were introduced by Republicans building an outer space agency upon NACA by amending the Act of 1915 and expanding NACA's mission.[195] Finally, Representative Keating introduced a concurrent resolution expressing the sense of Congress that the United States take the lead in efforts to gain an international agreement that outer space be devoted to peaceful purposes.[196]

As opposed to this scattering of bills, Johnson waited until the administration proposal was in before he chose to act. Giving no backing to any, he preferred to place the administration's legislation under severe congressional scrutiny. At the same time, Johnson exerted such influence over the administration and the rest of Congress that his views of the important issues in any impending space effort would set the agenda for this congressional policy-making.

ORGANIZING CONGRESS FOR SPACE   One further sign of the exceptional pattern of congressional activity was that body's special internal attempts to handle the new issue. Ordinarily, space legislation would be referred to existing committees according to the content of the particular bill. Now proposals appeared to grant jurisdiction in space to the Joint Committee on Atomic Energy; to create a joint Committee on Outer Space; and to establish separate House and Senate Standing Committees on space. An initial move was made by the Joint Committee on Atomic Energy when Carl Durham, its chairman, announced the establishment of a Special Subcommittee on Outer Space Propulsion, with Senator Anderson as chairman.[197] After a certain amount of negotiating over conflicting jurisdictions, Johnson, with Senator Knowland's support, introduced a resolution prepared by the Preparedness Subcommittee creating a Special Committee on Space and Astronautics to frame legislation for a national space program.[198]

The resolution passed the Senate on February 6 and the committee was "authorized and directed to conduct a thorough and complete study and investigation with respect to all aspects and problems relating to the exploration of outer space and the control, development and use of astronautical resources, personnel, equipment and facilities."[199] It consisted of seven Democrats and six Republicans, a blue-ribbon group which included eleven ranking members of the six standing committees whose fields of jurisdiction space might affect. The committee was considered so prestigious that the Senate leadership invoked the seniority rule to select its members: Bridges, the ranking member of the Appropriations Committee; Russell and Saltonstall, the chairman and ranking member of the Armed Services Committee; Anderson and Hickenlooper, the vice-chairman and ranking Senator of the Joint Committee on Atomic Energy; Green and Wiley, chairman and ranking member of the Foreign Relations Committee; McClellen and Mundt, chairman and ranking member of the Committee on Government Operations; Magnuson and Bricker, chairman and ranking member of the Interstate and Foreign Commerce Committee; Symington, a member of the Armed Services and Government Operations Committees who, although outranked on both, was selected on the basis of his wide experience in government; and Johnson, who had introduced the resolution and thereby traditionally qualified for selection. On February 20 Johnson was elected chairman.

This committee was especially qualified to execute Johnson's space policy. As a function of their status, its members were relatively autonomous political powers. Many had gained experience in the Preparedness Subcommittee hearings. Johnson himself chaired the group, thus guaranteeing the bipartisan, strongly congressional quality which had characterized his efforts throughout the year of the Sputnik.

Reflecting a certain amount of rivalry between the two chambers, the House leadership soon set up a parallel group. At the suggestion of Representative Vinson, Chairman of the Armed Services Committee, Overton Brooks introduced a resolution to create a select committee on space on February 11. The leadership of both parties supported this resolution at first, but later the measure was withdrawn in favor of one introduced on March 5 by McCormack.[200] This new solution permitted McCormack rather than Brooks to assume the chairmanship, an unusual provision since a House Majority Leader does not normally chair a committee. The House, however, sought an eminent spokesman on a par with Johnson to give added dignity to the new committee. Like the Senate, the House established a thirteen-member select committee to be chosen by the party leaders. In contrast to the Senate measure, however, which had established membership "on the principle of representation from specified committees with related interests," no such formal provision was made in the House resolution.[201] Joseph Martin, the Minority Leader, was appointed. Some members were chosen because of prior committee assignments: Brooks and Arends from the Armed Services Committee; Natcher and Ford from Appropriations; Hays and Fulton from Foreign Affairs; and O'Brien from Interstate and Foreign Commerce. Keating, Metcalf, Sisk, and McDonough were the other members.[202]

Besides these organizational moves, the Congress passed on February 12 PL 85-325, enabling the DOD to pursue basic and applied and research development for military requirements and authorizing the DOD to undertake, for one year, any advanced space projects designated by the President.[203] In effect, this law established the ARPA to pursue the ongoing nonmilitary space program until Congress made more permanent organizational arrangements. On the previous day the Supplemental Defense Appropriations Act of 1958 had appropriated funds for such activities.[204]

Thus, Congress indicated a broad concern with the organization of the space program. First, in setting up special committees to study the space effort, the houses of Congress were delineating a new area of congressional activity — a step not taken lightly in the national legislature, where new missions are more typically handled in old structures. Second, the specific authorizations of acceleration in the present space effort were tentative ones: signaling the congressional expectation that a new approach to space would soon be forthcoming. Third, Congress had, in effect, indicated that at least a portion of the space effort would be in civilian hands. There were no serious proposals to organize the entire space program under the DOD or to place congressional review of space in the Armed Services Committees. Indeed, by permitting ARPA responsibility for civilian space programs for only one year, Congress indicated its unwillingness to give the military an unlimited mandate in space.

Most important of all, these first steps made clear that Congress gave high priority to the future space program and its organization. Neither defensive nor moderate in its attitude toward space, disposed to push both civilian and military programs, Congress wanted a major space effort. It exerted its own authority in expressing these views, making it clear that the final space program would be a joint executive-legislative effort.

Like other participants in the formulation of space policy, Congress remained dependent upon the President to show his hand. With the scientists and the military spokesmen, the legislative branch required a focal point for its positions. Now having established its preferences and objectives, the leadership in Congress awaited the administration bill before making its final round of strategic choices.

## Presidential Choice: The Drafting of the Bill

The administration chose a visible, substantial response to Sputnik: the establishment of a high-level agency with a clear mandate to pursue broad programs of exploration and development in space. The bill submitted by the President proposed an independent civilian space agency under a single administrator, charged with the direction of basic research and nonmilitary projects in outer space. It was faithful in its provisions to Eisenhower's earliest reactions to the challenge in space, primarily his insistence upon civilian control for nonmilitary space programs.[205] It reflected, too, the aims and preferences of three special groups of influentials who came to dominate the drafting process.

That process, which began in the executive office just after the launching of Sputnik II, was a relatively secretive one. It initially involved officials from the White House, particularly from PSAC and Killian's office. Later it included the Bureau of the Budget and NACA, upon which the new agency was built.

The Killian appointment and the reconstitution of PSAC in the White House offices during November precipitated discussion about the form of the future space program. This initial evaluation lasted throughout November and into December. "As soon as the outlines of an expanded and accelerated space program emerged from the deliberations," the White House agreed that civilian and military aspects of space exploitation should be given organizational recognition in two separate agencies.[206]

The original suggestion to place the civilian and scientific space missions within an enlarged NACA and to permit continued DOD participation in military space programs appeared to come from NACA and from the Space Sciences Panel of the PSAC, the advisory group given primary responsibility for considering the new mission.* By January this proposal was the accepted position of the PSAC.[207] Given this decision, in late December Killian, in his dual capacity as chairman of PSAC and Special Assistant to the President, approached the Director of the Bureau of the Budget, asking that the bureau undertake organizational and administrative planning for the space program.†

---

*A source within PSAC cites Dr. James Fisk, a member of the panel, as the originator of the proposal.

†The Bureau of the Budget is statutorily charged by the Budget and Accounting Act of 1921 with responsibility for evolving and overseeing the organization of governmental activities. Thus, it was standard procedure for Killian to request assistance from the Bureau's Office of Management and Organization in establishing this new administrative structure.

Concurrent with the discussions within the PSAC, NACA initiated its public campaign for the space mission.[208] NACA itself did not participate in the PSAC's original consultations, but its chairman, Dr. James H. Doolittle, was a member of the PSAC during this period. NACA also made recommendations to the White House[209] at this time, and while NACA officials were not themselves involved in the final decision, certainly the administration was made aware of their preferences.

Thus, by the end of January, the group of scientific advisers whom Eisenhower had charged with designing a space program and the agency's leadership were agreed that NACA would be the base on which NASA would be built. The Bureau of the Budget, partly guided by Killian's report of PSAC's deliberations, reached the same conclusion. Rapidly a consensus emerged from separate appraisals of a rather complicated administrative problem, suggesting a high community of interests.

The interests were overlapping—but not identical. PSAC, vocally representing the interests of the scientific community, sought a primarily civilian structure in which basic research and important peaceful space missions could be pursued free from military control. NACA provided such a structure. Furthermore, NACA's ongoing nucleus of research facilities and staff could be expanded at a rate which the scientific advisers considered consistent with the overall scientific interests of the government.

PSAC's organizational preferences stemmed from that body's conception of the substantive space program. These guidelines—as later outlined in the Purcell Committee's report, "An Introduction to Outer Space"—identified four major factors which made the advancement of space technology imperative: "the compelling urge of man to explore and to discover"; defense objectives; national prestige; and new opportunities for scientific observation and experiment.[210] Of these four, the committee was primarily concerned with scientific inquiry, outlining a variety of research purposes for scientific satellites. It argued that in the past pure research had a "remarkable way of paying off" and that, while it could not predict the future utility of space ventures, the "scientific questions come first."[211]

Furthermore, the committee was skeptical about the potential military uses of outer space.

Much has been written about space as a future theater of war, raising such suggestions as satellite bombers, military bases on the moon and so on . . . for the most part, even the more sober proposals do not hold up well on close examination, or appear to be achievable at an early date . . . . In short, the earth would appear to be, after all, the best weapons carrier.[212]

With such emphasis on civilian space activities as a part of a total scientific program, building NASA around NACA seemed to PSAC the "natural" organizational solution.

On NACA's part, interests of organizational survival coincided with a substantive outlook similar to that of PSAC.[213] NACA acknowledged the importance of military objectives in space more readily than PSAC, but NACA spokesmen concurred that civilian and scientific objectives might well be subordinated in a military agency. Thus NACA favored separating civilian from military exploitation of space, viewing this two-space-agencies solution as parallel to the dual NACA–DOD structure which had supported aeronautical technology for forty years.

Finally, the Bureau of the Budget viewed NACA as an administratively neat solution by its own special criteria. The bureau as a rule does not enjoy creating new executive agencies, on the theory that current administrative resources should be utilized for new missions if at all possible. In Director Maurice Stans's words:

> Retrospectively, a major objective of the legislation was to build upon existing institutions and to avoid increasing the total number of Federal Agencies involved in aeronautical and space matters .... The bill accomplishes this aim by utilizing the NACA as the nucleus of the new agency.[214]

Thus, the upgrading of NACA offered an efficient and economic administrative arrangement.

Initially, the bureau expressed some difficulty in designing the structure for a new space program by conventional organization and management principles. Associate Director William Finan believed that the management planners had "read too much, or perhaps too little, science fiction in the past ... and that it required the applications of a special mental discipline to be sure that they were planning for the organization and administration of the program being officially conceived and not for the even more fantastic projects being speculated about in public."[215] When Killian specifically requested aid in drawing up the bill, however, the bureau had an opportunity to include its favorite tenets of streamlined administrative management.

Thus, by February 4, when Eisenhower publicly announced the establishment of the Purcell Committee and charged it with delineating America's future space program, the Executive Office had already agreed that a new civilian space agency would be built upon the NACA structure.[216] Thereafter, the drafting process proceeded with an increasing sense of urgency. Public and governmental uncertainties about the management of the space mission were rising, and the President was eager to send a bill up before

the Easter recess, eliminating any further opportunity for independent congressional space policy-making. Work on the legislation
was thus done under "crash" conditions by a selected and limited
group of policy makers in Killian's office, the NACA, and the Bureau
of the Budget.

The actual drafting committee met first in late January or early
February. The men worked under the overall aegis of the bureau's
Division of Organization and Management and consisted of William
Finan, the Assistant Director in charge of that division; Alan Dean,
one of its senior staff members; Paul Dembling, the legal counsel to
NACA; S. Paul Johnston, Director of the Institute of the Aeronautical
Sciences and temporarily a member of Killian's staff who also served
as staff for the Purcell Committee; and finally, Kenneth McClure,
assistant counsel to the Department of Commerce on loan to the
bureau.

The Bureau of the Budget took overall charge of evolving the
draft legislation. Killian had frequent contact with Budget Director
Brundage and Finan, as well as direct access to the drafting process
through Johnston. Killian took an active interest in the proceedings,
and one can best define this "Administration Bill" as Killian's bill in
his capacity as Eisenhower's personal adviser. Killian also was the
first agent of the administration to mobilize congressional support
for the legislation through several private discussions with House
Majority Leader McCormack with whom he remembered establishing a "heartening relationship."[217] PSAC also participated
in that the Space Sciences Panel of PSAC saw various drafts of the
bill as it evolved.

NACA's views were also well represented to the drafting committee. Director Dryden had three or four discussions with Finan,
and additional ones with Killian and Brundage. Dembling also
provided a channel of communication between NACA and the
drafting committee.[218]

Out of this convergence of interests, the administration's draft
of the National Aeronautics and Space Act of 1958 reflected consensus in general policy objectives and a special blending of particular philosophies and preferences in the detailed organizational provisions. The bill provided for "the solution of problems
of flight within and outside the earth's atmosphere and . . . for the
development, testing and operation for research purposes, of
aircraft, missiles, satellites and other space vehicles."[219] Such
activities were to be directed by a civilian agency "exercising
control over aeronautical and space research sponsored by the U.S.
except insofar as such activities may be peculiar to or primarily associated with weapons systems or military operations, in which case the
agency may act in cooperation with, or on behalf of the DOD."[220]

Below this level of generality, PSAC and Killian abandoned the long-standing preference of the scientific community for a multi-member, executive unit composed of private citizens with professional scientific backgrounds, thus breaking sharply from the pattern established in NACA, the AEC, and the NSF. The spokesmen for professional science had come to value the administrative pattern which the Bureau of the Budget had long espoused as a basic principle of public administration: the single-executive structure which placed reliance on generalized administrative competence and limited the plural-member, specialized body to an advisory role.

Thus, major operating authority in the new agency would be vested in the director, appointed by the President with the advice and consent of the Senate. He would control the shaping of the research program, the construction and management of facilities, and the establishment of the contract provisions for private enterprise. Such an administrative structure would be most amenable to clear executive coordination and control, thereby avoiding the pitfalls of vested interests, potential military domination, or powerful Congressional alliances which a more autonomous administrative structure might induce.

The National Aeronautics and Space Board was to consist of not more than seventeen members, of whom not more than eight would be from appropriate departments or agencies of the government, including at least one from the DOD. The others would be eminent private citizens. The board's role was to advise the President and the director—later the administrator—of the agency on government policies and programs in space. It would be consulted by the director prior to initiation or substantial modification of policies or programs.

Two other principles long favored by public management experts in the bureau were also incorporated. The drafters relied on administrative flexibility and interagency cooperation in place of detailed prescriptions to set the boundaries of agency operations. In the first instance, the enabling language was general, since the character of the space mission was so relatively unknown. Relatively unfettered executive discretion would permit the President and the director to continue to shape the substance of the space effort. Second, interagency coordination was to be secured through regular channels of the executive branch: the legislation avoided statutory liaison committees or specific designations of membership on the advisory board.

In short, the liaison process was to continue the informal relations with the DOD, NSF, AEC, Weather Bureau, and Department of State that NACA had previously established with considerable success. Where working-level liaison and joint participation in space projects broke down, the President would resolve disputes and ultimately determine overall national space policy. Thus NASA emerged not as an overall national policy-making agency for outer space activities but rather as a regular arm of the executive branch specifically devoted to pursuing basic research in space sciences, performing space experiments in conjunction with other government agencies, and cooperating with the military establishment in research and development of military interest.[221]

These concepts were supported both by NACA and PSAC, for they confirmed the old agency's working experience and appealed to the scientists as logical extensions of their basic aims. But the Budget Bureau provided the rationale for the arrangements. To Finan, the working group had a priceless opportunity to write a "kitchen stove kind of bill" based on optimal administrative theory, complete with such heretofore exotic touches as exemption from Civil Service classification requirements for scientific personnel and an extremely liberal patent policy.[222] This sort of design for NASA, the Budget Bureau felt, could both assure a superior American space program and provide a model agency which conformed to the purest tenets of administrative theory.

As for the specific relations between military and civilian space activities, the draft was almost cryptic—understandably so, given its basic tenets. There was enabling language included for DOD activities but, on the assumption that these projects could be clearly delineated, no specific liaison structure was proposed. In case of controversy the President would be the final authority.[223] Similarly, no specific references to other agencies appeared. The drafters considered it unnecessary, for example, to state that NASA should cooperate with the State Department to assure peaceful utilization of space or with the AEC to foster development of nuclear propulsion for outer space vehicles. A "straight line" operation required, especially in the Budget Bureau's view, no special statutory language to confirm the natural workings of the executive establishment and the plenary powers of the President.

Reasoned and reasonable as the administration's bill may have seemed, however, it remained the product of a limited group of congenial interests. Neither the State Department nor the Weather Bureau was consulted,[224] though each had a role to play in future space programs. More important, the military establishment was, for the most part, bypassed. A few individuals from DOD did participate: General Schriever had a discussion with PSAC scientists during January or February in which scientific exploitation of space was the sole topic; Dr. Herbert York in his capacity as a member of the PSAC Space Sciences Panel "sat in on many arguments" about the organization of the new agency before his appointment in February to the DOD as chief scientist of ARPA.[225] But no ARPA, Army, or Navy personnel were included. Instead, they heard "rumors" that a civilian agency was to be built upon NACA.[226]

To Executive Office personnel, these omissions appeared natural ones, for they assumed a relatively limited and clearly defined military space mission. Moreover, the military establishment may have inadvertently encouraged the deemphasis on liaison arrangements. As Roy Johnson noted later in May:

> Within the DOD, up until just recently, there was a feeling that [the new agency] was basically an extension of the relationship with NACA as it existed in the past and there was not much concern about the language [of the bill] or the change in relationship as I interpreted it.[227]

Nonetheless, what the narrowly based drafting group gained in initial unanimity, it paid for in later criticism and conflict. In early March the completed bill cleared the President's Advisory Committee on Government Organization. Dryden reviewed it for a week and suggested some changes, and then the Bureau of the Budget began the normal process of interagency clearance. Compared to the usual procedure, the period of circulation was short, lasting from the afternoon of Thursday, March 27, until noon on Monday, March 31, although the bureau accepted additional comments through April 1. The bureau took the position that those departments with a substantial interest were already familiar with the major provisions of the bill and thus were expected to keep their comments to a minimum.[228]

The bureau's expectations were not fulfilled. DOD, the State Department, the Weather Bureau and a few other agencies protested the short time period in which they had to comment. The general counsel's office, which was responsible for coordinating the DOD position toward the bill, allowed the various subdivisions of the department only twenty-four hours in which to comment. This restriction applied to the services and the ARPA and led to Senator Johnson's later observation that the draft had "whizzed through the Pentagon on a motor cycle."[229] York and Roy Johnson of ARPA and Assistant Secretary MacIntyre of the Air Force all testified later that they had discussed certain reservations about the bill's demarcation of military-civilian space jurisdiction with the general counsel and Quarles during the day allotted to them, but that their ideas did not get into the draft. Each was unhappy with the deadline and argued that a longer period could have produced a better bill. Brucker and Medaris, while not submitting formal comments to the OSD also expressed reservations to Quarles which did not see print.

Nevertheless, open interagency conflict did not result at this stage. The OSD concluded that essentially the bill was an extension of the DOD-NACA relationship and interpreted its enabling provisions to mean that the DOD was still free to pursue the military space mission as it chose.[230] Thus, dissent by the services and ARPA was foreclosed for the moment. Yet, significantly, the inter-agency clearance process did not produce full executive support behind the administration bill. The civilians continued to minimize the military program. The OSD remained content in its belief that NASA like NACA before it would function as a helpmate in projects that OSD was willing to relegate to it. And the legislation remained "a draft in which Dr. Killian's office, the Bureau of the Budget, and the NACA participated."[231] The compromise among them was the bill the administration sent to Congress.

Apparently, the President expected to surmount the latent conflicts arising from different expectations of the space program through executive action. On April 2, in a message to the Secretary of Defense and the Chairman of NACA, Eisenhower directed the DOD to coordinate space projects with NACA, the NSF, and the National Academy of Science.[232] He also asked the defense establishment to prepare an operating plan to assure support for the new agency either through cooperative arrangement or by transfer of facilities to NASA. Finally, he instructed NACA to prepare detailed plans for the assumption of its contemplated responsibilities both for the internal-management structure of the new agency and its projected space programs, including arrangements with the NSF and the NAS for the participation of the scientific community in setting program goals. Finally, Eisenhower asked NACA to present to Congress a full explanation of the proposed legislation and its objectives.[233]

By April 2, then, the President had made public his choice among the alternative organizational structures for the space mission. The administration bill aligned the President with the views of the scientific community, specifically those of his personal scientific advisers and the nonmilitary government scientists. The proposed solution also fulfilled the administration's desire to downgrade the military exploitation of outer space for both strategic and budgetary reasons and its wish to capitalize on the political appeal of space without an open-ended assignment of energy and resources.

This confluence of objectives made it difficult, of course, to estimate the force of the scientists' influence. Clearly, the scientists did make a substantive contribution to the initial design of America's space effort. Yet, like most men in politics, they were both manipulators and manipulated, members of the strategic alliance forged by the President to serve a number of potentially gainful political ends.

## The Second Round of Policy-Making: The Legislative Process

On April 14, Senators Johnson and Bridges introduced the administration's bill as S. 3609, and Representative McCormack filed the same measure as H.R. 11881. The filing of the bill provided Congress with its own opportunity to take formal and final positions on the organizational issue. It also offered other political activists their last chance to reassert their own policy interests. At this stage, interested elements of Congress could fashion informal alliances with unsatisfied elements within the executive branch. In this instance, Johnson's drive for an independent policy-making role, and the military services' concern that their own role in space was minimized combined to revise substantially the National Aeronautics and Space Act of 1958.

### ENTERING THE LEGISLATIVE ARENA

Hearings on the bill opened in the House on April 15 and in the Senate on May 6. During the subsequent weeks spokesmen for the administration, the scientific community, the DOD, and the services testified before two congressional bodies. Each of these groups developed distinct attitudes toward three key issues: the respective roles of the DOD and NASA in space; the sources of decisions allocating activities to each; and finally, the role and proper composition of the National Aeronautics and Space Board. In one way or another, all three issues concerned the distinction between military and civilian space efforts and the need to establish an organization which could at once insure both sufficient basic research in space without obvious program payoffs as well as research and development immediately relevant to the demands of national security. The military establishment appeared in the main not to recognize the need for sufficiency; the scientists often failed to acknowledge the need for relevancy. To many of the participants in congressional deliberations, the administration bill satisfied the first criterion but failed to give due weight to the second. The prospects for major organizational modifications in the legislative arena were thus evident at the outset.

Dryden and Doolittle, supported by Stans and Finan, presented the administration's case. They reiterated their conviction that in regard to the respective roles of the DOD and NASA, the military was empowered to engage in research and development peculiar to weapons systems or military operations. The civilian agency was to

be responsible for all others.[234] Decisions about which projects were
of military interest would be arrived at by joint consultation between
NASA and the DOD, with unresolved disputes left to the
President.[235]

Representatives of the civilian scientific community and nonmilitary government scientists — still persuaded of the noncontro-
versial character of many project assignments — also defended the
administration's position on this issue. As Dr. Van Allen argued,
NASA should have "primary and dominant cognizance of space
matters among all Government agencies and ... only in case it is
clearly demonstrated that an endeavor has a direct importance to
our military preparedness ... a direct and significant importance,
should the primary cognizance reside in the DOD."[236]

As for the basic decision-making for programing space activities,
administration spokesmen saw the process working this way. They
assumed that the basic research program which must precede any
exploitation of space would naturally be located in NASA.[237] Then,
they envisioned the DOD presenting its requirements to NASA,
which, in turn, would provide the research capabilities for future
military developments.[238] Thus NASA would naturally coordinate,
if not control, all basic research in the space sciences.[239]

So far as the board was concerned, Budget Bureau officials
and nongovernmental scientists alike were persuaded that the
scientific community ought to be amply represented on the board
and that its role was best conceived as advisory rather than liaison.
Though government scientists, such as Dr. Waterman and Dr.
Wexler, director of the Office of Meteorological Research in the
Weather Bureau, emphasized the need for agency representation,
they accepted the basic proposition that participation by scientists
was the crucial requirement.*

These assumptions were unacceptable to the scientists in military employ. Most of these scientists continued to support civilian
control of space but placed great emphasis upon the military utility
of the new mission.[240] Although they reasoned concomitantly that
scientific investigation would have to precede military applications,
national security considerations were to them the underlying impetus for space explorations.[241] Thus, they favored wide discretionary
authority for the military to pursue whatever research programs
it chose and to establish conclusively the military requirements
for the program. Acknowledging the need for coordination of
civilian and military aspects, most military scientists urged in-

---

*An editorial in the June 13, 1958, issue of *Science* rather bluntly made this
point by declaring that "the degree of favoritism incorporated into the
final version of the Space bill will be one measure of the importance that
Congress attaches to the scientific investigation of outer space." (p. 371)

creased representation of the DOD on the National Aeronautics and Space Board.[242] They foresaw a broad national space program, formulated jointly by the two agencies.[243]

DOD spokesmen were even more outspoken in their dissent and broader in the scope of their criticism, for they took exception to substantive as well as organizational matters. As they reflected on the legislation, they became increasingly uncertain that NASA would be just another NACA. In particular, they took violent exception to Section 2 of the bill, which declared that America's activities in aeronautics and space "should be directed by a civilian agency exercising control of aeronautical and space research sponsored by the U.S. *except insofar as such activities may be peculiar to or primarily associated with weapons systems or military operations, in which case the agency may act in cooperation with or on behalf of the DOD.*"[244] This provision, they believed, deprived them of control over their own space activities.

On April 2, another presidential action seemed to confirm these fears. In a letter to NACA and the DOD, Eisenhower ordered a division of the space mission in which "the DOD will continue to be responsible for space activities peculiar to or primarily associated with military weapons systems or military operations . . . . Responsibility for other programs is to be assumed by the new agency . . . . In this connection I commend to the attention of the Congress, the comments of my Science Advisory Committee in its statement on March 26, 1958, on the military applications of space technology."[245] The "peculiar to" clause, the ambiguous permission granted NASA to "cooperate" with the DOD, and finally the reference to the Purcell Committee report, with its highly restrictive view of the DOD's space mission, aroused the DOD to legislative counterattack.

Between March 27 and April 14 Roy Johnson, Director of ARPA and an early critic of the bill, convinced Deputy Secretary Quarles that the language of Section 2 threatened military operations. Subsequently, from mid-April until mid-May the OSD was outspoken in its defense of the department's space mission and, led by Johnson, department officials persuaded the administration to amend Section 2.

At the outset of the hearings, the OSD made clear its determination to acquire ample authority to shape its own space mission. Quarles argued that

> the Defense Department . . . must have the latitude to pursue those things that are clearly associated with defense objectives as stated here. It must also have the latitude to pursue things that are potentially important to defense and to pursue those within the Defense Department or in cooperation with the . . . civilian agency.[246]

I would construe this language as not limiting the clear responsibility of the DOD for programs that are important to the
defense mission, including the support of research that is
closely related to the defense mission.[247]

Herbert York, chief scientist for the ARPA, followed Quarles in reiterating the need for the military to pursue any research with a
"reasonable chance of fulfilling military ends"[248] without oversight
by the civilian agency.[249] In effect, the department supported the
concept of a civilian agency responsible only for aeronautical and
space research "beyond the proper military interests."[250]

So far as the locus of decision-making power was concerned,
in sharp contrast to the drafters' view of NASA as the creative
agent, the OSD wished the choice as to whether a given project was
military or not to rest with the DOD, under the overall direction of
the President. NASA and the DOD, as two independent agencies
responsible for separate missions, might coordinate or undertake
joint projects in space, but only if both agreed to do so. The OSD
interpreted the "on behalf of" clause in military space projects as
authorization for NASA to do certain work it was particularly qualified to undertake, but only upon request by the DOD. If disputes
should arise over the military character of a project, the military
could carry its claim up to the President. In its view, no other
agency could interfere in this direct line of command responsible
for national security affairs.[251] Quarles, at any rate, believed that the
two space organizations "will have such similar views and objectives
on this matter that it will not be a frequent problem for the Chief
Executive."[252]

Finally, DOD spokesmen saw the board as an informal co-
ordinator of space programs, rather than an agent of mandatory
liaison. In particular, they argued that the board should have no
power to allocate projects between the military and civilian agencies: this was a task of direct interagency negotiation.[253] In order
to insure that the board would sympathetically exercise even this
limited role, the DOD recommended increased military membership
beyond the single representative provided for in the administration
bill. In no event, however, was the board to have binding jurisdiction
over defense projects.

Within the context of the overall DOD position, each service
adopted a special position traceable to its initial attitude toward the
ARPA. The Navy, having opposed a centralized space agency within
the military, now faced an even less palatable alternative. A civilian
agency would remove scientific space projects even further from
Navy labs—and further reduce the service's roles and missions.

Thus, Navy spokesmen were highly critical in testimony.
Garrison Norton, Assistant Secretary of the Navy for Air, stated

his personal preference for an executive board representing both military and civilian interests which would control the new agency.[254] In stating the Navy's position he qualified his own view somewhat, but argued that the Navy had grave misgivings "about certain portions of the bill as drafted, notably section 2."[255] Its language, he felt, should be changed so that NASA would be required to cooperate with the DOD if requested to do so, thus assuring adequate military control over its own space research, development, and vehicles.

Other Navy representatives, such as Raborn and Hayward, also argued that the military's role in space should be anything which the DOD decreed necessary for the national defense. Each also urged increased DOD representation on the board, both to protect military needs and to ensure that DOD and service— hopefully the Navy's — capabilities would be considered and utilized. As their testimony continued, it was evident that Navy spokesmen wanted a reconstituted NACA, faithful to the tradition of passive support of and cooperation with the military services.

The Air Force also viewed the new agency as properly an extension of NACA. Unlike the Navy, however, it supported its establishment with real enthusiasm. Anxious to pursue the space mission as part of its own ballistic-missile mission, the Air Force had rigorously opposed the establishment of the ARPA, viewing it as a dilution of its own natural monopoly of the space effort within the DOD. Now NASA appeared as a convenient receptacle for space research in which the Navy and Army had been engaged, and which was not competitive with present Air Force projects. Hence Air Force personnel strongly backed the creation of a civil agency, secure that its own military space role would be unchanged, or indeed increased.

Testifying on the administration bill, witnesses for the Air Force thus adopted the theme that the military space mission should be recognized as paramount. Civilian and scientific exploration would be useful, but the Air Force "did not attach the same degree of urgency to space exploration per se as . . . to the development of those space weapons which will be vital to the national security during the next ten years."[256] NASA should properly have increased authority to pursue space research, but it should not impinge upon the freedom of the military to carry out its own requirements.[257] With such an interpretation, the Air Force did not view an upgraded NACA as a threat and was quite content to leave to NASA rather than to another service, residual, nonmilitary space activities.

Consistent with the OSD position then, the Air Force urged that a unit within the military establishment, preferably itself or a highly dependent ARPA, determine which fields were of military concern. Specifically, Schriever and MacIntyre urged that the Air Force be left free to refuse transfer of any space mission or vehicle to NASA if it deemed such a transfer detrimental to national defense.[258] To insure its own primacy within the DOD, the Air Force advocated service—as distinct from departmental—representation on the board.[259] If any conflict arose between the DOD and NASA over the military or civilian character of a given project, the Air Force assumed that the Secretary of Defense would carry the disagreement to the President rather than depending upon the board to effect coordination.

The Army's view of NASA was almost the precise opposite of that of the Air Force. Testifying before the House committee, Medaris feared "the more the scientific and military are divided, the more difficult it will be for us to really go forward in the research that must be done now if the next generation of military weapons will be as good as those which we may meet."[260] He recalled that he had opposed the establishment of a civilian agency before the Preparedness Subcommittee and stated that he had seen no facts which had yet persuaded him otherwise.

Such arguments, of course, were designed to save the space mission for the Army. Since purely military exploitation of space now seemed likely to be lodged primarily in the Air Force, the only way for the Army to retain a space capability would be through a centralized organization within the DOD.[261] Moreover, the Army advocated a broad spectrum of research as the only source of futuristic weapons systems, and feared that removal of such research from the DOD might seriously jeopardize future preparedness.

As a last line of defense, in the event that NASA were established, the Army supported as broadly integrated a national space effort as possible. It urged that the new NASA should exercise overall surveillance over military as well as civilian and scientific interests in order to insure close cooperation and to utilize available teams. Thus, the Army sought to have the DOD represented on the advisory board through ARPA, rather than the services, a position obviously consistent with the Army's aim of enhancing the role of ARPA within the DOD and ensuring close coordination between the ARPA and NASA.[262] Should disputes arise as to the placement of vehicles, teams, or projects between the two agencies, the Army looked either to joint resolution by the two agencies or ultimately the President.[263] Through such provisions the Army sought to avoid a situation in which the Air Force and NASA would gain respective control over the military and civilian space missions. To prevent this outcome, the Army worked to expand the space mission as far as possible; to retain an absolutely, if not relatively, large slice of the space pie; and to integrate the space research and exploration missions so that capability rather than roles and missions or civilian or military status would determine who would undertake a given project.

The services' differences never disappeared in the course of the hearings, but they were overshadowed by congressional action. The Senate and the House committees reopened far more trenchantly than the critics themselves the question of civil versus military control of space. Thus the OSD and the services found willing legislative allies to extract from a previously reluctant administration an enhanced space mission for the military establishment.

## THE HOUSES GO SEPARATE WAYS

What troubled both committees of Congress which were to deal with organizing the space mission went beyond service and agency roles. Congressional leaders concentrated their fire on the absence of criteria by which to determine civilian or military jurisdiction in space; absence of interagency coordinating mechanisms; absence of machinery for overall national space-policy-making; and, finally, absence of substantive provisions to support the sweeping generalizations of the bill's declaration of policy. Congressmen rejected as unworkable the administration's argument that through normal interagency coordination channels NASA and the DOD would either "get along" or take their disagreements to the President. In their view such permissiveness left major policy questions unanswered. These issues boiled down to a central question: should the NASA make policy for either part or all of the space effort or, alternatively, should it merely administer policy made elsewhere, and if so, where? Within this broad issue lay a host of complex questions of a scientific, strategic, and administrative nature on which the two houses of Congress differed in both emphasis and response.

For a number of reasons, the House Select Committee on Astronautics and Space Exploration chaired by McCormack was more civilian in orientation than its Senate counterpart. The committee lacked the background which the upper house had gathered through the Senate Preparedness Subcommittee; only two of its members served on the House Armed Services Committee,[264] and it was chaired and staffed by men particularly concerned with the scientific, civilian, and peaceful potentialities of outer space. McCormack and Keating, for example, viewed NASA as a basis for further government organization of science at the cabinet level.

They also repeatedly stressed the need to consider peaceful uses of outer space before military developments progressed so far that arms control would be overly difficult.[265] Several committee members, including McCormack, initially preferred a commission form of organization like the AEC, which would place both civilian and military exploitation of space under a single, civilian, controlling body. George Feldman, the committee's chief counsel and a close friend of McCormack, had worked on the AEC legislation in 1946 and was particularly interested in the commission model. In the face of total White House opposition they did not press this view, but it colored their response to NASA.[266] McCormack's close relations with Killian also added to this civilian-scientific bias.

Thus the House committee viewed the establishment of a civilian agency with primary responsibility for the exploitation of space as an urgent, necessary mission of the Congress and distrusted administration attempts either to downgrade the agency or to upgrade DOD responsibility in space. Specifically, Feldman suspected that the administration's proposal for a high-level agency in space was principally shaped by a desire to meet public concern, not to fashion a major new program. Both he and the individual committee members vented this suspicion upon administration spokesmen, particularly those from NACA. They distrusted NACA's capabilities for a large space effort and displayed marked disrespect for Dryden,[267] the presumed director of the new agency. Feldman more than once referred to the "deadwood in NACA," and McCormack indicated that the new agency would demand men of vision and dynamic leadership, "not men with a status-quo mind."[268] Dryden's reference to von Braun's proposal for a 150-mile shot of a man into space as akin to shooting a lady out of a cannon,[269] proved especially unpopular to the committee.* Increasingly the House came to view the administration's proposal as merely a way of updating and upgrading NACA—likely only to result in "doing business at the same old stand."[270]

The committee was especially disturbed by the traditional dominance which the military had exercised over the operations of NACA. The committee did not deny the DOD a substantial role in the space mission; indeed, McCormack claimed that no one on the committee had interpreted the language of Section 2 to exclude ARPA from conducting basic research or as inhibiting the DOD in the performance of its "proper functions." Nevertheless, the committee strove to assure NASA independent civilian status.[271] In contrast to the views of the military, the House interpreted the language of Section 2, which specified that the agency might act on behalf of or

---

*This anti-Dryden position of the House committee ultimately denied him his expected promotion as the administrator of NASA.

in cooperation with the DOD in activities related to weapons systems or military operations, as a possible authorization for the DOD to remove all original powers from NASA unless the DOD granted it express permission to pursue space activities. McCormack feared the language gave the DOD "a complete voice in determining to what extent the new civilian agency might operate" since almost all space missions might be associated with either weapons systems or military operations.[272] Only after two weeks of hearings was McCormack persuaded that the administration's safeguards for civilian initiative were sufficient. Then he acknowledged that Doolittle's testimony in firm support of a civilian agency had revived his enthusiasm for provisions of Section 2 which had previously seemed vulnerable to military domination.

A second major concern of the House committee was the specific form of NASA—DOD relationships. House leaders sought a civil-military liaison mechanism at the project level. This form of inter-agency coordination seemed to them the most effective means of handling the necessarily large "gray area" which existed between the military and civilian space missions: those projects that could be utilized for both. Feldman and McCormack were particularly adamant about this form of coordination: Feldman invited witnesses such as Herbert Loper, assistant to the Secretary of Defense for Atomic Energy, to testify specifically on this subject, and asked everyone else in sight what he thought of such a liaison system. The committee evidently backed him. In Metcalf's words, "I think it has been developed by Mr. Feldman that no matter what happens to the composition of the board, there has to be daily, constant and continuous liaison between the civil and the military agencies."[273]

The board did not fully satisfy the congressmen as an effective means of policy liaison. They objected to the requirements of prior consultation before the director could make certain policy decisions as limiting vigorous executive action. For the same reasons, they objected to the nongovernmental majority on the board. Instead, they advocated a purely advisory committee, vesting overall policy coordination and high-level space-policy-making in the director himself.[274] The committee saw NASA as responsible for overall national space policy under the direct control of the President, with the DOD undertaking certain operations and planning according to this policy in the special fields affecting national security. Thus, over-all problems of coordination between civil and military operations in space would be solved through "a civilian agency . . . with direct primary responsibility for an overall civilian, military, research, development, and exploratory policy, as well as the overall primary responsibility for implementing those various programs . . . thus combining all the functions under one policy-making civilian agency, with the military given its adequate place."[275] This high-level-policy execution was to be based upon lower-level coordination through an operating civil-military liaison committee placed in the DOD. Such a lower-level cooperative mechanism, in the committee's view, would permit NASA to take military needs into account while still retaining civilian planning and control.

The Senate committee, while sharing many of the reservations of the House, drew some sharply different conclusions from its deliberations. For a variety of reasons, the committee itself was more preoccupied with military concerns than was the House committee. First, it was operating in a context formed by the Preparedness Subcommittee Hearings. Second, five of its members, Chairman Johnson, and Senators Russell, Symington, Bridges, and Saltonstall, were all members of the Armed Forces Committee. Third, Johnson, having maintained close relations with the OSD over the past months, was thoroughly familiar with military requests for an undisputed sphere of decision-making authority. Finally, Johnson's whole emphasis upon the challenge in space was premised upon the principle "if you would have peace, prepare for war." America, in his view, could only achieve a lasting peace by retaining military control of outer space.[276]

From the outset, then, the Senate committee was openly hostile to major portions of the administration bill: its failure to insure military exploitation of outer space; to provide overall direction for the space effort; and to recognize various other necessary aspects of space developments, including international cooperation, the development of nuclear propulsion systems, and a reliable patent policy to protect the public interest. It questioned NACA's ability to become a large-scale contracting agency and expressed its initial judgment that the administration bill was only marginally preferable to the present situation of interagency competition in the space effort.[277]

The Senators were concerned with the difficulties inherent in pursuing both military and peaceful exploitation of space without incurring ruinous competition.[278] But they were more concerned that the military program might "deteriorate under perhaps certain imagined or possible civilian attitudes."[279] The problem of dividing space activities between civilian and military missions and responsibilities—in short, of insuring both sufficient and relevant space research and development—plagued the Senate as it had the House. As Symington put it: they were all concerned about "how to get as much as possible out of the military departments and at the same time not to affect the military requirement."[280]

As the hearings progressed, the Senators approached an informal consensus around the need to give the DOD primary operating responsibility in those aspects of the space mission which affected national security. Mundt and Hickenlooper explicitly remarked that the civilian agency had been given excessive responsibility for military space developments. They viewed the phrase that NASA "may act on behalf of or in cooperation with the DOD" as a clear statement of DOD dependence upon NASA for the definition of the defense mission.[281]

In order to correct this unnecessary restriction, the Senators reached two conclusions. First, they decided that the DOD should have independent authority in the field of its special responsibilities.[282] Johnson, in extracting declarations from less than reluctant DOD officials that they would appreciate such authority, in effect forced this powerful group to repudiate a basic tenet of its own administration's bill: that the military would pursue military exploitation of space with the agreement of the civilian agency. Johnson declared that some definite language providing the DOD with such autonomous authority to act in space should be written and wryly observed that he thought the "ingenious DOD" could produce some such wording.[283]

Second, the Senate evolved its own form of military-civilian liaison mechanism. The committee had noted throughout the hearings that in the administration bill there was no power vested in anyone except the President to decide what phase of the space mission belonged to which agency. As Symington noted:

> Now at the beginning of planning our outer space program, we have an opportunity to provide for some unification. S. 3609, however, does not provide for an overall organization which can plan with foresight for our national and international programs in outer space. Separate agencies are to be separate agencies and are to be separately administered, and voluntary cooperation among coequals is supposed to result in a kind of happy coordination. . . . There is even no provision for settling questions of jurisdiction among the various executive agencies which will be concerned with the exploration of space.[284]

Not only did such a system seem inefficient to the Senators; such dependence on presidential policy-making was distasteful to Congress in its current mood of autonomous policy-making. Moreover, the Senate committee believed that the President and his scientific advisers depreciated the military potentialities of space to an extent it could not accept. No simple solution such as the House's coordinating channel through a civil-military liaison committee seemed sufficient. The committee sought instead a broad comprehensive new procedure.

What was missing, in the Senators' view, was a high-level policy-making board which could exercise both responsibility and

authority over the national space program.[285] Since many conflicts, in the committee's view, would never be resolved if "no one
in any particular agency has the authority to make the decision," the
committee decided to provide a high-level policy board, empowered
to establish national space policy and to determine particular project assignments among various operating agencies according to
their military or civil nature.[286] Each operating agency would be
free to pursue its own specific mission, but this executive decision-
making body, under ultimate civilian control, would serve to
coordinate, weigh, and direct the various missions which America
was to undertake in space.

So, the two committees, occupied with similar concerns,
arrived at quite different concepts of how the space program should
be organized, and formed alliances with different interest groups
within the administration. Confronted with these contending coalitions, it fell to the administration to restyle its own proposal to gain
an acceptable compromise. It was this process of administration retreat and congressional bargaining which ultimately produced the
National Aeronautics and Space Act of 1958.

## THE ACTORS MEET

In May the military establishment, exploiting the concern of
both houses about the division of function between the civilian and
military space missions, expressed publicly its own reservations
about the administration bill. Its advanced spokesman was Roy
Johnson, whose flamboyant disregard of his role as a member of
the administration made him the natural instrument for such a policy
offensive. Indeed, Mr. Johnson took such an extreme position that
the administration's desire for civilian supremacy was virtually
forgotten. Only solitary voices like those of Dryden, Doolittle,
and Van Allen continued to call for a purely "civilian" bill.

Director Johnson launched his attack upon the administration
bill on May 5. Appearing before the House committee, he stated
that "the legislation setting up a civilian group should not be so
worded that it may be construed to mean that the military uses of
space are to be limited by a civilian agency. This could be disastrous
.... For example, if the DOD decides it is militarily desirable to
program for putting man into space, it should not have to justify
this activity to this civilian agency."[287] Johnson proceeded to
explain that the language as it stood required exactly this: that it
did not permit the military to proceed on its own without the
participation of the civilian agency.[288] He then offered, on his own
account rather than on behalf of the DOD, his own preferred version

of Section 2: the civilian agency should undertake all space activities except those which may be "in support of or presumed to lead to the use of space for national defense in which case the agency is authorized to act in cooperation with or on behalf of the DOD if so requested by the DOD."[289]

Johnson argued that the DOD should be free to operate in any field of space interesting to it without any prior civilian approval. The two agencies might work in parallel directions or share voluntarily in a single project, but would be authorized to act independently if they wished. Since only the military was qualified to judge what was of military significance it would be a tragedy, in Johnson's view, if the statute were in any way to reduce its independence by limiting it to clear-cut military objectives. Finally, in response to a pointed question from Representative Keating about his draft suggestion, Johnson acknowledged that he could barely think of a space mission which could not be presumed to be of utility to the national defense.[290]

Leaving the House to mull over his recommendations, Johnson headed for the other side of the Hill. Two days later he found the Senate committee receptive to his claims, since the committee had heard Quarles that morning say he had no personal objection to an amendment permitting the OSD initial responsibility in military space exploitation. Although Johnson's suggestion that the NASA-DOD relationship be something like the IGY-DOD relationship was too extreme for the committee, he held to his basic position.

> Let me put it this way, Mr. Senator. If the AEC had been set up on atoms for peace at that time...then I don't believe that Congress would have appropriated the money...nor the country supported it to the degree that it was supported. If (this) civilian agency is set up on the basis of space for peace or space for fun—I think that a parallel is there....I think that it has to be set up with a military connotation, with a full understanding on the part of the public that this is a threat. This isn't something we can sweep under the rug by just saying that it is civilian and it is something that by saying it is civilian we can then decide is not a threat.[291]

Receiving at least partial encouragement from Senators Bridges, Mundt, and Hickenlooper, Johnson reiterated the theme he had emphasized in the House: that the civilian and military agencies should be permitted free and independent opportunities to perform space research. In conclusion, Johnson remarked that he really didn't know why there should be a NASA at all, since the NACA was now capable of pursuing nonmilitary space research. As an afterthrought he told the Senators: "I understand that even though we are employed within the Government that when we testify before this Committee, we are supposed to tell what we really think and of course I do not know whether I will have a job when I leave here today but I am saying what I think."[292]

In the next few days of Senate hearings, Norton, MacIntyre, and Brucker endorsed the spirit, if not the letter, of Director Johnson's testimony. The Senators responded by expressing substantial concern about the language in Section 2. When McElroy stated in a news conference on May 8 that Johnson and he were very clear that the "departmental position is [Johnson's] position," the DOD's final position became clear.[293] Between May 7 and 12 the OSD prevailed upon the Executive Office to accept certain of Johnson's arguments, in return for which Johnson accepted administration policy in support of the new civilian agency.[294]

More amendments were afoot. On May 6 Doolittle publicly conceded to the Senate Committee that increased representation of the DOD on the board would be necessary, and indicated that the power of final decisions over space missions might not fall to NASA.[295] On May 11 the Bureau of the Budget conceded to the DOD a minimum of three members on the advisory board.

On May 12 the administration amended Section 2. Called to the House to explain discrepancies in his previous testimony, Johnson was a chastened man. Moreover, he was duly escorted by Dr. York and Mr. Robert Dechert, general counsel of the DOD and a man versed in the ways of administration solidarity. When Johnson appeared to be reverting to his former arguments, Dechert interrupted. "To shorten the procedure," he suggested,

> Mr. Johnson has language on the two items that have been mostly under discussion, which language is satisfactory to the Executive Department as a whole, although it has not finally gone through the ordinary reporting processes. I cannot commit the whole Executive Department to this exact language but I believe confidently it will be approved, having talked to the person in charge of policy decisions . . . . It was written in longhand on the way over, after various telephone calls.[296]

With this introduction, Johnson read the amendments. Section 2 was rewritten to read that NASA was responsible for space activities "except insofar as such activities may be peculiar to, or primarily associated with weapons systems or military operations, in the case of which activity the DOD will be responsible." The second amendment provided for nine members of the government on the advisory board, thus giving the government a majority, of which three would represent the DOD.

The House committee reacted to this announcement with understandable alarm. Given their earlier fears of military domination over the new agency, this new language disturbed at least the chairman and the staff. Subsequent testimony did little to allay their concern. Dechert, in emphasizing the administration's agreement on the amendments, stated that it was his understanding "the President does not want to go beyond what he said in his message through fear that, if we go beyond it, it will look as if we are trying to take this away from civilian control. Therefore . . . the administration wants to keep the expression of the DOD participation in the exact words that the President used . . . which are weapons systems and military operations . . . . Mr. Johnson has indicated that the research leading up to weapons systems and military operations is necessarily a part of these systems and operations themselves."[297]

Thereafter, the following exchange occurred:

| | |
|---|---|
| Feldman: | Would you interpret this language . . . as giving you the exclusive authority to decide without any cooperation or without cooperation with the new agency, what is military? |
| Johnson: | Yes, Sir. |
| McCormack: | We might as well put a bill out and put in military control. |
| Dechert: | Isn't that subject to the fact that both these agencies will be part of the executive department and if those in the civilian agency believed that the military agency had made the wrong decision they always have the right of appeal to the President on it. I think the President is the ultimate arbiter, if there is a disagreement. |
| Feldman: | Should not some person or agency plan and coordinate all aspects of space research in order to prevent gaps and to insure effective cooperation? |
| Johnson: | Definitely not, Sir. I think that would be the most tragic thing that could happen to this country. |
| York: | You do not do that with Maritime. The Maritime and Navy go on and both use the ocean. |
| Feldman: | Another Pearl Harbor with no coordination. |
| York: | Of course the purpose of ARPA is to make sure that the Army, Navy and Air Force are together on the space program. |
| Feldman: | Why not the civilian agency; why not have the same cooperation with them? |
| York: | If their purpose is primarily to explore space and planets . . . all we need is the information they get. If they are not getting the information that is necessary for defense, we get it ourselves. That is why I think these things can be almost independent. |
| Feldman: | In other words, when the President now is |

|          |                                                          |
|----------|----------------------------------------------------------|
|          | talking of a national space program, national space agency, what you are saying instead is that we should have one for the DOD and one for peace time. |
| York:    | I say space is a place and not a program at all. It is a place where you have different programs. |
| Feldman: | Then the President's message does not mean what it says.[298] |

Despite the sentiments of the House staff, in the following days endorsements for the amended version poured in. On May 13 the Bureau of the Budget submitted identical changes for the administration to the Senate, which generally received them as positive improvements, although by no means an adequate solution to the problem of overall coordination in space. Stans indicated at this time that the amendments had the unqualified support of NACA and Dr. Killian. At his news conference on May 14 Eisenhower formally endorsed the new version, and five days later Norton, MacIntyre, and Quarles did as well. Only the Army, now virtually fighting for its life in space, dissented, by proposing yet more drastic changes. In the week from May 20 until May 27, the Army reported no less than three separate versions of Section 2 to Congress. On the twentieth Brucker suggested as a last clause "in which case the DOD shall exercise control."[299] Medaris, predictably, was even more adamant. He repeated Brucker's wording for Section 2 but added the language that "the Congress, recognizing that the pre-determination of the primary application of such activities in the vast new field of space may be impossible, hereby declares that where such clear-cut determination appears impossible, the Secretary of Defense shall be responsible for the determination of whether such projects should be carried out by the civilian agency or by the DOD, unless he is otherwise directed by the President." Finally, on the twenty-seventh, Michaelis, chief of legislative liaison for the Army, suggested the following wording for Section 2: "except and insofar as such activities are closely related to missions of the DOD, in which case the agency is authorized to act in cooperation with or as an agent of the DOD." Michaelis, however, felt it necessary to specify that this wording did not represent a policy position of the DOD or of the Army.

Thus the administration had, in effect, completed its final drafting process by acquiescing to elements within itself which had been excluded from the initial writing of the bill. Now, with the exception of the Army, every major element within the administration deemed the compromise satisfactory. There remained the reconciliation between the two congressional committees, still widely separated in their views.

## CONGRESS MAKES A LAW

The alliance-building which occurred during the hearings eventually pitted the Senate and the military establishment against civilian scientists, the Bureau of the Budget and the House of Representatives. Each house of Congress consulted the White House to see which of its proposals might be acceptable, and trade-offs between various items in the respective bills were made within limits stipulated by the administration. The precise mix of the compromise, however, was determined by the relationships and relative influence of the two committees and their chairmen.

Since February, when the Senate had established its special committee, a substantial rivalry had existed between the two Houses. McCormack, apparently disturbed by the Senate action, had held the first hearings, an action which in turn aggravated Johnson. Subsequently, there was limited consultation between the two committees, and those contacts which did occur were principally between staff members or between Johnson and Rayburn. Thus each committee drew up its bill with a certain deliberate disregard for the known position of the other.

On May 24 the House committee unanimously reported out H.R. 12575, reflecting the main intent of the original administration bill with a draft providing civilian control for the entire space effort.* Indeed, the House proposal was more civilian than the administration bill after its May 12 amendment, since the committee had resisted administration attempts to persuade it to accept the rewording of Section 2. In the House bill, this section directed the new agency to undertake all space activities except such as may be "peculiar to or primarily associated with the development of weapons systems, of military operations or the defense of the U.S. (including the Research and Development necessary for the defense of the U.S.) in the case of which activities the Agency shall act on behalf of or in cooperation with the Department of Defense."[300] The House feared that the vesting of original authority in the DOD for military exploitation of space might hamper the research activities of the civilian agency. Thus, division between military and civilian operations granted the military freedom to pursue broad research and development efforts, but continued to vest final determination of the space program in civilian hands: in the administrator of the agency and ultimately in the President.

---

*A staff member has described McCormack's desire to achieve bipartisan support for the committee bill. He said that all votes on provisions were unanimous, although there were some partisan "discussions."

The House bill also included its creature, a Military Liaison Committee in the DOD. The administrator of NASA was to vest operating relations with the DOD in this committee as well as matters involving interagency jurisdiction and joint activities.[301]

In case of disputes not resolved at this level the administrator or the Secretary of Defense might refer the matter to the President for final decision. In addition, the House bill established an Atomic Energy Liaison Committee to effectuate similar coordination with the AEC.

The National Aeronautics and Space Board was renamed the Aeronautics and Space Advisory Committee, composed of nine government representatives, including three from the DOD, and eight private citizens. This committee was a purely advisory body which might consult with the administrator on national space policy and attempt to coordinate programs of various agencies. With responsibility for operational coordination already in the Liaison Committee, overall policy-making fell, in effect, to the administrator and the President, thereby constructing the "straight-line operation" under civilian control which the Bureau of the Budget and PSAC had originally favored.

Finally, the House bill authorized the establishment of a Joint Congressional Committee on Aeronautics and Space; specified that the agency could engage in programs of international cooperation under the foreign policy guidance of the Department of State; and inserted patent provisions modeled on the stringent patent policy of the AEC.

The bill went to the floor on June 2 and passed unanimously after a rather poorly attended two-hour debate.[302] The only significant floor amendment was to strike out the provision for a joint committee. This shift was due to a number of factors. Speaker Rayburn preferred a standing committee in order to provide an important chairmanship for Representative Overton Brooks. The House traditionally fears Senate domination in such joint settings. Finally, McCormack himself came to believe that the establishment of a standing Committee for Science and Astronautics, empowered to oversee all scientific activities including space, might contribute to the eventual establishment of a Department of Science.[303]

Nine days after the House passed its bill the Senate committee reported out S. 3609 as amended—a vastly different legislative product. The Senate bill provided for original DOD responsibility in those areas of space research and development which pertained to national defense, and for joint civil-military control of the national space program.[304] It expanded upon the administration's amended wording of Section 2, so that "activities peculiar to or primarily associated with the development of weapons systems or military operations shall be the responsibility and under the direction of the DOD."[305] The Senate argued strongly for the separation of the military and civilian space missions on the operational level. On the one hand, the report accompanying the bill stated that "great mischief could be wrought by delegating to the civilian space agency authority over military weapons systems and military operations."[306] On the other hand, the report argued that removing operational responsibility for military space projects from NASA would prevent the civilian agency's activities from being inundated by attention to the military applications of space.

Addressing itself to other issues which the House bill covered, the Senate bill established a Joint Committee for Space and Aeronautics, authorized the agency to pursue international cooperative efforts under the foreign-policy direction of the President, and included patent provisions similar to those of the House.

The major innovation of the Senate bill, however, was the establishment of a National Aeronautics and Space Policy Board. In contrast to the limited functions which the House and administration bills had assigned to what the administration called the board, the Senate established a high-level, policy-making organ. Despite the opposition of the Executive Office, particularly Killian and the Bureau of the Budget, to such an administrative structure, the Senate committee viewed this board as the answer to the vexing problem of general space policy-making. Established in the Executive Office of the President and composed of seven government officials (the Secretary of State, Secretary of Defense, Administrator of NASA, Chairman of the AEC, and representatives of three other agencies, only one of which might be from the DOD), the board was obviously a blue-ribbon body. It would direct NASA and the DOD – the two operating space agencies – and coordinate the work of ten other principal government agencies interested in space exploitation.

The Senate report argued that "any differences arising among the agencies concerned in the course of the execution of their functions must be established at a governmental level higher than that occupied by any of those operational agencies."[307] Interposed between the operating agencies and the President, the board was to conduct a continuing survey of space activities, recommend a comprehensive program in aeronautics and space exploitation, designate responsibility for major projects, and resolve interagency conflicts: in sum, evolve national policy in space. Its role in relation to aeronautics and space would be "comparable to that of the National Security Council with respect to the integration of the foreign and military policies of the U.S."[308] Like the NSC as well, it would function as a statutory, policy-making body vested with administrative responsibility and held accountable to Congress, through the

President. To support its functions, the Senate authorized the board to employ an executive director and other specialized staff.

The structure and functions of the Policy Board reflect the Senate's conviction that no single agency could be assigned total responsibility for the space field. They also reveal the Senate's determination that the military interest in space would not be abridged. While the board had a civilian majority in membership, the military departments would be included at this highest echelon of space policy-making. In addition, the Secretary of Defense—but not the administrator of NASA—was authorized to appeal separately to the President in any case where action or inaction by the board seemed to threaten his space mission.

On June 16 the Senate unanimously passed H.R. 12575 as amended by the entire text of S. 3609. The sole important amendment on the floor was offered by Senator Johnson, striking out the patent provisions pending review by the conference committee. With its passage, the alignments in the final struggle to pass a space act were drawn. The Senate had taken a stand on the division of functions between the DOD and NASA which aligned it with the administration (in its latest position) and against the House. But so far as the mechanisms providing for national space-policy-making were concerned it placed itself in opposition to both the administration and the House.

After the Senate passed its bill, neither body seemed disposed to compromise. The House considered its bill close to the original administration proposal. The Senate held the position that its bill alone recognized the characteristics of urgency and breadth necessary for a successful space program.

Preliminary attempts to resolve differences at the staff level failed. For several weeks the only contacts between the committees were those between Mrs. Eilene Galloway of the Legislative Reference Service and special consultant to the Senate committee, and Gerald Siegal, chief of staff of the Senate committee on the one hand, and Dr. Charles Sheldon, of the Legislative Reference Service and associate staff director of the House committee, and Glenn Wilson of the House staff, on the other.[309] The House staff tried subsequently to extend contacts without success. They believed that Johnson was striving to increase his bargaining position by holding out for the Senate bill or none at all.

At this impasse, the White House reentered the arena. The stimulus seemed to come from Senator Johnson. One Sunday late in June or early July, the Majority Leader called on the President.[310] During this interview the President—reputedly for reasons not directly related to the space program—agreed to a modified version of the Policy Board.

When Killian returned after the weekend, the President informed him of his wishes. With administration concurrence, and with a
record of support for administration space policies, McCormack
was now persuaded to reconsider the House position. In this atmosphere and with two major outstanding issues settled—the wording of
Section 2 and the interagency coordination mechanisms—negotiations for a conference committee meeting reopened. The issues at
hand were the formulation of congressional committees; provisions
for international cooperation; and patent procedures. Both houses
agreed that the agency could engage in international cooperative
ventures under the foreign-policy guidance of the President.[311] The
Senate abandoned its demand for a joint committee and accepted
two standing committees. The House accepted the Senate patent
provisions.* These staff negotiations completed, the Conference
Committee met for one session on July 15 with Johnson in the chair.
The agreements were ratified and the conference accepted the bill.†

In addition to these compromise proposals reached in conference, the final bill contained those agreements made by the two
houses with the administration. Section 2 finally read: "[aeronautics
and space activities] shall be the responsibility of and shall be
directed by a civilian agency exercising control over aeronautics
and space activities sponsored by the U.S. except that activities
peculiar to or primarily associated with the development of weapons
systems, military operations, or the defense of the U.S. [including
the Research and Development necessary to make effective provision for the defense of the U.S.] shall be the responsibility of and
shall be directed by the DOD."[312] This wording represents a victory
for the Senate, although incorporating the clarifying language about
research and development written by the House.

Section 204 provided for a Civilian-Military Liaison Committee
composed of representatives from the DOD, the services, and
NASA. This organ would permit the agencies to consult and in-

---

*These granted title to NASA except under certain specified conditions
in which the administrator could waive title to the contractor. The provisions were written in the O'Mahoney Subcommittee on Monopoly of
the Senate Judiciary Committee. During June some patent attorneys
and their clients had argued in favor of the original administration
assumption that NASA patent procedures would follow the DOD's, vesting
patent rights in the contractor in exchange for free use of the patented
invention by the government. Resisting such pressures, the Senate wrote
in restrictive provisions.

†The conference bill was principally drafted by the House staff. The
House Committee on Science and Astronautics was established on
July 21 in House Resolve 580 on the basis of H. R. Report # 1837, "Amend-
ing the Rules of the House to provide for a Committee on Science and
Astronautics." The Senate amended its rules to create a Committee on
Aeronautical and Space Sciences in Senate Resolve # 327 on the basis
of Senate Report # 1925.

form each other on matters within their respective jurisdictions. Its structure departed slightly from the original House proposal, since it was no longer placed in the DOD; however, it was designed to provide the project-level coordination which the House had deemed necessary for effective collaboration in space.

What had been the National Aeronautics and Space Board in the administration proposal, the Aeronautics and Space Advisory Committee in the House bill, and the National Aeronautics and Space Policy Board in the Senate bill, finally became the National Aeronautics and Space Council. This nine-member advisory organ was to be composed of the President as chairman, the Secretaries of State and Defense, the Administrator of NASA, the Chairman of the AEC, one other representative of the federal government, and not more than three private citizens appointed by the President. It was authorized to employ a staff and was to advise the President on all activities authorized by the act. Specifically, the council would survey all aeronautical and space activities of all government agencies engaged in such programs and develop "a comprehensive program of aeronautics and space activities to be conducted by the agencies of the U.S. Government."[313]

The bill passed both Houses on the day of the conference, and Eisenhower signed it into law as the National Aeronautics and Space Act of 1958 on July 29.[314] "In the long view of history," Johnson proclaimed a month later, "possibly the most important step we took during this session was to establish an agency to guide America's effort in the exploration of outer space."[315]

## Conclusion

The passage of the National Aeronautics and Space Act of 1958 was generally viewed by informed observers as a "victory" for the scientific community. From one perspective this interpretation seems plausible. NACA, one of the oldest scientific enterprises within the federal government, had been preserved and reinvigorated. The military had not assumed primary responsibility over the total space mission. Spokesmen for science had participated directly in the drafting of the administration's legislation and had indeed shaped some of its key concepts. Scientists outside and within the government had generally united in their preferences for an independent civilian-based space agency, emphasizing the exploration of outer space as a pursuit of knowledge as well as a strengthening of the nation's security.

Yet a moment's reflection on the events and actions incident to the act sharply modifies this plausible interpretation. For one thing, the interests of the scientists were shared by other powerful actors in the process. A separate civilian agency and a clear orientation toward the peacetime uses of a space program served the political and budgetary purposes of the administration very well. They also reflected the convictions of "generalist administrators" ably represented by the Bureau of the Budget.

Two other points should be noted. First, where the organizational and management viewpoints of the scientists appeared to threaten the interests of the military, they did not prevail. The military mission remained protected in large measure to the degree satisfactory to the office of the Secretary of Defense and the Air Force. Most important of all, the Congress of the United States, led by Lyndon Johnson, succeeded in broadening the conception of the space program and identifying it as a major national program far beyond the expectations and even the desires of the scientists and their allies within the office of the President. Johnson's concept of a Space Council that institutionalized the high priority he placed on the program, his equal emphasis upon military and civilian aspects, and the sense of urgency which the entire Congress attached to the total undertaking triumphed over the administration. In a fundamental way it was a broadly conceived and dramatic program which emerged in response to the political impact of Sputnik, not a carefully designed, reasoned policy for the support of space science per se.

The influence of these other components of the political process can lead a thoughtful observer to doubt not only that science "did it alone" but also to question whether science as a political force could ever do it alone. Prior to Sputnik I, the scientific backing and participation in the original Vanguard program had not been sufficient to generate political support. After Sputnik II the values the scientific community espoused were clearly joined with other values before the conflict was resolved and the space mission defined.

Two conclusions would seem to follow. First, the public management of the space enterprise after 1958 involved the pursuit of policy objectives which go far beyond the benefits for science and national security to be derived from space exploration. A successful administration of the program requires, so the history of the legislation suggests, the simultaneous pursuit of a number of objectives, some clearly nonscientific in character. Second, if the scientists and their spokesmen were to continue to achieve a substantial number of their aims they would have to proceed in concert with their allies and in conflict with their adversaries. The enactment of the law signaled a tentative and discernible deployment of forces. For men concerned with the overall scientific strength of the nation, the quality of research and development, and the training and recruitment of new scientific talent, the establishment of NASA in 1958 was the beginning of political activity, not the end.

## NOTES

1 U.S. House of Representatives, Select Committee on Astronautics and Space Exploration, *Hearings on H.R. 11881*, p. 275, testimony of Admiral John T. Hayward, Assistant Chief of Naval Operations for Research & Development.

2 U.S. Senate, Preparedness Investigating Subcommittee of the Committee on Armed Services, *Hearings, Inquiry into Satellites and Missile Programs*, p. 1699, testimony of General John B. Medaris, Commander, Army Ballistics Missile Agency. (Hereinafter, these Senate Preparedness Subcommittee Hearings will be referred to as *SPSCH*.)

3 See U. S. Senate. *Document #124*, "Special Report by the National Academy of Sciences for the Committee on Appropriations," 84th Congress, 2nd Session; Walter Sullivan, *International Conciliation*, "The IGY," #521, January, 1959; and Sullivan, *Assault on the Unknown* (New York, McGraw Hill, 1961), *op. cit.*, p. 28.

4 See U. S. House of Representatives, Select Committee on Astronautics and Space Exploration. *Hearings on H. R. 11881*, p. 275 ff, testimony of Admiral John T. Hayward, Assistant Chief of Naval Operations for Research and Development. (Hereinafter, these House Hearings will be cited as *HH*.) See also Eugene M. Emme, *Aeronautics and Astronautics* (Washington, D.C., U.S. Government Printing Office, 1961), pp. 59, 61.

5 U.S. House of Representatives, Committee on Appropriations, Subcommittee on Department of Defense Appropriations. *Project Vanguard: A Scientific Earth Satellite Program for the International Geophysical Year* (A Report . . . by the Surveys and Investigations Staff), Hearings, Part VI, 86th Congress, 1st session, pp. 56–57.

6 Erik Bergaust and William Beller, *Satellite!* (Garden City, N.Y., Hanover House, 1956), p. 36.

7 See U.S. House of Representatives. *Project Vanguard. . .*, *op. cit.*, p. 57; *HH.*, pp. 155, 48–49 (testimony of Chief Scientist of ARPA, Herbert York); see also Sullivan, *Assault on the Unknown, op. cit.*, p. 80.

8 U.S. House of Representatives, *Project Vanguard . . ., op. cit.*, pp. 57–58. See also Sullivan, *Assault on the Unknown, op. cit.*, chap. 6.

9 *HH*, p. 63, testimony of Dr. Werner von Braun.

10 U.S. House of Representatives, *Project Vanguard . . ., op. cit.*, p. 58.

11 *HH*, p. 63, testimony of Dr. Werner von Braun. See also U.S. House of Representatives, *Project Vanguard . . ., op. cit.*, pp. 58–59.

12 U.S. House of Representatives, *Project Vanguard . . ., op. cit.*, p. 59.

13 U.S. Senate, Preparedness Investigating Subcommittee of the Committee on Armed Services, *Hearings, Inquiry into Satellites and Missile Programs*, p. 148, ff. (Hereinafter, these Senate Preparedness Subcommittee Hearings will be referred to as *SPSCH*.)

14 See *SPSCH*, pp. 209, testimony

of Secretary of Defense Neil McElroy, 165, testimony of Dr. John Hagen, Director, Project Vanguard, Naval Research Laboratories. See also U.S. House of Representatives, *Project Vanguard . . . , op. cit.*, p. 74; see also Sullivan, *Assault on the Unknown, op. cit.*, p. 86, U.S. House of Representatives, *Project Vanguard, op. cit.*

15 *SPSCH*, p. 1701, testimony of Gen. John B. Medaris, Commander, Army Ballistic Missile Agency.

16 See *SPSCH*, pp. 1700–1701, testimony of Gen. John B. Medaris, and *The New York Times*, October 15, 1957. (Hereinafter, *The New York Times* will be cited as *NYT*.)

17 See *SPSCH*, p. 510, testimony of Gen. James M. Gavin, Deputy Chief, Office of Research and Development, U.S. Army.

18 Sullivan, *Assault on the Unknown, op. cit.*, p. 87. See also U.S. House of Representatives, *Project Vanguard . . . , op. cit.*, pp. 68–70.

19 See Sullivan, *Assault on the Unknown, op. cit.*, pp. 29, 49, 56–57; *NYT*, June 2, 1957, and *NYT*, June 27, 1957; and Survey Research Center, *Satellites, Science, and the Public: A Report of a National Survey on the Public Impact of Early Satellite Launchings* (Institute for Social Research, University of Michigan, 1959).

20 *NYT*, October 5, 1957.

21 See *NYT*, Oct. 5, 1957, and *Science*, Oct. 18, 1957; see also, Richard Witkin, editor, *The Challenge of the Sputniks*, New York, 1959, p. 4.

22 Survey Research Center, *Satellites, Science, and the Public: A Report of a National Survey on the Public Impact of Early Satellite Launchings*, Ann Arbor, Mich., 1959; See also Gabriel Almond, "Public Opin-

ion and Space Technology," in Joseph Goldsen, editor, *Outer Space in World Politics*, New York, 1963, pp. 71–96 especially p. 92.

23 See *NYT*, Oct. 5, 1957.

24 *NYT*, Oct. 10, 1957.

25 *NYT*, Oct. 24, 1957.

26 *NYT*, Oct. 16, 1957.

27 See *NYT*, Oct. 17, 1957.

28 See *NYT*, Oct. 18, 1937, and Oct. 29, 1957.

29 See Bernhard G. Bechhoefer, *Postwar Negotiations for Arms Control*, Washington D.C., 1961, and *NYT*, Oct. 7–8, 1957.

30 See *NYT*, Oct. 14, 1957.

31 See *NYT*, Oct. 10, 1957.

32 *NYT*, Oct. 16, 1957.

33 See *NYT*, Oct. 11, 1957, and *infra*, Chap. 3, Secs. 1 and 2.

34 *NYT*, Oct. 11, 1957.

35 See *NYT*, Oct. 28, 1957. At this meeting, Dr. Alan Waterman submitted the National Science Foundation's Report on "Basic Research—A National Resource" to Eisenhower, who received it favorably.

36 *NYT*, Oct. 5, 1957.

37 See *NYT*, Oct. 23, 1957 and *NYT*, Oct. 29, 1957.

38 See *NYT*, Nov. 3, 1957, Sec. 4.

39 *NYT*, Oct. 5, 1957.

40 *HH*, p. 279, testimony of Rear Admiral Hayward.

41 *NYT*, Oct. 9, 1957.

42 See *NYT*, Oct. 10, 1957.

43 *NYT*, Oct. 17, 1957.

44 See *NYT*, Oct. 15–16, 1957.

45 See *NYT*, Oct. 17, 1957.

46 See *NYT*, Oct. 5–6, 1957, particularly the statements of Dr. Lloyd V. Berkner, Dr. Vannevar Bush, Dr. Joseph Kaplan, and others.

47 *NYT*, Nov. 3, 1957.

48 *NYT*, Oct. 24, 1957.

49 *NYT*, Oct. 6, 1957.

50 *NYT*, Oct. 16, 1957.

51 *NYT*, Oct. 6, 1957.

52 *NYT*, Oct. 5–6, 1957.

53 *NYT*, Oct. 12, 1957.

54 *NYT*, Oct. 19, 1957.

55 *NYT*, Oct. 6, 1957; see also *NYT*, Oct. 8, 1957.

56 *Ibid.*

57 Samuel P. Huntington, *The Common Defense*, New York & London, 1961, p. 220.

58 *NYT*, Nov. 10, 1957.

59 *NYT*, Jan. 21, 1958.

60 See *NYT*, Jan. 21, 1958.

61 *NYT*, Feb. 2, 1958.

62 See *NYT*, Jan. 21, 1958.

63 See *NYT*, Feb. 1, 1958, and *NYT*, Feb. 3, 1958.

64 See *NYT*, Dec. 7, 1957.

65 See *NYT*, March 10, 1958.

66 *Business Week*, Nov. 16, 1957.

67 See *Science*, Jan. 2, 1958.

68 *NYT*, Nov. 13, 1957. See also *NYT*, Nov. 15, 1957.

69 See *NYT*, Dec. 5, 1957.

70 See *NYT*, Jan. 14, 1958.

71 *NYT*, Nov. 14, 1957.

72 *NYT*, Feb. 6, 1958.

73 For further discussion of the evolution of the administration's position on space, see *infra*, pp. 232–239.

74 *NYT*, Feb. 18, 1958.

75 *NYT*, Mar. 27, 1958.

76 U.S. House of Representatives, *Message from the President of the United States Relative to Space Science and Exploration*, Document No. 365 (85th Cong. 2nd Sess., 1958).

77 See *NYT*, Nov. 12, 1957.

78 *SPSCH*, pp. 361–362, testimony of Director of Guided Missiles William Holaday.

79 See *ibid.*, p. 250, testimony of Secretary McElroy.

80 *Ibid.*, p. 207, testimony of Secretary McElroy, emphasis added.

81 See *NYT*, Dec. 8, 1957, *NYT*, Dec. 30, 1957, and *NYT*, Feb. 1, 1958.

82 *SPSCH*, pp. 236–237, testimony of Secretary McElroy.

83 See *NYT*, Nov. 16, 1957.

84 See *SPSCH*, p. 211, testimony of Secretary McElroy.

85 *NYT*, Dec. 12, 1957.

86 *SPSCH*, p. 413, testimony of Mr. Holaday.

87 *Ibid.*, p. 218, testimony of Secretary McElroy.

88 *Ibid.*, p. 424, testimony of Mr. Holaday.

89 See *infra*, pp. 199–212.

90 See *Aviation Week*, Dec. 23, 1957, statement of Mr. Dan Kimball, president of Aerojet Gen. Corp. See also Robert Coward, Unpublished seminar paper on ARPA [M.I.T.], pp. 2–4.

91 See U.S. House of Representatives, Committee on Government Operations, *Hearings, Organization and Management of Missile Programs* (1959), p. 133.

92 *NYT*, Jan. 10, 1958.

93 Department of Defense, Directive #5105.15.

94 See *HH*, pp. 716–719, testimony of Dr. Herbert York.

95 *SPSCH*, p. 235, testimony of Secretary McElroy.

96 *Ibid.*, p. 237, testimony of Secretary McElroy.

97 *Ibid.*, p. 415, testimony of Mr. Holaday.

98 See *NYT*, Nov. 9–10, 1957, and *NYT*, Dec. 4, 1957.

99 See *NYT*, Mar. 3, 1958.

100 See *SPSCH*, p. 1757.

101 *Ibid.*, p. 1952, testimony of Admiral Arleigh Burke, Chief of Naval Operations.

102 See *ibid.*, p. 159, testimony of Dr. Hagen.

103 *Ibid.*, p. 172, testimony of Dr. Hagen.

104 *NYT*, Nov. 9, 1957.

105 See *NYT*, Nov. 10, 1957; see also *SPSCH*, pp. 1701 ff., testimony of Gen. Medaris.

106 *SPSCH*, pp. 560–561, testimony of Gen. Medaris.

107 See *NYT*, Dec. 11–12, 1957, *NYT*, Dec. 19, 1957, and *NYT*, Jan. 28, 1958.

108 *NYT*, Feb. 1, 1958.

110 *Ibid.*

111 *SPSCH*, p. 464, testimony of

Wilbur Brucker, Secretary of the Army.

112 *Ibid.*, p. 1509, testimony of Gen. Gavin.

113 *Ibid.*, p. 505, testimony of Gen. Gavin.

114 *Ibid.*, p. 507, testimony of Gen. Gavin.

115 *Ibid.*, p. 1511, testimony of Gen. Gavin.

116 *Ibid.*, p. 558, testimony of Gen. Medaris.

117 See *ibid.*, p. 613, testimony of Dr. von Braun.

118 See *NYT*, Nov. 4, 1957; see also, *SPSCH*, p. 517, testimony of Gen. Gavin.

119 See *SPSCH*, p. 1709, ff.

120 *Ibid.*, p. 575, testimony of Gen. Medaris.

121 *Ibid.*

122 *Ibid.*, p. 613, testimony of Dr. von Braun.

123 *Ibid.*, p. 618, testimony of Dr. von Braun.

124 *Ibid.*, pp. 1708–1709, testimony of Gen. Medaris.

125 *Ibid.*, p. 1453, testimony of Gen. Gavin; see also *NYT*, Jan. 5, 1958 and *NYT*, Jan. 9, 1958; see also *infra*, pp. 220–231.

126 See *NYT*, Mar. 6, 1958.

127 *SPSCH*, p. 858, testimony of Secretary of the Air Force Douglas.

128 *Ibid.*, p. 977, testimony of Richard E. Horner, Assistant Secretary of the Air Force for Research and Development.

129 See *NYT*, Nov. 19, 1957.

130 *SPSCH*, pp. 1678–1679, testimony of Gen. Bernard A. Schriever, Commander, Air Force Ballistic Missile Agency.

131 *Ibid.*, p. 1678, testimony of Gen. Schriever.

132 See *ibid.*, p. 841, testimony of Secretary Douglas.

133 See *NYT*, Jan. 15, 1958, and *NYT*, May 25, 1958.

134 See *NYT*, Feb. 9, 1958, and *NYT*, Feb. 19, 1958. See also, *SPSCH*, p. 1675, ff., testimony of Gen. Schriever.

135 See *supra.*

136 See *SPSCH*, p. 1675 ff., testimony of Gen. Schriever; see also, *NYT*, Nov. 22, 1957.

137 See *NYT*, Nov. 22, 1957, and *NYT*, Nov. 30, 1957.

138 See *SPSCH*, p. 1674 ff., testimony of Gen. Schriever; see also, *NYT*, Jan. 9, 1958.

139 *SPSCH*, p. 1674, testimony of Gen. Schriever.

140 *NYT*, Nov. 30, 1957.

141 *SPSCH*, p. 976, testimony of Lt. Gen. Clarence S. Irvine, Deputy Chief of Staff for Material, USAF.

142 *Ibid.*, p. 1588, testimony of Gen. Thomas D. White, Chairman of the Joint Chiefs of Staff.

143 *Ibid.*, p. 1678, testimony of Gen. Schriever.

144 *Ibid.*, pp. 1679–1680, testimony of Gen. Schriever.

145 *Ibid.*, p. 1593, testimony of Gen. White.

146 *Ibid.*

147 *Science,* Nov. 29, 1957.

148 The journals reviewed include: *The New York Times; Science; Scientific American; The Bulletin of the Atomic Scientists; Foreign Affairs; Harper's;* and *The Atlantic Monthly.*

149 See *SPSCH*, testimony of Dr. Edward Teller and Dr. Vannevar Bush, pp. 6 ff.; see also C. C. Furnas, "Why Did the US Lose the Race: Critics Speak Up," *Life*, Oct. 21, 1957; see also, Arthur R. von Hippel, *Bulletin of the Atomic Scientists*, Vol. XIV, No. 3, Mar., 1958, p. 115; see also E. Rabinowitch, *Bulletin of the Atomic Scientists*, Vol. XIII, No. 12; Dec., 1957, p. 346; see also *NYT*, Jan. 1, 1958, speech by Dr. Isidor I. Rabi.

150 See *SPSCH*, pp. 6 ff., testimony of Dr. Teller and Dr. Bush.

151 *NYT*, Jan. 1, 1958.

152 *NYT*, Feb. 4, 1958.

153 See *NYT*, Nov. 9, 1957, especi-

ally the comments of Dr. Arthur Compton, Dr. Lee duBridge, and Dr. Detlev Bronk.

154 See *NYT*, Feb. 7, 1958; see also *Science*, Apr. 18, 1958.

155 See *Science*, Feb. 21, 1958.

156 U.S. Senate, Special Committee on Space and Astronautics, *Compilation of Materials on Space and Astronautics*. No. 1, "A National Space Establishment," p. 17.

157 *Ibid.*

158 *Ibid.*, p. 18.

159 *Ibid.*, pp. 18–19.

160 *Ibid.*, p. 19.

161 See *NYT*, Dec. 5, 1957, and *NYT*, Dec. 13, 1957; see also, *Missiles and Rockets*, Nov. 7, 1957.

162 See *SPSCH*, Appendices.

163 See U.S. Senate, Special Committee on Space and Astronautics, *Compilation of Materials . . .*, "Basic Objectives of a Continuing Program of Scientific Research in Outer Space," pp. 23, ff.

164 *Ibid.*

165 *Ibid.*, p. 44.

166 See *The Bulletin of the Atomic Scientists*, Vol. XIV, No. 2, Feb., 1958, editorial.

167 *NYT*, Nov. 16, 1957.

168 See *NYT*, Jan. 13, 1958.

169 See *SPSCH*, Appendices.

170 See *supra*, p. 201 for Dr. Hagen's view, and pp. 204–206 for Dr. von Braun's opinion.

171 U.S. House of Representatives, Select Committee on Astronautics and Space Exploration, *The National Space Program*, Report No. 1758 (85th Cong. 2nd Sess., 1958). "NACA— Resolution on the Subject of Space Flight, adopted January 16, 1958," p. 118, emphasis added.

172 *Ibid.*

173 *Ibid.*, "Space Technology and the NACA," pp. 112–113.

174 See *supra*.

175 See *NYT*, Nov. 14, 1957, and *NYT*, Nov. 24, 1957.

176 See *NYT*, Nov. 9, 1957.

177 *SPSCH*, p. 2057.

178 *NYT*, Nov. 11, 1957.

179 *SPSCH*, pp. 1–3, statement of Sen. Johnson.

180 See *ibid.*, p. 2428.

181 See *NYT*, Dec. 16, 1957.

182 *SPSCH*, pp. 280–281, remarks of Sen. Johnson.

183 See *ibid.*, pp. 249 ff., testimony of Secretary McElroy, and *ibid.*, pp. 282 ff., testimony of Under Secretary Quarles.

184 *Ibid.*, p. 249, remarks of Sen. Symington.

185 See *ibid.*, p. 344, statements of Sen. Johnson.

186 *Ibid.*, p. 508, remarks of Sen. Johnson.

187 *Ibid.*, p. 1459, remarks of Sen. Johnson.

188 *Ibid.*, p. 2429.

189 See *NYT*, Dec. 5, 1958, Johnson's speech before the Texas Testimonial; see also *NYT*, Jan. 10, 1958, Johnson's statement preceding the President's State of the Union Message; see also *NYT*, Jan. 15, 1958, Johnson's speech to CBS affiliate stations.

190 See *NYT*, Jan. 8, 1958, column of James Reston.

191 *NYT*, Jan. 8, 1958, text of Sen. Johnson's speech to the Democratic caucus.

192 *Ibid.*

193 S. 3117, H.R. 10352, and H.R. 10271, respectively, all of which were referred to the Joint Committee on Atomic Energy.

194 S. 3233, introduced by Sens. Yarborough, Mansfield, Hill, Sparkman, Carroll, Morse, and Humphrey, and referred to the Interstate and Foreign Commerce Committee. H.R. 9847 and H.R. 9966, introduced by Reps. Thomas Lane and Melwin Coad, respectively, and referred to the House

Armed Services Committee.

195 S. 3604, introduced by Sen. Francis Case and referred to the Special Committee on Space and Astronautics. H.R. 11188 and H.R. 11860, introduced by Reps. Frelinghuysen and Fulton, respectively, and referred to the House Armed Services Committee.

196 H.R. Con. Res. 265, referred to the House Foreign Affairs Committee.

197 See *NYT*, Jan. 17, 1958; see also, Alison Griffith, *The National Aeronautics and Space Act: A Study of the Development of Public Policy*, Washington D.C., 1962, p. 12.

198 Sen. Res. 256.

199 Sen. Res. 256, Sec. 1.

200 H.R. Res. 496.

201 Griffith, *op. cit.*, p. 21.

202 See *ibid.*, p. 22.

203 See *supra*, pp. 193–199.

204 See *ibid.*

205 See Frank Gibney, "The Missile Mess," *Harper's*, Jan., 1960, p. 43, where he describes Eisenhower's insistence upon civilian control as "fanatic: his one piece of enthusiasm in the whole space picture."

206 See William F. Finan, "Organizational and Administrative Problems of the Government's Space Program," *unpublished paper*, p. 1.

207 Private interview sources.

208 See *supra*, pp. 217–220.

209 U.S. Senate, Special Committee on Space and Astronautics, *Hearings on S. 3609* (85th Cong. 2nd Sess., 1958), p. 249, testimony of Dr. Hugh Dryden, Director, National Advisory Committee for Aeronautics. (Hereinafter, these Senate Hearings will be referred to as *SH*.).

210 See U.S. Senate, Special Committee on Space and Astronautics, *Compilation of Materials . . .*, "An Introduction

to Outer Space," p. 45.

211 *Ibid.*, pp. 48–49.

212 *Ibid.*, p. 52.

213 See *supra*, pp. 217–220. See also lecture by James R. Killian on the establishment of NASA, at M.I.T., Mar., 1962.

214 *SH*, p. 282, testimony of Bureau of the Budget Director Maurice Stans.

215 Finan, *op. cit.*, p. 2.

216 See *NYT*, Feb. 5, 1958.

217 See Killian, *op. cit.*

218 Private interview sources; see also *HH*, p. 421, testimony of Dr. Dryden.

219 *SH, S.* 3609, p. 1.

220 *Ibid.*, p. 2.

221 See *HH*, p. 133, testimony of Dr. Dryden.

222 See *SH*, p. 279, testimony of Director Stans.

223 See *SH*, p. 195, "Statement of the Bureau of the Budget on Certain Statements made by Assistant Secretary of the Air Force MacIntyre before the Senate Committee, on May 8, 1958."

224 See *SH*, p. 342.

225 *HH*, p. 1542, testimony of Dr. York.

226 See *SH*, testimony of ARPA's Director Roy W. Johnson, Secretary Brucker, and Dr. Hagen.

227 *SH*, p. 168, testimony of Director Johnson.

228 See *SH*, testimony of Director Stans.

229 *NYT*, May 10, 1958.

230 See *supra*, p. 238, statement of Roy Johnson.

231 *SH*, p. 25, testimony of Dr. James Doolittle, Chairman of the National Advisory Committee for Aeronautics.

232 See *HH*, p. 5.

233 *Ibid.*

234 See *SH*, p. 195.

235 See *SH*, p. 15, ff., testimony of Dr. Dryden.

236 *HH*, p. 866, testimony of Dr. James A. Van Allen.

237 See *SH*, p. 15, ff., testimony of Dr. Dryden.
238 *Ibid.*
239 *Ibid.*
240 See *SPSCH*, appendices.
241 See *HH*, testimony of Dr. Herbert York, Chief Scientist, ARPA.
242 See *ibid;* see also *ibid.*, testimony of Dr. Hagen and Dr. von Braun.
243 See *HH*, pp. 312–313.
244 *SH*, p. 2, text of S. 3609, emphasis added.
245 *HH*, p. 5.
246 *HH*, p. 1110, testimony of Under Secretary Quarles.
247 *SH*, p. 67, testimony of Under Secretary Quarles.
248 *HH*, p. 178, testimony of Dr. York.
249 See *SH*, p. 47, testimony of Dr. York.
250 *SH*, p. 66, testimony of Under Secretary Quarles.
251 See *SH*, pp. 111, ff., testimony of Under Secretary Quarles.
252 *SH*, p. 74, testimony of Under Secretary Quarles.
253 See *SH*, p. 67, testimony of Under Secretary Quarles.
254 See *SH*, p. 245, testimony of Garrison Norton, Assistant Secretary of the Navy for Air.
255 *SH*, p. 238, testimony of Assistant Secretary Norton.
256 *HH*, p. 656, testimony of Gen. Schriever.
257 See *HH*, p. 648, testimony of Gen. Schriever.
258 See *SH*, p. 198, testimony of Assistant Secretary of the Air Force Malcolm MacIntyre.
259 See *SH*, p. 197, testimony of Assistant Secretary MacIntyre; see also, *HH*, p. 672, testimony of Gen. Schriever; see also, *HH*, p. 527, testimony of Gen. Boushey.
260 *HH*, p. 145, testimony of Gen. Medaris.
261 See *HH*, p. 146, testimony of Gen. Medaris.
262 See *HH*, p. 690.
263 See *SH*, p. 221.
264 Reps. Leslie Arends and Overton Brooks, neither of whom participated actively in the hearings on the space bill.
265 See *HH*, pp. 75–76.
266 See Griffith, *op. cit.*, Chap. 6.
267 See *HH*, p. 1121, and *HH*, p. 1158, comments of Mr. George Feldman, Staff Director and Chief Counsel to the House Committee.
268 *HH*, p. 893, statement of Rep. John McCormack, Chairman, House Select Committee on Astronautics and Space Exploration.
269 See *HH*, p. 415.
270 *HH*, p. 470.
271 See *HH*, p. 427; see also *HH*, p. 435.
272 *HH*, p. 862, remarks of Rep. McCormack.
273 *HH*, p. 676, remarks of Rep. Lee Metcalf.
274 See *HH*, pp. 462 ff.
275 *HH*, p. 136.
276 See *SH*, pp. 6–7, statement of Sen. Johnson.
277 See *SH*, pp. 297, ff.
278 See *SH*, p. 30, remarks of Sen. Leverett Saltonstall.
279 *SH*, p. 24, remarks of Sen. Bourke Hickenlooper.
280 *NYT*, May 10, 1958.
281 See *SH*, pp. 229, ff; see also, *SH*, p. 73.
282 See *SH*, p. 85.
283 See *SH*, p. 219.
284 *SH*, p. 55, remarks of Sen. Stuart Symington.
285 See *SH*, p. 58, statement of Mr. Edwin Weisl, Consulting Counsel to the Senate Committee.
286 See *SH*, p. 37; see also *SH*, p. 276, comments of Mr. Weisl.
287 *HH*, p. 1165, testimony of Director Roy Johnson.
288 See *HH*, p. 1168, testimony of Director Johnson.
289 *Ibid.*
290 See *HH*, p. 1191, testimony of Director Johnson.

291 *SH*, p. 150, testimony of Director Johnson.

292 *SH*, p. 169, testimony of Director Johnson.

293 *NYT*, May 9, 1958.

294 See Coward, *op. cit.*, pp. 7–12.

295 See *SH*, p. 17, testimony of Dr. Doolittle, where he suggests that the President appoint a committee consisting of Killian, Quarles, the director of NASA, Strauss, and Waterman to "resolve questions as to which specific items should be in NASA and which should be in the DOD and which should be joint projects."

296 *HH*, p. 1528, testimony of Mr. Robert Dechert, General Counsel of the DOD (statement cleared with Gerald Morgan, Assistant Counsel to the President.)

297 *Ibid.*

298 *HH*, pp. 1534–1540, *passim*.

299 *SH*, p. 236.

300 U.S. House of Representatives, Select Committee on Astronautics and Space Exploration, *Establishment of the National Space Program, Report on H.R. 12575* (Report No. 1770, 85th Cong. 2nd Sess., 1958).

301 See Griffith, *op. cit.*, p. 79.

302 See *ibid.*, Chap. 8; see also,

303 See *NYT*, June 3, 1958.

304 See Griffith, *op. cit.*, Chap. 8. The bill itself was largely written by Gerald Siegal, Chief of Staff for the Senate Committee, in Johnson's office. It was accepted in one meeting of the Senate Committee, practically as drafted.

305 U.S. Senate, Special Committee on Space and Astronautics, *National Aeronautics and Space Act of 1958* (Report No. 1701, 85th Cong. 2nd Sess., 1958).

306 *Ibid.*, p. 4.

307 *Ibid.*

308 *Ibid.*, p. 7.

309 Private interview.

310 Private interview, see also Killian, *op. cit.*

311 U.S. House of Representatives, Committee of Conference, National Aeronautics and Space Act of 1958 (Report No. 2166, 85th Cong. 2nd Sess., 1958), Sec. 205.

312 *Ibid.*, Title I, Sec. 102(b).

313 *Ibid.*, Title II, Sec. 201.

314 *PL 85–568.*

315 Congressional Record (daily edition), Aug. 23, 1958, p. 17884.

# 6

# Comsat:

## The Inevitable Anomaly

ROGER A. KVAM

IN THE· SUMMER of 1962, two events occurred in a sequence that emphasized both the promise and the problems of a new era in American life. On July 10, the world's first communications satellite, designed and built by a private company for a commercial market, was launched into orbit by the joint effort of the company, American Telephone and Telegraph, and a government agency, the National Aeronautics and Space Administration. In August the Communications Satellite Act of 1962 was signed into law by President John F. Kennedy.[1] This act was the result of two years of arduous legislative effort in the executive and Congress to design a legally, politically, and economically viable entity to preside over the national effort to develop a system of space communications in association with other countries.

The technological feat earned plaudits from all sides. The legislative achievement was not so widely appreciated. Senator Russell Long of Louisiana said of the new statute: "When this bill first started out I thought it was as crooked as a dog's hind leg. I am now convinced that that would be a compliment. This bill is as crooked as a barrel of snakes."[2] Duly allowing for senatorial hyperbole and mixed metaphor, the Senator's complaint illustrates the contrast between the political neutrality of the technological development and the politically charged character of the effort to organize and control this development.

In the fashioning of the statute, all the classic ingredients of American legislative politics were on hand in abundance. Private groups jockeyed for position in the pursuit of whatever commercial

ROGER A. KVAM *is Assistant Professor of Political Science, the University of Akron. This paper is drawn from a larger work in preparation.*

advantages outer space might hold. Political figures in both parties responded to new challenges with exactly the well-worn clichés a cynic might have expected. Spokesmen for the public agencies were alternately unanimously in favor of the administration's bill and willing to give vent to their more limited interests and anxieties whenever opportunity arose.

In addition, there was a new element—the novelty of outer space as a policy issue. Was the new communications system merely a "cable in the sky," like more familiar systems for transmitting information—or was it something so unprecedented that it required a different system of exploitation and control? What of the international complications? Here was a system that could be a very potent instrument of political expression. Was it proper to put it primarily in the hands of a private profit-making company? And what of the problem of monopoly? It hardly seemed advisable or practical to open outer space to a scramble for advantage among industrial competitors, but was it any more proper to confer a monopoly on a single firm? Should the public funds that had already been invested in space activities and that would continue to be invested go for the support of a venture in private profit?

It is understandable that the statute should have emerged from Congress only after it had undergone an extraordinary career of scrutiny and reconsideration. Senator Mike Mansfield of Montana, the Majority Leader, normally known for his patience and equanimity, introduced debate on the bill by noting that it had been studied by five committees in the Senate and one in the House and that it had been the subject of 3,000 pages of testimony that took over 45 days to present. On the Senate floor, he pointed out, it had consumed 308 pages of debate in 14 days. Now the bill was coming up for the third and, he hoped, the final time: "In the light of this generous legislative history, the Senate must now squarely face the question of whether it will legislate or vegetate."[3]

Legislate it did, for better or worse. As finally passed, the law provided for a corporation that would be a blend of public and private enterprise. On its board would sit not only representatives of shareholders but also directors appointed by the President and confirmed by the Senate. The business of the corporation was to be guided by the profit motive, but under the regulation of the Federal Communications Commission, NASA, the State Department, and the President—and with public subsidy. Samuel F. B. Morse's apotheosis of telegraphy—"What hath God wrought?"—might have been repeated, with less piety but the same wonder, for the creature brought forth by Congress to oversee satellite communications.

President Kennedy thought that the result was an important achievement in the effort to use science and technology in the public interest, but in accordance with the traditional American reliance on private enterprise. As he put it, when he signed the bill into law:

> The statute provides many safeguards to protect the public interest. No single company or group will have the power to dominate the Corporation. The general public, the comunications industry, and the Federal Government all will have a voice. All will contribute their resources, and all may reasonably hope to benefit. In this way, the vigor of our competitive free enterprise system will be effectively used in challenging new activity on the frontier of space.[4]

There were many, particularly in Congress, who disagreed with the President and thought that space activities belonged in the public domain. Their objections were overridden in favor of an instrument that was neither wholly private nor wholly public but a mixture of the two. To those familiar with the pattern of postwar relations between science and government, this result should have come as no great surprise. Comsat was only the latest instance of the partnership between government and the private sector that has grown up as the matrix of government support for research and development.[5] Given the precedents and the need for speedy action, some such hybrid anomaly was probably inevitable. But the fact that it was in a certain sense inevitable does not mean that it must pass unexamined. We may still ask with profit whether the Communications Satellite Act serves the public interest well or badly; whether, indeed, it is possible to define the public interest in this instance and others involving major technological innovations, with so many unforeseeable consequences; whether, finally, the decision to create Comsat reflected a careful consideration of principle and practicality or whether it came about primarily through a play of forces—forces like the self-interest of private business and the fear of Soviet competition. We may ask, in short, how it was that this experiment in government as well as science came to be undertaken and what it indicates about our ability to cope with the products of modern science.

## Administrator Glennan Sets the Stage

In the early consideration of communications satellite policy during the Eisenhower administration, the most crucial decision that had to be faced was unquestionably that dealing with ownership. Was private enterprise to control the American share of any worldwide system? Once this issue was decided, other decisions could be made concerning participation by government in the production of satellites and launch vehicles and in the orbiting operations. If ownership was to be in private hands, plans could be drawn up for the eventual recovery of public funds already committed to the program. The basic decision was therefore bound to be far-reaching.

It is hard to pinpoint the considerations that weighed most heavily in the balance. The traditional Republican belief in the virtues of free enterprise under government regulation was undoubtedly one important factor, especially since the communications companies lost no opportunity to remind the administration of its principles. Another consideration was the fact that the companies were spending large amounts of money on their own to develop satellite technology,[6] enabling government to keep public expenditures down. Still another factor in the decision was the belief in private ownership held by the man most immediately concerned with the issue, Dr. T. Keith Glennan, Administrator of NASA.

Dr. Glennan, who was appointed to his post when NASA was first established in 1958, believed strongly that the entire communications system should remain in private hands. He agreed with the contention of the Bell System that the new facilities should be integrated into the country's existing system because under private control that system had provided America with eminence in communications.[7] There were members of his staff who thought otherwise. They contended that communications satellites required public ownership and they had grave suspicions that AT&T, by absorbing the new technology that was being developed at government expense, would acquire a vast addition to its already enormous wealth and power.

Glennan acknowledged that there was a certain danger of monopoly in the private exploitation of space communications, but he preferred to see the project advanced quickly, as it would be with the help of private enterprise, even at a certain risk of monopoly. When the Bell System offered in September 1960 to spend as much as $30 million for three satellite flights, and more if the results warranted, Glennan was easily persuaded that such positive action would hasten the day when government could reserve its funds for other projects less feasible commercially. He had no exact idea when and how the government's role should be phased out, but it was clear to him that the government should not finance efforts that would yield private profits beyond the point at which the venture could stand on its own. He was inclined to dismiss the criticisms of the civil servants around him as the misconceptions of people who had worked for government so long that they could not appreciate how well private enterprise could serve the public interest.[8]

During the last months of the Eisenhower administration, Glennan sought diligently to win the support of the President and other high officials for this policy. The first public disclosure of what the administration's policy might be came in a speech by Glennan on October 12, 1960, at a luncheon sponsored by the Oregon State Department of Planning and Development in Portland. In this talk the administrator pointed out that "NASA has a statutory duty to preserve the leadership of the United States in space technology and in the application of it to the conduct of peaceful activities." But he made it quite clear that he expected NASA's role in space communications to be that of an initiator only. "NASA," he said, "will continue its research and development efforts in this field only so long as is necessary to assure that timely development of a commercially feasible communications system will be completed by private industry."[9]

This was a remarkable statement in several respects. It was the first commitment by a government official to the policy of turning the ownership of the forthcoming system over to private enterprise. It was also the first commitment of the government to the idea of permitting private companies to become its partners in the early stages of development. Since the statement was so important, it might be supposed that it would have been cleared before delivery. In fact, however, Glennan had not cleared the speech with the White House or, indeed, with any of the other agencies concerned with satellite communications.[10] "I was not sure how government policy was made in those areas," he observed in retrospect, "but I was going to try and find out."[11]

Glennan's hope was that before he left NASA he would succeed in getting communications policy "on the right track." To this end he prepared a policy statement which he circulated among the other interested political officers of the Eisenhower administration. Late in December the policy statement was presented to the Cabinet, where it secured Presidential approval. Part of the paper was issued as an official policy statement by the President on December 31, 1960, barely twenty days before the new administration was to take over. In the statement Eisenhower urged that the government encourage private enterprise to establish a profit-making satellite communications system. He directed NASA to cooperate with other government agencies such as the FCC with this object in mind. He closed the statement with a clear commitment to private enterprise:

> To achieve the early establishment of a communication satellite system which can be used on a commercial basis is a national objective which will require the concerted capabilities and funds of both Government and private enterprise and the cooperative participation of communications organizations in foreign countries.[12]

The Eisenhower commitment was not immediately confirmed by the new administration. On May 25, 1961, President Kennedy appeared in person to present a message on "Urgent National Needs" to a joint session of Congress. In this address he stressed his determination to emphasize activities in outer space. He proposed committing the nation to landing a man on the moon by the end of the decade and stepping up the effort in space communications. The new President clearly meant to pick up the pace of the entire space program, and the use of satellites for communication promised one of the earliest "payoffs" in the effort to recoup lost prestige. The supplemental appropriations requested totaled $531 million, with a projected $7 to 9 billion additional to be committed over the next 5 years.[13] This was the sort of recommendation that left no doubt among the interested parties both in government agencies and private industry that the time had come for vigorous action. But it was no longer clear what the policy of the government would be with respect to private participation and control.

### The Industrial Rivalry

As the government accelerated activity on the space front in general, and in communications satellites in particular, the various interested firms were quick to make known their views on the disposition of any new system of communications. A wide group of companies had interests in the subject, ranging from the international and domestic common carriers to the manufacturers of space hardware. Within the industry there were divisions of interest. The international carriers and the domestic carriers had conflicting points of view. There was also a conflict between the companies that carried voice transmission services and those that carried only recorded transmissions. The Bell System controlled virtually the entire international voice transmission business, while the record transmissions were carried by several companies, including the Radio Corporation of America, International Telephone and Telegraph, Western Union, and several smaller companies. This group of companies argued that since the distinction between voice and recorded transmissions had been outmoded by technical advances their companies ought to be permitted to provide a full range of services to their customers. The Bell System naturally opposed this potential inroad upon its lucrative market. As a result of these conflicts of interest, the communications industry was badly split in its effort to influence the formation of policy.

A division of interest that was still worse, from the point of view of the communications industry, was the one that ranged the communications carriers against several aerospace companies—

Lockheed, Hughes, General Electric, and Bendix, among others. Through their experience in supplying and managing the hardware used in civil and military space efforts, they had gained considerable knowledge and skill that could be put to use in space communications. The aerospace firms were quite aware that several of the communications companies, notably Bell, RCA, and IT&T, had manufacturing subsidiaries of their own from which they were in the habit of purchasing virtually all of their equipment. They were therefore frankly fearful that if Bell or the other carriers were given the satellite system, their own competitive position as equipment suppliers would be hopeless.

AT&T was destined for the role of villain from the start. As the largest privately owned corporation in the world, with over $22 billion in assets at the end of the 1960 business year,[14] and with a reputation for business acumen and ability in research that inspired universal envy and admiration, it was bound to be feared by its competitors. Bell had already made overtures to NASA and other government agencies in the hope that it might be permitted to launch an experimental satellite system. Not to be outdone, Lockheed had in 1960 submitted a study prepared by a management consulting firm on the business implications of a commercial satellite system. On January 19, the day before the new administration assumed office, these preliminary efforts led to more advanced ones. Lockheed sought approval from the Department of Justice for a joint study, in collaboration with RCA, General Telephone & Electronics, and other companies, to examine the feasibility of such a system and to consider the type of business organization that might best develop and operate it. The Justice Department gave its approval.

The same day the FCC announced that it was authorizing the Bell System to establish the first space communication link across the Atlantic on an experimental basis. NASA would do the launchings for Bell, and the company would reimburse the government for all costs. The commission made clear that the authorization was for an experimental system only and not for a commercial one. This restriction did not trouble Bell so much as the fact that the advent of a new administration meant that the policy line laid down by Administrator Glennan might no longer be in force. If not, Bell might find itself in a position where it would be spending funds for an experiment that it would not be permitted to exploit commercially. Nor could Bell proceed with the experiment without further ado. Before the FCC permit could be acted upon, a new group of administrators would have to be convinced that Bell wished only to advance the state of the art by the experiment rather than preempt the field.

The very fact that Bell received a license for such an advanced project stirred fears among its many industrial rivals that even if the company were not ultimately selected as a "chosen instrument" it would nevertheless still acquire a predominant position through its projected research. There was a lively awareness of the same possibility within government. As a result, the agencies that were to cooperate with Bell were reluctant to carry out the agreement until the policy regarding ownership was established. The agencies' reluctance aroused criticism from at least one important member of Congress. "I am trying to find out," Senator Clinton F. Anderson of New Mexico told NASA Administrator James Webb, "why we want to spend $50 million of Government money to do what AT&T says it would like to do free."[15] Webb took the position that until policy was declared, it was advisable that costs of research and development be borne wholly by the government.

In order to clarify its own position, AT&T issued an elaborate press release rehearsing its "Space Policy." The statement sought to reassure equipment suppliers that they would not be frozen out if Bell obtained control of the system. In a section on "The Question of Monopoly," the release declared:

> The Bell System does not seek a monopoly in space communications, either in use or ownership of satellite systems, or in manufacture of hardware. In fact, much of the money spent in realizing Bell's proposal would be for equipment and services supplied from sources outside the Bell System. Rockets and launching for a Bell satellite system, for example, would be supplied by private industry, although the Government would doubtless exercise appropriate controls over rocket launchings. . . . If the Bell System's proposal for an experiment is adopted, other international common carriers will be welcome to conduct their own tests using the Bell satellite . . . . If the Bell System's plans for a commercial satellite system are accepted, such a system and its use, would come under public regulation just as are all other common carrier communications facilities and services. . . .
>
> Meanwhile, of course, creation of the satellite system Bell proposes would not under any circumstances preclude the development of other space communications systems. As AT&T President Frederick R. Kappel noted in a speech at Raleigh, North Carolina March 22: "Space is a great big place and we don't expect to fill it."[16]

This euphoric and partly disingenuous reassurance could not still the apprehension of many in government and business who believed that the Bell System was indeed quite big enough to fill the whole of space if given the chance. Still, the fact that Bell had an idea and an experiment and abundant resources that could all contribute to an early payoff in space had an appeal that was to overcome the qualms of the new administration. It was to prove practically impossible to withhold the opportunity for Bell to undertake its experiment and thereby gain an important competitive advantage.

At first, however, the administration hesitated. It was not clear how the matter would be resolved until the FCC took the initiative and led the administration to decide on a policy. No one on the commission was more influential in this effort than its new and dynamic chairman, Newton Minow. Satellite communications had been one of the first matters brought to his attention by the White House upon his appointment.[17] At first he had no policy leanings one way or the other, but after studying the problem he became convinced that the approach of the international carriers was the most sensible one. In the interagency negotiations he became a vigorous champion of their point of view.

Minow's position soon became that of the FCC. In 1960 the commission had invited the interested commercial companies to present their views. On May 24, 1961, the commission reported its conclusions. These clearly supported the idea of a joint venture by the international carriers, although the FCC took pains to assure the equipment manufacturers that their interests would be safeguarded in any plan that would have FCC approval.

The FCC's report aroused interest in Congress, where the antitrust subcommittees of both houses announced hearings on the subject. Indeed the debate ranged beyond the Capitol. Almost all of official Washington was arguing about the ambiguities of government policy in this field. John Finney reported in *The New York Times* that certain congressmen were reviving the idea of a government-owned system, while at the same time an FCC *ad hoc* committee of industrial representatives was meeting with government officials to draft a plan for a private consortium that would operate the American part of an international system. Finney also reported that Senator Long's Anti-Monopoly Subcommittee, by conducting the first comprehensive inquiry into the public policy problems involved, was arousing "some jurisdictional interest and jealousy in committees more directly concerned with the problem, such as the Space and Commerce Committees." The "sudden upsurge of congressional interest," he observed, has apparently been stimulated by "some intensive industrial lobbying. It was also becoming evident that the question of ownership of a communications satellite system was likely to be settled ultimately in Congress, rather than in the White House and the Federal Communications Commission."[18]

Every day criticism of the proposal for private ownership could be heard on the floor of both houses and in the subcommittee rooms. Representative James Roosevelt said that if AT&T, "whose assets of $23 billion are greater than those of Standard Oil of New Jersey,

General Motors, and United States Steel combined," were to be given a prime position in the development of a satellite system, "it can be expected to do as it has done in the past—namely, purchase virtually every piece of equipment from its wholly owned supplier, Western Electric, and conduct its research in the Bell Laboratories . . . ." Courtlandt S. Gross, President of Lockheed, agreed with the congressman. As he told the Long Subcommittee, "It is extremely difficult to envision free competition in the hardware market for the system where the owners of the system are themselves both operators and manufacturers."[19]

To complicate matters still further, a good deal of controversy had been boiling up over the question of which was the best system of satellite communications, from a technical point of view. AT&T favored an initial system of 25 to 30 satellites in orbit at an altitude of about 7,000 miles. This was called a "low random orbit" and would give coverage to the United States and Europe and, at stated times, links with other locations. According to AT&T, such a system could become operational within three or four years. The other mechanical system in contention was a high-altitude, synchronous orbit system championed as the ideal and eventual mechanism by IT&T, RCA, and General Telephone. NASA, with fine impartiality, was negotiating a contract with Hughes Aircraft Corporation for an experimental synchronous satellite while this very debate was in progress. This instrument would orbit at an altitude of 22,300 miles in a polar orbit that would keep the satellite in the same general position and enable three such instruments to give global coverage.

Bell's objection to this system was not only that the government did not have the rockets necessary to thrust it into position, but also that from a technical voice transmission viewpoint, the distance a voice signal had to travel produced an unacceptable echo that made conversation awkward. While not ruling out an eventual Syncom System (the system being developed by the DOD for its military satellite communications system under the name of Project Advent), the Bell spokesmen thought their proposal would provide the best immediate system.

The synchronous satellite supporters countered with the claim that General Telephone and Electronics Laboratories had been working on an echo suppressor that would solve the echo and time-delay problem. They claimed that a low-random-orbit system would not fulfill the President's policy directive calling for global coverage. Their system, they claimed, would cover 91 percent of the globe with only one satellite.[20]

This technical debate, with its parade of reputable scientists taking opposite sides, was quite enough to confuse mere legislators struggling with the already complex questions of public policy in regard to ownership and operation. Dr. Edward C. Welsh, Executive Secretary of the National Space Council, testified before the Long Subcommittee that the United States was likely to launch a random-orbit system before a system of the Advent type. This testimony was contradicted by Brigadier General William M. Thames, Commander of the Advent Management Agency, who presented a rather more optimistic view of the progress of his project in testimony to the House Committee on Science and Astronautics. He assured the committee that an "operable" Advent System, using one satellite, would be achieved by late 1963 or early 1964. If the Army were assigned a mission for a system of three satellites, which would provide global coverage, he thought it could be put in operation "prior to 1965."[21] In view of the series of difficulties plaguing the Advent Project at the time, one can only wonder at the general's confidence. In any case, the immediate result was that legislators began to feel free to choose the expert testimony they preferred to believe on nontechnical grounds.

While this debate was proceeding in and around Congress, another important debate was in progress at the offices of the FCC where the international carriers were attempting to work out a proposal for a joint venture. The carriers were having difficulty over a number of issues. There was some fear that if American equipment manufacturers were included in the consortium, foreign manufacturers might also demand admission through cooperating governments. There were also disagreements concerning the distribution of control within the proposed consortium. But all these difficulties were overshadowed by a common fear that delay occasioned by such bickering would only lead Congress to legislate public control regardless of what policy might be hammered out under the auspices of the FCC.

One result of these deliberations came in late September, when General Electric withdrew its application for part ownership of the system, leaving the field to existing communications carriers. GE's official reason for dissolving its Communications Satellites, Inc., was that it did not wish to "divert its resources into the carrier communications field, but to concentrate on its traditional role as a manufacturer of space vehicles and related equipment."[22] Since this was hardly more necessary in September than it had been in January, many industrial commentators speculated that the recent "unpleasantness" in and around Capitol Hill had some relation to GE's decision. In its "Washington Roundup," *Aviation Week* commented:

> General Electric's abrupt decision to drop its bid for a share in ownership of a commercial communications satellite system resulted primarily from concern of its top officials that efforts

made by its subsidiary, Communications Satellites, Inc., had unintentionally strengthened the hands of those who favor government ownership.[23]

Following GE's withdrawal, the *ad hoc* committee proposed, on October 13, the formation of a nonprofit corporation to develop and operate a commercial satellite system. The corporation would be owned by the companies engaged in international communications, but the government would have three representatives on the board of directors, out of a total of from fourteen to eighteen American members. Under the plan the corporation would manage the satellites while the ground stations would be owned and operated by individual member companies. Each member company with an ownership of more than $500,000 would name two directors. Companies which did not wish to make such a capital contribution but did wish to lease facilities in the system could collectively designate one director to represent their interests.

The attitude of the firms whose interests were affected by the proposal varied. AT&T indicated its willingness to contribute $50 million or more. Other companies indicated a willingness to join on a smaller scale. RCA chose to withhold its reaction pending further research. Western Union vigorously dissented from the plan on the ground that it would give AT&T overwhelming predominance. Instead, Western Union proposed the creation of a public stock corporation that would be open to carriers, equipment manufacturers, and the general public. Such a proposal, if adopted, would have been likely at least to decrease the degree of control that AT&T and the other carriers could have exercised through the extent of their investments, if not through control of the board of directors. Hughes aircraft made a similar proposal.

## The Congressional Debate

The international carriers, however, were not without powerful allies. The most important of these for the coming congressional phase of the battle was the senior Senator from Oklahoma, Robert S. Kerr, Democrat, and Chairman of the Senate Committee on Aeronautical and Space Sciences. Kerr, a large, genial, and somewhat overwhelming product of the southwest, gloried in the many newspaper and magazine stories of 1961 that had described him as the most powerful man in the Senate. As it happened, the major issues in the presidential program for the second session of the eighty-seventh congress — reciprocal trade, medical care, and tax revision — were due to come before the Finance Committee on which he was ranked number two in seniority after Harry F. Byrd, Democrat of Virginia. With Chairman Byrd unfriendly to the

President's proposals on all three subjects, it was Senator Kerr to whom the President would have to turn for someone to carry the burden of such proposals in the Senate. He was one of those Democrats who are hard to classify. He had come out of the Populist tradition of the West but was also a "self-made" oil man, chairman of the board of Kerr-McGee Oil Industries, Inc., and generally a conservative on economic matters. He was to perform magnificently for the President on the Trade Expansion Act of 1962, taking it through the Senate when Byrd defaulted, and yet he was to stalemate the President's Medicare Program.[24]

It was Senator Kerr who would become, in company with the President, the real formulator of the Communications Satellite Act of 1962. In this effort his first act was an attempt to preempt jurisdiction for his Aeronautical and Space Sciences Committee over the legislation creating any communications satellite system. He determined to do this, according to Dr. Glen Wilson, the chief clerk of the committee, not to undercut the prior rights of the Commerce Committee in communications matters, but rather to attempt to end "the pulling and hauling all over the town by liberals in Congress and out over various ways of making the new system more responsible to the public investment in it."[25] This intense activity on the part of the industry's opponents had created, according to Wilson, such a welter of confusion that it seemed a good idea to get the only actual proposal made so far, that of the *ad hoc* carrier group, down in the record as an item for legislative disposition.

Although the Kerr bill, S. 2650, accepted the main features of the *ad hoc* Carrier Report restricting ownership and control to international common carriers, it differed from the report's recommendations in several important respects. It sought to establish a "profit-seeking" rather than a "non-profit" corporation; required the ownership of United States earth terminals by the Satellite Corporation rather than by the owning carriers; provided no government or public representation on the board of directors of the corporation; established the private corporation by an act of Congress, rather than permitting the carriers to set it up themselves under FCC supervision; and lastly, it required, rather than permitted, the corporation to purchase from NASA the necessary launch vehicles and services.[26]

The administration, meanwhile, had been assessing the results of the carrier negotiations in the light of the President's general goals. The criticisms of the carriers' proposal were taken seriously, and the Space Council was given the job of coordinating an effort to draft a bill that would incorporate several of the carrier's suggestions and also include provisions designed to meet some of the objections raised by the industrial critics. The bill finally produced was the product of many minds, but Attorney General Robert Kennedy and his deputy, Nicholas Katzenbach, along with Dr. Welsh, seem to have played important roles in determining the ownership and control provisions.

The President's bill was introduced on February 7, 1962, by Senator Kerr as S. 2814 and by Representative George P. Miller (D.-Calif.) as H. R. 10138. In essence the bill followed the principle first laid down by Administrator Glennan in the Eisenhower administration of placing the ownership of the new corporate entity in private hands under public regulation. To allay fears of domination by the carriers, stock in the corporation was to be opened for sale to the public as well as to industry. In a statement accompanying the bill, the President explained that since the corporation would be by its nature a government-created monopoly, it was advisable that there be widespread ownership.

To achieve the goal of widespread ownership, a formula was proposed whereby the common stock of the corporation would be divided into two classes. Class A stock would be open to the public and would earn dividends and carry voting rights. Class B stock, which could be purchased only by carriers approved by the FCC, would have no voting rights and receive no dividends other than through liquidation. It was also provided that a carrier's investment in class B stock would be eligible for inclusion in the carrier's rate base to the extent allowed by the FCC. The directors of the corporation were to be chosen only by holders of class A stock, and no stockholder or trustee was to vote for more than two members of the board of directors.[27]

The President's bill made tortuous progress in Congress throughout the late winter, spring, and summer months of 1962. The Senate Committee on Aeronautics and Space Sciences initiated hearings on the bill in February and reported it out on April 2, when it was immediately referred to the Committee on Commerce. The House passed a version of the bill on May 3. On June 11 the Commerce Committee reported the bill out with a minor amendment spelling out the President's duty to supervise the corporation's relationships with foreign governments. The Foreign Relations Committee then received the bill for further study as part of a unanimous consent agreement whereby a small band of recalcitrant liberal Senators agreed to permit emergency and priority legislation to come to the vote while the satellite bill was delayed in committee. The bill was released by the Commerce Committee on August 10 without amendment. A liberal filibuster was cut off by the invoking of cloture for the first time since 1927, and the bill was passed by a vote of 66 to 11.

Congressional consideration touched chiefly on several key

issues. One was the question of the power of the corporation to act on behalf of the United States in foreign policy. The bill introduced for the President (S. 2814) stipulated in Section 402:

> The corporation shall not enter into negotiations with any international agency, foreign government, or entity without a prior notification to the Department of State, which will conduct or supervise such negotiations. All agreements and arrangements with any such agency, government, or entity shall be subject to the approval of the Department of State[28]

Spokesmen for industry criticized the provision as an unprecedented and unwarranted interference with private business management, resulting only in confusion and a dampening of initiative. The section was amended by the Senate Committee on Aeronautical and Space Sciences to read:

> Whenever the corporation shall enter into business negotiations with respect to facilities, operations, or services authorized by this title with any international or foreign entity, it shall notify the Department of State of the negotiations, and the Department of State shall advise the corporation of relevant foreign policy considerations. Throughout such negotiations, the corporation shall keep the Department of State informed with respect to such considerations. The corporation may request the Department of State to assist in the negotiations, and the Department shall render such assistance as may be appropriate.[29]

Thus revised, the section survived (except for a minor change in wording) all subsequent revisions of the bill. But if the change pacified industrial critics, it aroused fresh antagonism from liberal critics who charged that it amounted to an unprecedented delegation of the presidential prerogative in foreign affairs to a private monopoly. The furor was diminished somewhat when the Secretary of State let it be known he saw nothing objectionable in the provision as amended.[30]

Although the bill itself said nothing about the type of system the proposed corporation was to employ, the issue arose in Congress nonetheless because the legislators realized that if AT&T was to be in a controlling position in the organization, the company might use its position to its own advantage. Since AT&T had already committed a substantial investment to research on the low-altitude system, it would very likely not prove anxious to promote the rapid development of the synchronous system by the new corporation. If the synchronous system were to be developed rapidly and adopted as soon it was ready, AT&T's expensive system of over forty satellites and ground stations would suddenly become obsolete—"junk," in the word of Senator Long. AT&T was more likely to defer development, said the critics, until its investment had been paid off.

Senator Long thought AT&T might be inhibited by other considerations as well:

> Another reason why A. T. & T. might want to adopt the low orbit system is that while it would be unprofitable for a great number of years, corporations which are not regulated utilities would find it a poor investment, and therefore A. T. & T. would find it easier to chase other companies out of competition in this field, because such companies would not be able to make the money back at the expense of the public. However A. T. & T. would [by including the cost in its rate base].[31]

The Senator's point was well taken. Since a public utility is allowed a fair return, determined by the regulatory body, on its capital investment, it can take losses on immediate operations and expect to make up for its losses by raising charges to its customers. But the point was also appreciated by those who framed the legislation. In fact, it was just this peculiar ability of the international carriers that was one of the chief arguments in their favor. It was generally agreed that communications satellites would not be profitable for some years. Ordinary investors and companies were therefore unlikely to find them an attractive investment. Given their legally guaranteed ability to recoup any losses, however, the carriers would not suffer the same disabilities.

AT&T's critics also charged that the company had a notorious habit of witholding innovations that would provide better and more economical service until existing facilities had been fully depreciated. Would not the same attitude serve to prevent the new corporation from making effective use of its satellites so long as AT&T continued to have a sizable investment in underwater cables? AT&T spokesmen answered that satellites would only be one of many types of communication and that, in any case, AT&T would not be in a position to determine policy arbitrarily. [32]

The issue which might be correctly, if inelegantly, described as the "gut" issue of the hearings and the legislation was that of ownership. Much of the preparatory work in the field of satellite communications had been done by the government; yet much more work remained to be accomplished before the system would yield a profit. The FCC decided to support the idea of a joint effort of private carriers primarily in the belief that, all things considered, it was the fastest and most efficient way to develop the system. The Justice Department, with its concern for the antitrust laws, was inclined to be more dubious about such an arrangement. As Attorney General Kennedy explained,

> There were disputes within the Government as to how the legislation should be written.

In fact, I believe that it was quite clear that Mr. Minow and the Federal Communications Commission took a different position than we did at the Department of Justice in connection with the public ownership of the communications satellite.

From their vast experience they felt that the carriers could make such a major contribution to moving this communications satellite forward that the carriers should play a very major role.

We felt, and, I think, like most of the other branches of the Federal Government, that since so much money had been expended by the Federal Government in this operation — some $175 million — and would continue to be spent, that the general public should have a right to play a major role in the development of the communications satellite.

Mr. Minow testified for the Federal Communications Commission and I went up and testified for the Department of Justice, and we took different positions.

Ultimately, a compromise was arrived at, and in my judgment the compromise is most acceptable.[33]

Senator Morse was not satisfied that the compromise was in fact in the public interest. He pressed the Attorney General to justify what he felt was bound to be a device that would enhance the monopoly position of AT&T:

*Senator Morse.* Could you explain for the record why the compromise? Will you give the reason for the compromise that, in effect, selects A. T. & T. as the corporate entity?

*Attorney General Kennedy.* I wouldn't agree with that conclusion, Senator. I don't think A. T. & T. has been selected as the corporation to be the entity in connection with the commercial satellite.

There were differences within the Government in which it was felt that the carriers, A. T. & T., RCA, and seven or eight others, had had tremendous experience in this field, had had tremendous expertise, that if you turned this corporation over and just permitted the public to buy generally that frequently you would miss all of this experience, all of this background, all of this expertise, all of this knowledge which might be necessary in order to make this corporation a success. It was that argument which led to the compromise.

The original argument that was made by Mr. Minow and by others in the FCC as well as certain of your colleagues in the U. S. Senate, in my judgment, would have turned this corporation too far over to A. T. & T., and to the other carriers, and we battled and fought that over an extended period of time.

We came out with a compromise which is this bill, in which, in my judgment, we received 90 percent of what we struggled for.

I am perfectly satisfied with this bill [H. R. 11040], and I would say, Senator, that it was — the Department of Justice, myself as Attorney General — that led the struggle and led the battle in the fight against A. T. & T. dominating and controlling the commercial satellite.[34]

The fact that the bill did embody a genuine compromise — at least one between the Justice Department and the FCC — is indicated by the misgivings expressed by the FCC in connection with the provision for widespread ownership by the general public. The FCC pointed out that these investors would put pressure on the new corporation for immediate returns. As a result, that long-range development might be slowed and the cost to users of the system might be made prohibitively expensive. As an FCC statement observed:

> During the early operational years it is unlikely that the satellite system will operate at a profit. It will probably be a number of years before traffic demands increase to a point where the high channel capacity of the costly system will be sufficiently employed to put the system on a profitable basis. Thus, the cost per satellite channel in use will be very high for some time, compared to existing facilities.
>
> Under ordinary circumstances involving the introduction of new facilities, carriers are able to include in their general rate bases the relatively high cost of their new facilities with the lower costs of their existing plant and thus, in effect, average such costs for ratemaking purposes. Thereby, a return on the capital invested in new facilities is not dependent solely upon revenues produced by those facilities during their initial years of operation. This has the advantage of facilitating the introduction and application of new facilities in an orderly systematic manner with a minimum of impact on rates charged the public.
>
> Were only carriers to be owners of the corporation, their investments would be eligible for inclusion in their respective rate bases, so that a return on the total capital invested in the corporation would come from general service revenues produced by all facilities. By permitting investment by noncarriers, to the extent capital contributions are made by such noncarriers, a return to such capital can only come from revenues of the corporation from its satellite operations. *Since those revenues will be derived from channels furnished at high cost during initial operational years, its charges, particularly during those years, will be commensurately high if there is substantial investment by noncarriers.* This will have the undesirable effect of diminishing the amount of use made of the system by our common carriers and their foreign counterparts, who will use less costly facilities to the extent possible and thereby defeat out Nation's objective of fostering the most widespread use that can be made of the system.[35]

The provision calling for the appointment of directors whose duty it would be to represent the public interest was another aspect of the compromise that aroused acrimonious debate, as indicated in an exchange between Senator Morse and FCC Chairman Minow:

*Senator Morse* ... By the way, you said something this morning which I will try to paraphrase. I think you will agree this is a fair summary of your statement:

For the first time the President of the United States will appoint three members of a board of directors of a corporation. The question is: Do you think that is a desirable precedent?
*Mr. Minow.* Yes, I do.
*Senator Morse.* Do you think that the President of the United States ought to get into the business of appointing members to the boards of directors of corporations?
*Mr. Minow.* I think in a unique situation like this, which represents, as I see it, a joint effort by government and business, that it is very desirable, yes, sir.
*Senator Morse.* And—a business that has many foreign relations implications?
*Mr. Minow.* Yes, sir.
*Senator Morse.* Do you think he ought to appoint, therefore, some members to the board of directors of the United Fruit Co.?
*Mr. Minow.* No, sir.
*Senator Morse.* You do not think United Fruit has anything to do with American foreign policy in Latin America?
*Mr. Minow.* I am not familiar enough with that, but I am talking about this bill, and this situation of communications satellites.
*Senator Morse.* I am talking about your word "unique."
*Mr. Minow.* Yes, I think that is right.
*Senator Morse* ... My point, Mr. Commissioner, is that you are going to talk about foreign policy. We have to take a look at these corporate entities. When we have the President appoint three members of the board of directors of this corporation by way of a precedent, you are going to have someone coming in and suggesting that he ought to do it to United Fruit. I happen to be against this appointment in all these instances. I think that certainly is one thing that the President of the United States should not be doing, and that is appointing members to the board of directors of any corporation. Jefferson must be revolving in his grave with that suggestion.
*Mr. Minow.* I must very respectfully disagree. I think this is a very admirable thing to do, given the circumstances of this unique communications satellite system.[36]

Other critics of the legislation agreed with Morse that the appointment of public representatives was more dangerous than beneficial because it would give the appearance of official sanction to whatever the corporation might choose to do in furtherance of the private interest of its owners. A colloquy between Senator Albert Gore of Tennessee and attorney Benjamin V. Cohen expressed this uneasiness:

...Now, I would like to ask you another question as a lawyer.

Would you find it remarkably strange that the President of the United States should be the director of a private corporation organized for the profit of its stockholders?

*Mr. Cohen.* I am very much troubled by the suggestion.

*Senator Gore.* I mean to give direction and supervision.

*Mr. Cohen.* I am very troubled that the President of the United States should be given that responsibility over a corporation that is supposed to be independent of the Government and supposed to be a private corporation.

I am also deeply troubled that the President of the United States should appoint three directors of a corporation that is going to sell common stock—without any profit record at all— to the public in this country. *It will be difficult to convince those who buy the stock that the President has not recommended its purchase.*

My experience with the SEC legislation makes me really react most violently against the idea that the stock should be sold to the public with the Government unable to avoid certain implied responsibilities that come from its appointing three directors.

*Senator Gore.* You have referred about three times, I believe, in your testimony, in response to questions, to the fact that three members of the Board will be appointed by the President.

As a lawyer, to whom, in your opinion, does a member of the board of directors of a corporation owe its fiduciary trust?

*Mr. Cohen.* Primarily to the shareholders, I should think. *That is why I am troubled by this act that looks in different directions, but does not clearly define the responsibilities of these directors as being any different from those of the other directors.*

...If there is any [public responsibility], it is derived and implied only from the fact that they are appointed by the President, but there is nothing otherwise that would indicate that they do not bear the same responsibilities as the other directors.

*Senator Gore.* I agree that insofar as the proposed bill is concerned, once they become members of the board, their responsibility is no different from the other members, and under the charter of the corporation, chartered under the laws of the District of Columbia, as I understand those laws, the fiduciary trust and responsibility of the board of directors is not only primarily, but solely, to the stockholders.

*Mr. Cohen.* I think that is true.

*Senator Gore. Then this tends to give it a color of public responsibility but no substance.* Would you agree with that?

*Mr. Cohen.* I agree. That expresses my viewpoint better than I have been able to express it.

As I say, the nearest thing I can think to this sort of thing is the old code authorities in the NRA, and while many of us had high hopes of what NRA might accomplish, *I think that particular type of hybrid instrument which is neither public, nor private, is generally conceded not to be effective or workable.*

*Senator Gore.* Now, to further emphasize the fact that no public responsibility is involved here, the bill specifically provides that the corporation shall be organized for profit. I do not cite this as an effort to demean that corporation or the profit motive, but this is one further evidence that no public responsibility is vested.[37]

## The Virtues of Being an Anomaly

Gore and Cohen did indeed put certain important provisions of the act in question. How, after all, can a director stand in fiduciary trust to the stockholders of a company organized for profit and still bear true allegiance to the public when those interests are in conflict? But the belief that he can serve two masters is not unique to the framers of this legislation. Thoughtful students of American enterprise have argued that unless corporate managers take the interest of the public into account along with the interests of their various corporate constituencies, the basis of a free society is bound to erode.[38] Comsat is an experiment, a social experiment, as its satellites are an experiment in nature — to see whether new forms can be developed that will transcend the obsolete notion of society as a competition between the individual and the state. It is an experiment in cooperation linking the private sector of society with the public, an experiment that has been fostered not alone by developments in science but by the effort of the representatives of a people concerned both with excellence of accomplishment and with the prevention of a monopoly of power in any social institution, public or private. If it should prove to be a successful experiment it may well set a pattern for many other developments to come.

## NOTES

1 Public Law 87–624, 87th Cong. 2nd Sess., 1962, 76 *Stat.* 419.

2 108 *Congressional Record* 15111 (daily ed., Aug. 10, 1962).

3 *Ibid.*, p. 15088.

4 Statement of President John F. Kennedy, Department of State *Bulletin*, Sept. 24, 1962, p. 477.

5 For the path-breaking study of this development see Don K.

Price, *Government and Science,* New York, 1954.

6 U.S. Congress, House, *Satellites for World Communications, Hearings Before the Committee on Science and Astronautics* (86th Cong. 1st Sess., 1959) pp. 40, 116.

7 Interview with T. Keith Glennan

8 *Ibid.*

9 U.S. Congress, Senate Committee on Aeronautical and Space Sciences, *Policy Planning for Space Communications* (Staff Report; 86th Cong. 2nd Sess., 1960), pp. 191–192.

10 *Ibid.,* p. 198.

11 Interview with T. Keith Glennan.

12 Department of State *Bulletin,* Jan. 16, 1961, p. 77.

13 *Public Papers of the Presidents of the United States, John F. Kennedy,* Jan. 20 to Dec. 31, 1961, Washington D.C., 1962, p. 404.

14 *1960 Annual Report,* American Telephone & Telegraph Co. p. 24.

15 U.S. Congress, Senate Committee on Aeronautics and Space Sciences, NASA authorization for fiscal year 1962, June 7, 8, 12 (87th Cong. 1961), p. 45.

16 Press release, "Space Communications, Who–What–Why", American Telephone & Telegraph Co., Apr. 13, 1961.

17 Interview with Newton Minow.

18 *The New York Times,* Aug. 4, 1961, p. 3.

19 *Aviation Week and Space Technology,* Aug. 14, 1961, p. 33.

20 *Aviation Week and Space Technology,* Aug. 7, 1961, p. 34.

21 *Loc. cit.,* p. 28.

22 *Aviation Week and Space Technology,* Oct. 2, 1961, p. 35.

23 *Loc. cit.,* p. 25.

24 *Congressional Quarterly,* 1962, pp. 37, 204, 399, 1556, 1560.

25 Interview with Glen Wilson.

26 *Policy Planning for Space Communications,* p. 166.

27 *The New York Times,* Feb. 8, 1962, p. 1.

28 U.S. Senate, *Communications Satellite Legislation, Hearings, Committee on Aeronautical and Space Sciences,* (87th Cong. 2nd Sess., 1962, p. 10.)

29 U.S. Senate, Committee on Commerce, *Communications Satellite Legislation, Hearings* (87th Cong. 2nd Sess., 1962), pp. 174–175.

30 See the testimony of Secretary of State Dean Rusk, U.S. Senate, Committee on Foreign Relations, *Communications Satellite Act of 1962, Hearings* (87th Cong. 2nd Sess., 1962), pp. 174–175.

31 *Congressional Record* (87th Cong. 2nd Sess., June 15, 1962).

32 See the testimony of James Dingman, Vice-President of AT&T, *Commerce Committee Hearings,* p. 187.

33 *Foreign Relations Committee Hearings,* pp. 23–24.

34 *Ibid.,* p. 36.

35 *Commerce Committee Hearings,* pp. 69–70.

36 *Ibid.,* pp. 89–90; emphasis added.

37 *Ibid.,* pp. 353–354; emphasis added.

38 See for example Richard Eels, *Corporation Giving in a Free Society,* New York, 1956.

# 7

# Smoking and Health:

## *The Congress and Causality*

### STANLEY JOEL REISER

IN THIS GENERATION, legislators have found it necessary to establish communication with the scientific community in the roles of benefactor, judge, and critic. While this relationship has become of increasing social importance, the subjects of common interest have grown increasingly complex. Even under the best of circumstances, the relationship is bound to be difficult. The legislator, living in a "world of common sense," appears to be perplexed when visiting the "world of scientific objects,"[1] where logic and order prevail and events are woven into rational sequences of causally related occurrences. The scientist, on the other hand, supposedly at home in both worlds, is assumed to possess an ability to pass between them which he does not necessarily have. In the debate over the relation of cigarette smoking to health the two worlds of the scientist and legislator have come together in a focal policy issue. The results have not been altogether satisfactory. The reasons are worth examining.

## The Controversy

In the decade preceding 1962, a large number of scientific studies were conducted which developed evidence indicting cigarette smoking as the leading cause of cancer of the lung[2] and which hypothesized a strong, but less well documented, relationship between the smoking of cigarettes and the increasing incidence of several widespread respiratory and cardiovascular diseases.[3] During this same period, several foreign governments issued

STANLEY JOEL REISER, M.D., *is now pursuing graduate studies in the History of Science at Harvard, where he prepared this essay for the Science and Public Policy Seminar.*

reports citing the dangers of cigarette smoking. In this country leading health-oriented voluntary organizations warned the public against the dangers from smoking and called for government measures to deal with the evidence against cigarettes that science was uncovering. The period produced statements such as these:

> Resolved, that there is sufficient evidence available of a relationship between smoking and lung cancer to justify advising the public to stop smoking cigarettes. [Resolution of the Public Health Cancer Association, October 11, 1954]

> The sum total of scientific evidence establishes beyond reasonable doubt that cigarette smoking is a causative factor in the rapidly increasing incidence of human epidermoid cancer of the lung. The evidence of a cause-effect relation is adequate for considering the initiation of public health measures. [Joint Report of the American Cancer Society, the American Heart Association, The National Cancer Institute, and the National Heart Institute, March 6, 1957.]

> ... it is the view of the [Research] Council [of Sweden] that ... substances in tobacco smoke constitute, in all probability, an essential factor in the occurrence of certain types of lung cancer. ["Statement to the King on ... Effects of Tobacco Smoking," May 12, 1958]

> The Study Group [of the World Health Organization] unanimously agreed ... that cigarette smoking is a major causative factor in the increasing incidence of human carcinoma of the lung. [Report of a WHO Study Group, Nov. 20, 1959][4]

Neither the United States government nor the American public paid much heed to these statements. It was only with publication in 1962 of the report of the Royal College of Physicians of London[5] on smoking and health (which confirmed the charges against the cigarette), the intense lobbying by private organizations, and after the appointment of a receptive Surgeon General (who had spoken out publicly against the cigarette)[6] that an Advisory Committee on Smoking and Health was convened by the Surgeon General with presidential approval. This committee of scientific experts was charged to undertake a comprehensive review of all data on the relationship of smoking to disease and was then to submit to the Surgeon General a technical report containing its evaluations and conclusions. It was enjoined from conducting new research or from making recommendations for political action. The formation of the committee began with Federal, private, and tobacco industry representatives compiling a list of approximately 150 well-qualified people in the scientific community who had taken no public position on the issue. From this list, the Surgeon General selected ten men and the advisory committee was born.

## The Advisory Committee

Generalizing about advisory committees, Mort Grant observes that although they are rarely established for the sole purpose of detached counseling, the justification for convening an advisory committee must involve "prima facie (if superficial) concern with advice alone—pure, pristine, and uncontaminated.... The real objective, the forms, the practices, which follow may defy classification but the nominal purpose remains steadfastly simple—the administrator wishes advice."[7]

At the time Surgeon General Terry created his advisory committee, the quantity and quality of scientific evidence accumulated against the cigarette was such that reevaluation of it seemed duplicative and patently superfluous. It is apparent that the committee's purpose was extrascientific. The advisory committee may be regarded as a political *deus ex machina*. Professor Wheare[8] has cataloged four political advantages gained by convening a committee like the Surgeon General's. They are to pacify, to postpone, to gain support, and to camouflage. These purposes were quite evident in this case.

The assembling of an advisory committee was an expedient method of pacifying the advocates of action which, at the same time, made it possible for the government to avoid taking an immediate political stand on the issue. By putting the cigarette manufacturers on notice that it was contemplating action, the government postponed a difficult decision and left open a chance (admittedly a slim one) that prompt execution of scrupulous self-regulatory measures by the industry might stave off the need for remedial action.[9] Alternatively, if industry were to prove unwilling to inaugurate such procedures, the government could hope that time, acting as opiate, would make action at a future date easier and that the report of a prestigious committee of experts would help rally the public and legislature to the cause. The camouflage function served by the advisory committee is also obvious. In the committee, the Surgeon General presumably saw a political shield which would protect him from the congressional backlash sure to follow proposals for remedial legislation on cigarettes. The wrath of opposing legislators, he could hope, might be deflected from himself if he could claim "lack of responsibility" for its findings. Having said this in one breath, however, he might indicate in the next that he was compelled to seek restrictive legislation in light of public awareness of the committee's findings.

The potential power of the advisory committee would have remained in the realm of the "might have been" had not two conditions been fulfilled: first, it was required that the committee arrive at the decision desired by the Surgeon General (i.e., that cigarette smoking was a substantial health threat), and second, that it do so unanimously. The odds were quite good that both conditions would be met, for by 1962, when the advisory committee was brought into existence, the scientific evidence against the cigarette was substantial. Hence, there was little chance that the nonpartisan, highly qualified group of scientists on the committee could arrive at any conclusion but that cigarette smoking presented a considerable hazard to health. The Surgeon General presumably realized that disagreement among the scientists in the final report would mean political disaster. Congress would have likely interpreted a split decision as testimony to the inadequacy of the scientific evidence against the cigarette. But in order to translate the scientific consensus on the health threat of cigarette smoking into social action, the Surgeon General required political ammunition. He could obtain this ammunition not simply through the knowledge that his scientific experts might provide—for this was already available—but rather by the support he could claim from their testimony. The words of Niccolo Machiavelli are yet true today: "Therefore, it must be concluded that wise counsels, from whoever they come, must necessarily be due to the prudence of the prince, and not the prudence of the prince to the good counsels received."[10]

## The Report

The advisory committee's report, issued in January 1964, unanimously condemned cigarette smoking as a major element (though not a proven cause) in the genesis of several prevalent respiratory and cardiovascular diseases. In addition, and most notably, it cited cigarette smoking as the most important causative factor in the rising incidence of cancer of the lung. "Cigarette smoking," the report said, "is causally related to lung cancer; the magnitude of the effect of cigarette smoking far outweighs all other factors. In comparison with non-smokers, average male smokers of cigarettes have approximately a nine to ten fold risk of developing lung cancer and heavy smokers at least a twenty fold risk."[11]

The public initially reacted to the report by decreasing its cigarette consumption. A five percent decline in cigarette sales occurred in the six-month period following its release. But soon thereafter sales began to rise and, at the time of this writing, had returned approximately to their prereport level.

The advisory committee's judgment that "cigarette smoking is a health hazard of sufficient importance in the United States to warrant appropriate remedial action,"[12] quickly led the Federal Trade Commission to take action. Soon after the release of the report, the FTC convened public hearings on the issue and in June 1964 set forth in a memorandum its intention to compel cigarette companies to disclose on their packages and in their advertising a message indicating that cigarette smoking is dangerous to health and may cause death from cancer and other diseases. The Congress, motivated in great part by tobacco-state pressure and also by a traditional disinclination to cede authority to administrative agencies, persuaded the FTC to forestall action until it had an opportunity to attempt enactment of legislation. Congressional hearings began in June 1964. They resulted in a proposal, which has presently passed both houses of Congress, to require that manufacturers place on their cigarette packages a statement warning of the relationship of cigarette smoking to ill-health, but not requiring them to have such a statement incorporated into their advertisements (as the FTC had advocated). This is at most a small first step in dealing with a practice described by Surgeon General Terry as one "formerly accepted as harmless and now scientifically determined as harmful."[13] The barriers to overcoming this widespread practice include not only the habits of millions of individuals but the interests of an $8-billion industry. Human habit and modern industry have combined in a formidable alliance. Against them, or so it might seem, stands only the weight of modern science. However, though scientific knowledge may precede, it does not guarantee, action. For social action to result from this scientifically based controversy over public policy, an explanation of the meaning that the scientific knowledge had for public welfare had eventually to be provided in a convincing form. But the scientific knowledge concerning smoking and health was not altogether cohesive. In fact, the scientific community contributed three distinct theories[14] on the association between cancer of the lung and cigarette smoking—a circumstance which, though hardly unusual in science, made matters difficult in the legislature.

## The Scientific Theories

According to one postulate, cigarette smoking causes lung cancer either directly through the action of smoke on the tissue lining the human bronchial tubes or indirectly by making the individual susceptible to some other cancer-causing agent in the environment. According to a second postulate, cigarette smoking and lung cancer both have a common cause, usually specified as a certain constitutional makeup (possibly genetic in origin) which predisposes certain individuals to lung cancer and also makes them cigarette smokers. Finally, it has been proposed that in reality lung cancer causes cigarette smoking, on the theory that a precancerous condition sets up a process which leads to a craving for tobacco.

This last hypothesis, advanced by the eminent British statistician Sir Ronald Fisher, was apparently presented for the sake of logical completeness and has found no supporting evidence.

The first hypothesis has received general acceptance in the scientific community and forms the theoretical basis of the report submitted by the advisory committee. It is known as the causal hypothesis. The second has come to be called the constitutional hypothesis. "Nothing short of a series of independently conducted, controlled, experiments on human subjects," comments Cornfield's study group, "continued for 30 to 60 years, could provide a clear-cut and unequivocal choice between them [the causal and constitutional hypothesis]."[15]

The meaning and significance of a causal relation and thus the validity of the statistical evidence in the advisory committee's report used in establishing such a relation, received considerable discussion in the congressional hearing room, where the fate of the proposed remedial legislation on cigarette smoking depended upon the clarification of its meaning for the lawmaker. The task of clarification fell to the expert witnesses, the scientists. But in wrestling with causation, they and the legislators were grappling with an elusive concept.

### Causality Considered

"Objects," wrote David Hume, "have no discoverable connection together: nor is it from any other principle but custom operating upon the imagination, that we can draw any inference from the appearance of one to the existence of the other."[16] The definition of and search for causal phenomena are central to the concept of science. But how valid a description of natural phenomena are laws affirming cause-effect sequences? How do we justify the deductions we make from them? Hume saw acutely that there is a profound philosophical dilemma in every attempt to answer such questions. Understandably, the determination of the validity of a cause-effect relation was the largest issue that had to be decided by the advisory committee. The painfulness of the process is evident in its report:

> Various meanings and conceptions of the term cause were discussed vigorously at a number of meetings of the Committee and its subcommittees. These debates took place usually after data had been studied and evaluated, and at the times when critical scrutiny was being given to conclusions and to the wording of conclusive statements. In addition, thoughts about

causality in the realm of this inquiry were constantly and inevitably aroused in the minds of the members because they were
preoccupied with the subject of their investigation.[17]

Unfortunately, this preoccupation with causation did not lead
to a lucid exposition of the meaning of the concept. In its report, the
committee laid down only that the word *cause* should convey "the
notion of a significant, effectual relationship between an agent
and an associated disorder or disease in the host."[18] It then indicated
its intention to use four variations of the term: (1) "a cause," (2)
"a major cause," (3) "a significant cause," (4) "a causal association."[19]
It was never made explicit whether all of these terms were to carry
the same weight of causal meaning. Introduced to "cause" in these
various senses at the beginning of the report, a reader found to his
dismay that in later sections causal connections (in their four
variations) would be referred to without specification. In cancer
of the larynx, cigarette smoking is "a significant factor"; to emphysema, cigarette smoking assumes "a relationship"; but only an
"association"[20] stands between the cigarette and the peptic ulcer.
The failure to distinguish more clearly between types of causality
was partly responsible for the subsequent difficulties scientists
had in interpreting it.

It does not appear that the lay community was expected to appreciate the technical nuances of what the report had to say on causality.
Instead the scientist was relied on to explain the technicalities inevitable in such a report. But some scientists felt that the report
contained conclusions that were unfit for scientific consumption.
Though a decided minority, these critics challenged the committee's
reliance upon statistical rather than experimental evidence as the
main basis of its conclusions. The public dialogue sounded like
this. Said the Council for Tobacco Research:

> After ten years the fact remains that knowledge is insufficient
> either to adequately prove any hypotheses or to define the basic
> mechanisms of health and disease with which we are concerned.
> It is true now as it was in 1954 that continued research in all
> areas where knowledge is deficient offers the best hope for the
> future.[21]

The advisory committee, on the other hand, claimed that "cigarette
smoking contributes substantially to mortality from certain specific
diseases and to the over-all death rate,... [and this warrants]
appropriate remedial action."[22]

The dialogue was, in essence, an argument about the validity
of statistical as distinct from experimental evidence. Long before
publication of the report of the advisory committee, this issue had
become a focal point of debate within the scientific community.

With the publication of the report, the debate left the laboratory and entered the public domain. In this transfer, the technicalities could not be shaken off.

Ernest Nagel notes that the word "cause" suffers from the variety of senses that have been attached to it, "varying from ancient legal associations of the word, through the popular conception of causes as efficient agents, to the more sophisticated modern notions of cause as invariable functional dependence."[23] In scientific experimentation, when one variable is investigated, a pair of systems is sought differing in that variable, but matched in all others which are possibly relevant. As Nash indicates,

> when many such variables come into question, we are committed to a huge effort of preparing great numbers of paired systems matched in all but one variable .... [In so doing] we are entirely debarred from certain investigations in which no matching of all the potentially interesting variables is possible.[24]

When it is impossible or inconvenient to do a strictly controlled experiment (as in the case of the cigarette smoking–lung cancer relationship), by using statistical analysis, the knowledge one seeks may be extracted from "the superficially more obscure data yielded by what may be described as controlled observation."[25] Nash concludes that whether the scientist uses the experimental or statistical method in seeking knowledge he is "always in the end brought back to human judgments dependent on fallible, preconceived ideas."[26]

Such judgment, in fact, had formed the basis on which the advisory committee decided causal significance. The report states categorically that "statistical methods cannot establish proof of a causal relationship in an association. The causal significance of an association is a matter of judgment which goes far beyond any statement of statistical probability."[27] Nevertheless, the committee used the word "cause" in the belief that it was the term that best described a "significant, effectual relation" between agent and disease. The results were unfortunate. The ambiguity of the term was bound to evoke criticisms, but in the subsequent dispute over semantics, the considerable abilities of the scientists on the advisory committee, and therefore the high quality of their scientific judgment, were never really brought to bear on the issue.

## The Congressional Hearings

The congressional hearings[28] on the relationship between cigarette smoking and health may be characterized as a study in the development and change in the meanings of words. The presence of an interpreter who could have directed language traffic between the scientific and legislative establishments would have done much to prevent the resulting bottleneck. The Surgeon General was perhaps in the best position to play this role. Unfortunately, he was not successful.

The principal scientific dispute of the 1957 and 1964 hearings concerned the problem of establishing causation on the basis of statistical rather than experimental evidence. In the 1957 hearings, Dr. Clarence Cook Little[29] contended that statistics alone are inadequate:

> To establish a cause-and-effect relation on statistical association without experimental evidence is not safe. It cannot be done . . ..
> The factor which is first discovered by statistical studies as being in excess in the background of an individual who develops cancer, may simply indicate the presence or even absence of some other factor entirely which is actually of predisposing or causative significance.[30]

Dr. Ernest Wynder,[31] on the other hand, said of the statistical evidence linking cigarette smoking with lung cancer, "If you doubt statistics, why do human work, which is statistics. So actually, you have already cut off every possible road to coming to an answer to the problem before you even start it."[32]

In the 1964 hearings, the split was just as wide. "Even if you had the finest statistical information," statistician Alan Donnahoe insisted, "you would still not have a proper scientific basis for saying that a causal connection existed between the two [ cigarette smoking and lung cancer]."[33] An eminent thoracic surgeon, Dr. Thomas H. Burford, added his support: "What we are going to have to do to prove this thing is to find an agent where we can duplicate time after time a set of experiments which prove that this agent (cigarette smoke) will in a given animal cause a cancer."[34]

On the other hand, Dr. Wendell G. Scott, President of the American Cancer Society, in effect denied that more evidence was needed:

> This report [of the advisory committee] established beyond any doubt the causative relationship between cigarette smoking and certain types of cancer — particularly cancer of the lung — and also an association with other disabling and frequent fatal diseases such as coronary heart disease, and chronic bronchitis, emphysema and peptic ulcer.[35]

Surgeon General Terry, testifying from his advisory committee's report, agreed. "Cigarette smoking," he said, "contributes substantially to mortality from certain diseases and to the overall death rate . . . . is causally related to lung cancer . . . the report removed all doubt of the existence of an overall health hazard of cigarette smoking."[36]

The legislator's inevitable frustration in the face of this conflicting scientific dialogue is evident in the following exchange:

Rep. Meader: You say there's a causative relation (between cigarette smoking and lung cancer) that is established by the evidence and Dr. Little says it's dangerous to take the statistical associations and from them deduce a cause-and-effect relation. I would like you to comment on what appears to be a conflict.

Dr. Heller: Certainly, Mr. Meader. Dr. Little is a distinguished and beloved scientist of the Nation... Dr. Little is indeed a very fine gentleman, both as a man and as a scientist. But there are differences in interpretation among scientists.[37]

The dilemma of the legislator is obvious. Plainly he did not have sufficient scientific knowledge to measure the merit of the conflicting scientific statements. How could he decide what weight to assign to statistical as opposed to experimental evidence in determining the validity of the scientific propositions being advanced? From his own experience with the manipulability of statistics, the legislator may well have felt that in this case, as in others, statistics could be used to prove or disprove almost any contention. But what was the alternative?

The only alternative would have been to await the results of further experimentation. "The Experiment" to prove the relation between cigarette smoking and lung cancer was still waiting to be done. Why had it not been completed? The scientists never adequately explained why only a thirty- to sixty-year experiment using human subjects would provide an unequivocal answer. Experimental evidence might well have been more satisfactory. It would have reinforced the common lay belief that experimental evidence is by nature a constant and certain entity as contrasted with the manipulable statistic. But it was not to be had.

In their longing for experimental proof, the legislators failed to appreciate the significance of judgment both in experiments and statistical studies. Nor did the scientists help them to understand that whether they used the statistical or experimental method in searching for knowledge, scientists are always, in the final analysis, "brought back to human judgments dependent on fallible, preconceived ideas."[38]

To be sure, although the statistical evidence constituted the essential core of the advisory committee's report, it was by no means the only evidence considered. Experimental, clinical, and pathological evidence were also important factors in the committee's conclusion. These kinds of evidence, however, were somewhat neglected both by the congressmen and the Surgeon General, perhaps inevitably. Just as in a play a protagonist sometimes over-shadows his supporting actors, so the statistical star dominated the legislative proceedings. Occasionally, witnesses like Dr. Wendell Scott reminded the legislators of the supporting players. "There is also considerable experimental proof," he pointed out, "on which the Surgeon General's report was based. So it was not just based on statistics."[39] The upshot was, nevertheless, that the Surgeon General had to win his argument on the statistical evidence.

The cosmology of the citizen, Ashby observes, "is based on hearsay and a vague deference to authority."[40] Lacking firsthand scientific knowledge, the legislator might have hoped to reach a decision in this issue by discriminating between scientific authorities on the basis of their prestige or numerical superiority. Surgeon General Terry and others used both these elements in an effort to persuade the lawmakers that they were in the right. The Surgeon General often emphasized that the overwhelming majority of scientists with special knowledge on this issue had expressed concurrence in the strong relationship between cigarette smoking and certain diseases. The lawmakers were cautioned against being deluded about the facts of the issue by a small minority of scientists. The Surgeon General had not only numerical superiority but also the prestige of the members of the advisory committee. The commit-tee stood, collectively, as a "super-expert" to whose side, amid the conflicting statements of other scientists, the uncertain legislator might come for assurance.

Terry's opening statement at the 1964 hearings revealed the high place the advisory committee had in his strategy.

The effect of the January 1964 report of my expert Advisory Committee on Smoking and Health has been to strengthen our earlier position and emphasize the need for bolder and broader programs. The report did this by removing all doubts about the existence of the overall health hazard of cigarette smoking. The report furnishes the scientific basis for the proposed legislation.[41]

The Surgeon General's powerful ally in the hearings, Paul Rand Dixon, Chairman of the Federal Trade Commission, also relied heavily upon the Advisory Committee's prestige to support his commission's stand on the smoking issue, as the following dialogue illustrates:

Rep. Pickle: There are a lot of questions [about the effect of smoking on health] it would seem to me that are

> still unanswered. . . . How can you be sure these
> answers will be forthcoming?

Mr. Dixon: [After remarking that conclusions had already
been reached in the advisory committee's report,
such as the one stating that a causal relation existed
between cigarette smoking and lung cancer.]
This is a flat finding of the greatest group of scientists in this subject that were ever put together,
sir.

Rep. Pickle: Then you take that [the report] as your bible and
as your sole source of issuing the rule [requiring
a health warning statement on cigarette packages
or in cigarette advertising].

Mr. Dixon: Together with other things that are in our record
of rulemaking.[42]

On another occasion, Chairman Dixon went even further in his use
and praise of the advisory committee:

> There is a consensus of medical and scientific opinion that
> cigarette smoking is a significant cause of certain grave diseases
> and contributes substantially to mortality and to the overall
> death rate. These were the findings of the Surgeon General's
> blue-ribbon Advisory Committee on Smoking and Health.
> These findings are authoritative, reliable and stand essentially
> unchallenged. They provide a compelling basis for prompt and
> effective government remedial action.[43]

The emphasis of the Surgeon General on majority rightness and
superior expertise encountered legislative resistance. Was not
science a synonym for the uniform and exact? Did not scientists
have equal knowledge and capability? The lawmaker could accept
a split judicial decision and compromise congressional bills, but it
was disconcerting to find public policy advocated on the basis of a
divided scientific decision. Was not such debate an indication that
the issue was far from settled? The lawmaker was bound to be
troubled by this divergence of scientific opinion. What was he to
make of statements such as that of Dr. Thomas Burford?

> I do not believe that lung cancer is caused by cigarette smoking
> and I do not believe that smoking is responsible for any shorten-
> ing of life. The oft-quoted statistics purporting to prove that
> smoking does cause lung cancer or does shorten human life
> have done nothing more than perhaps establish certain statisti-
> cal associations which fall far short of proving a causal relation.[44]

Later in the hearings, Dr. Scott rebutted Dr. Burford's statement. He was asked by Representative Younger, "Then how do you
account for the fact that he . . . says there is no relationship between
smoking and lung cancer [?]" Dr. Scott replied: "This is Dr. Bur-

ford's personal opinion. It is not supported by a series of scientific studies and investigations. An opinion to which he is perfectly entitled but with which I disagree, sir." Younger replied: "I can't understand how he can differ so much with the other reports."[45]

Confronted by such scientific disagreement, to whom does the legislator turn? Does he — can he — rely upon the majority consensus or on the prestige of the advisory committee, or does he wonder, in indecision, why the minority scientists are unconvinced by the evidence?

## Misunderstanding About Research

In this situation it is understandable that congressmen should have been tempted to avoid a decision by calling for more research. In voting for the research alternative, the legislator could postpone the pains of arduous decision. If he came from a tobacco state, he could certainly please his constituents; even if he did not, by deciding for research, he would receive plaudits for supporting the "institutional idol" of the American public.

When even the Surgeon General seemed to ask for more research, the temptation was bound to be even stronger, as the following exchange indicates:

Rep. Kornegay: Dr. Terry, as a matter of fact, the report on Smoking and Health was not original research with the fifteen [the correct number is ten] man Advisory Committee.

Dr. Terry: That is correct; it was not original research.

Rep. Kornegay: It was the pulling together, the compilation of past studies made by various and sundry groups, institutes, and research organizations throughout the country.

Dr. Terry: It was an attempt to make the most comprehensive review of all of the existing scientific information on the question of smoking and health in the world, sir.

Rep. Kornegay: Is there any clinical or laboratory work in this report?

Dr. Terry: There are reports of many laboratory studies. It is a highly technical report on various aspects of reported scientific studies.

............................................................................

Rep. Kornegay: I think you and I both agree that enough research has not been done.

Dr. Terry: Yes, sir.

Rep. Kornegay: And that there are many gaps as I think you

stated in your statements that need to be filled
in before we have the complete picture.

Dr. Terry: Yes, sir.[46]

Perhaps the most fundamental difficulty in the legislator's
predicament is the confusion of two kinds of research: research for
science and research for policy. The evaluation of research concerning science qua science must take place within a frame of reference
totally different from that applied to an appraisal of research concerning science qua policy. The difference is easily understood by
recalling the dissimilarity between the medical investigator and
medical practitioner. Their roles vary when measured by two essential parameters—objectives and time.[47] The objective of the medical
investigator is to acquire knowledge; for the practitioner it is to
maintain the health of his patients. The investigator is held to no
time limits. He may stretch his activities along the time line to fit
the needs of his research. For the practitioner, on the other hand,
time is of the essence. He must protect and preserve human life before the pathologic process has crept too far. The Surgeon General
is practitioner to the public. Like the personal physician he is required to act on pathologic processes affecting the health of the
nation. He cannot wait upon complete knowledge. He cannot dwell
in the utopian atmosphere of perfect scientific procedure. His command is action—time is not on his side.

The Surgeon General should have carefully explained to the
legislators that the quantity and quality of research evidence linking
cigarette smoking to disease, especially lung cancer, was sufficient
for making a social policy decision (in view of the magnitude of the
postulated health hazard of the cigarette), but not sufficient to establish proof of a causal relation within the policy-neutral and more
exacting framework of basic scientific research. He should have
made it quite explicit that when he asked for more research on the
subject, he meant "research for science" and not "research for
policy." Lack of clarity on this point created a misunderstanding
which persisted between legislator and scientist throughout the
hearings. Time and again, the legislators confused the necessary
degree of proof required in establishing causal relations in scientific research with that needed to make social policy. Indeed, how
could they help but be confused in the face of such seemingly contradictory statements as this one made by the Surgeon General:

> The publication in January of the Advisory Committee's Report
> on Smoking and Health marked an end to a long period of uncer-
> tainty. We still have much to learn about how cigarette smoking
> damages the human body—but we know beyond reasonable
> doubt that the damage is done. We must not use the need for
> further research as an excuse for lack of action.[48]

In this statement the Surgeon General seemed in effect to be telling the legislators that on the one hand uncertainty was at an end, but that on the other, "we still have much to learn." Later in the hearings, we find the Surgeon General again failing to differentiate the goals of medical research from those of medical practice:

Surgeon General Terry: I think we need to move forward on a two pronged attack—information and education, and in certain instances expand our research program.

Chairman Harris: Each answer raises another question, because you said as you concluded your statement, we must not use the need for further research as an excuse for lack of action.

Surgeon General Terry: That is right.

Chairman Harris: Now you say, you need further research.

Surgeon General Terry: I don't find any conflict between those statements, Mr. Chairman.[49]

But the chairman did, as did other lawmakers. For them the conflict was never resolved.

## Conclusion

I. I. Rabi has observed that fear of making decisions on less than complete knowledge motivates people to seek and accept what they believe (sometimes wrongly) to be a more informed judgment.[50] It was evident that the legislators feared to take a position on the smoking-health issue because of a felt lack of personal scientific competence. Because of the patent disagreement among the scientists, the lawmakers had to decide which scientists to believe. Further research offered a tempting alternative to making a decision on the present evidence. Whatever course he took, however, the legislator was destined to exert influence on substantial health or economic interests. On the one hand, the cigarette represented an hypothesized health threat to hundreds of thousands of people. On the other, the same cigarette stood for an $8-billion industry which made use of one of the basic crops of the nation. There was no easy route for the legislator to travel. By vote, abstention, or delay he would harm one of these interests. He was forced to judge, and he could not ask his scientific guides for certitude, because in this issue there was none available.

In the hearings, the legislator was required to balance scientific merit against social necessity and arrive at a legislative decision. He was not up to the task. If, moreover, he had poor success as judge, he most certainly could not play critic. This was unfortunate, for the role of critic is an important legislative function. The critic, as Barzun has remarked, "redirects fundamental thought . . . (making) two thoughts grow where only one grew before."[51] The critic reconstructs situations, giving to them a different and revealing cast. The smoking-health issue called for a legislator who could be both judge and critic. Though he tried, the lawmaker could be neither. It is sometimes said, in defense of democracy, that, though individually laymen may be worse judges than those with special knowledge, collectively they are as good. The hearings, alas, cannot be said to support this hope. The collective legislative mind, it turned out, offered no better insight into the issue than that of the individual.

Must we conclude, then, that in a scientific age replete with scientific problems, the concept of democracy (i.e., of amateurs electing amateurs), as Raymond Aron puts it, is an "attack on common sense and ultimately a ruinous absurdity?"[52] If blame for the misunderstandings in these hearings could be placed entirely on the legislative side, then perhaps this question could be answered affirmatively. But the scientists provided the second half of this legislative dialogue and their actions and responsibilities can be equally criticized. The scientist has a greater potential ability than the layman to relate science to social purpose; to determine how much scientific verification is needed for social action; and then to explain the issue to the layman. The scientists, divided on the issue of validity and perhaps unaware of the need for explanation, failed conspicuously throughout the hearings to meet these responsibilities. If blame is to be assigned for the resulting misunderstandings it must be shared.

The hearings on cigarettes and health forced the legislator to question the charisma and the exactitude he imputed to the scientist and science. He saw the exact scientific world give way to one of merely approximate accuracy. The word *science* seemed to lose some of its stability and to fall prey to the limitations of all that is tentative. Moreover, could scientists who so disagreed with each other have equal competence? If not, how does the lawmaker judge who is the more competent? The legislator was in a position like that of the man in the *New Yorker* cartoon seated in his armchair before a television set, listening to an announcer advocating a headache pill which "four out of five doctors recommend!" With a less-than-confident facial expression the viewer is saying to his wife, "I wonder if that fifth doctor knows something the other four don't."

"For the scientifically educated," remarks Barzun, "the authority of science [rests] on the strictness of its method—for the mass, it [rests] on its powers to explain."[53] To some scientists involved in this controversy, the strictness demanded by the scientific method seemed challenged—for conclusions were being drawn from evidence which appeared to them to be less than conclusive. However, the debate among the scientists over the evidence needed in the realm of pure scientific research became merged with a simultaneous debate concerning the evidence needed to institute social policy. They thereby confused not only themselves but also the legislators.

The legislative hearings on smoking and health disclosed the difficulty facing the nonscientific lawmaker when he seeks to weigh scientific evidence in a matter as complicated, technical and not fully understood as that of health. They also revealed the difficulty the scientist has in separating scientific thoroughness from social need and in explaining the difference to the layman. The hearings demonstrated, if demonstration were needed, that technical knowledge is a necessary but not a sufficient requisite for the scientist who seeks to play the catalyst in the conversion of scientific discovery to social action.

## NOTES

1 Jacques Barzun, *Science: The Glorious Entertainment*, New York, 1964, p. 116.

2 It is estimated that lung cancer kills an average of 36,000 people per year in the United States, a toll approximately equal to the number of deaths caused by traffic accidents. See E. Cuyler Hammond, "The Effects of Smoking," *Scientific American*, Vol. CCVII, July 1962, pp. 4–5.

3 Emphysema (a disease of the lung) and coronary artery disease (the most common form of heart disease) are the most important ailments in this category of cigarette-linked diseases in terms of number of people afflicted with them. The postulated relationship between cigarette smoking and coronary artery disease is quite alarming considering that this disorder accounts for nearly 29 per cent of all deaths in the United States. See *ibid*.

4 The above quotations and ones of a similar nature are cited in Ruth Brecher, *et al.*, *The Consumers Union Report on Smoking and the Public Interest*, Mount Vernon, N.Y., 1963, pp. 62–64.

5 *Smoking and Health*, A Report of the Royal College of Physicians of London on Smoking in relation to Cancer of the Lung and other Diseases, London, 1962, p. 69.

6 In 1962, Surgeon General Terry made the following statement: "The weight of scientific evidence ... demonstrates that cigarette smoking is a major cause of the increase in cancer of the lung.... Everyone should be aware of [this conclusion] because of [its] importance to health." As quoted in Brecher, *op. cit.*, p. 65.

7 Mort Grant, "Advisory Committees in Congress," *Public Policy* (1960), pp. 92–95.

8 K. C. Wheare, *Government by*

*Committee*, London, 1955, pp. 88–92.

9 A code of advertising ethics was in fact established by the cigarette industry in May 1964, but it contained too little and came too late to forestall consideration of remedial action.

10 Cited by Grant, *op. cit.*, p. 92.

11 *Smoking and Health*, A Report of the Advisory Committee to the Surgeon General of the Public Health Service, Public Health Service Publication No. 1103, Washington D.C., p. 31.

12 *Ibid.*, p. 33.

13 Luther L. Terry, statement read before the House Interstate and Foreign Commerce Committee, Washington D.C., April 7, 1965, p. 9 (mimeographed).

14 Jerome Cornfield, et al., "Smoking and Lung Cancer: Recent Evidence and a Discussion of Some Questions," *Journal of the National Cancer Institute*, Vol. XXII (Jan. 1959), pp. 191–192.

15 *Ibid.*, p. 191

16 David Hume, *A Treatise of Human Nature*, Selby-Bigge, ed., Oxford, 1960, Book I, Part III, Sec. 3.

17 Advisory Committee to the Surgeon General, *op. cit.*, p. 20.

18 *Ibid.*, p. 31.

19 *Ibid.*

20 *Ibid.*, pp. 212, 302, 340.

21 Council for Tobacco Research, as quoted in D. S. Greenberg, *Science*, Sept. 4, 1964, p. 1022.

22 Advisory Committee to the Surgeon General, *op. cit.*, pp. 31, 33.

23 Ernest Nagel, *The Structure of Science*, New York, 1961, p. 73.

24 Leonard K. Nash, *The Nature of the Natural Sciences*, Boston, 1963, p. 166.

25 *Ibid.*, p. 167.

26 *Ibid.*, p. 168.

27 Advisory Committee to the Surgeon General, *op. cit.*, p. 20.

28 The testimony to be quoted from in this section is taken from two congressional committee hearings on smoking, held in June 1957 and June 1964. No new major piece of scientific evidence on the relation between cigarettes and disease was uncovered in the seven-year span encompassing the two hearings. In these years there was an accumulation of evidence of a similar and confirmatory nature. The dialogue in the 1957 hearing therefore has the same essential tone and meaning as that in the 1964 hearing.

29 Dr. Little is a Doctor of Science, former Director of the American Cancer Society, former President of the University of Michigan and presently Chairman of the Council for Tobacco Research.

30 United States Congress, House, Committee on Government Operations, *False and Misleading Advertising (Filter-tip cigarettes)*, Hearings before Subcommittee (85th Cong. 1st Sess., 1957), pp. 112, 228. Cited hereafter as House Committee on Government Operations, *Cigarette Hearings* (1957).

31 Dr. Wynder at that time was Chief of the Epidemiology Section at the Sloan-Kettering Institute for Cancer Research.

32 House Committee on Government Operations, *Cigarette Hearings* (1957), p. 113.

33 United States Congress, House, Committee on Interstate and Foreign Commerce, *Cigarette Labeling and Advertising*, Hearings before Committee (88th Cong. 2nd Sess., 1964), p. 194. Cited hereafter as House Committee on Interstate and Foreign Commerce, *Cigarette Hearings* (1964).

34 *Ibid.*, p. 209.

35 *Ibid.*, p. 292.

36 *Ibid.*, p. 40.

37 House Committee on Government Operations, *Cigarette Hearings* (1957), p. 146.

38 Nash, *loc. cit.*, p. 167.

39 House Committee on Interstate and Foreign Commerce, *Cigarette Hearings* (1964), p. 303.

40 Eric Ashby, "The Administrator: Bottleneck or Pump?" *Daedalus*, Spring 1962, p. 264.

41 House Committee on Interstate and Foreign Commerce, *Cigarette Hearings* (1964), p. 40.

42 *Ibid.*, p. 119.

43 Paul Rand Dixon, "Statement on Proposed FTC Regulations against Cigarettes" (statement read before the Committee on Commerce, United States Senate, Washington D.C., March 29, 1965), pp. 7–8 (mimeographed).

44 House Committee on Interstate and Foreign Commerce, *Cigarette Hearings* (1964), p. 201.

45 *Ibid.*, p. 296.

46 *Ibid.*, pp. 57–58.

47 Lewis C. Robbins, "Medical Practice and Lung Cancer," *Minnesota Medical Journal*, Feb. 1962, p. 132.

48 House Committee on Interstate and Foreign Commerce, *Cigarette Hearings* (1964), p. 44.

49 *Ibid.*, p. 47.

50 I. I. Rabi, *Atlantic*, Aug. 1960, pp. 41–42, as quoted in Barzun, *op. cit.*, p. 8.

51 Barzun, *op. cit.*, p. 7.

52 Raymond Aron, "The Education of the Citizen in Industrial Society," *Daedalus*, Spring 1962, p. 253.

53 Barzun, *op. cit.*, p. 22.

# PART 2

# Governing Science

# 8

# Scientists and Statesmen

## A Profile of the Organization of the President's Science Advisory Committee

CARL WILLIAM FISCHER

IN PRESIDENT EISENHOWER's farewell address, remembered now for its warning against the dangers of a cohesive and committed interest group in a loose and pluralistic system, the retiring President also laid down what must be the ultimate presidential concern:

> Crises will continue to be. In meeting them...there is a recurring temptation to feel that some spectacular and costly action could become the miraculous solution of all current difficulties.
>
> But each proposal must be weighed in the light of a broader consideration; the need to maintain balance in and among national programs.[1]

Such balance should be taken to mean the optimum allocation of the nation's resources to its needs as they are realistically and honestly appraised. This ultimate concern was expressed again by President Kennedy at the one-hundredth anniversary of the National Academy of Sciences, when he said: "Scientists alone can establish the objectives of their research. But society, in extending support to science, must take account of its own needs."[2] These needs are simply priorities established in the presidential perspective. As Theodore Sorenson has said so well, "No amount of tinkering with the presidential machinery, or establishment of new execu-

CARL WILLIAM FISCHER is currently Chief of the Evaluation Branch, Office of Research, Plans, Programs and Evaluation, of the Office of Economic Opportunity. He holds an M.P.A. from the Littauer School, Harvard, where he submitted a more extensive version of this essay to the Science and Public Policy Seminar in 1964.

tive offices, can give anyone else *his* perspective."[3] Nevertheless, the worth of an advisory staff group must be judged by its contribution to that ultimate synthesis of goals and resources which is the function of the presidency. What does the President need from scientists to help him develop this grand perspective?

Several frameworks have been developed recently which help to clarify these needs. The one developed by Dr. Harvey Brooks of the President's Science Advisory Committee seems to be the clearest conceptual scheme.[4] It was used by the former Chairman of PSAC and Special Assistant to President Kennedy for Science and Technology in his statement of general federal research and development policies before committees of the House of Representatives in 1963.[5] According to Dr. Brooks' scheme there are two functions of the scientific adviser: the first is *science in policy*, which describes generally the use of the scientist's expertise to analyze various programs and proposals on the basis of their technical merits; the second is *policy for science*, which is meant to cover the scientist's advice on programs and measures which affect the fostering and nurture of the scientific enterprise itself.

In order to describe fully the needs of the President for the scientist as an adviser, we will here add a third function. It is *scientists for policy*, meaning the use of the scientists as a human resource in roles of policy-making and policy advice which go beyond the questions of technical feasibility and technical consequences and beyond the means of strengthening science itself. This function was implicit in the first of Dr. Brooks's two categories but it needs to be made explicit in order to emphasize what may be the President's deepest need for the scientist as an adviser. It should also be recognized that these functions are not mutually exclusive but overlap to some degree.

## Science in Policy

Science in policy, as a function of PSAC and its panels, meets the needs of the President in ways familiar to the layman. One need is for an appraisal of the technical merits and consequences of specific programs, existing or proposed. It draws upon the general familiarity of the scientist with the "state of the art" in various fields of endeavor and in some cases requires his specific or detailed knowledge of the project in question. This need is filled in part by the adviser's knowledge of the leading scientists and technicians in the field of endeavor under consideration, so that an appraisal can be made of the human resources which can be brought to bear on the technical problems to be solved. Here it may be the scientist's subjective judgment which is being used, but it is applied to the competence, insight, motivation, and other characteristics of those who propose to develop the program.[6]

Another aspect of science in policy is the President's need for technical assistance in the endless evaluation of competing claims for the allocation of national resources between scientific and technical programs and between other fields *when technical factors are controlling in the choice.* It is clear from recent developments that this need for scientific advice is increasing. Dr. Donald F. Hornig, now the Special Assistant to the President for Science and Technology, stated in an interview with *The New York Times* that the need for establishing priorities in the fields of science and technology is already upon us. He said that even in basic science some system of national priorities will have to be established.[7] The federal budget for fiscal year 1965 supports this statement completely.

The phenomenal rate of growth in federal support for research and development activity over the last decade is without doubt coming to a close. While it will probably continue to rise absolutely in amount, its relatively extreme expansion by almost a factor of 5 from 1954 to 1964 appears to be over. It is significant that the military research and development explosion, which led all other fields in both the rate of growth and the time of "takeoff" in 1956[8] should have undergone its first absolute reduction, in terms of new obligational authority (the budget's term for appropriated amounts), at the same time that its rapid rate of growth ended. This happened in the congressional action on the President's 1964 budget in the late fall of 1963. This action has been followed by a second absolute reduction, even below this 1964 appropriated amount, in the 1965 President's budget.[9] This evidence foreshadows a future in which research and development will have to withstand more comparison in the competition for dollar resources in the years immediately ahead.

To realize that this is not simply a shift in allocation to the civilian side of the research and development spectrum, we need only notice that the reduction in the overall growth rate in total federal expenditures for research and development is from 24 percent growth in the 1963–1964 period to 3 percent growth in the 1964–1965 period.[10] The growth rate for nondefense research and development expenditures falls from 45 percent in the 1963–1964 period (mostly NASA) to 11 percent in the 1964–1965 period. Clearly, this is a turning point in the growth curve of federal support for civilian research and development as well. In this climate, as never before in the history of PSAC, the President will need sound and courageous technical advice as to the relative worth of technical programs within and between agencies and scientific disciplines. A top official in the Bureau of the Budget has made the need plain in these terms:

And so that next billion dollars will come under both executive and legislative scrutiny of a kind previously unknown. And the scientific community will have to take a major responsibility for being sure that the Government chooses to put its dollars behind the best of many choices.[11]

Another need for *science in policy* is to assist the President in *reviewing the reviewers.* First, the departmental review echelons within the government must be held under surveillance so that the President may be assured that they are not being so diligent in fulfilling their responsibility for the program of one segment of the government that they are distorting the balance of the whole. In addition, in recent years there has been developed such a high degree of technical competence in the departmental review agencies (especially in the Department of Defense) that the reviewers are often the innovators of development projects and programs themselves. As with all innovators there is a considerable aversion to seeking out the weaknesses in one's innovation.[12] This professional "second-guessing" of the departmental review echelons has the added value of strengthening the review mechanisms of the department itself, as was the case with PSAC's scrutiny of the defense programs in the early and middle fifties, leading to the establishment of the Office of the Director of Defense Research and Engineering. Both review and actual recommendation were actually used in that case.

Also, in this age of "not-for-profit" firms doing systems and policy analysis outside of the government itself, there is a need to have technical expertise available to the government in reviewing their products of advice and advocacy. With reference to these analysis corporations, Don K. Price has said ". . . that the function of creating them, coordinating them, and judging their products requires an equally high level of competence within the Government."[13] The validity of this point was recognized by one of the operating members of a leading "think factory," the Rand Corporation, in a recent article,[14] and also by the government itself in the "Bell Report" on Contracting for Research and Development which recommended the establishment of government "institutes" for this purpose.[15] Until and unless these institutions are established, however, this role of review falls most importantly to the part-time science advisers, as they supplement the government's own capabilities.

## Policy for Science

The second presidential need for scientists as advisers has to do with the support and development of science itself. The specific activities usually mentioned as filling this need are as follows:

1. To provide advice on government organization and procedures for the most positive administration of scientific programs.

2. To identify gaps and "growth points," as they have been called, where rapid advances in science and technology are being detained by a lack of resources alone.

3. To provide advice on programs for the production of scientific and technical manpower through programs of education and promotion.

4. To provide advice so as to assure provision of adequate research facilities and equipment in balance with available manpower and technical promise.

5. To provide advice on international cooperative research efforts which will foster the growth of the scientific enterprise.

6. To identify and supply scientific and technical talent for top-level management positions.

## Scientists For Policy

In a speech before a national scientific body, McGeorge Bundy, then Special Assistant to the President, stressed the need of the government for scientists at top policy levels to offer their intelligence, imagination, and optimism in deliberations on policy matters extending far beyond their areas of expertise. He put this need very sharply:

> You don't solve the problem of nuclear weapons and their relation to the world by saying, "Here is a nuclear core — that's scientific; here is a nuclear weapon — that's military; here is a treaty — that's political." These things all have to live with each other. There are elements that are indeed military, or technological, or diplomatic, but the process of effective judgment and action comes at a point where you cannot separate them out.[16]

This is truly a *third dimension* of the relationship of scientific advice to national policy formulation. The reason for giving this dimension special emphasis in our thinking is so that we can more clearly assess the scientist's role as a nonexpert in the process of policy formulation. This role is as inevitable and inescapable as the intermeshing of factual and value elements in national policy questions. Examining this function as a separate activity (which it can never really be at the presidential level) enables us to appreciate its inherent value in the advisory process instead of fearing it as an insidious danger to be avoided at all costs.

To be sure, this deeper dimension of need was not the primary reason that scientists were originally brought to their present ascendency in the policy councils of government, even at the presidential level. It was primarily for their value as experts.[17] However, this

third dimension developed quite naturally as a result of the proximity to the "grand perspective" which figures so largely in the
presidency. The phenomenon has been reflected upon by many of
those who have experienced its effects. When asked if he thought
that scientists should be asked for, or allowed to express, moral or
social or political viewpoints in advisory sessions with government
leaders, Dr. Hans Bethe, former member of PSAC, said: "It is
unavoidable in the advisory sessions." He also said: "Only very few
scientists are involved in actually advising the President or the
Secretary of Defense, or whoever it might be. Usually these are
scientists in whom the political official has confidence. They are also
usually the ones who have some general thoughts about the world."[18]

The basis for this metamorphosis, which induces the expert to
offer his intellectual acumen and perspective beyond his explicit
technical specialty, has been explained well by others equally exposed to the situation. Dael Wolfle has said:

> There is a necessarily inverse relationship between an adminis-
> trator's closeness to the center of high policy responsibility and
> the singlemindedness with which he can concentrate on any
> particular element that goes into total policy. Top-policy con-
> trol cannot be divided. Budgetary, scientific, political, defense,
> economic, social, and other factors must be closely intermeshed.

He added:

> In order to be effective at this level, one must be more than an
> able and vigorous spokesman with a wide understanding of
> scientific and technical matters. One must also accept the fact
> that these matters constitute only a part of the basis for decision
> making.[19]

Let us turn to the specific ways in which the scientist fulfills
this third dimension of his relationship to national policy. *First*, and
perhaps most important, he brings a *unique perspective* or "set of
mind" to the policy council table. It was not too long ago that the
president of the American Political Science Association chastised his
peers in a presidential address denouncing the failure of political
scientists to take the initiative in anticipating the political and social
problems caused by the impact of accelerating scientific and technical advances. To overcome this failure he suggested, in part, that the
solution lay in inculcating forward vision and imagination through
the recruitment of scientifically trained personnel in order to
broaden the time perspective of political science.[20] The scientist's
"set of mind," he was suggesting, is oriented to the future; while he
is probably not capable of predicting human reaction to technical
change, he does have a measure of foresight concerning the technical
change itself. He also has a sense of urgency about the application

of scientific knowledge to man's material problems. Finally, he brings a different method of attacking or analyzing the problems of policy, which, while not always adequate, may provide a starting point.

*Second,* the scientist provides the President with a needed "lens" and channel for the executive branch, through which top-level scientific advice and conclusions may be focused and transmitted to the Congress, foreign nations, and back to the domestic scientific community.

*Third,* the President needs the scientist to help him achieve a national consensus in support of major policy decisions. This need is not a manifestation of duplicity, but rather a means for attaining legitimacy, authority, and national unity. As Don K. Price has said:

> ... the Presidency could easily be weakened if it were not supported by the general consensus of the nation. That consensus cannot be based—as at bottom the loyalty of the British to their King is based—on a traditional, indeed almost mystical, allegiance. It must rest on a belief in the law (especially the Constitution) and in an objective if not scientific approach to the facts.
>
> It is an attitude of willingness to adjust one's partisan views to the facts (rather than vice versa) that enables the Presidency to produce something like an integrated national program.[21]

*Fourth,* the President needs a respected and recognized interlocutor for the scientific community to facilitate communication and confidence between himself and this recently developed and powerful sector of the national policy. This will be especially true if there is to be an adjustment by this sector to more austere levels of support.

*Fifth,* the President needs the skills and viewpoints of the scientist in advice on the problems of optimum allocation of effort and resources between scientific and technical fields and other fields of national interest. As the first progress report of the Select Committee on Government Research of the House of Representatives has recognized,

> Without minimizing the importance of science for its own sake, the ultimate question which Government agencies must resolve before obligating funds for research and development is: What is the relationship of the program to the national interests and the responsibilities of the Government?[22]

Dr. Jerome Wiesner, the President's former Special Assistant for Science and Technology, provided an excellent insight into this more comprehensive need of the President for scientists as policy advisers in testimony on a "Civilian Nuclear Power" report of the Atomic Energy Commission. He mentioned his role as chairman of a presidentially requested Interdepartmental Energy Study, which included on its steering group the chairmen of the AEC, the Council of Economic Advisors, and the Federal Power Commission; and the directors of the Bureau of the Budget, the National Science Foundation, the Office of Science and Technology (also Dr. Wiesner at the time), and the Office of Emergency Planning. He said:

> As the Administration confronts this whole major question of development and conservation of energy resources, it is acutely aware that the amount and allocation of Federal research and development in the energy field will affect the efficiency of various components of our energy system, and, consequently the rate and pattern of our national economic growth.[23]

The former British Minister for Science also recognized "...there must be, of course, somebody to perform the more generalized function of supervision, looking for gaps or signs of imbalance, and fitting the parts into the general economic, cultural, and social pattern of the entire community."[24]

*Sixth*, and finally, the President needs the scientist's singular ability to visualize new ways and means of applying scientific and technical knowledge to major national and international problems of a social, economic, and political nature.

## The Organization and Structure of the Presidential Scientific Advisory System

This section deals primarily with (1) the skills, sources and associations of PSAC members, PSAC panel members, and the staff of the Office of Science and Technology, and (2) the organizational structure of these groups, both internally and in relation to other organizations in the executive hierarchy. This is an inventory of the raw material of the President's personal scientific advice. How it functions to meet the President's needs is deferred to the next section.

### THE PRESIDENT'S SCIENCE ADVISORY COMMITTEE

Since December 1, 1957, PSAC has been comprised of fifteen to eighteen of the nation's most eminent natural scientists. With the exception of the chairman, and since 1963 the deputy director of the Office of Science and Technology, the members serve as part-time paid consultants who meet regularly two days a month in Washington and in addition give large amounts of their time for special meetings with the panels of consulting scientists on particular problems. It has become a matter of custom and usage that the committee elects as chairman the presidentially appointed Special Assistant for Science and Technology. It has also been true that since 1963 the Special Assistant has been the director of the office of Science and Technology, within the executive office of the President, and his deputy director has been a member of the committee. This has meant that the leadership of the committee has, in fact, been full-time staff to the President.

In addition to the members themselves, there are seventeen consultants who are made up of "consultants-at-large" (normally appointed from the roster of prior members of PSAC) and a number of "government consultants" (appointed from the top-level departmental or agency scientific administrators). Two to five of these consultants make it a point to attend the regular meetings of PSAC, and several more are active on the PSAC panels of consultants described later.

PSAC and its consultants, over its six-year life in the Executive Office of the President and at present, can fairly be said to exhibit a very high degree of homogeneity and a more or less common scientific and vocational background. At the time of this writing 70 percent of the total six-year membership of forty-one received their graduate academic training at seven universities. Of the present sixteen members, 67 percent received their graduate academic training at five universities. Of all forty-one past and present members, twenty-eight are currently affiliated with universities on a vocational basis and 76 percent of these are associated with eight schools. Of the sixteen present members, thirteen are affiliated with universities and 61 percent of these are attached to three schools.

Concerning scientific skills and disciplines the same degree of likeness is apparent. For example, of the total forty-one members 63 percent are from the physical sciences and 77 percent are from the "hard" sciences (i.e., physical, mathematical, and engineering sciences); only 19 percent are from the life sciences; and none is from the behavioral and social sciences. The same pattern is true for the current membership, but it is a little more heavily weighted toward the "hard" sciences. Finally, it should also be noted that the average total tenure of the members in the physical and hard sciences is substantially longer, indicating greater individual opportunity for significant contributions.

PSAC exhibits therefore quality, cohesiveness, and, finally, continuity. Of the present sixteen members, seven have served double tenures, and of the seventeen present consultants, nine are former members. These characteristics are very important to the values and limitations of PSAC as it carries out its functions.

On the subject of PSAC's structure, it is most important to note that the organization's depth, if not breadth, of talent goes far beyond its formal outlines. The average age of the members centers on fifty. This is true even among those who are usually the youngest of physical scientists, the physicists. Quite often, however, the brilliant young colleagues of the PSAC member are informally called upon back at the universities and laboratories which so many of the members call home (subject of course to the limitations of security regulations). These scions of science are not brought directly into the fray, however, for several reasons. First, since they are in their most productive years scientifically, neither they nor their mentors want that important productivity destroyed. Second, they have not had what one present PSAC member has called "the training of the rough and tumble," that is, the collision of the facts and philosophy of science with the elusive objectives of public policy. However, the home environs of the PSAC members do make available other competence to deepen the base of expertise, if not experience.

## PSAC'S PANELS

Throughout its short life, PSAC has called upon an increasing number of experts from almost all major disciplines to augment its own skills and to provide full-time and intensive study of particular problems. This pool of talent presently numbers about 300 individuals. Primarily specialists, these people are called upon at different times as paid consultants. The amount of time that they spend varies greatly. It extends from the short-term analysis of a passing problem to the longer study of ever-present problems that essentially require a panel to serve as a standing *ad hoc* source of intelligence and criticism. In the latter cases, some of these groups have established themselves as units of expertise and experience with more continuity on a given subject than any other group inside or outside the government. These long-standing panels of PSAC are more dynamic and flexible than their parent organization.

There have been approximately eighty panels called into existence since 1957. The average size of these panels has been about ten. The size of the groups has ranged roughly from five to fifteen people. Many scientists have served on more than one panel.

The members of PSAC provide close supervision of the groups. Of twenty-two groups in existence at a typical point in time, fifteen had at least one active PSAC member. Ten were chaired by an active PSAC member. Two others were chaired by an active PSAC member. The remaining five had neither an active nor a prior PSAC member on them. The staff support for these groups is primarily provided by the staff of the Office of Science and Technology (OST) which is under the direct supervision of the chairman of PSAC in all three of his roles.

The broader base of skills and professional affiliations of the groups can also be seen in their composition. The twenty-two-group sample included data on 154 panel members. While, unlike PSAC proper, the social and behavioral sciences are included, the "hard" sciences still account for 75 percent of the total group members, compared with their 77 percent ratio in the total PSAC membership. While the number of universities awarding the highest degree is greater, there is still a concentration of 73 percent of the members from eleven schools. And, of those currently affiliated with educational institutions, 69 percent come from seven schools. As would be expected, six of these schools are among the eight with which 76 percent of PSAC's academicians are associated. It is also interesting to note that 26 of the 154 group members are also members of at least one of the following advisory groups to governmental agencies with large research and development programs: National Science Board (NSB); Defense Science Board (DSB); Naval Research Advisory Council (NRAC); Army Science Advisory Panel (ASAP); Air Force Science Advisory Board (AFSAB); and General Advisory Committee of the Atomic Energy Commission (AEC–GAC). In addition, it should be noted that 28, or roughly 18 percent of the group members are permanently affiliated with contractors (both profit and nonprofit) whose business is primarily military in nature. However, of the twenty-three members affiliated with the government, only six come from defense agencies, and the balance of seventeen come from civilian agencies with research and development programs.

These associations, it should be noted, are far more of an asset to the operations of PSAC and its panel structure than they are a detriment. The exercise of undue influence among one's peers, whose function is a critical and objective review of merit, is well-nigh impossible, even if it were intended. Rather, these associations provide invaluable channels of information by which much useless effort is saved and an important amount of coordination is achieved.

Finally, a word on the dynamism of the panel-group structure as compared with PSAC itself. A later section of this study discusses the significant addition of the realms of civilian technology, including strong emphasis on the life sciences, to the working agenda of PSAC and its panels. These areas were present in the first three years also, but not nearly to the degree that is now the case. It is as a direct result of this development that the panels began to shift to include problems in these areas, while continuing to give attention to the military area, which still makes up by far the largest portion of the federal research and development program.[25] This reorientation of the field of view of PSAC toward a broader perspective brought the life and behavioral scientists to panel groups in significant numbers. It has not resulted in a similar change in the skill groups from which PSAC itself has continued to draw its membership. It is true that eight of the forty-one members on PSAC have been from the life sciences. However, five of these were members before January 1961, and with the exception of one, their tenures were extremely short. Of the three appointed since that time, one has served very successfully for three years, and the other two have only been appointed for one year and one month respectively. Also, of course, there has never been a behavioral or social scientist appointed to PSAC.

The problems of trying to make PSAC more heterogeneous are discussed in a later section of this study. The basic difference between PSAC and its panels in this regard is that the panels can be made homogeneous by the disciplines associated with the particular problem at hand, and they generally are—and in this respect they are similar to PSAC. However, PSAC must consider their product reports and studies, which may be well outside of the area of skill, training, or appreciation of the scientists on PSAC proper faced with such a report.

## PSAC'S STAFF

While the staff of the Office of Science and Technology has been a relatively small group,[26] its size has a little more than doubled in recent years to its present overall number of thirty-eight, including eighteen professionals, as of October 1, 1963. In addition to providing the bulk of the staff assistance to their triple-hatted director, they also serve PSAC, the panels, and the Federal Council for Science and Technology.[27] This group also carries out the working liaison with the White House staff, Bureau of the Budget, National Aeronautics and Space Council, National Security Council, Council of Economic Advisors, and Office of Emergency Planning —all within the Executive Office of the President. It also has the responsibility for maintaining close contact with the top-level management of the various executive branch agencies and non-government scientific and technical groups, such as the National Academy of Sciences and the various not-for-profit research and analysis groups. Regularized procedures for such liaison and contact are of course impossible with the limited number of people available. Therefore the ability to move freely across the whole spectrum of areas under PSAC's purview is at a premium for these staff members and their more generalist character is a result of this need.

Of the eighteen professionals on the staff, seventeen hold graduate degrees. Of these, ten are in the sciences with seven being in the humanities or practical arts, such as law or administration. It is interesting to note that of the three staff members trained and working in the life-sciences area, one started in 1960, one in 1962, and one, Deputy Director MacLeod, started in 1963.

## The Functions of Presidential Scientific Advisers

There have been fundamental changes in (1) the problems with which PSAC has had to wrestle, and (2) the means which PSAC has developed for dealing with these problems. These changes have taken place over the six year period from 1957 to 1963. Furthermore, they indicate further and more difficult changes in the demands which may be placed upon this institution in the future. These changes will be shown by tracing the emphasis of PSAC's efforts over the six years as they have been applied to those presidential needs outlined above. The values and limitations of the PSAC organization in adapting to and meeting these fluctuating demands are handled in the following sections.

### THE PROBLEMS

The problems that were initially pressing to the President in 1957 were those of military and space technology. One PSAC member has described these as "the easy problems" as he reviewed the sweep of attention of the committee over the last six years. What he meant was that these were problems more or less confined to questions of the *technical* feasibility and consequences of weapons systems proposals. There was little question as to whether or not they should be done if they could be deemed feasible and necessary to the accepted objective of a superior military force. These were problems which the scientist as a member of PSAC and the panels could approach with a relatively high degree of confidence growing out of their war experiences in the nuclear weapons and electronics laboratories. The radiation laboratory at M.I.T. was an especially good training ground for these scientists because, unlike the nuclear weapons laboratories which were more or less separated from the rest of the defense establishment and its complex weapons interrelationships, radar and electronics groups had to understand the entire mix of fighting machines and strategy. This was an area where explicit factual information was more available as a base for the application of the traditional methods of the physical scientists and engineers that made up the bulk of the committee and its panels at that time. It was also easier to sort out those problems with policy implications where the factual data were ambiguous, and that obviously needed presidential attention.

This heavy emphasis on military "hardware" and space problems has abated somewhat as the Department of Defense has developed its own greater review capability and as the military situation is thought to have stabilized vis-a-vis the Soviet Union. Dr. Wiesner cited this change in the problems facing the presidential scientific adviser in testimony before a congressional committee:

> While this characteristic of constant change continues to dominate scientific activities, we may have reached a point of relative stability in that aspect of our technology—the development of weapons for military purposes—which has stimulated much of our scientific progress over the last ten years.[28]

He also pointed out that while national security will remain an area of great concern, it has been joined by completely new fields of endeavor. Dr. Wiesner also noted the reorientation of panel activity:

> Originally focussing primarily on the impact of technology on national security policy, these studies now embrace an ever increasing range of topics in fields of science; the impact of technology on questions of health, welfare, and education; and key aspects of government participation in scientific and technological activities.[29]

From an analysis of panel activity over a six-year period, it is clear that there has been a shift in emphasis to domestic and international civilian technology for economic prosperity and a rise in the number of panels concerned with the life sciences.

Under the leadership and demands of President Kennedy, the presidential science advisers were confronted with worldwide problems in the application of scientific knowledge which he himself so well described:

> The earth can be an abundant mother if we learn to use her with skill and wisdom—to tend her wounds, replenish her vitality and utilize her potentialities. And the necessity is now urgent and worldwide; for few nations embarked on the adventure of development have the resources to sustain an ever-growing population and a rising standard of living.
>
> This seems to me the greatest challenge to science in our time: to use the world's resources to expand life and hope for the world's inhabitants.[30]

Education is another area in which the effort of PSAC and the panels have been broadened. The whole area of the behavioral sciences has emerged as a new concern for PSAC. Finally, the life sciences have been given increasingly more attention by PSAC. It is significant to note that on January 4, 1960, Dr. Kistiakowsky called together a life sciences exploratory discussion group to identify aspects of federal activities in the life sciences which would justify studies by PSAC. This was the first formal attempt to bring the life sciences to the group's attention. Not only has PSAC undertaken studies of specific problems in the life sciences, but it has also been announced that "at presidential request" it is undertaking a study of *the quality of program decisions* by the National Institutes of Health.[31]

In the area of "Policy for Science," another problem that has developed over the six years is that of promoting more intense interest and support in special fields of science. These fields are those which are supported by more than one agency and most of them are interdisciplinary in nature. So far, oceanography, atmospheric sciences, natural resources, water resources, materials, and high-energy physics have been chosen for special study and coordination. The mechanism that has been used for this function is the Federal Council for Science and Technology. As Dr. Wiesner has said: "The nature of this body as a council determines both its weaknesses and its strengths."[32] It is composed of the chief scientific officers of the nine federal agencies most heavily involved in scientific activity. The impact of the council is limited to persuasion and agreement between the member agency's representatives. One area where very little progress has been made is in the allocation of the different portions of the integrated programs to the various participating agencies on a functional basis.[33]

The special fields are chosen on the initiative generated by agencies of the government, the National Research Council of the National Academy of Sciences, and special committees of experts established by the Federal Council as well as by PSAC concerns. Special panels of PSAC have been set up to review some of the long-range plans produced by the Council and the National Academy. In this area, more than in any other, PSAC, with the help of the FCST has tried to achieve an integration and balance of agency efforts across entire fields of science and technology. It is relevant for the future, however, to note that the degree of cooperation produced has been achieved where the emphasis from the center was on "strength, growth, the exploitation of new opportunities, and additional emphasis"[3] and not where it has been on the problems of allocating scarce resources.

At the same time that the range of problems with which PSAC must cope are broadening, the general tightening up of fiscal sup-

port for research and development is placing another burden upon
the organization it has never been eager to accept, even in times of
plenty. That is the problem of aiding the President in the hard job
of choosing between projects and programs in the allocation of
scarce resources. Dr. Wiesner was well aware of the difficulty of
performing this function:

> The attempts at development of national science policy have
> shown the need to judge the usefulness of a scientific activity
> not only in terms of an agency's mission needs, but also in rela-
> tion to wider areas of scientific need and opportunity and the
> availability of talent and interest. They have pointed to the impor-
> tance of relating fragmented research efforts of several agencies
> to a particular social or other national problem that transcends
> the mission of a single agency, and of attempting to assess the
> relative importance and promise of different avenues of re-
> search in order to guide the allocation of resources, a task of
> extreme difficulty and one that I approach with great trepida-
> tion.[35]

In the past, this problem has been far less critical. A former staff
member notes that PSAC has rarely been called upon to advise
on choices:

> Although long confronted with the necessity for choice, the
> President's science advisors have been understandably reluc-
> tant to establish priorities and thereby confer either damnation
> or assent on the aspirations of fellow scientists. . . . [PSAC] has
> looked at only a few of the costly disciplines, and these one at
> a time as they come along, without basis for comparison.[36]

A congressional committee, however, has urged that the President's
technical advisers assume a larger role in comparing proposals:

> While the science advisors now give their chief and the Bureau
> of the Budget technical counsel in a number of areas, this Pre-
> sidential-level staff assistance is needed on a broader front.[37]

And a present PSAC member laments the fact that PSAC has been in
no position to make budgetary comparisons:

> The problem of the responsibility of advice comes to the fore
> in the field of budgetary decisions affecting science. Unfortu-
> nately, advisory committees of scientists are seldom presented
> with the hard choices between attractive alternatives which
> usually concern the budgetary officer or administrator. The
> competing claims of different fields of science have yet to be
> squarely presented to a scientific advisory committee.[38]

Against this background, Professor Frederick Seitz, President
of the National Academy of Science and current PSAC Member, has

asked whether the present institutional structures and scientific administration developed in an era of plenty "will be able to preserve balance and objectivity through all of this, or will they be overwhelmed by emotional factors when they must make hard choices among individuals, programs, and institutions when so much of a complex nature is at stake?"[39] He offers no suggestions, however, as to how these institutions should or might be altered to gird for the coming onslaught. That the onslaught is coming was confirmed by the deputy director of the Bureau of the Budget in testimony to the Select Committee on Government Research:

> The Bureau has found the work of the Science Advisor and his predecessors to be extremely valuable on the budgetary side of the problem, and we are counting heavily on the Office of Science and Technology for help in the development of better criteria for judging research needs and priorities and the quality of research and development programs.[40]

Of course, the whole problem of first-line foreign policy in the area of arms control and limited conflict has forced itself upon the scientific adviser more and more heavily. The nuclear test ban negotiations were as much a test of the relationships between scientists and politicians in both principal nations as they were a trial of co-existence between the political systems themselves. Dr. Wolfgang Panofsky, a member of PSAC and one of the chief technical representatives to the Geneva negotiations, said recently: "In the whole disarmament problem the military, political, and scientific facts are so interwoven that they cannot in reality be separated."[41] Later in the same speech he remarked that "many of our top Government officials simply do not have the background to appreciate this limitation of science in political decisions; some underestimate the power of science, and some overestimate the power of science."[42]

Another way in which the scientific adviser's role has been complicated has been the addition of the duty to represent the executive branch in testimony before congressional committees. This was one of the reasons for institutionalizing the special assistant's office as the Office of Science and Technology. These new duties were carried on before, but in a very informal manner. However, they are much more extensive now and require large amounts of staff time, which might be devoted to review and analysis.

## THE MEANS

The means for meeting these new and different problems have been developing, too. Many of them have been in process

since the very beginning in 1957. Earlier we pointed out how the
the structure and makeup of PSAC and its panels and staff have
been changing to incorporate more life scientists and other relevant
disciplines. There are serious limitations on the extent to which
vastly different intellectual disciplines can be mixed in a group like
PSAC itself if it is to remain cohesive and productive. It also has to
be recognized that the *modus operandi* of a group at the level of
PSAC and its panels has to be to marshal the intelligence and
talents of the various operating agencies of the government itself,
instead of doing firsthand research and analysis of the problems.
PSAC has always acted to take advantage of these sources of skill.
In addition, due to its direct influence and efforts, outstanding
people have been found and appointed as assistant secretaries for
Research and Development in the Departments of Defense and
Commerce, and as advisers to the departmental secretaries in the
Departments of Interior and State. In the case of the State Department, Dr. Ragnar Rollerson is the principal scientific officer with
rank equivalent to assistant secretary. The full result of these
appointments in the agencies other than defense cannot yet be
legitimately appraised. It is somewhat discouraging to note that the
initial science adviser to the Secretary of the Interior has resigned
after a relatively short tenure.[43]

Since 1957, PSAC, and especially the staff which now makes up
the Office of Science and Technology, has been developing a close
working relationship with the other staff agencies within the Executive Office of the President. This was immediately necessary in the
case of the Bureau of the Budget, since the major military programs
had to be assessed in terms of their technical and fiscal resource
requirements. The staffs of these two agencies have grown to rely
on each other to a substantial degree, as have their political leaders.
It will not be a strange experience for these two agencies to have to
work closely together to aid the President in his allocation problems,
although the existing rapport will have to be relied upon more
intensively in the near future. "As an executive office agency, the
Office of Science and Technology can work alongside the Bureau
of the Budget in formulating the budget and advice on research
priorities and levels of support, as well as in evaluating particular
programs as the need arises."[44] In like manner, the PSAC organization has worked with the staff of the National Security Council, and
to an increasing extent in recent years with the Council of Economic
Advisors and the operating agencies on the civilian side of the
government.[45]

There is a day-to-day working relationship between the staff of
PSAC and the operating and policy officers of all the executive
branch agencies; with the staff of not-for-profit contractors; and with

the other staff organizations. These relationships are very informal. As anyone with experience in government will agree, this is the basis on which the most accurate information on major problems will flow to the center. Government is an accomplishment of people. Without the development of mutual trust and confidence between people in responsible positions, which go far beyond status, power structures, and authority by ascription, the business of government would not be carried forward with anything like the facility that usually exists. Continuity is a necessary ingredient for the development of these confidences and since the average tenures of the PSAC and panel members are both short and part-time, the staff helps to provide this valuable continuity.

In order to free itself to cover the broader range of problems PSAC has followed the pattern of most top-level staff units and has resorted to concentrating the major policy problem areas and relying on other staff and operating groups to point up the emerging trouble spots. This has permitted PSAC and its panels to give more attention to the "systemic" problems and avoid being swamped with "symptoms" of the more basic difficulties.

There is one common element in the new problems clamoring for presidential action and hence scientific advice as an input to this action. This common characteristic is that the problems are calling for far more than the formal skills of the natural scientist. President Kennedy stressed the universal nature of the problems with which science must cope and he called upon the scientist to broaden his sphere of action.

> For science is the most powerful means we have for the unification of knowledge; and a main obligation of its future must be to deal with problems which cut across boundaries, whether boundaries between the sciences, boundaries between nations, or boundaries between man's scientific and human concerns.[46]

He also noted that such an expansion of the scientist's influence means abandoning strict scientific technique as the sole instrument of this influence.

> I know few significant questions of public policy which can be safely confided to computers. In the end, the hard decisions inescapably involve imponderables of intuition, prudence, and judgement.[47]

Dr. Wiesner describes this type of attack as "a process that must combine the skills of the statesman, the scientific expert, the engineer, and I might add, the entrepreneur or industrialist, and it is a task that demands a major effort and the utmost imagination of all concerned."[48]

Many of the scientists who have been most directly involved in the work of PSAC in recent years think that the greatest unsolved problem for the committee and for the government at large is the need to develop mechanisms by which the goals and products of government and university research can be related to the needs of, and can inspire progressive change in, the "user" sectors of the national community. Such mechanisms seem to be lacking for the areas of civilian industrial technology, clinical medicine, public health, and foreign assistance.

As a means by which the PSAC organization can function to meet the President's growing need for scientific advice, this "process" must be more than an interpenetration of staff and leadership between cells of specialization, as is already the case to some extent in the Executive Office. It requires a wholehearted effort by scientist, politician, administrator, and industrialist alike to understand each other's assumptions, perspectives, and language. This too is in part recognized by present PSAC members. Several have described the unwritten criteria for membership on PSAC as the possession of (1) very high scientific competence and (2) intellectual breadth to see and work beyond one's field of specialization. The difficulty of finding these somewhat inconsistent qualities in one man is apparent. A man with this combination, however, is a *scientist for policy*.

To recapitulate, then, what is the function of presidential scientific advice? It is not wholly scientific; it is not primarily research; and it is not to provide explicit answers to well-defined questions. No matter how much the politician yearns for them, he cannot have definite answers to *his* problems even from the most well-defined of intellectual endeavors. The function of presidential scientific advice is to marshal the knowledge, the perspectives, and the intelligence of scientists which are relevant to political problems. It is a *contribution* to the comprehensive synthesis of all national and international interests and insights — it is not a *substitute* for it.

## The Value of Presidential Scientific Advisers

Specific values of presidential scientific advisers in the realms of "Science in Policy" and "Policy for Science" have been recounted earlier. The purpose of this section is to provide some elaboration of the characteristics of the *perspective* which is offered by the idea of the "Scientist for Policy." Other than his intimate knowledge of certain fields of science,[49] their rates of growth, and most promising investigators, what does the scientist bring to the policy councils of government which qualifies him as a contributor to the economic, social, and political problems for which his advice is being both sought after and offered?

## THE SCIENTIST AS AN INDIVIDUAL

It would be hard to establish that compared to other men a scientist is more objective and less prejudiced; more prescient and less myopic; more principled and less cynical *as a man* because he is a scientist. Some writers almost appear to say just that.[50] Others, writing in light of the Pauling-Teller and Foster-Bradbury debates on fallout and test bans, make what seems to be a more convincing case to the contrary.[51] Along the same line, Dr. Brooks points out that in the process of establishing PSAC's panels "if the issue to be resolved is politically controversial, a special effort is made to insure representation of a wide spectrum of viewpoints on the panel even though such a variety may not be represented on the parent committee."[52] He also cites another pressure at work on the humanity of the scientists: "There is also, of course, the problem of having to get along in the scientific fraternity—a road made somewhat rougher if the national interest must be placed before the advisor's own field."[53]

Despite these efforts to assure objectivity, the discipline and life-training of the natural scientist very likely does build in a penchant for the particular. Working with the explicit seems to produce an instinct for the relevant details which are controlling in any comprehensive situation. Even those who hold a rather extreme view of the scientists as a dangerous "power group" recognize their value in the evaluation of the facts of a situation.[54] It must be recognized, however, that the natural scientists must fight their own impatience with social and political factors which, to them, seem a little too fuzzy to be honored as "facts."

When he is at his best, the scientist's approach also has an *openness* to new data which may reverse the balance of the whole problem under study. Dr. Oppenheimer describes this in simple terms: "It is the nature of research, that you pay your two bits first, that you go in and you don't know what you are going to see."[55] Coupled with this openness is the willingness to "make an about face." In *Physics and Politics,* Max Born shows that scientists push a concept or theory to its limit in experience (data) and then must be willing to make revolutionary changes in approach when the facts warrant it.[56] This is surely a practice well adapted to politics. As a *caveat,* however, it should be noted that Nobel prizes are awarded partly because of the scarcity of these open and reversible people, even in the sciences.

Finally, the scientist brings to the policy table his nonobjective

skills. Josiah Willard Gibbs, one of America's first theoretical
scientists to achieve foreign recognition, observed that "one of
the principal objects of theoretical research in any department of
knowledge is to find the point of view from which the subject
appears in its greatest simplicity."[57] He was describing a transposi-
tion in thought—an observation of known facts from a new perspective. It is the intuitive, or metaphorical means to knowledge. The
mathematician Polanyi calls this "tacit" as opposed to "explicit"
knowledge and says that "tacit powers achieve their results by re-
organizing our experience to gain intellectual control over it."[58]
Just as the scientist must have a penchant for the particular or explicit he must also have a sense for the whole or comprehensive
entity that goes beyond its description in terms of specifics. The
politician's need for this skill may be greater than for those skills
which are more objective and explicit. But the transfer is not easy.
One of the strongest barriers to this transfer is the fact that in the
sciences this rather free conceptualization is based on a disciplined
identification of well-defined and measured facts. In the social system such "facts" are scarce. Nevertheless, where the skill of the
scientist can be brought to bear, it will plainly have great value. As
Dr. Brooks has said, "The advice of a committee is not the sum of
the individual expertise of its members but a synthesis of viewpoints
of people accustomed to looking at problems in the broadest terms."[59]

Valid questions have been raised as to whether or not the
scientist's habits of thought and "set of mind" can be usefully transferred to other areas of problem-solving activity. James B. Conant is
doubtful. "Those who contend that the habits of thought and the
point of view of the scientist as a scientist can be transferred with
advantage to other human activities have hard work documenting
their proposition."[60] And yet, Dr. Conant goes on to write the book
On Understanding Science in the hope that "a greater knowledge of
the genesis of scientific methods would probably reinforce certain
habits of mind ... the demonstration day after day of the success of
such methods is bound to have profound influence on public opinion.
If properly understood, the demonstration strengthens those rational
elements in our civic life which make for the adventurous yet
orderly development of our free society."[61] Scientists and humanists
share this hope and this confidence.[62]


## THE SCIENTISTS ASSEMBLED

Natural scientists, like any other people who share the same
life work and professional objectives, have a natural camaraderie.
Any advisory committee or staff must weather severe storms of

discouragement and criticism, and PSAC is no exception. In fact, the newly developing problems discussed earlier augur for more and not fewer storms of criticisms and struggles in the "market place" of policy.[63] The fact that they are serving together in what they recognize to be a meaningful and important cause gives them a natural drive and cohesiveness that is difficult, if not impossible, to create artificially. It may not be too wide of the mark to conclude that much of the success and productivity of PSAC is due directly to this close relationship.

The problem of communication between committee members is made considerably easier by the fact that most of the members are from the same or similar disciplines. This provides a very strong basis for group deliberation and confidence. It also affects the inputs to the group. The witness appearing before such a group feels entirely different from one who must make his case before a congressional committee, for example, where not only diverse political interests but diverse and incompatible backgrounds and training often detract from a sustained, consistent, and incisive examination of a problem of policy. The fraternal spirit of the group actually forms a part of the enticement to a busy and dedicated scientist to take part in the process of policy advice. This aspect should not be lightly regarded as a value of "Scientists for Policy."

The assembling of scientists has the value of providing the President with another means for a reasonably objective evaluation of the facts. This has the important value of contributing to public confidence and support for a coherent program. In the *Discourses*, Machiavelli points up the special value in a republic of a man or of men in whom the public has confidence. Speaking of the public, he says that if they have ill-founded fears

> resort is had to public assemblies where the mere eloquence of a single good and respectable man will make them sensible of their error. "The people," says Cicero, "although ignorant, yet are capable of appreciating the truth, and yield to it readily when it is presented to them by a man whom they esteem worthy of their confidence."[64]

One of the criteria for public confidence today is the scientist's loyalty to his professional standards. In order to perpetuate this criterion for confidence, the operations of an advisory group must be made as public as possible, without destroying the advisory process. Further, the public must be helped to understand the values and the limitations of science and scientists in the public councils.

An incidental but important side effect of the professional status and prestige of scientific advice and method is that it commands respect among the other professional groups making contributions to policy development. The scientist is able to "get the attention" of the military or economic specialist in a way that the generalist-administrator finds very difficult, simply because "science" is a rigorously defined system of thought that has made distinct contributions to human knowledge. In this way, the scientific group's value is a counterweight to other specialized intellectual methods—not to obliterate the other viewpoints, but to balance them.

An example of this balancing effect between science and technology and two other specialized fields can be observed in the introduction and influential use of the discipline of economics in the Department of Defense under Assistant Secretary Hitch, to balance the expertise of the professional military staff. In that case, there has been a simultaneous growth of the scientific and technical staff in the office of the Secretary of Defense under the director of Defense Research and Engineering. Hence, a triumvirate of economic, military, and scientific-technical skills has been developed which often results in a standoff of status and a healthy contention among these perspectives. This is especially true in the rapidly advancing and highly important area of military research and development, where all three points of view have relevance.

## The Limitations of Presidential Scientific Advisers

Presidential scientific advisers labor under a whole continuum of limitations which run from those over which they have almost no control, through those which they can help to eliminate, to those which are almost their own sole responsibility. This section deals with this range of limitations and provides examples of what seem to be the most troublesome.

### LIMITATIONS OF THE LISTENERS

The recipients of scientific advice at the presidential level are, for the most part, people from fields other than the sciences. In the area of "Science in Policy" and to a lesser degree on matters of "Policy for Science," this means that the listener cannot make accurate assessments of the scientific certainty or probability of many of the adviser's predictions of the technical feasibility and consequences of programs and proposals. Under these conditions the counseled should insist that the scientist make such an assessment for him. He should also insist that independent assessments of the probabilities be made. Often, however, the listener does not recognize that there is actually technical uncertainty in the process of estimating the degree of risk involved in a proposal because he does not know how little data the scientist had at his disposal when he made his estimate. This is a "second-order" probability problem. It involves a judgment of the probability that the probability estimates are correct. For example, it is one thing to estimate a circular error probability (CEP) of a missile system based on ten test flights and another to base it on a hundred test flights. It is one thing to base it on firings conducted under research and development testing conditions and another to base it on firings under operational conditions.

In this same vein, there is also a danger of using a "double double standard" in the field of policy planning for national security programs. First, a double standard is applied to technical programs. It says that we have to accept high-risk endeavors in national security because the stakes are high and the unknowns of enemy potential are great. That is a legitimate double standard distinguishing civilian and military programs. In civilian programs more certainty is usually possible with regard to the primary risks. In military programs, however, there is the danger of saying, "Since the risk is high, and we cannot know precisely how high, we will not be as exacting in our examination of the degree of risk as we are in non-military programs." This is piling risk upon risk. Many policy-level officers are not as keenly aware of this pitfall as one who has spelled out his own recognition of the problem as follows:

> ... there are many things that are important for the layman to understand which he does not automatically understand in his own ignorance. One of them is how much is *not* known, even to scientists... What one means by probable accuracy, how normal it is to be off by an order of magnitude, how uncertain, at the edges, quantities are—these are things which non-scientists do not immediately appreciate and to which their attention must be directed.[65]

Both the policy maker and his scientific adviser must work to point up this limitation. The use of marginal analysis principles, often called the "economics of choice," have not been effective enough in forcing emphasis on these problems of secondary uncertainty.

There is a danger, in other words, of ignoring the full meaning of scientific advice in scientific matters. The failure of the policy maker to seek scientific advice at all is equally dangerous. This happens occasionally when decisions are not recognized to have technical factors which are relevant if not integral to the choice. The answer to this difficulty also appears to be twofold. The generalist-administrator must be educated to see these relationships and the scientific adviser must be alert and sensitive to emerging problems where such an oversight is probable.

Another limitation of the listener is that, in his zeal to avoid the painful exercise of political judgment, he is often unable to understand that science frequently cannot produce a clear answer even on completely technical matters. Dr. Killian, the first Special Assistant to the President for Science and Technology, put it this way:

> It is important, as science gets involved more and more in controversial policy decisions, that the public understand that scientific method and analysis do not always yield a single, mathematically exact, incontrovertible answer. It will help the relation of science to policy-making to have it recognized that the scientist, however objective, must sometimes be limited to dusty answers when policy makers understandably are "hot for certainty."[66]

Finally, there is an ultimate and legitimate limitation on scientific advisers which must be exercised by the President, for he himself is limited by it. That is, of course, when he must say to his science adviser, as he must at some time to others, "Your advice is sound from your point of view, but in this case, from my perspective, other considerations are controlling." These other considerations are weighed with the scientific in most cases. A present member of PSAC has cited a case in point involving a presidential decision on a military weapons system — the cancellation of the Aircraft Nuclear Propulsion Program — which was a decision involving many technical problems:

> the responsibility for the ANP decision was shared by many administrators and advisors; the voice of PSAC was only one among many voices, and this voice was probably not decisive. Such decisions within the executive branch are seldom reached through the advice of a single group or individual but are the result of a gradually evolving consensus among many advisors.[67]

A more recent example of this limitation of the political and social context is the consideration of the merits of the partial nuclear test ban treaty. In an address given at Tufts University on March 4, 1964, Dr. Panofsky of PSAC described the presidential decision on the treaty as a "balance of risks." Among the nine factors which he listed as making up the "balance of risks" were several that were not at all technical: "The effect of the agreement on world opinion and on the prospects for further arms limitation measures; the effect of any control measures agreed on in decreasing secrecy barriers; and, the economic effects of an arms limitation step."

## LIMITATIONS OF STRUCTURE

A review of the structure and organization of PSAC, its panels and its staff, as they are changing, illuminates other limitations. There is a heavy preponderance of the physical and engineering sciences on both PSAC itself and on the panel structure. There is also a high percentage of people from the academic as opposed to the industrial and/or operational fields. As one person long associated with PSAC put it, "these people tend to resonate together." He was not talking about collusion but about the lack of varied perspectives in the face of problems containing an almost infinitely broad range of human experience and difficulty. Albert Wohlstetter points out that in both the type of national policy problems that can be quantified and the type that cannot, elements of military operations, industrial and production economics, mass psychology, and other such factors are controlling and they "do not fit into any of the narrowly technical traditional disciplines of natural science or engineering."[68] He then points to the discrepancy between the broad range of controlling elements and the relatively narrow background of the scientific advisers appraising them.[69]

One of the limitations due to the homogeneity of PSAC is the lack of firsthand experience relevant to broad sectors of the technology-related enterprises. Although it would be impossible to place a complete range of detailed expertise on the limited advisory groups even if that were deemed advisable, it is not impossible to draw scientific advisers from the fields of industrial management and project engineering who would be generally experienced in the problems of organizing and carrying through development and production programs, both domestically and in underdeveloped areas. Werner von Braun has pointed out that

> the missile business, particularly once a project gets going, involves many questions which are, I would say, non-scientific in nature; they have something to do with project management or time schedules. For example, a physics professor may know a lot about the upper atmosphere, but when it comes to making a sound appraisal of what missile schedule is sound and how you can phase a research and development program into industrial production, he is pretty much at a loss . . .[70]

Many of the policy problems of military and civilian technology involve practical production and management factors which may be controlling. The lack of a general familiarity with these problems on the part of at least some members would seem to limit PSAC's ability to appraise a panel report. Also, many of the programs subject to review and analysis by PSAC and its structure of panels are heavily interdependent with economic, social, and political conditions. The lack of representatives of these disciplines on the committee would seem to impede its ability to ask many relevant and critical questions and generally identify the merits and the alternatives involved in the President's policy problem.

Another limitation, stemming from the fact that the membership of PSAC is made up from closely related sectors of the national community, is the difficulty of making this type of advisory group really sensitive to the needs and desires of the users of science and technology. This seems to be especially true of the industrial sector of the nation at a time when the impact of technology, as one of the "residual factors" of economic growth, is being emphasized as never before.[71] To be sure, the panel structure is being used increasingly for the purpose of bringing in these interests and their problems. However, with the exception of two people from nonprofit affiliates of profit-making industrial concerns, PSAC itself does not include members who could serve this purpose at their level of review. Attempting to bring such people to the committee itself and even the panels involves the very difficult matter of conflict of interest. There is also the problem of the considerable reluctance on the part of American industry to encourage or stimulate the government to enter the field of civilian commercial research. Nevertheless, finding ways and means for overcoming these difficulties may become imperative if we are to escape the pessimistic conclusion that "a class of experts is inevitably so removed from common interests as to become a class with private interests and private knowledge, which in social matters is not knowledge at all."[72] One means for overcoming both the conflict of interest and the hesitancy of commercial industry to support such a government effort might be to have PSAC direct its attention to the means for developing the fundamental research base necessary to the advance of civilian technology. This work would be far enough advanced so that it would not have any immediate commercial impact nor advantage through monopolization. It is interesting to note that in England, where the government-industrial relationship is somewhat different, the Trend Committee Report on the Organization of Civil Science took as a basic assumption "that it will be the Government's purpose to promote industrial research and development more intensively than hitherto, as an essential element in the sustained growth of the economy."[73] On this basis, the report went on to recommend a change in the structure of the Advisory Council on Scientific Policy so as to split the membership 50 percent–50 percent between scientists, and economists and industrialists.[74] The value of this sort of interdisciplinary advisory group is both that it provides multiple perspectives and also that it assures at least a degree of close communication between the government and industry at the highest levels.

The "mutual resonance" phenomena resulting from the similar backgrounds of the PSAC and the panel members apparently also produces a strong tendency toward consensus which limits the examination and exploration of conflicting ideas. A PSAC member has indicated this danger with the following statement: "On the whole, the greatest occupational hazard of advisory committees is not the conflict but rather platitudinous consensus."[75] As indicated earlier, special steps are taken in the process of panel formation to overcome imbalances in view.[76]

Dr. Alvin Weinberg, a former Member of PSAC (1960–1962) and the director of the Oak Ridge National Laboratory, has indicated his concern over the lack of representation of other competing interests within the individual panels.

> The panel system, however, suffers from a serious weakness. Panels usually consist of specialized experts who inevitably share the same enthusiasms and passions. To the expert in oceanography or in high-energy physics, nothing seems quite as important as oceanography or high-energy physics. The panel, when recommending a program in a field in which all its members are interested, invariably argues for better treatment of the field—more money, more people, more training. The panel system is weak insofar as judge, jury, plaintiff and defendant are usually one and the same.[77]

While Dr. Weinberg has chosen to limit the practical portion of his discussion to the problem of choosing between fields of fundamental or basic science, the same problem of limited perspective pertains to choices between major developmental efforts in both military and civilian technology. The problem would seem to be even more critical in these broader areas since here the social, political, and economic interactions are much more immediate and direct. Yet, even here, the physical and engineering scientist's hold forth in numbers out of proportion to their perspective. Dr. Weinberg recommends a broadening of the base of review committees. It is a limited broadening which would enlist only "representatives of neighboring fields," but he is concerned only with fundamental research in suggesting this solution.[78] Also, moderation in degree of change may be wisdom to match the valor of proposing a more drastic change in principle. In fact, Dr. Weinberg goes to the logical conclusion later when he writes:

> I believe, however, that it is not tenable to base our judgments entirely on internal criteria. As I have said, we scientists like to

believe that the pursuit of science as such is society's highest good, but this view cannot be taken for granted.... Society does not *a priori* owe the scientist, even the good scientist, support any more than it owes the artist or the writer or the musician support.[79]

One more limitation, which results partially from the use of internal criteria only, is the concentration on the aim of *assuring the adequacy of support for promising fields* of science to the exclusion of needed effort on establishing priorities and advising as to the *optimum allocation of resources between fields.* This situation would seem to argue for a broadening of the base of perspective on the committee itself, as well as on the panels.

Time of tenure is really a conflicting and paradoxical limitation on the structure of PSAC. As the tenure now stands (a norm of three years), it would seem as if the members are rotated off the active committee at the high end of their learning curve as presidential advisers. On the other hand, due to the practice of drawing these people from the pool of scientific advisers who have gained considerable experience on the panels and other advisory groups, it may be that their value is quite high throughout their three years of PSAC membership. In addition, many of those who have proved themselves to be most effective are retained informally as consultants-at-large. The conflicting consideration is that if the scientist or expert of any discipline is away from his full-time profession very long he is in danger of losing (1) his professional stature (a possibility which would discourage scientists from serving on PSAC) and (2) the peculiar perspective and knowledge that gives him his value as an adviser.

Finally, there is the structural limitation which plagues every staff group, be it composed of full-time generalists or part-time specialists. This is the tendency to slip into the rut of negative criticism and to provide little or no positive stimulation for the operating agencies. PSAC seems to have successfully avoided this danger in the area of "Policy for Science," where it has been very active as the initiator of schemes for bolstering the support and development of the scientific enterprise. However, according to one former PSAC member, there is some feeling that PSAC has not done as much as it might have to initiate new departures in specific areas of technology. This is a natural result of two circumstances. The plethora of good, mediocre, and poor proposals from the operating agencies keeps the docket of PSAC full to overflowing. Secondly, should this presidential staff agency actually initiate a new project or idea, who would have the qualifications to review an invention of the nation's highest scientific group? Perhaps one solution to this last problem could be to utilize the panel structure to develop new and interesting departures in various fields of technology, subject to the review of the committee itself, which would then be passed on to the responsible operating agencies. Of course, it should be recognized that in the process of study and review of other proposals, many new ideas are in fact uncovered and passed on to the initiating agencies informally. This spontaneous stimulation may be more helpful than an attempt to develop a more formal process.

## LIMITATIONS OF THE SCIENTIST AS AN INDIVIDUAL

Many of the limitations of the scientist as an individual adviser have already been discussed. What remains is to develop a more complete understanding. Almost all of these limitations can be reduced or eliminated by the effort of the scientist himself. The first limitation is that quite often the scientist does not appreciate or understand the process of political choice as differentiated from technical analysis. He is sometimes unable to enter into a process of thought in which irreversible decisions and actions have to be taken without the complete accumulation and analysis of measurable and controllable data. In fact, it almost seems to require a surrendering of his professional standards for him to take part in such a process. This is hardly an inevitable barrier. The hesitancy of the natural scientist to come to a conclusion or to act without complete evidence is based upon a legitimate desire to achieve a high degree of certainty about the result. But in the case of human society the elements are adaptive, so that even if the social sciences were able to develop to the point where their data were measurable and controllable and where action and results were predictable and capable of being reproduced, human nature itself would be conditioned by these predictions and the response-effect would be uncertain. "For increased knowledge of human nature would directly and in unpredictable ways modify the workings of human nature and lead to the need of new methods of regulation, and so on without end."[80]

A second limitation of the natural scientist which sometimes stands in the way of his developing a better understanding of politics and society is a belief that adequate knowledge of these fields can be acquired without intensive study. For example, one leading natural scientist has said:

> I think most intelligent scientists get their human values and their humanistic education more or less on their own. I don't believe you need much formal training in this. Some of the scientists are deeply interested, some are not. Those who are

interested will talk to people in other departments of the university, and will read books and broaden their competence.[81]

Some natural scientists have acquired a deep understanding of the processes of government and of man in his social environment without academic training in the humanities, but few, if any, have done so without long personal exposure to the writings and actions of men steeped in the art and knowledge of the social process. This has been recognized by the injection of humanities courses in most of the leading technical and scientific curriculums of our major universities. The unfortunate effects of a lack of political education among scientists in policy positions have been observed in the operations of scientific attaches in the State Department.[82] Quintin Hogg (formerly Lord Hailsham), former British Minister for Science, has written that the difficulty with scientific advice is

> how to provide the scientist in his training with adequate perception of the social aspects of his environment. This is hardly less important than the companion problem, which is to provide those whose education is primarily classical or humanist with a sufficient understanding of scientific aims and methods.[83]

A third problem is the *time element*, which is so crucial in many presidential decisions. Quite often, the scientist legitimately believes that, given a technically "reasonable" amount of time, he could come up with a fairly conclusive analysis for the political figure. Just as often, the politician cannot wait. It is a real test of the scientist's understanding of the political process to attempt to contribute his judgment under these conditions. Christopher Wright adds to our understanding of both the timing and methodology problems of merging scientific and political judgment when he points out that

> while the avoidance of difficult problems in the natural sciences until they are ripe for solution may actually contribute to their more rapid solution, social goals and values and the quest for them can be effectively destroyed if these [social] objectives and the problems associated with them are neglected.[84]

Fourth, there is a limitation based on a utopian view of natural science as the answer to the problems of the economic, political, and social organization of man. Don K. Price writes that while this belief was realized to be naive by European scientists some time ago it lingers on to an unfortunate degree among American scientists today.[85] It would seem that as long as any discipline or profession is burdened by such an impression of its own ultimate role in solving mankind's problems it cannot optimize its contribution to a cooperative and maximum assault on those problems. In fact, it has a divisive effect, as Hogg has wisely observed:

> If there is a real division inside the realms of scholarship it is
> not between the artist and the scientist, but between the man —
> scientist or humanist — who views his own specialty in isolation,
> and the man who regards his specialized knowledge as placing
> him indeed in a position of vantage, but within the wider con-
> text of an undivided world of civilized values and academic
> standards.[86]

More and more, American scientists are coming to positions which
exhibit the kind of view that would place them in Hogg's latter
category. Speaking of social and political issues, Dr. Oppenheimer
has given an appraisal of the relative position of science *vis-a-vis*
the humanities that warns against undue scientific pretensions:

> There is to my view no reason why we should come to these
> [questions] with a greater consensus or a greater sense of valid
> relevant experience than any other profession. They need
> reason, and they need a preoccupation with consistency; but
> only insofar as the scientist's life has analogies with the artist's —
> and in important ways it does — only insofar as the scientist's
> life is in some way a good life, and his society a good society,
> have we any professional credentials to enter these discussions,
> and not primarily because of the objectivity of our communica-
> tion and our knowledge. But if I doubt whether we have special
> qualifications for these matters, I doubt even more that our
> professional practices should disqualify us, or that we should
> lose interest and heart in preoccupations which have ennobled
> and purified men throughout history, and for which the world
> has need today.[87]

## The Future of Presidential Scientific Advisers

Science and technology, as such, are only a part of the problems of the President which are being addressed today by his
scientific advisers. Likewise, scientific knowledge and skills are
only a part of the value of the scientist as an adviser. The problems
of applying science and technology to the goals of human welfare
are becoming much broader and interwoven with other disciplines
and other professional points of view. Social, political, economic
and technical elements must be synthesized in the process of
presidential advice. The essential question for the future is where
shall this synthesis take place? Alternative solutions to this problem
will be examined in this final section.

### SYNTHESIS AT THE POLITICAL LEVEL

One solution to the problem would be to use the present
structure of advisory groups and staff officers in the Executive Office
of the President, and depend upon the President's own political

staff in the White House to mold, balance, and integrate the expert
advice from PSAC and the other organizations. In the "real world," at
the point where judgment and action come together, the President's
personal staff will always have to play a major role in the synthesis.
If personal trust and confidence are crucial anywhere in government, they reach their greatest importance at the center of power
in the executive. Also, the President can never allow himself to
become dependent upon one source of advice. It is for this reason
that he must use his closest staff to keep open the channels to all
of the operating agencies of the government and the legislature
as well as the whole realm of private institutions. Such freedom
cannot be adequately achieved by any single presidential staff
advisory group. The question is, should the synthesis be essentially
limited to this high level of presidential assistance, or should it be
spread downward through the permanent staff institutions and the
President's Science Advisory Committee in particular?

If the function of synthesis is to be carried on at lower levels
of presidential assistance, that is, at the levels where the primary
contributions are from people with more specialized roles, the
problem of limited perspectives becomes clear. This problem is
evident in the statistical analysis and personal comments of the
members of PSAC.

## BROADENING THE BASE OF EXPERTISE

The second possible solution to this divergence between the
scope of the Presidential problems and the breadth of the scientific
advisers is to broaden the base of expertise on PSAC and its panel
structure so as to include persons from other disciplines and sectors of the community. This is not only a hypothetical possibility.
It has been done with a considerable measure of success at the level
of detailed systematic analysis within some of the leading research
and development establishments in the nation. It has been done in
top-level government advisory committees. And it is being recommended as the basis for organizing expert advisory groups in the
United Nations and other international development organizations.
Finally, it is a part of the day-to-day operations of the planning
offices of most major private corporations.

The Rand Corporation is probably the leading example of a not-
for-profit private institution organized to perform intensive analysis
of major policy questions in the area of military operations and
military development. It has since broadened its scope to include operational and development problems of a civilian nature.
The interdisciplinary approach was started early at Rand with the

incorporation of economics and social science departments along with the scientific departments. As a study of Rand has pointed out,

> the important characteristic to note about RAND's research staff is its *diversity*. An enormous variety of professional skills are represented and each has some contribution to make to the total research effort. The systems analysis work seems to benefit particularly from the range of talents available. If RAND's experience is any guide, it would seem evident that effective systems analysis work demands a variety of different professional talents.[88]

An excellent example of this melding of disciplines is the effort involved in Rand Research Memorandum 2925 entitled "Communications Satellites and Public Policy: An Introductory Report," December 1961. In this report, which was done under contract with NASA, 3 economists, 1 political scientist, 1 professor of law, and 1 physicist provided the professional effort. Apparently there was considerable initial disagreement between the economists and the political scientists on the matter of the correct approach. However, Smith reports that

> The final form that the report assumed, however, not only reconciled these divergent original approaches but it also reflected a healthy stimulus and leavening of views which greatly strengthened the study. As in the usual RAND systems analysis, the emphasis on describing the costs and consequences of alternative policy choices was strong. As well, attention was focused on such broad policy considerations as the implications of a global communications system for achieving U.S. foreign policy objectives, its relations to foreign economic aid programs, the role of foreign participation in the system even at possibly greater cost in money terms to the United States, and problems in organizing and controlling such a mammoth undertaking in the public interest.[89]

A senior staff member of the Rand Corporation has noted the importance of the political scientist in joint endeavors and has observed that "much is gained from putting the representatives of the several relevant disciplines together and getting them to work jointly on the same problems, along with physicists, engineers, and other technologists; but the interdisciplinary transference of insights is not always easy."[90]

The present membership of the British Advisory Council on Scientific Policy is made up of scientists, industrialists, and generalist-administrators.[91] As mentioned earlier, there is some pressure to broaden the membership even further by the imposition of a formula for the distribution of the posts among various related disciplines.[92] The same is true of the present National Council on Scientific Policy of Belgium.[93] The Scientific Advisory Council (*Wissenschaftsrat*) and the German Research Association (*Deutsche Forschungsgemeinschaft*) also have broad professional representation.[94]

The working combination of scientists and economists is being used in France, the Netherlands, Norway, and Sweden.[95] The Organization for Economic Co-operation and Development (OECD) recommends to its member nations that, for the purposes of both short-term economic plans and longer term economic evolution, "It is important that this work of analyzing the lines of research to be developed be undertaken parallel with the economic plan, and partly with the same personnel."[96] In the United Nations, partly as a result of the recently completed Conference on the Application of Science and Technology, the same tendency may be observed.

> In recommending the [United Nations] Economic and Social Council to set up its own advisory committee on science and technology, the Secretary-General said that its contribution would be the greater if the Committee were so constituted as to include scientists, economists, and administrators of the highest caliber with an intimate knowledge of the activities of the United Nations agencies, . . .[97]

Conant has described the intertwining of the scientist and the professional in the more "practical" arts in the realm of business and its decision-making processes.[98] He also points out how the layman, in these circumstances, has been able to develop a skill in appraising the commercial worth of the proposed programs of innovation.

The greatest disadvantage of broadening the base of expertise is that it threatens to destroy the values of the partial but pointed contribution of the single discipline.[99] Joseph Schumpeter put the problem very clearly:

> Synthesis in general, i.e. coordination of the methods and results of different lines of advance, is a difficult thing which few are competent to tackle. In consequence it is ordinarily not tackled at all and from the students who are taught to see only the trees we hear discontented clamor for the forest. They fail to realize however, that the trouble is in part an *embarras de richesse* and that the synthetic forest may look uncommonly like an intellectual concentration camp.[100]

This is especially true at the level of detailed research investigation.[101] However, it seems to be much less a problem at the more generalized levels of policy formulation and policy analysis as is shown in the examples of the Rand Corporation and other cases cited earlier.

## LIMITING THE FIELD OF VIEW

A third possible solution might be the attempt to limit the problems that are posed to the scientific adviser to those elements which are strictly technical or scientific in nature. Earlier discussion of the impossibility of separating these elements at the presidential level, as well as the remarks by the political figures themselves, show the futility of this approach, as well as the possible danger of losing the nonobjective contribution of the scientist to the problems of national policy.

Problems of political or value judgments are involved any time decisions must be taken or advice rendered on a question of increasing or reducing support for a sector of the whole federally supported program. Planning is done for periods of time, and for any given period there are limitations on resources. The limitation may be a politically established budget ceiling (in itself a product of the allocation between public and private activity), or the Gross National Product, or available manpower. Therefore, recommending an increase in the federal program for oceanography, for example, involves a value judgment between that field and another which must be reduced to provide the added support. At the level of national decision it is foolish to say that advice on allocative decisions can be purely technical, especially where alternatives for additional support involve more than one field. There is also a considerable amount of centralized control of research activity involved in such decisions.

To attempt to limit advice and action to the technical material involved would be difficult, but not impossible in most cases. However, it would be, in Philip Selznick's phrase, a "retreat to technology."[102] It suggests a positivist theory of administration.[103] It would involve narrowing the field of view not only in subject matter but also in the method of attacking presidential problems. It would be a means of avoiding the integration of scientific perspective and overall national purposes and a conscious dismissal of the need for "Scientists for Policy."

## A NEW CLASS OF EXPERTS

Other writers have proposed that perhaps what is needed is a new class of experts. This might either be a scientist turned generalist or a systems analyst.[104] The development of this type of skill group is held to be inevitable, due to the need for better communications between the scientists, the political figures, the other advisory specialists, and the generalist-administrator. In fact, the development of this type of talent can now be observed both within the government and in the private scientific community itself. The staff of the Office of Science and Technology is a good example of the emergence of this type of person. However, as we have seen, one of the greatest values of the scientist as a presidential adviser is that he does have a distinct perspective. This value would be reduced or eliminated if there was an attempt to replace the scientist with a "universal man," instead of supplementing the activities of specialists in the presidential advisory councils with a corps of experienced staff, which is able to bridge the communication gap between dissimilar disciplines. If the price of developing coherent policies and plans, in scientific or nonscientific areas, is set as the forfeiture of unique or individual genius, we might well ask if it is not too high. To be sure, becoming a generalist may be the "opportunity cost" of switching from a full-time career in science to one of "pure" administration as an agency head or a bureau chief. But you do not have a "scientific adviser" if you have an adviser who *was* a scientist.

## A WORKING COMPROMISE

There are no final solutions to this problem because the staff of a President must be subject to constant change and reorganization if it is to serve him in promoting and meeting change. This survey has attempted to show the change in the problems directed to the PSAC organization and its adjustments over time to meet them. Synthesis between fields at the level of specialist-advisers appears to be both advisable and unavoidable. The problem is one of degree. The following suggestions for further change in the PSAC structure and functions are calculated to maximize the synthesis between the interests of science and the needs of society, while protecting the values of scientific advice for national policy.

1. Broaden the official membership of PSAC itself to include the behavioral sciences and production management and engineering, as well as the life sciences that are now represented. In addition, on a reciprocal basis, have nonparticipating observers in the PSAC meetings from the Council of Economic Advisors, the Bureau of the Budget, and other relevant executive office agencies as a matter of routine. This practice is followed now to some degree.

2. Broaden the panel structure so as to: (A) assure that *all* relevant disciplines, including the social sciences, are represented on given subject panels; (B) provide panel activity directed toward stimulation of new ideas in the development and application of technology;

(C) include industrial representatives wherever possible in observance of conflict-of-interest principles; (D) provide a panel to look into the possible legitimate relaxation of the conflict-of-interest orders; and, (E) include qualified staff of operating agencies whose programs are active in the area of concern.

3. Expand PSAC's involvement in the development of economic forecasts so that the effect of scientific innovation and automation on economic growth (planned and possible) may be taken more directly into account.

4. Expand PSAC's activity in the realm of priority establishment and the role of allocation of resources between fields of science and technology. This point involves nothing more than an intensification of the present relationship between the PSAC and the Bureau of the Budget and the operating agencies of the executive branch.

These suggestions are not meant to produce, in the PSAC structure, a staff agency which is capable of a complete and comprehensive analysis of all the national and international interests. By definition, that is impossible for any advisory group. It would have serious disadvantages in any staff agency to the President even if it could be accomplished—the primary one being that, should the group's assessment of the importance of its advice become too inflated, that group's usefulness to the President would be diminished. Should a staff institution become confident that *it* had the proper presidential perspective, the President would not be able to use freely or discard its advice without destroying the mutual confidence that must exist between the chief executive and his advisers.[105] Rather, the suggestions offered above are intended to broaden the perspectives of the institution and deepen the means of interpenetration between it and other staff agencies of the President. It is hoped that this would accelerate its growing usefulness to the President in a rapidly changing world.

It is remarkable that Machiavelli, writing early in the gestation period of the modern republican nation-state, should have so clearly perceived one of its most basic paradoxes. Concerned with the viability of governmental institutions he wrote:

> It is this which assures to republics greater vitality and more enduring success than monarchies have; for the diversity of the genius of her citizens enables the republic better to accommodate herself to the changes of the times than can be done by a prince.

But his perception went one disturbing step further, as he added:

> The ruin of states is caused ... because they do not modify their institutions to suit the changes of the times. And such

changes are more difficult and tardy in republics; for necessarily circumstances will occur that will unsettle the whole state, and when the change of proceeding of one man will not suffice for the occasion.[106]

It is not clear from his writings or his life that this early bureaucrat ever decided where he stood—whether he preferred the unity and limitation of a monarchy or the diversity and liberty of a republic. But we have chosen, and our problem is to ensure that our government institutions are kept receptive to change, and that our citizen genius circulates through them.

## NOTES

1 Dwight D. Eisenhower, "Farewell Address," *The New York Times*, Jan. 18, 1961, Sec. 1, p. 22.

2 John F. Kennedy, "Address to National Academy of Sciences," *New York Times*, Oct. 23, 1963, Sec. 1, p. 24.

3 Theodore C. Sorenson, *Decision-Making in the White House*, New York, 1963, p. 84; see also Richard E. Neustadt, *Presidential Power*, New York, 1960, pp. 164 and 179.

4 Harvey Brooks, "The Scientific Advisor" (unpublished paper, Dec. 1962); later published in *Scientists and National Policy Making*, R. Gilpin & C. Wright, New York, 1964, p. 76.

5 Jerome B. Wiesner, "Federal Research and Development: Policies and Prospects," statement before the Subcommittee on Science, Research and Development. House Committee on Science and Astronautics, Oct. 16, 1963, pp. 4–5.

6 P. Cherington, M. J. Peck, and F. Scherer, "Organization and Research and Development Decision Making Within a Government Department," *The Rate and Direction of Inventive Activity*, Princeton N.J., 1962, p. 405.

7 Donald F. Hornig, an interview, *The New York Times*, Nov. 16, 1963, p. 12.

8 Bureau of the Budget, *Budget of the United States Government* for the Fiscal Year ending June 30, 1965, Washington D.C. Jan. 1964, p. 407.

9 *Ibid.*, p. 208.

10 *Ibid.*, p. 408, Table H–1.

11 William D. Carey, "Research, Development, and the Federal Budget," an address before the seventeenth National Conference on the Administration of Research, Estes Park, Colo., Sept. 11, 1963.

12 For an excellent discussion of British and American cases of this phenomenon see Albert Wohlstetter, "Strategy and the Natural Scientists," in *Scientists and National Policy Making, op. cit.*, pp. 198–203.

13 Don K. Price, "Organization of Science Here and Abroad," *Science*, Mar. 20, 1959, p. 764.

14 Chalmers Sherwin, untitled article, *Science, Scientists and Politics*, Santa Barbara Calif., 1963, p. 11.

15 Bureau of the Budget, *Report to the President on Government Contracting for Research and Development, Washington D.C.* Apr. 30, 1962, pp. 51–52.

16 McGeorge Bundy, "The Scientist and National Policy," this volume, p. 429.

17 Warner R. Schilling, "Scientists, Foreign Policy and Politics," in *Scientists and National Policy Making, op. cit.*, extrapolates the original relationship to the present situation.

18 Hans Bethe, "Science: An Interview on the American Character," Santa Barbara Calif., Mar. 1962, pp. 15–16.

19 Dael Wolfle, "Government Organization of Science," *Science*, May 13, 1960, pp. 1407–1417; the article is based on a seminar discussion held in January 1960 which included Lloyd V. Berkner; A. Hunter Dupree; James McCormack; James M. Mitchell; Emmanuel Piore; Don K. Price.

20 Harold D. Lasswell, "The Political Science of Science," *American Political Science Review*, Dec. 1956, pp. 961–979.

21 Don K. Price, *Government and Science*, New York, 1954, pp. 195–196.

22 U.S. Congress, House Select Committee on Government Research, *First Progress Report* (88th Cong. 2nd Sess., 1964), pp. 12–13.

23 Jerome B. Wiesner, Testimony Before the Joint Committee on Atomic Energy, U.S. Congress, Section 202 Hearings, Feb. 20, 1963.

24 Viscount Quintin M. H. Hailsham, *Science and Politics*, London 1963, p. 17.

25 Another very real reason for the absolute and relative reduction in the number of panels having to do with military and space technology in the second three years is the appointment of Dr. Wiesner as special assistant. His vast prior experience in military and related "hardware" development programs no doubt reduced his need for outside technical assistance. Also, as the Office of the Director of Defense Research and Engineering became effective in the Pentagon under Dr. York and Dr. Brown, the need for military panels was diminished. This does not account, however, for the upsurge of panels on civilian technology.

26 Robert Kreidler, "Science Advisors," in *Scientists and National Policy Making, op. cit.*, p. 120, n. 7. This former staff member of OST writes that there had never been more than eight full-time staff members.

27 For a brief but useful description of the Federal Council see Office of Science and Technology, *Federal Council For Science and Technology: 1962 Annual Report*, Washington D.C., 1963, 21 pp.

28 Wiesner, "Federal Research—Policies and Prospects," Oct. 16, 1963, p. 3. For an extensive and clarifying dialogue on Dr. Wiesner's meaning see U.S. Congress, *House Hearings on Government and Science*, Subcommittee on Science, Research and Development of the Committee on Science and Astronautics, Washington D.C., 1964, pp. 183–187.

29 *Ibid.*, pp. 17–18.

30 Kennedy, "Address to the National Academy of Sciences," Sept. 22, 1963.

31 "Contemporaries," *Modern Medicine Magazine*, Feb. 3, 1964, p. 64; Statement by Colin MacLeod, Deputy Director of OST.

32 Wiesner, "Federal Research—Policies and Prospects," p. 18.

33 *Ibid.*, p. 19.

34 Office of Science and Technology, FCST, 1962 Report, pp. 6–7.

35 Wiesner, "Federal Research—Policies and Prospects," p. 16.

36 Kreidler, "Science Advisors," *op. cit.*, p. 139.

37 U.S. Congress, Senate Committee on Government Operations, Subcommittee on National Policy Machinery. *A Study on Science Organization and the President's Office* (87th Cong. 1st Sess., 1961), p. 4.

38 Brooks, "The Scientific Advisor," *op. cit.*, p. 87.

39 Frederick Seitz, "Science and Government," *Physics Today*, Dec. 1963, p. 32.

40 Elmer B. Staats, Testimony before the Select Committee on Government Research, Nov. 19, 1963, p. 9, (mimeographed).

41 Wolfgang K. Panofsky, "Science in Government and the Test Ban," speech given at Tufts University, Boston Mass., Mar. 4, 1964, p. 4, (mimeographed).

42 *Ibid.*, p. 8.

43 Dr. Roger Revelle resigned May 1, 1963, and was replaced by Dr. John C. Calhoun, Jr.

44 Staats, *op. cit.*, p. 9.

45 See reference to the Interdepartmental Energy Study now in progress on page 000.

46 Kennedy, "Address to the National Academy of Sciences," Oct. 23, 1963.

47 *Ibid.*

48 Wiesner, "Federal Research — Policies and Prospects," *op. cit.*, p. 4.

49 Not all fields, since any committee or panel membership is necessarily limited to numbers that must exclude representatives from all related fields; in addition, there is the fact that the present membership criterion of high distinction in a field requires a degree of specialization that prohibits detailed knowledge of other fields even in the same major discipline.

50 See Robert Gilpin, "Civil-Science Relations in the United States: The Example of the President's Science Advisory Committee," unpublished paper presented to the American Political Science Assn. Convention, Sept., 1961, p. 8 — noted in R. C. Wood, "An Apolitical Elite," in *Scientists and National Policy Making, op. cit.*, p. 63; Bertrand Russell, *Has Man A Future?* New York, 1962, p. 59; and C. P. Snow, *Science and Government*, Cambridge Mass., 1962, p. 6.

51 Wohlstetter, "Strategy and the Nuclear Scientists," *op. cit.*, pp. 217–222; J. Robert Oppenheimer, "Communication and Comprehension of Scientific Knowledge," *Science*, Nov. 29, 1963, pp. 1143–1144.

52 Brooks, "The Scientific Advisor," *op. cit.*, p. 83.

53 *Ibid.*

54 James L. McCamy, *Science and Public Administration*, Birmingham, 1960, pp. 178–179.

55 J. Robert Oppenheimer, *The Open Mind*, New York, 1955, p. 7.

56 Max Born, *Physics and Politics*, New York, 1962, pp. 67–86.

57 From a letter to the American Academy of Arts and Sciences accepting the award of the Rumford Medal, Jan. 10, 1881, published in Lynde Wheeler, *Josiah Willard Gibbs*, New Haven, 1951, p. 89.

58 Michael Polyani, *The Study of Man*, Chicago, 1958, p. 20.

59 Brooks, "The Scientific Advisor," *op. cit.*, pp. 82–83.

60 James B. Conant, *On Understanding Science*, New Haven, 1947, p. 9.

61 *Ibid.*

62 Sir Frederick Brundett, "Government and Science," *Public Administration*, Autumn, 1956, pp. 245–256; Polanyi, *op. cit.*; Born, *op. cit*; Kennedy, "Address to National Academy of Sciences," Oct. 23, 1963. The

article by Sir Frederick is an exceptionally strong argument for what he calls a "partnership" between scientists and policy officers.

63 Carey, "Research, Development—Budget," *op. cit.*, p. 4.

64 Niccolo Machiavelli, *The Discourses*, New York, 1950, p. 120 (Modern Library Ed.).

65 Bundy, "The Scientist and National Policy," *op. cit.*, p. 426.

66 James R. Killian, Jr., Phi Beta Kappa—Sigma Xi Address to 125th National Meeting of the American Association for the Advancement of Science, Dec. 29, 1958.

67 Brooks, "The Scientific Advisor," *op. cit.*, p. 87.

68 Wohlstetter, "Strategy and the Natural Scientists," *op. cit.*, p. 178.

69 *Ibid.*, p. 228.

70 U.S. Congress, House Committee on Government Operations, *11th Report: Hearings on Organization and Management of the Missile Programs* 1959, pp. 589–592.

71 Organization for Economic Cooperation and Development, *Science, Economic Growth and Government Policy: Background Paper*, Paris, 1963, pp. 9–12.

72 John Dewey, *The Public and Its Problems*, Denver, 1954, p. 207.

73 Great Britain, *Committee of Enquiry Into the Organization of Civil Science* (Trend Report) London, 1963, p. 38.

74 *Ibid.*, p. 49. It is interesting to note however, that the Trend Committee's authorization excluded the more comprehensive problem of organization for review of the priorities of civil versus military research programs and research programs versus other major programs in the national interest.

75 Brooks, "The Scientific Advisor," *op. cit.*, p. 89.

76 See note 63 above.

77 Alvin M. Weinberg, "Criteria for Scientific Choice," this volume, p. 409. See also the letter of Dr. George B. Kistiakowsky to Congressman Daddario of Sept. 11, 1963, wherein he states the same conclusion, U.S. Congress House Subcommittee on Science, Research and Development, *Government and Science Hearings* (88th Cong. 1st Sess., 1964), p. 421.

78 Weinberg, *op. cit.*, p. 409.

79 *Ibid.*, p. 411.

80 Dewey, *op. cit.*, p. 197.

81 Bethe, *op. cit.*, p. 16.

82 D. S. Greenberg, "Science and Foreign Affairs: New Effort Under Way to Enlarge Role of Scientists in Policy Planning," *Science*, Oct. 12, 1962, p. 123.

83 Hailsham, *op. cit.*, pp. 38–39.

84 Christopher Wright, "Establishment of Science Affairs," in *Scientists and National Policy Making, op. cit.*, p. 299.

85 Don K. Price, "The Scientific Establishment," *The George Washington Law Review*, Apr. 1963, pp. 713 and 714 n. 3.

86 Hailsham, *op. cit.*, p. 33.

87 J. Robert Oppenheimer, "Communication and Comprehension of Scientific Knowledge," *Science*, Nov. 29, 1963, pp. 1143–1144.

88 Bruce Smith, work in progress on a doctoral dissertation on "The Rand Corporation: Its Development and Operation," Harvard Univ., March 1964 (emphasis added).

89 *Ibid.*

90 Bernard Brodie, "The Scientific Strategists," *Scientists and National Policy Making, op. cit.*, pp. 247–248.

91 Great Britain, *op. cit.*, pp. 21–22.

92 *Ibid.*, p. 49.

93 OECD, *Country Reports on the Organization of Scientific Research: Belgium*, Paris, Oct. 1963, pp. 13–14.

94 National Science Foundation, *International Science Reports: No. 2: "The Organization of Science in Germany,"* Washington D.C., June, 1963, pp. 12–14.

95 OECD, *Science, Economic Growth and Policy: Background Paper, op. cit.*, p. 28.

96 *Ibid.*, pp. 36–37.

97 United Nations, *Report on the U.N. Conference on the Application of Science and Technology for the Benefit of the Less Developed Areas*, UNCAST New York, 1963, Vol. I, p. 230.

98 James B. Conant, "Science and Practical Arts," *Harvard Business Review*, Autumn 1947, pp. 545–546. The use of "laymen" in the evaluation of technical program decisions by industry was strongly affirmed by Dr. Samuel Lenher, Vice-President for Research, E. I. Du Pont De Nemours & Co. in Congressional testimony on Nov. 20, 1963. See U.S. Congress, *House Hearings on Government and Science*, Subcommittee on Science Research and Development, Washington D.C., 1964, pp. 336–339.

99 See the values outlined on pp. 335–338 above.

100 Joseph A. Schumpeter, *Capitalism, Socialism and Democracy*, New York, 1962, p. 46.

101 For an excellent treatment of the difficulties encountered in the interdisciplinary approach at the research level see Margaret Barron Luszki, *Inter-disciplinary Team Research: Methods and Problems*, No. 3 of the Research Training Series, New York, 1958, esp. Chap. 14, pp. 299–304.

102 Philip Selznick, *Leadership in Administration*, New York, 1957, pp. 74–82.

103 See Herbert A. Simon, *Administrative Behavior*, New York, 1947, pp. 45 ff.

104 Wright, "Establishment of Science Affairs," *op. cit.*, p. 301.

105 The writer is indebted to Don K. Price for this observation. The danger has also been expressed in Sidney Hyman's *The American President*, New York, 1954, pp. 322 and 323.

106 Machiavelli, *op. cit.*, pp. 442–443.

# 9

# Scientific Advice for Congress:

## *Analysis of Three Proposals*

EILENE GALLOWAY

THE NEED for more congressional information on science and technology has been expressed by a number of Members of Congress and scientists. There are two major reasons why proposals are being made to meet this problem. The first is the mounting uneasiness of Members who are asked to vote increasing budgets for executive agencies spending billions of dollars on research and technological developments. Growing out of this situation is the second reason, that there is a prevailing distrust by the legislature of the scientific and technical information and advice furnished by the executive branch in order to justify its expenditures.

Several proposals have been made recently to strengthen congressional sources of information and advice in the fields of science and technology. Each proposal is based upon assumptions concerning the nature of the problem to be solved, and differences of opinion regarding congressional requirements have resulted in a variety of proposed solutions.

Suggestions on the functions of congressional staffs, for example, range from furnishing information without advice, information with recommendations for and against proposed courses of action, advice which is tantamount to relieving committees and the Congress of responsibility for making decisions, to purely educational opportunities for Members of Congress to learn chemistry, physics,

EILENE GALLOWAY *is a specialist in national defense in the Legislative Reference Service of the Library of Congress and special consultant to the Senate Committee on Aeronautical and Space Sciences. This analysis was written at the request of the House Select Committee on Research and Development and was published originally in U.S. Congress, House Committee on Science and Astronautics, Government and Science No. 3,* Scientific-Technical Advice for Congress, Needs and Sources, Staff Study for the Subcommittee on Science, Research, and Development *(88th Cong. 2nd Sess. 1964), pp. 71–82.*

biology, and mathematics. Ideas concerning the required size of the staffs vary from 300 to 3 each for the Senate and House of Representatives. Organizational patterns contemplate one office of Science and Technology for the entire Congress, separate offices for the House and Senate, one service attached to the Library of Congress or an expansion of the staff of the Legislative Reference Service.

The pros and cons of three proposals are examined in this report in order to facilitate debate: (1) An Office of Science and Technology advanced by Senator E. L. Bartlett, in S. 2038, 88th Congress, 1st session; (2) a Legislative Scientific Service suggested by R. A. Carpenter; and (3) a Science Advisory Staff, one each for the Senate and the House of Representatives, as proposed by H.R. 6866, 88th Congress, 1st session, introduced by Congressman Abner W. Sibal.

## Pros and Cons of Three Proposals on Congressional Staffing in Science and Technology

### A. CONGRESSIONAL OFFICE OF SCIENCE AND TECHNOLOGY (COST)

Senator Bartlett introduced S. 2038, 88th Congress, 1st session, to establish the Congressional Office of Science and Technology to include separate offices in the Senate and House supervised by Directors appointed by the President pro tempore of the Senate and the Speaker of the House without regard to political affiliation. Each Director, subject to the approval of the officer by whom he was appointed, shall employ and fix the compensation of assistant directors and employees (with adequate provision for security clearances).

The duties of the Office of each House are to advise and assist Members, committees, and joint committees, as they may request, on matters relating to science and technology; to make studies as directed by the House, Senate, or any committee; to maintain a register of consultants who are experts in science and technology; to report significant scientific and technological developments to relevant committees. Priorities for authorized directions and requests are to be determined by the Senate Committee on Rules and Administration and the House Committee on Administration. Necessary appropriations are authorized by the proposed bill.[1]

*Pros*

1) Our system of separation of powers and checks and balances creates a requirement that Congress have its own source of objective

information and advice in science and technology. In planning their budgets, executive agencies recognize this system and expect to have congressional committees exercise surveillance over their operations. For example, in testifying before the Senate Committee on Aeronautical and Space Sciences on the NASA authorization for fiscal 1963, NASA Administrator James E. Webb said that—[2]

> ... we are here in the traditional role of defending the President's budget. I assume that this means the Congress will perhaps attack it and look at it with great care and decide whether the President's recommendations are the correct ones for the Nation.... It is an adversary kind of proceeding. We have a Government of division of power and we are told to come here and defend the President's budget.

Senator Symington asked, "Would you like us to attack the budget?" and Mr. Webb replied, "I think it is a healthy thing to examine it with great care. The adversary proceeding is not a bad way to do it."

2) Just as the President receives advice and counsel from the scientific community through his Office of Science and Technology, Science Advisory Committee, and Federal Council for Science and Technology, so does the Congress need its own source of independent scientific wisdom and advice. Such a service is needed because Congress is requested by the executive branch to appropriate billions of dollars for research and development, and during recent years the accelerated increase of such appropriations means that the time has come when Congress must have an organization to oversee, coordinate, and evaluate R.&D. requests and expenditures. COST would provide a focal point in the House and in the Senate where Members, committees, and joint committees could turn for advice and assistance on matters relating to science and technology.

3) COST would be a nonpartisan professional service of "scientific generalists ... who know who and where the specialists are."[3] The permanent staff would be composed of three or four professional members in each House. The Directors of the House Office and the Senate Office would be appointed without regard for political affiliation, and a register of outstanding specialists maintained.

4) COST would play an active role in advising Congress because it would have authority to undertake, on its own initiative, scientific and technological reports deemed of interest to the committees. At the same time, COST would not interfere with existing committee staffs since it "will act as a clearinghouse; it will help congressional committees and Members find the men with the experience they need. If the committee and Members wish to employ the services of the expert, compensation will be paid by the Member or com-

mittee, not by COST."[4] Committees would not be obliged to use the services of COST. As the author of the bill points out, "COST should be a tool of the Congress. It should in no way reduce the authority of any committee or of either House. COST will operate in a purely advisory capacity to be used or not used as each Member and each committee shall determine.[5]

5) COST would enable Congress to establish regular procedures whereby communication between scientists and Members of Congress could be improved, thus overcoming the present situation in which "Congress does not understand science and . . . science does not understand Congress."[6] The most important issues in the scientific field could be identified and analyzed in terms of public policy. Such information would then be transmitted to committees which might be involved in a consideration of the problems involved. Individual Members could also be assisted. This is very important because the development of science produces problems which are of concern to all Members and not merely to those on the committees to which legislation is referred. For example, all the Members and all the people are affected by radiation hazards resulting from nuclear tests, the pollution of water by detergents, the pollution of air by exhaust fumes, and the pollution of land by pesticides.

6) COST would enable Congress to perform its role of representative government in a democracy by making its own informed decisions on matters having great implications for the people. This would be an improvement over the present method whereby decisions are often made in secret by a few "unknown administrative officials," known to Congress only when "the implications are already upon us."[7] Congress has been making decisions since its establishment, many have been on questions involving highly technical matters, and it is recognized that numerous Members have become expert in handling subjects referred to their committees. But it is not to be expected that large numbers of Members could become experts in all the disciplines involved in analyzing scientific and technical problems whose solution is sought by legislation. These sciences need to be studied separately, and in combination, in order to produce the type of information and objective advice required by congressional committees. A central office in the House, and another in the Senate, to handle matters concerned with science and technology would provide the kind of evidence needed to make informed judgments.

7) The determination of priorities in the workloads of the Senate and House Offices of Science and Technology will be made, respectively, by the Senate Committee on Rules and Administration and the House Committee on Administration. This will enable the

Congress to maintain direction and control over matters which it considers of paramount importance, i.e., the scientists will be "on tap" and not "on top."

*Cons*

1) The possibility of employing sufficient top scientists and engineers on a permanent basis to staff two congressional Offices of Science and Technology is indeed remote, considering present attempts and those made during the past few years to strengthen the scientific and engineering staffs of the House Committee on Sciences and Astronautics, and the Senate Committee on Aeronautical and Space Sciences. At the present time there are not sufficient numbers of qualified scientists and engineers to establish permanent, separate, and duplicate groups in the executive and legislative branches. Top part-time consultants outside the Government are likely to be the same persons for both the executive and legislative branches because there are so few such experts; this means that even though it becomes possible to set up duplicate sets of permanent scientific staffs, this practice could not extend to the very top consultants. Thus, the same most distinguished consultants would still be called upon by both the President and Congress. It should be noted that this situation is different from that which exists in the fields of economics and foreign affairs where there are enough qualified experts for highly qualified separate staffing of both branches of the Government.

2) Aside from the fact that most top-level scientists and engineers wish to pursue psychologically and financially rewarding careers in their chosen fields, they would not be qualified to work on the Hill if they could not translate specialized subjects into language understandable to laymen and also be able to write reports. The science administrators in Government, universities, and industry have these extra qualifications of being able to express opinions by speaking and writing, but they can get much more personal satisfaction and public recognition by working in the places where they are now employed than by accepting anonymous staff positions in Congress. At present they are working in the executive branch in charge of operating programs, in universities where they are educating new scientists and engineers, and in industry where they can earn much more money by carrying out Government contracts in defense, space, and atomic energy.

3) Scientists and engineers differ among themselves on matters involving their own specialized fields and on public problems where they take positions as citizens rather than as experts. When they present pro and con advice on the nuclear test ban, for example,

they are apt to give the same advice to Congress as to the President. When experts in COST disagreed in estimating purely scientific and technological facts, what method could be used to resolve differences of opinion—and given such contending opinions—what would a congressional committee do that is any different from what is now being done when decisions have to be made?

4) If outstanding scientists and engineers had much experience in having their advice disregarded, especially in cases involving political, economic, or foreign policy decisions which they deemed less important than their own input, it is likely that they would not wish to remain employed on Capitol Hill.

5) Science and technology are not involved in the legislative process as separate fields but are elements in bills and investigations including economic and political, national and international factors, which must also be evaluated when decisions are made. For example, research and development in agriculture, atomic energy, advanced aviation, and spacecraft are indigenous to functional locations in executive agencies and congressional committees, and decisions with regard to such varied matters usually depend upon value judgments involving nonscientific and nontechnical factors with which scientists and engineers are often unfamiliar. The function of elected representatives of the people is to balance all significant points of view within our society and arrive at decisions in the public interest. The scientific and technical facts involved in a supersonic airplane may be similar whether presented by experts to the executive or legislative branches, or at least may be capable of resolution on a purely technical level; but whether or not Congress decides to appropriate money for a supersonic airplane will depend upon the assessment of other factors, notably the relationship of the plane to defense, estimates of Soviet progress in aviation, and the future commercial growth of our aircraft industry.

6) Trying to separate science and technology from other and equally important factors involved in making legislative decisions may have unsatisfactory results. A congressional Office of Science and Technology would either be regarded by Members and committees as too far removed from congressional committee staffs to be taken into account when actual work on a bill is underway; or a group such as COST could overlap with presently constituted committee jurisdictions. Considering that at any one time there are a number of bills and investigations involving many sciences and numerous specialized branches of engineering, it is likely that a bottleneck might develop in the proposed system whereby priorities are assigned to the requests made of COST. At least the committees designated to act as control towers would have to develop special staff facilities to direct the flow of information between

scientific talent and the Congress, and if simultaneous committee workloads became too heavy, it is likely that COST would be bypassed.

7) It isn't necessary for Congress to establish an Office of Science and Technology because existing sources of information on these subjects can be strengthened by adding to the staffs of the standing committees and to the Legislative Reference Service if qualified applicants are available. There is also the possibility of working out better arrangements with the National Science Foundation and the National Academy of Sciences-National Research Council. The President of the NAS–NRC, Dr. Frederick Seitz, testified on June 11, 1963, before the Senate Committee on Aeronautical and Space Sciences that the National Academy would be glad to assist Congress more than in the past, pointing out that the NAS–NRC has a large permanent staff and excellent arrangements for mobilizing in a short time the opinions of the Nation's top experts in science and engineering. Dr. Seitz also reminded the committee that the National Academy's Committee on Science and Public Policy (COSPUP) was ready to help Congress with the broad issues of scientific and technical problems.

## B. A LEGISLATIVE SCIENTIFIC SERVICE

R. A. Carpenter has proposed that a Legislative Scientific Service of 100 professional and 200 supporting personnel be established in Congress with responsibility "(1) to analyze the Federal involvement in science and technology, (2) to recast the major issues coming up for decision in the structure of scientific principles and the state-of-the-art, and (3) prepare various means of imparting to the Congress the necessary information for understanding." This service would be supported "in information handling and mechanics of operation" by the Library of Congress but "should report only to Congress, perhaps a joint committee." "The role of such a legislative scientific service would be solely that of raising the level of scientific understanding in individual legislators and their staffs." It would not advise, recommend, make decisions or issue reports. "It would educate."[8]

*Pros*

1) Modern informational techniques, including audiovisual presentations, "to correspond to the specialization of congressional committees and subcommittees, would educate Members of Congress so that they could comprehend the whole spectrum of science

and technology." This is a much better method than hearings which "do not produce a favorable climate for education." Raising the level of understanding of scientific problems among individual Members of Congress is the most reliable way of insuring informed decisions on research and development programs costing billions of dollars. Unless this method is employed, the Members would have to depend upon the advice of their professional staff in science and technology, and to such an extent that the staff would really be making the decisions. The Members would also be better able to explain situations involving science and technology to their constituents, thus raising the level of understanding of such matters among the whole people.

2) An important result of establishing a Legislative Scientific Service would be that Congress could perform its intended role under the Constitution of making decisions contributing to the public welfare. Members, committees, the House, and the Senate would no longer be put in the position of merely acquiescing in decisions made by experts in the executive branch. Furthermore, executive decisions could be checked to see whether more money is being requested than necessary to meet policy objectives which have been agreed upon.

3) It is more realistic to educate Members of Congress in science and technology than to try to elect scientists to Congress because "the public has inherent distrust of scientists." This distrust, which may be compared to that which exists concerning the military, arises because scientists have invented or created certain devices and substances which are potentially harmful. The regulation and control of such harmful products, radiation and pesticides, for example, comes within the sphere of interest of the elected representatives of the people. Politicians who are generalists are better equipped than specialist scientists to measure the various factors required for formulating public safety.

4) The proposed Legislative Scientific Service would be an improvement over the scientific advisory groups which some of the congressional committees have established. Such committees meet infrequently, and lacking familiarity with security classified technical literature, can discuss scientific problems only in a superficial manner.

5) The Legislative Scientific Service will also relieve the Congress from any dependence on trade organizations, technical sources, industrial corporations, and other lobbies. Most of these organizations and industries have special interests, being the recipients of Government contracts in the aerospace and atomic energy fields, and they naturally wish to sell their point of view to Congress. The continuous process of education by the Legislative Scientific Service

will help Members to deal judiciously with those whose special interests must be recognized but checked for accuracy and relation to the general public interest.

6) The proposed Scientific Service would enable Members of Congress to deal with those occasions when scientists disagree or express personal bias. Members would have the information and advice whereby they could make their own evaluations of whether or not the Air Force should send a band of copper needles into orbit, whether or not nuclear tests should be conducted in outer space, and whether or not the formula for pesticides should be altered to avoid harmful effects upon people and crops.

## Cons

1) The Carpenter proposal overemphasizes science and technology in the legislative process. There are many types of legislation which are just as difficult and technical as science and technology, e.g., taxation, foreign aid, and social security. If an elaborate system employing 300 people to educate Members of Congress in the many disciplines involved in science and engineering can be justified, then similar systems could be justified in all other branches of human knowledge, e.g., in international economics so Members could understand tariff rates, the Common Market, the International Monetary Fund, etc. This line of reasoning obviously overlooks the fact that broad legislative fields and specific bills require a combination of ingredients, each measured to the degree necessary to attain desired objectives contributing to the public welfare. These other elements are legal, political, economic, military, psychological, national, and international. The legislative task requires a generalist who can identify those elements whose consideration is essential to the passage of laws which regulate and guide public affairs. In making generalist decisions involving science and technology, it is not necessary for Members of Congress to know physics, chemistry, biology, electronic engineering, etc., in detail. For example, a legislator need not know the chemical formula for liquid and solid propellants in order to make up his mind whether or not to vote money to develop both fuels. If it is important for national defense that the Navy have missiles, if ships and men would be endangered by liquid-fueled rockets, a decision can be made to develop Polaris missiles on the basis of these additional factors. Similarly, if the feasibility of separating salt from water is established, if some regions in the United States need more water, it is not necessary to know the molecular structure of ocean water in order to decide upon appropriations for research and development looking toward a desalinization program.

2) This proposal overemphasizes science and technology in analyzing the relations between the executive and legislative branches. The responsibility of Congress is not to staff itself merely for the purpose of checking and balancing the executive branch. Representative democracy requires legislation based upon a consideration of all pertinent factors, significant interests, and informed opinions so that the results will reflect the majority will.

3) The proposed system would give Members and committees too much information of a scientific and technical nature, actually impeding the decisionmaking process in the legislature in much the same way that flooding the motor of a car can stall the engine. A pool of 300 specialists and supporting personnel who are prohibited, under this proposal, from advising, recommending, deciding, and issuing reports, would not be able to put information in a form which would enable Members to identify the main scientific and technical factors and put them on a scale with all the other elements which must be weighed before a decision is reached. Some of the committees are already combining the latest audiovisual aids with hearings in order to inform the Members.

4) Considering the difficulties experienced by existing standing committees in employing professional staff personnel trained in science and engineering, it is unlikely that 100 professional and 200 supporting personnel could be found to engage in raising "the level of scientific understanding in the U.S. Congress." If they could be employed, and if office space were available, the system would be expensive.

5) The administration of the proposed Legislative Scientific Service is not altogether clear. It is to receive "support in information handling and mechanics of operation from the Library of Congress," thus giving rise to the impression that the Service will be located in the Library; but the Service is apparently not to be organized or administered by the Library of Congress nor is its relationship to the Legislative Reference Service clarified. The plan provides that reports should be made only to Congress, "perhaps a joint committee," an arrangement which would bypass the Library of Congress and the Legislative Reference Service.

6) It would be difficult to figure out the relationship between the proposed joint committee of the Legislative Scientific Service and other committees of the House and Senate. In the technology—specifically the engineering—involved in flood control and construction of military facilities, for example, what would be the relationship between the new Service and the permanent committee staffs which have been handling such matters for many years?

7) The proposal places more emphasis on science than technology. Thus the record of Congress in dealing with engineering as an

element in legislation is overlooked. In making plans for future staffing, it is well to remember that most of our present problems in the use and exploration of outer space involve engineering rather than science. Use of the word "science" to include engineering is not popular with engineers and might on occasion, lead to recruitment policies which would neglect a proper balance between the different types of professional employees needed to meet congressional requirements.

## C. A SCIENCE ADVISORY STAFF IN EACH HOUSE AS PROPOSED BY H.R. 6866, 88TH CONGRESS, FIRST SESSION

The proposal is to establish in the Senate and in the House of Representatives a science advisory staff composed of a director and two associates, each staff chosen for competence in biology, chemistry, and physics. Two scientists for each House would be appointed by the majority party (one to be designated as director), the third scientist being appointed by the minority party, but appointments would be made without reference to political affiliation. Appointed to 3-year staggered terms, the scientists would be under 55 years of age and could serve no more than two terms. The director would be authorized to appoint temporary scientific personnel.

The function of each science advisory staff would be "to give scientific advice and assistance in the analysis, appraisal, and evaluation of legislation or proposed legislation" to Members, committees, and conference committees.

### Pros

1) The science advisory staffs "would remove the present dependence of the legislative branch upon the executive and occasional outside experts for technical advice and counsel" by establishing "a permanent source of scientific talent solely responsible to Congress."[9] The separation of powers between the Executive and the Legislature makes it necessary to have a reliable system whereby checks and balances can be made truly effective. We cannot expect to develop a situation in which Congress will be able to depend upon the validity of information and advice furnished by the executive branch on scientific and technological matters. One reason for this is that many programs are divided among a number of Government departments, and if their activities have not been coordinated by the Bureau of the Budget (which has far too few persons to do the job adequately for all agencies) the only place where infor-

mation on duplicating facilities comes to light is in connection with the legislative process. The other reason is that some of the executive agencies are in the position of competing for funds and their administrators are not apt to give congressional committees information which might tend to cut down on their prerogatives. Thus it becomes necessary for Congress to have its own source of objective, unbiased information.

2) Members of Congress, untrained in science, would have the kind of staff assistance they need to translate technical scientific information into language which can be understood by laymen. As a result, the Members could question executive programs more effectively. It would also be possible to have the kind of professional staff which could keep track of continuing space and defense programs thoughout the year instead of questioning operations only during hearings. This would enable the appropriate committees to head off developments which could be estimated to be undesirable, wasteful, and inefficient.

3) The science staffs would be a focal point for liaison between Congress, executive agencies, and the scientific community. From such sources of information, the staffs could provide Members of Congress with information, advice, and suggestions on all important scientific problems. A forward look could be taken toward projects which appeared to have potential value for future development, and Congress would be able to initiate positive programs in the field of science and technology.

4) The science staffs would keep track of executive expenditures on science in order to curtail waste and duplication and to evaluate programs. They would be invaluable particularly to the Committees on Government Operations which have responsibilities for all Government agencies.

5) The method of appointing top scientists would insure consideration of the needs of the majority and minority parties, but at the same time insure the selection of highly qualified scientists without reference to political affiliation. Considerable dissatisfaction has been expressed by some of the minority party members over the fact that they do not have sufficient professional staff assistance. The composition of the science advisory staffs would dispel any dissatisfaction on this score. If additional scientific assistance were needed, the director of each science advisory staff could select experts on an ad hoc basis, so that neither the majority nor the minority party need ever feel inadequately staffed for the purpose of making prudent decisions on scientific legislative matters.

6) Youth and creativity would be insured by providing that the director and his two associates be under 55 years of age and new viewpoints would be infused into the operation by the provision

for staggered terms and the prohibition against the scientists serving for more than 6 years.

*Cons*

1) Although the purpose of the proposal is to provide "Congress with a staff competent in science and technology," the bill mentions only the appointment of scientists and omits any reference to engineers. Engineering problems predominate in space programs as well as in the construction of military facilities, flood control, etc. Furthermore, not all the sciences are represented. Among the scientists needed to analyze Project West Ford, for example, are astronomers. (Project West Ford was an Air Force program concerned with orbiting a belt of copper needles for military space communications purposes.)

2) Three scientists for the House and three for the Senate would not be sufficient personnel to achieve the objectives of the proposed bill in analyzing and evaluating the legislation and answering requests for information. It is unlikely that the three scientists would be required to work as a team on each legislative task because not all problems would involve these sciences, the result being that the House would have one biologist, one chemist, and one physicist, with a similar situation prevailing in the Senate. The three House scientists would be expected to serve too many masters: 435 Members, 21 committees, 125 subcommittees, and perhaps 7 joint committees. An imbalance is created by proposing fewer scientists for the House than for the Senate which has 100 Members, 18 committees, and 100 subcommittees. Even so, three scientists could not adequately serve the Senate.

3) It would be difficult to work out a satisfactory relationship between the science advisory staff in each House and the staffs of the standing and joint committees. So many committees and subcommittees would be conducting investigations and holding hearings at the same time that those which are well staffed would not be likely to wait their turn for the comments of one or more of the three congressional scientists. They would be far more likely to call in as many consultants as they needed from all over the country to evaluate the different aspects of the situation being considered. On the other hand, the science advisory staff would have no means of seeing that studies they initiated would have the effect desired.

4) The budget of $50,000 per year to cover travel, clerical personnel, and office expenses is too small to permit the appointment of temporary scientific personnel when additional staff is needed for important legislation and increased workloads.

5) Top-level scientists willing to give up working in their own

fields with opportunities for public recognition of individual work are unlikely to accept positions to advise and write reports for Congress; at least such persons are hard to find and this difficulty might be compounded by the provisions for appointment and tenure in the proposed bill. Even though appointments are to be made without reference to political affiliation, outstanding scientists are unlikely to think that nonpartisanship is the governing factor when appointments are also made by the main officials of the majority and minority parties. Whether or not the limitation of tenure to a total of 6 years is a drawback remains to be seen.

6) Specialist scientists are unlikely to have the qualifications to identify and analyze all the pertinent elements necessary for the formulation of Government policy. The additional elements which must be weighed are economic, political, military, national, and international. If a biologist explained various forms of cancer, for example, it would still be necessary for someone on a committee staff to relate this information in a meaningful way to committee decisions on appropriating more or less money for the construction of health research centers, medical personnel, and fellowships; how to prevent overlapping and duplication among Government departments; and what criteria should govern Federal grants to universities.

The partial role that could be played by a biologist, a chemist, or a physicist can be estimated by analyzing the component parts involved in the decision by the President and Congress to create the Space Communications Satellite Corporation. This subject has scientific and technical aspects but in addition the following elements are involved: the relation between the Government and industry; antitrust legislation; international relations, particularly with Western Europe, the Soviet Union, and the conduct of foreign policy in the United Nations; assistance to underdeveloped areas; conflicting patent provisions in U.S. law; interdepartmental relationships; the regulation of rates; ownership of stock; and the impact upon other forms of communication. An analysis of such factors, individually and in combination, can only be made by staff members who are qualified as generalists to assist in the legislative process.

*(The following conclusions were appended by the staff of the Committee on Science and Astronautics — Ed.)*

## Conclusions

In view of the data and information provided through the foregoing channels, it may be useful to suggest certain findings and recommendations for the consideration of the subcommittee and the full committee. These findings and recommendations should not necessarily be regarded as conclusive, since subsequent inquiries or developments may disclose a need for amendment.

## FINDINGS

The scientific community, or an important segment of it, appears to feel that—

Congress may need to solve its informational problems on a fluid, case-by-case basis rather than through some permanent formal mechanism.

Since scientists themselves often disagree, as well as possess individual interests, care must be taken to avoid one-sided advice.

Few national issues, even those of a scientific nature, are resolved solely by technical decisions. Most are tempered by a multitude of other interests which in themselves do not present a clear-cut solution. The element of judgment and the weighing of all factors precludes the likelihood that Congress will find a ready answer, regardless of the methods of securing information and advice.

Scientific advisers should not be used to make decisions, but only to provide insights that will be useful to Congress in its policy determinations.

Congress could and should make better use of existing sources of information and advice, both in Government and out, than it does today.

Inquiry made of the staffs of various House committees suggests that—

It is necessary to draw a distinction between demonstrated congressional needs of a purely technical nature and those of a policy or managerial nature with scientific overtones. The incidence of the former is rare, of the latter numerous.

The problem of overlapping committee jurisdiction is a real one, but it is unlikely to be much alleviated so long as the activities of Federal agencies are mission oriented and involve a variety of scientific disciplines.

Depending on committee staffs for scientific aid has the advantage of operating through an entity which is familiar with congressional needs and the interests of individual Members, which is knowledgeable about agencies and companies performing scientific work, and which has access to virtually all sources of technical information. The disadvantage is the difficulty which staffs with many other duties experience in keeping abreast of all scientific activity as well as current on new developments.

Inquiry made of executive agencies dealing in scientific and technical matters, emphasizes these points:

The most consistent and detailed contact with industry, universities, and other nonprofit organizations engaged in scientific and technical work is maintained by those in executive branch departments or agencies.

Most scientists employed by the Government itself are to be found in executive branch agencies.

Nonetheless, few inquiries of a true technical nature are made to executive branch agencies by the Congress — usually less than 1 percent of those received from congressional sources.

Executive branch personnel are ready and willing to go into detail with Congress on scientific matters relating to their own work — but are reluctant to discuss the work of others.

Some officials in the executive branch now believe that administrators and managers of technical programs in Government should take the initiative in getting scientific information and advice about their programs to Congress.

Background briefings and situation reports on difficult scientific problems should be given to Congress *before* they become major issues.

Advice on certain technical programs may often have to come from the same people advising the executive agencies since there may be a limited number of experienced persons with knowledge of that program.

Inquiries made of personnel representing the professional societies disclosed these points:

Few professional organizations are set up to provide rapid response to technical queries.

All such groups, however, appear willing to organize special committees or subgroups to handle such requests if asked to do so on any consistent basis.

Present limitations on the professional societies include (1) lack of time and funds to perform detailed studies for Congress unless costs can be reimbursed, and (2) necessity for limiting work to areas of special interest to the individual society.

Societies may have problems of maintaining tax-exempt status if they take the initiative in offering their services to Congress — although this obstacle appears surmountable. (See study C, p. 63).

The professional societies receive more inquiries of a scientific or technical nature from the executive branch than from Congress.

Inquiries made of industry representatives accustomed to dealing with Congress brought out the following:

Congressional requests to this source for purely technical information and advice seem extremely rare. More tend to come from the executive branch than the legislative.

Most congressional inquiries are directed to the status of ongoing or prospective company projects.

Most technical interplay between industry and Congress seems to occur in the course of company-planned briefings initiated by industry rather than Congress.

As with the professional societies, industry is ready to gear itself to more technical use if requested and, unlike the societies, is generally able to do so with a minimum of delay and without the requirement for special funding.

While industrial groups are ready to provide technical information and advice—or even loan personnel—to Congress on request, they are reluctant to evaluate scientific matters involving competitors or work in technical areas other than their own.

The survey of the use made of the Legislative Reference Service by Members of Congress and congressional committees has resulted in these findings:

The bulk of congressional requests involving science and technology are not so much for detailed scientific or technical information as they are for information bearing on management or engineering problems in relation to one of the broad fields of Government interest—such as defense, economics, foreign affairs, space, natural resources, communications, etc.

The Legislative Reference Service has been able to meet most congressional requests to date with personnel trained largely in Government and the social sciences.

There is a definite need, however, for additional Legislative Reference Service staff with scientific or technical training.

It must be kept in mind that congressional needs, as indicated by requests placed with the Legislative Reference Service, almost always carry strong overtones of governmental or public policy and that scientific and technical studies requested will usually have to be couched in such terms. The pure laboratory scientist, therefore, may be ill equipped to perform this kind of work unless he has had considerable experience with the nature of the problems Congress normally faces.

## RECOMMENDATIONS

Since it is virtually certain that Congress, in the years ahead, will have to deal increasingly with issues affected by science and technology, it is recommended that the subcommittee and/or the full committee give special consideration to the promotion of these activities:

1. Utilization, either by informal arrangement or contract, of highly trained ad hoc groups of scientists and technicians to provide evaluation of problems and issues which are mainly technical in nature. Such groups could be employed as consultants on the particular matter to be handled, so long as the need exists, then disbanded.

2. Formulation of improved mechanisms for liaison with the executive Office of Science and Technology, the National Academy of Sciences, and, when created, the proposed National Academy of Engineering.

3. Strengthening of committee staffs through the addition of personnel with technical backgrounds—but bearing in mind (1) the desirability that such personnel be familiar with the workings of Government and the Congress, and (2) the fact that the bulk of staff work, even for technically oriented committees, requires more application of the social and political sciences than the purely physical ones.

4) An increase of scientific and technical personnel within the Legislative Reference Service in order to facilitate handling requests from Congress of a scientific or technical nature.

5) A continuing survey both by individual members of the Congress and by those committees dealing with scientific and technical matters, of their needs for scientific advice—and the immediate disclosure and publication of any such needs for the benefit of all those concerned.

6) Close cooperation among congressional committees and their staffs, especially those dealing with facets of the same scientific or technical problems, so that sources of technical advice may be more efficiently utilized and important information may be readily disseminated on a broad basis.

## NOTES

1 *Congressional Record*, Aug. 13, 1963, pp. 14002–14003. See also the Congressional Record, July 30, 1963, pp. 12896–12898.
2 "NASA Authorization for Fiscal Year 1963," hearings before the Senate Committee on Aeronautical and Space Sciences, 87th Cong., 2nd sess., on H. R. 11737, June 13, 1962, pp. 26, 27.
3 Remarks by Senator Bartlett, *Congressional Record*, Aug. 13, 1963, p. 14003.
4 *Ibid.*
5 *Ibid.*
6 *Congressional Record*, July 30, 1963, pp. 12896–12898.
7 *Ibid.*, p. 12898.
8 The quotations in this section are from "A Proposal To Raise the Level of Scientific Understanding in the United States Congress," by R. A. Carpenter, 709 DuPont Circle Bldg., Washington, D. C. Multilithed. Five pages.
9 Hon. Abner W. Sibal, speaking in the House of Representatives on June 6, 1963, *Congressional Record*, June 6, 1963, p. 9847.

# 10

# The Scientific Establishment and American Pluralism

SANFORD A. LAKOFF

I

IN THE process of coping with the technological challenges of the last two decades the United States has indeed created what Don K. Price has called "the scientific establishment." As Price has shrewdly observed, the establishment of science in the United States can in certain respects be profitably compared to the establishment of religion elsewhere. "The plain fact is," Price has written, "that science has become the major Establishment in the American political system; the only set of institutions for which tax funds are appropriated almost on faith, and under concordats which protect the autonomy, if not the cloistered calm, of the laboratory."[1] And yet, in one crucial respect, this establishment is a very peculiar one, in that, as Price has also pointed out, it is far from the cohesive and even monolithic structure that we usually think of when we speak of a state church.[2] If anything, the scientific establishment is about as fragmented and pluralized as anything could be, even in a country distinguished for its pluralism in so many respects.

In general our political pluralism takes two forms: first, a system of society in which public government has a preeminent but not exclusive place—a system in which there are also private governments, with more limited power, but with a vital role and a real share in the exercise of power—private governments like those of corporations, labor unions, universities, professional associations, political parties, and even churches; secondly a system of public government in which there is a deliberate effort to encourage fragmentation and decentralization, whether through the separation of powers, through federalism, or through the dispersal of executive and legislative powers among a variety of relatively autonomous agencies and committees.

These two forms of pluralism are very much in evidence in what we may call the scientific establishment. This is clear if we

377

examine any of the statistics concerning the diffusion of scientific activity. In fiscal 1964, when total federal expenditures for research and development reached a record high of $14.9 billion, most of these funds paid for work actually performed outside government itself. Based on the 1962 figures, which are roughly comparable, almost two-thirds (63 percent) of these federal government disbursements were received by private industrial contractors; 17 percent went to universities, university-affiliated research centres, and not-for-profit corporations; and only 20 percent paid for work done in government laboratories.[3]

The distribution of scientists and engineers according to employers tends to follow the distribution of expenditures. One survey indicates that 81 percent of the country's engineers are employed by private industry, 13 percent by all levels of government, and 3 percent by colleges and universities. According to the same source, 43 percent of our scientists are employed by industry, 30 percent by colleges and universities, and 17 percent by government, particularly the federal government.[4] Of all scientists now engaged in research and development it is also estimated that 60 percent work on projects directly or indirectly supported by government funds.[5]

Indeed, even if we confine our examination to scientific activities within the public sector, which is to say to the government agencies that undertake or supervise work in this general category, it is apparent that they do not fit into some neatly integrated administrative structure. For the most part the agencies that are heavily involved in scientific and technical work are housed in separate entities and jurisdictions, sometimes for reasons of historical accident rather than logical fitness. Scientific activities in the federal government range over ten departments and involve twenty-seven independent agencies.[6] The Department of Commerce houses the Weather Bureau, the National Bureau of Standards, the Census Bureau, and the Coast and Geodetic Survey. The Geological Survey, however, is in the Department of the Interior, as are the Fish and Wildlife Service, the Office of Saline Water, and the Bureau of Mines. The Agricultural Research Service is of course in the Department of Agriculture. The Department of Health, Education, and Welfare includes the Public Health Service, which, in turn, oversees the research and disbursements of the National Institutes of Health. The Department of Defense maintains its own supervisory agencies, the Office of Defense Research and Engineering and the Advanced Research Projects Agency, as well as advisory committees and R & D organizations run by each of the armed services. And even the Post Office contains an Office of Research and Engineering.

In all these instances, scientific activities are components of the more comprehensive missions of cabinet-level departments of the executive branch. In addition, however, there are also in the executive branch agencies outside the departments which exist solely for the sake of undertaking, supporting, and supervising scientific activities in particular areas. All of recent creation, they are the Atomic Energy Commission, the National Science Foundation, and the National Aeronautics and Space Administration. In other independent line (or operating) agencies, scientific activities are incidentally important to specific responsibilities, as in the case of the Agency for International Development and the Arms Control and Disarmament Agency. The regulatory agencies—the Interstate Commerce Commission, Federal Power Commission, Federal Trade Commission, Federal Communications Commission, and Federal Aviation Agency—also perform functions involving scientific research and technical evaluation. And to add to the confusion, or perhaps merely profusion, there are the variously public corporations—the TVA, which is a mixture of public and private, and the non-profits, such as Rand, which are privately managed but publicly supported.

The pluralism of the scientific establishment in the executive branch is one example of the general situation. Scientific activities also claim the attention of Congress, for the most part through the committee system. The programs conducted within most of the executive agencies are scrutinized and authorized by the regular standing committees charged with oversight of the general areas in which the agencies function. In addition, several new committees have been established to deal with the programs of the newer autonomous agencies: the Joint Committee on Atomic Energy and the House and Senate committees on space. The Legislative Reference Service has only recently acquired a new division of science and technology. Congress maintains long-standing relationships with two quasi-governmental bodies, the National Academy of Science and the Smithsonian Institution, both chartered by act of Congress.

In short, if we consider only this one sector of the scientific establishment, the public sector, we see a structure made up largely of horizontally parallel rather than vertically integrated segments. The scientific establishment in the government is hardly monolithic or regimented. It too is distinctly pluralistic. If we were to add to this picture the structure of the nongovernmental sectors, we should have a vison of a pluralistic universe capable of impressing even a modern astronomer. Fortunately for the political scientist, it is not necessary to intuit, deduce, or leave aside the question of how this universe is regulated and by whom. The rulers of governments, and the rules by which they proceed, may be difficult to describe with perfect accuracy, but they are not shrouded in impenetrable mystery.

## II

In considering the coordination of science in the present day, it may be well to remind ourselves of Henri Saint-Simon's project for a Supreme Council of Newton which was to propagate the new religion of science and its chief dogma, the law of universal attraction. Saint-Simon even went so far as to suggest that to guide its affairs the council elect a secretariat which would be considered the "Pope and clergy of the physical scientists."[7] As audacious or merely amusing as this proposal now appears, we had better not dismiss it as altogether out of the question. Too many of the even more fantastic prophecies of Aldous Huxley's *Brave New World* have come close to realization for us to be smugly confident of the impossibility of a kind of global sacro-technocracy. For the time being, however, the world has not yet come to this pass, and in the United States, at any rate, we are still addicted to a more limited notion of what science stands for and a more pragmatic and freewheeling attitude toward the way it ought to be managed. In fact, the present system by which American science policy is coordinated, as it has so far evolved, is almost as pluralistic as the medium in which it tries to operate.

The evolution began with the experience of World War II. The Office of Scientific Research and Development, under Vannevar Bush and James Bryant Conant, had served the War Department well as a means of establishing and maintaining contact between the military and the private institutions upon whose facilities the government had to draw for much of its military R&D. After the war the Defense Department experimented with a number of efforts designed to perpetuate the essential characteristics of OSRD. During the Korean War, when it became plain that Cold War tensions required a stepping up of weapons research, the DOD established a Science Advisory Committee within the Office of Defense Mobilization. By 1957, however, pressures had built up which all but demanded that scientific advice be available at a higher level than the ODM. Accordingly, President Eisenhower issued an executive order which in effect transferred the Science Advisory Committee from the Defense Department to the Executive Office of the President, where it was reconstituted, and continues its existence, as the President's Science Advisory Committee (PSAC). At the same time, President Eisenhower also appointed a Special Assistant for Science and Technology who was elected chairman of PSAC, a custom which continues to be followed.

From the point of view of the President, the creation of PSAC and the office of the Special Assistant were necessary steps because through them he would have access to a source of advice on technical questions completely free of commitments to the operating agencies under his direction.[8] PSAC was to be composed of qualified scientists from outside the government who would be brought together to serve as a kind of board of review for controversial proposals which might emanate from the agencies. From the point of view of the scientific community, these steps offered an opportunity to restore the links between nongovernmental scientists and the presidency that had been badly damaged, if not altogether severed, by the change from a Democratic to a Republican administration — relations which were both symbolized and exacerbated by the widely resented withdrawal of J. Robert Oppenheimer's security clearance.

In time the functions of PSAC and the Special Assistant expanded to include not only questions in which scientific matters were important ingredients, as in the case of weapons systems, but also questions pertaining to government policy toward science and scientists in general — questions such as those arising in connection with the training of scientists, university-government relations, and the identification of national needs in science. PSAC has drawn help from two satellite bodies, a group of consultants-at-large, composed of former PSAC members, and another group composed of consultants from government agencies, as well as from panels able to call on a roster of over 300 scientists in the universities and industry. In cooperation with the National Science Foundation, the staff of the Special Assistant began to collect information designed to provide a basis not only for the review of existing programs but for the initiation of new efforts where they might prove to be advisable. When the NSF was created in 1950, some of those instrumental in bringing it about entertained the hope that it would become the focus of concern for the overall objectives of the science programs and also that to some extent it would oversee the operation of at least the major programs. But for various reasons, among them the controversy over the definition of its objectives and its relatively low position on the administrative totem pole, NSF has chosen to confine itself to the more modest role of supporting and advocating basic research.

PSAC and the Special Assistant have taken full advantage of their relatively high position and their presidential mandate to review and initiate programs along a broad front. PSAC's recommendations contributed to the decision to cancel the B-70 program and proposals for nuclear-powered aircraft. Its advice was also heeded in the establishment of the Office of Defense Research and

Engineering in the DOD. And PSAC has also directed a good many studies designed to suggest improvements in government science policy. Since 1957 no less than eighty panels and subpanels have been convened by PSAC from its roster. PSAC itself has been composed of from fifteen to eighteen scientists, until recently almost all from the physical sciences, who have come to Washington for monthly two-day meetings and have, in addition, individually chaired and participated in the work of the panels.

Through PSAC the Special Assistant has sought to fulfill the President's need for qualified and unbiased advice. If this were the only direction in which the Special Assistant could move to aid the President, however, he would not have much leverage with which to work for the President's objectives within the executive branch. As Richard Neustadt acutely observes, in our system of shared powers and under modern conditions "federal operations spill across dividing lines or organization charts; almost every policy entangles many agencies; almost every program calls for interagency collaboration." Although the President is formally in command of the executive branch and although he is vitally interested in every aspect of its operation, the agency administrators are responsible not only to him but also to "Congress, to their clients, to their staffs, and to themselves."[9] Clearly, if the Special Assistant was to be at all successful in implementing the advice of PSAC and in helping to coordinate ongoing programs, he needed another arm — an arm that would not be directed outward, as PSAC is, toward the university and industrial research laboratories, but inward toward the executive agencies.

The special assistant received such a second arm with the creation in 1959 of the Federal Council for Science and Technology. The FCST, which was also set up under an executive order, brings together the highest officers with policy rank and scientific responsibilities from each of the nine departments and agencies having the largest scientific programs. As in the case of PSAC the Special Assistant serves as chairman, again by custom rather than prescription. And again, as in the case of PSAC, the FCST appoints committees to study and report on specific problems. In two respects, however, there are important differences between the operation of these complimentary bodies. When the Federal Council adopts a report of one of its committees, or when, in a less formal way, it comes to certain conclusions about what ought to be done in any given area, its decision amounts to a kind of treaty among the major agencies. In addition, in several instances the FCST has been instrumental in setting up interagency coordinating committees, notably the Federal Radiation Council, the Interagency Committee on Oceanography, and the Interagency Committee on Atmospheric

Sciences. It is still too early to assert with confidence that these interagency committees will succeed in overcoming the gaps and duplications in federal programs they are designed to avoid or in securing the more intensive cooperation they are designed to promote. There is no doubt, however, that the Federal Council is significantly successful in providing a forum for the exchange of ideas among agency personnel on a number of levels which might never take place otherwise. The council has also been clearly successful in enabling the Special Assistant to keep a running check on the operations of the major agencies and to offer his services, as the President's broker, in smoothing out any interagency tangles and disagreements.

Through the establishment of PSAC and the FCST the powers and responsibilities of the Special Assistant were considerably strengthened and extended. But this very enlargement helped to make his job more difficult to perform. It was in order to alleviate this difficulty that in 1962 Congress transformed the staff activities which the special assistant had begun to accumulate into a permanent statutory agency, the Office of Science and Technology. OST was formed along lines first proposed by Senator Henry M. Jackson's subcommittee of the Senate Committee on Government Operations. This proposal won support because the staff of the Special Assistant, the members of PSAC, and the responsible officials of the Budget Bureau all agreed that a change was necessary and all preferred that it take the form of a moderate rather than a radical reorganization. A number of considerations weighed heavily with these scientists and administrators:

1) The budget for the various activities, including PSAC, under the direction of the Special Assistant, had to be drawn from the funds available to the President for all White House activities. This budget had grown to a figure in the neighborhood of $750,000. So as not to impose too great a strain on the general White House budget, it was considered advisable to ask Congress to allocate separate support for the work of the Special Assistant. This would enable him to expand his staff and his activities to whatever extent became necessary, subject to congressional approval.

2) The Jackson subcommittee had recommended the creation of an office of Science and Technology partly to improve the ability of Congress to inform itself about the government's science programs. Understandably, responsible congressmen wanted easier access both to information about the science programs and to the opinions of those in a position to review them. Inasmuch as Presidential assistants are customarily considered responsible to the President but not to Congress, the obvious solution was to establish a formal channel through which the legislators could reach the one

man in government with a broad understanding of what was afoot. It was also felt by congressmen that just because the Special Assistant is a key contributor to the making of policy involving science, he ought to be "more visible," or, in other words, available to Congress, as he would be if he were performing an analagous function as a political appointee in the State Department or the DOD.

3) There was a possibility that if this relatively moderate reorganization proposal were not accepted, pressure might build up in Congress for a more radical change, along the lines previously indicated in the various proposals for a Department of Science, proposals which have met with all but universal disfavor within the executive.

4) Events had demonstrated convincingly that science and technology would continue to be a vital area of policy concern for the forseeable future. It was therefore advisable to put the operations of the Special Assistant and his staff on a permanent basis. If matters remained on an *ad hoc* basis, staff members would find themselves at the mercy of political considerations every four years and the removal of valuable documents as personal papers could not be prevented. No harm had yet come to the staff or their functions due to the impermanence of their mandate, but without a regular statutory charter there was no guarantee against future damage.

Since there seemed to be several advantages and no obvious drawbacks to the proposal, the reorganization plan was submitted to Congress and OST was established. With this last touch effected, it soon occurred to the Members of Congress to take advantage of their new access to information. In 1963 a Select Committee on Government Research was appointed under the chairmanship of Representative Carl Elliott of Alabama and began a broad series of inquiries into the techniques of coordinating and supporting science. At the same time, a subcommittee of the House Committee on Science and Astronautics, which had until then been preoccupied with the space program, was set up under the chairmanship of Representative Emilio Daddario of Connecticut with a roughly similar, if somewhat less ambitious, purpose.

## III

If these congressional investigations have resulted in no major overhauling, it is because neither committee discovered much to find fault with in the system of advice and coordination which has so far been evolved. All those who have had important experience in this system, including all three past special assistants, indicated in their testimony before both committees that on the whole they were well pleased with the system now in operation.

This widespread satisfaction no doubt reflects an appreciation of the improvements that have been made in recent years rather than any unshakable conviction that the changes which have been set in motion will necessarily prove adequate. Indeed, such is the system that the very strengths it exhibits could become the sources of serious weakness.

Perhaps the greatest of these strengths is that in its pluralistic structure it shares the chief characteristic of the scientific establishment itself. As a result it is able to represent and mobilize all of the components of the constituency with which it deals without becoming the special preserve of any one of them. Through its relations with the National Research Council of the National Academy of Sciences, it secures highly valued estimates of long range needs. Through the Federal Council, which Jerome Wiesner has referred to as a "subcabinet for science and technology,"[10] and the informal relations which develop between the Special Assistant and the agency heads, it oversees programs in being, adjusts differences, and promotes cooperation. PSAC, meanwhile, stands somewhere in the middle, trying to integrate long-term estimates and on-going programs in the form of practical proposals. The Special Assistant acts as the President's lieutenant in matters where settled policy needs to be enforced, operating both by persuasion and by invoking the implicit threat of presidential sanction. At the same time he serves the President by bringing to the attention of the Chief Executive matters of importance which reach him through the various channels he now has open to the agencies, to university and industrial laboratories, to the professional associations, and to Congress; and by providing technical assistance and clarification whenever the President needs such help. The staff of OST, few in number but high in quality, can be used to assist wherever their help is most needed, and can also be relied upon to identify issues that might otherwise escape the attention of one or another of the elements in the network. Meanwhile, of course, the operating agency and bureau chiefs are free to run their programs without irresponsible interference and with the tacit assurance that, provided they maintain good relations with the Special Assistant, they are not likely to find any of their programs suddenly canceled or cut back because their viewpoints are unknown or misrepresented in the White House.

Another very considerable strength of the present system is that it provides welcome assistance to the Bureau of the Budget. In some respects it might have been expressly designed to help the Budget Bureau perform its important functions more efficiently. With the help of the OST staff, the PSAC panels and FCST committees all produce information and evaluations which make it considerably easier for the Bureau to do an effective job of reviewing appropriation requests. In addition, the Special Assistant and the FCST act as a buffer between the Budget Bureau and the agencies whenever conflicts arise between overall executive policy and the interests of particular agencies. These conflicts can be ironed out in the forum provided by the Federal Council or through the good offices of the Special Assistant without requiring the Budget Bureau to engage in a direct confrontation of strength with the departments and agencies, which the Bureau understandably prefers to avoid.

These strengths are surely considerable. But so are the potential weaknesses. It is quite possible that the long range projections of the National Academy, just because they are made by a relatively independent body outside the policy-making system, will not be translated into programs, The Federal Council is a subcabinet for science *only* in the sense that it brings operating agency heads together and not in the sense that these agency heads are appointive agents of the presiding officer. It is therefore possible that FCST will not secure the degree of cooperation that may be necessary if competition for appropriations is keen or if serious sacrifices are called for by the recommendations of the NAS and PSAC. As to PSAC, perhaps its chief potential weakness is that just because it need not embody a representative cross section of the scientific community, it may become an overly homogeneous pressure group working on behalf of narrow institutional or disciplinary interests.[11] Since it is in no formal way responsible to the constituency it represents, there can be no assurance that it will be balanced and objective in its judgments.

Nor, finally, is the Special Assistant in an unambigiously strong position. Under his various hats, he carries the key to the effectiveness of the entire system, but the key does not belong to him. His ability to achieve implementation of the advice he solicits and to coordinate the work of the agencies depends to a very great degree on the influence he has with the President. Even when relations are very good, as between President Kennedy and Dr. Wiesner, the Special Assistant can never be perfectly sure of his ground. Although the evidence for a definite judgment is not yet publicly available, it would seem that Dr. Wiesner had considerable influence with the President in connection with the negotiations leading to the nuclear test ban treaty with the Soviet Union. In at least one other case, it is known that he was overruled. Reportedly, Dr. Wiesner and James Webb, the director of NASA, disagreed over the question of whether an earth orbit or a lunar orbit would be the most advisable course for the manned lunar landing project. Dr. Wiesner is said to have favored the earth orbit, in part because of the dividends it might have for other programs, including the military space program.

President Kennedy reportedly overruled Dr. Wiesner on the ground that since the space agency had the responsibility of carrying out the assignment, it would be best to allow the agency to decide upon the method, regardless of secondary considerations. Apart from any experience, however, it is clear that without considerable and sustained presidential support, the Special Assistant would find it extremely difficult to carry out any recommendation that might meet with agency objections.

One somewhat subtle consideration which militates against these potential weaknesses should be noted. In only a few years the Special Assistant and PSAC have managed to extend their influence into the operating agencies by persuading the departments to create new high-level positions for scientist-administrators. At the instigation of PSAC, several departments, including State, Agriculture, Commerce, and Interior—and in effect though not in name, Defense—now have assistant secretaries for research and development. All these posts have been filled by people associated with or approved by PSAC. These appointments, together with those in the Office of Defense Research and Engineering, have enabled the Special Assistant and PSAC to establish better ties to the departments and agencies than might otherwise exist. It would be a mistake to think that appointees to these posts become catspaws of the Special Assistant. In each case they have been men of excellent qualifications and proven independence. As members of a department they are bound to develop loyalties to it and feel great concern for its special missions. Nevertheless, their previous association with PSAC undoubtedly makes informal coordination and communication easier than it would be with personnel who have come up through the ranks of the agency or who are appointed without PSAC approval.

## IV

In general, then, the American scientific establishment is regulated according to the same pluralistic principles that define its very structure. This pluralism surely distinguishes the modern establishment of science from the traditional establishment of religion. Nevertheless, there are certain ways in which the comparison remains suggestive.

Both types of establishment confer benefits and run certain risks. In each case regular and assured public support frees the practitioners to pursue their callings, releasing them from the need to divert much of their energy to the job of finding sources of financial assistance. Establishment may also be said to encourage dedication, whether it be to the practice of faith or the pursuit of knowledge, by conferring a measure of public approbation upon those willing to undertake the training and the discipline necessary to the work. On the other hand, any institution or set of institutions enjoying such a protected position is vulnerable to corrupting influences, and certainly to constant imputations of corruption.

For just this reason, in ages past, the question of ecclesiastical establishment provoked considerable critical debate. In seventeenth century England, while modern science was still in its swaddling clothes, zealous Puritans denounced the Church of England as corrupt and tyrannical. In reply, the formidable Anglican spokesman, Richard Hooker, only needed to cite the example of Scotland, where the Puritan churches were no less firmly established. The English Puritans, he charged, were fanatic enthusiasts, enemies to all order and to reason, and not even faithful disciples of Calvin. If established churches could become temporarily corrupt, he asked, how much more corrupt would matters be if they were left to the private judgment of everyone who claimed to be directly inspired?[12]

Although the critics of the modern scientific establishment form no united party or sect, they nevertheless do exist, and again the accusation of corruption has arisen. One type of criticism concerns the role of the scientist as an adviser to government. Scientists are accused of suborning their noble pursuit of truth to the inhumane rattle of the war machine, presided over by the "High Brass" in the Pentagon.[13] It is said that their participation in government permits them only to provide technical service while compelling them to acquiesce in policy decisions they can have no part in making. Others contend that scientists can have far too great an influence with statesmen unable to question their technical judgment, and that they may use their proximity to power to intrigue against colleagues with whom they disagree.[14]

Apart from such accusations of political compromise, there are also critics who suggest another kind of corruption — intellectual corruption. The acceptance of government subvention is criticized because it is said to rob the scientist of the freedom to follow his creative instinct wherever it leads him. Instead, by a Machiavellian process mixing carrots and sticks, inducement and coercion, he becomes committed to paths prescribed by others — paths which often lead him to the temptations of power and pelf. Because government spending must be justified in terms of well-defined social goals, a kind of Gresham's Law is said to operate, by means of which applied research drives out basic reasearch, and the development of useful instruments drives out both forms of research. In the process, the solitary and more genuinely creative ways of "little science" allegedly are slighted in favor of "big science,"[15] with its stifling bureaucratic overorganization, its penchant for team research, its disease of "projectitis." Seemingly innocuous university research projects, installed at the behest of government agencies, are said to represent harmful interference both with the academic freedom of faculty members and with the goals of effective and balanced education.

A defender of the scientific establishment would probably answer these critics, much as Hooker answered the Puritans, by arguing that some kind of establishment is better than none. He might well reject most or all of the criticisms as exaggerations of problems the system is well prepared to deal with on the whole, if not in every instance. When scientists give advice they merely contribute one strand to a much larger fabric of decision-making. When they accept funds, it enables them to do research of all kinds, and not merely pragmatic and military work. At the same time, if the defender of the establishment were completely candid, he might well confess to some doubts of a different sort—doubts which assail even those who value government support for science in its present form.

In abstract terms these doubts might be summed up as the difficulty of reconciling the demands of constitutional democracy with the requirements of effective scientific research. Representative government may be said to work best when its decisions embody a broad consensus, when the goal of the decision is clearly defined, and when the method of achieving the goal is appropriate and easily made subject to public scrutiny. In science, however, decisions must be made by those best qualified to make them, results are often uncertain, multiple approaches may be advisable, and processes are so esoteric that no one but a few experts—often the ones at work on the projects—can say whether things are being well managed or not. In more practical terms this difficulty takes a host of forms. Should decisions on such allocations be made by the most qualified scientists, even if they represent a relatively small number of institutions, or should they be made by a more representative body? How much should it cost to learn a scientific truth? Should funds go to institutions where the level of work is relatively high or to those where the level might be improved? How is it possible to compare what may possibly be learned from an investment in research with what could be obtained by the same expenditure in the form of goods and services required by some other socially desirable goal? How, indeed, can anyone make intrascientific comparisons of space exploration with high-energy physics, or of oceanography with weather forecasting? Scientists, moreover, no less than clerics, are subject to human bias and self-interest. When, like churchmen and monastic orders, they disagree over matters of doctrine and compete for control of the benefices, how is any collegial assembly, whether of cardinals or Nobelists, to choose between them fairly?

No amount of academic or congressional investigation will fully answer these criticisms and doubts. Some of them involve questions of value more than matters of fact. Others are inherent as problems in any attempt to govern something as ungovernable as the pursuit of truth. To govern, as Pierre Mendès-France once said, is to choose. To an extraordinary degree, the choices that face modern nations, the United States in particular, involve our response to, and our direction of, science and technology. It is no exaggeration to say that most of the public dilemmas we are compelled to live with are profoundly affected by what is done with and through science and technology. Nor are these forces by any means beyond our control, as the philosophers of technological determinism have tried to persuade us. If we cannot have the same confidence as Marxists claim to have in the happy influence of progress in the "mode of production," nevertheless, we should not be paralyzed by the prophets of doom who depict the advance of knowledge as a Frankenstein monster about to turn on its creator. We cannot assume, it is true, that under modern conditions the freedom of choice may not itself turn out to be fatal. The balance of terror in which we live must constantly inhibit any such overconfidence. But at the very least we can say with Raymond Aron: "We have lost our taste for prophecies; let us not forget the duty of hope."[16]

The experience of the United States, in the years since World War II, does in fact provide some grounds for hope. Throughout this difficult and challenging period we have been trying, with considerable success, to expand our knowledge of nature and to make use of what is learned. It would be naive to say that we have always done so out of pristine idealism. Most of the time our motivation has been a compound of the desire for security, for power, and for prestige. But whatever our immediate motives, the result has been that as a nation we have gradually come to recognize that we can no longer afford the luxury of borrowed genius, the romantic reliance on backyard hits and misses, and the all but open contempt for learning and theorizing that has so often diminished the value of our pragmatic inclinations.

In historical terms, even this is no mean improvement. For the longest period of American history, the support of science was not considered a proper activity of government. The founding fathers rejected the proposal for a national university. Our first federal observatory came into being disguised as a naval storehouse. The Smithsonian Institution was only created when Congress reluctantly agreed to accept the bequest of an Englishman. The atomic bomb came to us with the physicists expelled from Europe. Until very recently, Americans excited by the progress of science could only express embarrassment—as Jefferson, Franklin, and John Quincy Adams did—that this great republic, from which the philosophers of the Enlightenment expected so much, should in fact have done less to foster science than royalty and revolutionary dictatorships across the Atlantic.

Recent experience, however, shows convincingly that with respect to science at least, we are a changed country. Nor is this change, of course, only a matter of our attitude toward science. Ours is a social system far removed from the state of nature in our dependence upon artificial conveniences and upon one another. It is a highly organized society where all of us, whether we are in business or government or in the professions, are to some extent compelled to become organization men. Few would seriously wish to go back to the state of nature, whether it be to Walden Pond or the Everglades. Nor could we go back, even if we wanted to, because the progress of knowledge is irreversible. We can learn, but we cannot unlearn. Our problem is rather how to balance our desire for knowledge and technical innovations with our desire for a good life and a good society. Our problem is to determine how we can enjoy the blessings of growth and enrichment without suffering what Justice Brandeis feared would be "the curse of bigness."

It is for this reason that the involvement of government in the promotion of science demands close attention. For in this effort the United States has sought to achieve just such a balance. On the one hand we have sought to develop an enormous and diversified capacity to produce and to utilize knowledge; and on the other hand we have tried to arrange and manage this far-flung system in a way that respects intellectual initiative and personal responsibility, that promotes cooperation rather than coercion, and that provides as much decentralization of decision-making as is compatible with the demands of our most urgent priorities.

## NOTES

1 Don K. Price, "The Scientific Establishment," in Robert Gilpin and Christopher Wright, eds., *Scientists and National Policy-Making*, New York, 1964, p. 20.

2 See particularly his path-breaking discussion of support for science as "federalism by contract" in *Government and Science*, New York, 1954, Chap. 3.

3 Statement of Dr. Jerome B. Wiesner, *Hearings Before the Select Committee on Government Research*, House of Representatives (88th Cong. 1st Sess., 1963), Washington, D.C. 1964, p. 96.

4 Statement of Leland J. Haworth,

*Hearings Before the Subcommittee on Science, Research, and Development of the Committee on Science and Astronautics*, House of Representatives (88th Cong. 1st Sess., 1963), Washington, D.C. 1964, p. 370, Table 3.

5 Testimony of Dr. James R. Killian, Jr., *Hearings Before the Select Committee on Government Research*, Part 2, p. 757. (See Footnote 4 for complete reference.)

6 *Federal Organization for Scientific Activities, 1962*, National Science Foundation (NSF pp. 62–37), Washington, D.C. 1963, p. 3. Four agencies—the Weather Bureau, Coast and Geodetic Survey, Institutes for Environmental Research, and Environmental Data Service—have recently been consolidated into the "Environmental Sciences Services Administration" (ESSA) within the Department of Commerce.

7 Frank E. Manuel, *The New World of Henri Saint-Simon*, Cambridge Mass., 1950, p. 126.

8 For fuller discussions of PSAC see the essays by Harvey Brooks and Robert N. Kreidler in *Scientists and National Policy–Making, op. cit.;* and Carl William Fischer, Jr., "Scientists and Statesmen: A Profile of the Organization and Functions of the President's Science Advisory Committee," this volume.

9 Richard E. Neustadt, *Presidential Power: The Politics of Leadership*, New York, 1962, p. 89.

10 Jerome B. Wiesner, *Hearings Before the Select Committee on Government Research, op. cit.*, p. 273.

11 Fischer, in his paper on PSAC, this volume, p. 323, notes that 63 percent of all PSAC members have been from the physical sciences and 77 percent from the physical, mathematical, and engineering sciences; and that 70 percent received their graduate academic training at seven universities.

12 See Richard Hooker, *Laws of Ecclesiastical Polity* (1593), London, 1954 (Everyman's Library Ed.).

13 See Edward Speyer, "The Brave New World for Scientists," *Dissent*, Vol. VIII, No. 2 (Spring 1961), pp. 126–136.

14 See C. P. Snow, *Science and Government,* Cambridge Mass., 1962.

15 See Derek J. de Solla Price, *Little Science, Big Science*, New York, 1963.

16 Raymond Aron, *War and Industrial Society*, London, 1958, p. 60.

# PART 3

# Knowledge and Power: The Overview

*11*

# Federal Support of Science

### ALAN T. WATERMAN

IN THE EARLY days of Federal support of science after the war, it was expedient to justify this support by its specific contributions to essentially practical objectives, such as defense, health, and atomic energy. This was natural, since the technical industries had amply demonstrated the value of research in their developmental programs and in the profits resulting, and also since this kind of justification is quickly understood by those holding the purse strings. Was not the use of atomic energy "science," and also radar, and were they not designed and developed by scientists? It is true that in the war emergency many scientists worked on both these projects, but none would think of calling either of these science. Both were engineering developments. Neither would have succeeded without first-class, highly practical engineering.

Both atomic energy and radar had their origins in science, which, however, merely pointed out that there existed a theoretical possibility for application, but it took much applied research to establish the practical possibility, and it took extensive development to prove the feasibility and make the possibility a reality. As a matter of fact, both these enterprises had their origins in research so basic that it would never have been attempted as applied research, much less financed.

These two familiar examples precisely illustrate my first point; namely, that capital discoveries almost invariably have their origin in basic research, but which, since it explores the unknown, cannot foretell its findings, much less whether they will ever be practical. Consequently, the idea that one should only undertake basic research which is sure to be useful is a most short-sighted policy and,

DR. WATERMAN, *the first director of the National Science Foundation, was President of the American Association for the Advancement of Science when he presented this statement to Congress. It was first published in U.S. Congress, House Select Committee on Government Research, Hearings. H. Res., 504, Part 2 (88th Cong. 1st and 2nd Sess., 1964), pp. 808–815.*

as a rule, will miss entirely the outstanding advances which science may make possible. I had thought we had learned this lesson, but it seems we have not.

The magic words "scientific research" and "basic research" are applied indiscriminately to all manner of products brought to public notice. National expenditures for research and development are quoted as expenditures for science or research, e.g., "national funds invested in research this year will total nearly $16 billion"; "the current Federal budget for science is $12 billion." The implication is that all of this money goes to scientists for their research in science. It does no such thing. Almost 90 percent of this goes to Government and industrial laboratories whose mission is the development of useful equipment and devices for production.

## The National Budget for Research and Development

What are the facts? The national budget for the current year is indeed estimated at about $16 billion for research and development. But 70 percent of this sum—over $11 billion—is for development, and not for research at all. Only 10 percent is for basic research, which alone is directed toward strictly scientific objectives. It is only this portion which carries out the scientists' own programs. The entire country is the beneficiary for the developmental programs, in items directly useful in the national and the public interest.

But do not misunderstand me. I am not implying that this large and rapidly growing investment in research and development should not be reviewed; indeed it should be examined with great care. What I am saying is that we should know what it is that we are examining and for what purposes the funds are to be used. In particular, and this is my next point, we should not make the mistake of assuming that major economies can be brought about by an investigation of science and the activities of scientists, unless indeed one wants to jeopardize our future technology.

What does require special attention is the review and analysis of what we are spending large amounts of money for, whether national goals are truly served by these programs, whether the programs presently planned will indeed attain their objectives, and whether these operations are conducted efficiently and economically.

## Character of the National R. & D. Effort

I believe that it would be most appropriate and helpful if I were now to put before you a brief picture of the nature and background of the country's effort in science and technology. As you know, the National Science Foundation has since 1953 made comprehensive studies of many phases of this effort. Its distribution among the major economic sectors and the trends that are apparent over the last decade I believe would be especially illuminating from the standpoint of your study.

As I have just stated, the national total for research and development is currently estimated at about $16 billion. This is nearly 3 percent of the gross national product, an increase from 1.4 percent in 1953–54. Of this, the Federal Government provides about 65 percent, while about 32 percent is provided by industry. Thus industry and the Federal Government are paying practically the entire research and development costs, in the ratio of 1 to 2.

In this national effort, industry is doing most of the work. Seventy-four percent of the total funds are used by industry in performance of research and development, 14 percent by the Federal Government in its own laboratories, and 12 percent by nonprofit institutions.

The distribution of scientific and technical manpower among these economic sectors is similar. Thus of the total number of scientists and engineers employed in research and development activities in 1960, 68 percent were in industry, 15 percent in the Federal Government, 12 percent in academic institutions, and the rest in other nonprofit institutions.

Although the total national funds for research and development have about tripled since 1953, this distribution of funds and scientific and engineering manpower has changed very little, and practically not at all since 1957. During this period the labor force has increased by 15 percent, and scientific and technical manpower by 57 percent. As a percentage of the labor force, scientific and technical manpower now stands at 3.6 percent; it was 2.5 percent in 1953.

The distribution of effort in basic research is somewhat different, but it is similar in its stability. National funds for basic research currently amount to nearly $1.5 billion, which is about three times the amount in 1953. As a percentage of the total funds for research and development, basic research funds remained nearly constant at 8 percent until the past two years, when they rose to about 10 percent. This largely reflects costly new projects in such subjects as oceanography, high-energy accelerators, and space research, where research facilities are especially expensive. The Federal Government is the source of less than 60 percent of national funds for basic research, industry about 25 percent, while academic and other nonprofit institutions provide the remaining 15 percent, in the ratio of about 2 to 1.

Colleges and universities have consistently performed nearly half of the Nation's basic research, industry about one-third, and Government about one-sixth.

What is especially important to note is that the Nation's effort in research and development has been a remarkably consistent one in its distribution of funds and technical manpower for the past decade. In recent years, increasing apprehension has been voiced over the large increases in the Federal budget for scientific research and development. While these increases have indeed been large, you will note that they have been quite effectively matched by the increases in contributions from the other sectors of the economy. Of particular significance is the fact that the Federal Government is not acquiring a monopoly or control over scientific and technological activities any more than it has been exercising for the past decade. In view of this stability in distribution of effort, it would seem that one should proceed with caution in the formulation of any radical change in the extent of Federal participation. Obviously such could lead to serious dislocations and loss of valuable time and effort in the process. Besides, one must never forget that we live in a highly competitive world, and the modern key to successful competition lies in science and technology.

## Review of R.&D. Programs

In undertaking the task of review, it is relatively easy to state what should be reviewed, and quite another matter to specify how one should go about it. In the case of developmental or research and development programs, I believe it is helpful to conduct the review under two major aspects: (a) study of the R.&D. programs per se, and (b) study of the management and organization of the agencies involved in planning and operating R.&D. programs.

Thus, under (a), program content, one should consider:

1) what are its objectives and what are their relative priorities?
2) will the program, if successful, meet these objectives?
3) is the program technically feasible?
4) is the estimated cost of the effort justifiable, in dollars, manpower, and facilities?

Under (b), management and organization: The operating agency should be held strictly responsible for carrying out its mission; for this purpose it should have adequate authority and funds. Fundamental to this kind of review are the following considerations:

1) competence of agency leadership and staff, and its organization;
2) selection of objectives toward carrying out its mission;
3) selection and use of experienced and competent consultants and advisory committees;
4) planning of programs to further objectives;
5) efficiency of management and administration.

These are fairly obvious principles, to be sure. But many a review is wasteful of time and effort in that its initial approach may disregard them—especially the first premise, that the operating agency be held responsible. If an agency has experienced and competent leadership, and if it selects and heeds advisers of the highest qualifications, then in scientific and technical programs, caution should be exercised against attempting to find higher authorities to make findings on the same technical points and plans.

In this connection, a most perplexing problem arises—what to do about conflict of interest. In principle, conflict of interest must by scrupulously avoided, especially by the Government, for obvious reasons. However, when carried to its extreme, this means that no expert may qualify for consulting service if he is receiving any direct or indirect support from the Government for R.&D. projects or programs which relate to his consulting. Since in carrying out the R.&D. programs which the Government supports it is obviously important to secure the services of the ablest individuals in the field, rigorous application of this extreme policy means disqualification of this top group for consultation. Clearly this is an extremely grave matter. It is not soluble by asking such individuals to drop out of related activities. In the first place, many will refuse; in the second, if they accept, they are then lost to the programs involved. I have no good answer to this dilemma, except to say that such individuals are essential in both capacities, and that therefore one must select individuals with high integrity and objectivity, and count upon their performance accordingly.

In the analysis of the feasibility of a given developmental program, and the planning of its procedures and operations, there are a number of modern techniques that are being developed to a high degree of effectiveness which can greatly improve the quality and time spent in decisionmaking. These include systems analysis and operations research especially, together with data-processing methods, information theory, and computer applications. Full use of these techniques and processes is especially desirable as the scope and complexity of technical programs increase.

## Overall Program Limitations

From the overall national point of view, a question of first importance is naturally whether the country can afford to carry out a program of this magnitude and technical character. As I have already stated, curtailment of basic research is not the answer to this question. Insofar as funds alone are concerned, it seems reasonable to me to assume that the country can certainly carry on an undertaking of the present or greater magnitude, provided its objectives are sound and fully endorsed by the Nation. A far more stringent limitation is the available supply of scientific and engineering manpower necessary to carry on the work. We need to know the present number of available scientists and engineers, their rate of output, and whether the future numbers will be adequate. Clearly this is the factor in this situation which most calls for long-range planning, since it takes seven or eight years beyond high school to carry through the advanced training which is needed.

Recent studies of this subject by the National Science Foundation[1] have shown a remarkably consistent trend in the production of scientists and engineers which has remained the same for forty or fifty years. The rate has been an accelerated one, but the acceleration has remained constant. Thus, the number of advanced degrees in science and engineering for a given age group has been doubling every twelve years. Taking into account the abnormally high birth rate following the war, one can conclude, therefore, that if no major change occurs, the output would about double by 1970. This would make the total available number also double by that time. This estimate was based on the number of graduates from academic institutions with advanced degrees. Furthermore, a study of the number of scientists and engineers employed in the various sectors leads to approximately the same conclusion, namely, that unless the situation changes, the number of scientists and engineers employed by 1970 will be doubled. This gives us some assurance that the future situation will be satisfactory. But, and it is a large but, we have fallen badly behind in providing the facilities for this training. Badly needed at our educational institutions are teachers, increases for teachers' salaries, laboratories, classrooms, and operational funds. Unless we can come to grips with this situation, and do so promptly, the requisite manpower will not be forthcoming, or, what is very bad, the quality of training will deteriorate. It is also especially important to note that in order to carry out this training program at least 40 percent of the output of scientists and engineers will have to be employed by colleges and universities in order to train the increasing numbers with the same degree of effectiveness.

## Review of Basic Research Programs

Any review of the Federal Government's program in basic research and its responsibilities therefore must recognize that the field of basic research requires a quite different approach. As I have already stated, the program is a relatively small one in terms of money, and therefore no great economies can be achieved which will be of appreciable relative importance. The second point rests upon the distinction which I have already mentioned between basic research and its applications, development, and technology. Basic research is undertaken for the advancement of knowledge and not to accomplish particular practical objectives. The distinction, then, rests primarily upon the motivation of the research worker. This distinction often cannot be determined from the title of the research project, since one of two projects with the same title may be carried out as basic and the other as applied research, with findings of different kinds. Typical examples of basic and of applied research are easy to find, but the two classes admittedly overlap. Why, therefore, do scientists stress the distinction so strongly? The first reason is that basic research is true pioneering, and unless it is given completely free rein, it may miss important contributions to knowledge, many of which, as history shows, pave the way for sensational technological progress. Another and eminently practical reason was stated by Dr. Vannevar Bush in "Science, the Endless Frontier," his epoch-making report which you recall resulted from a request by President Franklin Roosevelt to make recommendations concerning the future role of the Federal Government in science, and which recommended the establishment of the National Science Foundation in order to assign specific responsibility for the support of basic research. The statement to which I refer is that applied research drives out basic—a sort of Gresham's law. That is to say, under budget limitations and pressures to achieve high priority, practical objectives, preference tends to be given to those items which are aimed directly at meeting practical needs.

My concern at the moment, and it is a deep one, is that we are now observing a verification of this law in the critical attitude which is developing toward provision of funds for the support of scientific activities. The reason for this attitude lies first in the failure to make the distinction between basic research as compared with applied research and development, and, second, in too little understanding and appreciation of the role which basic research plays in our national security and welfare for the future. One of the chief misconceptions is the notion that one can identify in advance where important discoveries will be made. How, for example, could one have projected in advance a program for the discovery of X-rays or radioactivity when these phenomena were not known to exist?

From the point of view of the Federal Government, basic research should be regarded as a national investment. As such, it should be comprehensive in nature, covering all fields of science. Like a financial investment, it should include solid, conservative projects which guarantee a small but reliable return, and others which are more problematical but which, if successful, might bring a handsome return. Such a program, soundly conceived by those experienced and skilled in the art, will, on a statistical basis, guarantee substantial returns of a practical nature even though the individual successes may not be foretold in advance.

One final but no less important aspect of basic research is that it is an essential ingredient in the advanced training of scientists and engineers. Its natural habitat is the colleges and universities where these are trained and where the association of young, inquisitive minds gives added  impetus and effectiveness to the research performed.

Any review of a basic research program should depend primarily upon the advice of leaders of basic research. The consideration of prospective programs must be largely a subjective process, depending as it does upon the judgment of experienced individuals.

Questions are often raised regarding the degree of coordination and duplication which exists in programs for basic research. One must realize at once that a certain degree of duplication is necessary, since an important research finding must always be checked by other observers, preferably using somewhat different techniques. The proper word to use for basic research is undesirable duplication, and again this is a matter which the scientists are most competent to decide. A further important point is that basic research has a remarkable, built-in coordination. This follows from the fact that each basic research investigator has as his goal a sound and original contribution to his field. Indeed his standing among his colleagues is judged by this standard. Therefore, in order to determine whether his work will be unique and original, he must make it his business to learn as best he can about all research currently being carried on in his particular speciality. To attempt to duplicate unnecessarily the work of another researcher is to commit professional suicide. It follows that a competent research scientist or a panel of competent scientists in a particular field of science will know remarkably well the current work that is going on in the field, and will not undertake or recommend projects which do not have this original quality. This fact, which is commonly misunderstood, provides the greatest possible safeguard against needless duplication. At the same time, quite obviously it  also makes for a high degree of coordination in overall plans.

At the present time, 14 percent of the Federal research and development budget is for the support of basic research, as compared to 10 percent for the country as a whole. This appears justifiable, since basic research has a universality about it in the overall progress of science and the training of scientists and engineers throughout the Nation.

There has been occasional criticism regarding the ease of securing Federal funds for basic research. I would estimate roughly that only about 50 percent of the applications for Federal support of research from competent investigators are granted support, and on the average only about one third of the total funds requested. Thus there is a high degree of selectivity.

## Education and Training in Science and Engineering

On the general subject of education and training in science and engineering, there are several issues which are of considerable national importance and which I am sure will be of interest and concern to this committee and to the Congress. First, the encouragement and support of research is closely related to education and training, especially in graduate schools. In universities, simultaneous encouragement and support should be given to undergraduate teaching and to graduate teaching and research in order to provide the proper degree of continuity in the total educational scheme. One of the important current issues is the extent to which the Federal Government should broaden the base of its support to academic institutions of all kinds. A few comments on the present distribution of support may be in order. There are about 2,100 colleges and universities of all types in the country. These include universities, liberal arts colleges, medical, engineering, and technical schools, agricultural schools, and junior colleges. To what extent should public funds from the Federal Government be used to support this large and heterogeneous group of academic institutions? Some idea of the characteristics of these institutions, the distribution of scientists and engineers among them, and the degree of present R. & D. support may be gained from the following:

Of the 2,100 institutions, only about 1,100, or 52 percent, give bachelor's degrees in science and engineering.

Of the 1,916 colleges and universities surveyed in 1958 by the National Science Foundation,[2] only 377, or 20 percent, made any appreciable provision for research in science or engineering.

This group of 377 institutions employed 99 percent of the total professional scientific personnel on the faculties of the entire list of institutions.

This same group of 377 institutions also used 99 percent of the total R. & D. funds expended by the entire list.

Thus we see that about half of all our academic institutions have no basis for research support, since they do not award baccalaureate degrees in science or engineering. Of this half, only about one-third, or one-sixth of the entire list, employ practically all of the scientists and engineers on their faculties, and they have practically all of the R. & D. funds.

This is the extent and the nature of the concentration of the research and development, and its support, among the country's academic institutions. As you see, the funds are available in and to the institutions which have research competence among their faculties.

Incidentally, the National Science Foundation, with the broad mission of supporting scientific research and education, provides research support to somewhat less than 500 academic institutions, and support for a variety of scientific activities to approximately 800.

A criticism frequently heard is that Federal support goes in increasing amounts to the large universities most active in graduate work and research, and that the Federal Government should pay more attention to the distribution of public funds to the medium-sized and small institutions. It is certainly a most desirable goal to improve the education provided in our academic institutions and also to give general encouragement to research. However, there are a large number of small institutions which do not wish to encourage graduate work of research, but which concentrate their attention upon undergraduate teaching. Surely this is a matter of their own decision.

Futhermore, it is highly questionable, in my opinion, whether the 1,000 institutions that do not now provide a bachelor's degree in science and engineering should at this stage be considered for research support; their immediate problem is the extension of their teaching to include science and engineering. Attention should be paid to this class of institution, to be sure, in the direction of improving their general educational activities and, in this modern day and age, to strengthening their science instruction.

My personal view of this question is that the support of research by the Federal Government must first of all be such as to enable the country to progress in scientific and engineering research as soundly, imaginatively, and rapidly as possible. In doing this, the support of high-quality work is the major consideration. High standards must be set and adhered to. Otherwise, our science is in serious danger of deteriorating. Bad science is worse than no science, and it is appallingly expensive. My view, therefore, is that the policy adopted by the National Science Foundation is the proper one, namely, to provide for the needs of the highest quality research projects and the most competent investigators wherever they may be found. As one approaches the limit of available funds, one then has to choose from among a large number of projects, approximately equal in merit and quality, coming from large and small institutions, from all sections of the country and from experienced and youthful scientists. Under these circumstances, with similar quality, one can furnish preferred support to young investigators, to small institutions, and to improving geographic distribution. Under this policy, the NSF finds that the distribution of funds for research follows quite closely the graduate research population in different sections of the country. Thus while it is true that the largest institutions receive the most support, it is because they have the largest number of capable scientists and engineers; the distribution follows very closely the distribution of those capable of performing research of good quality wherever they may be found. Under the policy I have outlined, a broadening of the base of support can be accomplished automatically by providing more total funds.

To me this is the most justifiable point of view to take with respect to the distribution of research support. On the other hand, it is certainly true that the Federal Government should pay attention to improving the growth and strength of institutions in their science and engineering. But in my opinion, the wise and sound manner of doing this is to provide support to the institution for strengthening its science in general rather than to attempt this by a wider distribution of research project support.

## NOTES

1 "Investing in Scientific Progress," 1961; "Profiles of Manpower in Science and Technology" 1963.

2 "Scientific Research and Development in Colleges and Universities Expenditures and Manpower, 1958." National Science Foundation, 1962.

# 12

# Criteria for
# Scientific Choice

## ALVIN M. WEINBERG

### I

AS SCIENCE GROWS, its demands on our society's resources
grow. It seems inevitable that science's demands will eventually be
limited by what society can allocate to it. We shall then have to make
choices. These choices are of two kinds. We shall have to choose
among different, often incommensurable, fields of science—between,
for example, high-energy physics and oceanography or between
molecular biology and science of metals. We shall also have to choose
among the different institutions that receive support for science
from the government—among universities, governmental laboratories and industry. The first choice I call scientific choice; the
second, institutional choice. My purpose is to suggest criteria for
making scientific choices—to formulate a scale of values which
might help establish priorities among scientific fields whose only
common characteristic is that they all derive support from the
government.

Choices of this sort are made at every level both in science and
in government. The individual scientist must decide what science
to do, what not to do: the totality of such judgments makes up his
scientific taste. The research director must choose which projects
to push, which to kill. The government administrator must decide
not only which efforts to support; he must also decide whether to do

ALVIN M. WEINBERG *is Director of the Oak Ridge National Laboratory of the*
*Atomic Energy Commission. This essay originally appeared in* Minerva *(Winter*
*1963), pp. 159–171, and was later reprinted in* Physics Today *(March 1964),*
*pp. 42–48. A subsequent article, in which Dr. Weinberg develops his ideas*
*further, appears under the title "Criteria for Scientific Choice II" in* Minerva
*(Autumn 1964), pp. 3–14. The article is discussed in Stephen Toulmin, "The*
*Complexity of Scientific Choice, A Stocktaking,"* Minerva *(Spring 1964), pp.*
*343–359. Dr. Weinberg's and Professor Toulmin's articles will also be reproduced*
*in* Science and Policy: Minerva Papers, *E. Shils and S. Dedijer, eds., to be*
*published in 1966.*

a piece of work in a university, a national laboratory, or an industrial laboratory. The sum of such separate decisions determines our policy as a whole. I shall be concerned mainly with the broadest scientific choices: how should government decide between very large fields of science, particularly between different branches of basic science? The equally important question of how government should allocate its support for basic research among industry, governmental laboratories, and universities will not be discussed here.

## II

Most of us like to be loved; we hate to make choices, since a real choice alienates the party that loses. If one is rich—more accurately, if one is growing richer—choices can be avoided. Every administrator knows that his job is obviously unpleasant only when his budget has been cut. Thus the urgency for making scientific or institutional choices has in the main been ignored both in the United States and elsewhere because the science budget has been expanding so rapidly: the United States government spent $1,600,000,000 on research and development in 1950, $9,000,000,000 in 1960, $14,000,000,000 (including space) in 1962.

Though almost all agree that choices will eventually have to be made, some well-informed observers insist that the time for making the choices is far in the future. Their arguments against making explicit choices have several main threads. Perhaps most central is the argument that since we do not make explicit choices about anything else, there is no reason why we should make them in science. Since we do not explicitly choose between support for farm prices and support for schools, or between highways and foreign aid, why should we single out science as the guinea pig for trying to make choices? The total public activity of our society has always resulted from countervailing pressures, exerted by various groups representing professional specialities, or local interests, or concern for the public interest. The combination that emerges as our Federal budget is not arrived at by the systematic application of a set of criteria: even the highest level of authority, in the United States, the President, who must weigh conflicting interests in the scale of the public interest, is limited in the degree to which he can impose an overall judgment by the sheer size of the budget if by nothing else. But because we have always arrived at an allocation by the free play of countervailing pressures this does not mean that such free interplay is the best or the only way to make choices. In any case, even if our choices remain largely implicit rather than explicit, they will be more reasonable if persons at every level, representing every pressure group, try to understand the larger issues and try to mitigate sectional self-interest with concern for broader issues. The idea of conflicting and biased claims being adjudicated at one fell swoop by an all–knowing supreme tribunal is a myth. It is much better that the choices be decentralized and that they reflect the concern for the larger interest. For this reason alone philosophic debate on the problems of scientific choice should lead to a more rational allocation of our resources.

A second thread in the argument of those who refuse to face the problem of scientific choice is that we waste so much on trivialities – on smoking, on advertising, on gambling – that it is silly to worry about expenditures of the same scale on what is obviously a more useful social objective – the increase of scientific knowledge. A variant of this argument is that with so much unused steel capacity or so many unemployed, we cannot rightly argue that we cannot afford a big cyclotron or a large manned–space venture.

Against these arguments we would present the following considerations on behalf of a rational scientific policy. At any given instant, only a certain fraction of our society's resources goes to science. To insist or imply that the *summum bonum* of our society is the pursuit of science and that therefore all other activities of the society are secondary to science – that unused capacity in the steel mills should go to 'Big Science' rather than a large-scale housing program – is a view that might appeal strongly to the scientific community. It is hardly likely to appeal so strongly to the much larger part of society that elects the members of the legislature, and to whom, in all probability, good houses are more important than good science. Thus as a practical matter we cannot really evade the problem of scientific choice. If those actively engaged in science do not make choices, they will be made anyhow by the Congressional Appropriations Committees and by the Bureau of the Budget, or corresponding bodies in other governments. Moreover, and perhaps more immediately, even if we are not limited by money, we shall be limited by the availability of truly competent men. There is some evidence that our ratio of money to men in science is too high, and that in some parts of science we have gone further more quickly than the number of really competent men can justify.

### III

Our scientific and governmental communities have evolved institutional and other devices for coping with broad issues of scientific choice. The most important institutional device in the United States is the President's Science Advisory Committee, with its panels and its staff in the Office of Science and Technology.

This body and its panels help the Bureau of the Budget to decide what is to be supported and what is not to be supported. The panel system, however, suffers from a serious weakness. Panels usually consist of specialized experts who inevitably share the same enthusiasms and passions. To the expert in oceanography or in high-energy physics, nothing seems quite as important as oceanography or high-energy physics. The panel, when recommending a program in a field in which all its members are interested, invariably argues for better treatment of the field—more money, more people, more training. The panel system is weak insofar as judge, jury, plaintiff and defendant are usually one and the same.

The panel is able to judge how competently a proposed piece of research is likely to be carried out: its members are all experts and are likely to know who are the good research workers in the field. But just because the panel is composed of experts, who hold parochial viewpoints, the panel is much less able to place the proposal in a broader perspective and to say whether the research proposal is of much interest to the rest of science. We can answer the question "how" within a given frame of reference; it is impossible to answer "why" within the same frame of reference. It would therefore seem that the panel system could be improved if representatives, not only of the field being judged but also representatives of neighboring fields, sat on every panel judging the merits of a research proposal. A panel judging high-energy physics should have some people from low-energy physics; a panel judging low-energy physics should have some people from nuclear energy; a panel judging nuclear energy should have some people from conventional energy; and so on. I should think that advice from panels so constituted would be tempered by concern for larger issues; in particular, the support of a proposed research project would be viewed from the larger perspective of the relevance of that research to the rest of science.

In addition to panels or the bodies like the President's Science Advisory Committee as organizational instruments for making choices, the scientific community has evolved an empirical method for establishing scientific priorities, that is, for deciding what is important in science and what is not important. This is the scientific literature. The process of self-criticism, which is integral to the literature of science, is one of the most characteristic features of science. Nonsense is weeded out and held up to ridicule in the literature, whereas what is worthwhile receives much sympathetic attention. This process of self-criticism embodied in the literature, though implicit, is nonetheless real and highly significant. The existence of a healthy, viable scientific literature in itself helps assure society that the science it supports is valid and deserving of support. This is a most important, though little recognized, social function of the scientific literature.

As an arbiter of scientific taste and validity, scientific literature is beset with two difficulties. First, because of the information explosion, the literature is not read nearly as carefully as it used to be. Nonsense is not so generally recognized as such, and the standards of self-criticism, which are so necessary if the scientific literature is to serve as the arbiter of scientific taste, are inevitably looser than they once were.

Second, the scientific literature in a given field tends to form a closed universe; workers in a field, when they criticize each other, tend to adopt the same unstated assumptions. A referee of a scientific paper asks whether the paper conforms to the rules of the scientific community to which both referee and author belong, not whether the rules themselves are valid. So to speak, the editors and authors of a journal in a narrowly specialized field are all tainted with the same poison. As Einstein said, 'Eigener Dreck stinkt nicht.'[1]

Can a true art of scientific criticism be developed, *i.e.*, can one properly criticize a field of science beyond the kind of criticism that is inherent in the literature of the field? Mortimer Taube in *Computers and Common Sense*[2] insists that such scientific criticism is a useful undertaking, and that, by viewing a field from a somewhat detached point of view, it is possible to criticize a field meaningfully, even to the point of calling the whole activity fraudulent, as he does in the case of non-numerical uses of computers. I happen to believe that Taube does not make a convincing case in respect to certain non-numerical uses of computers, such as language translation. Yet I have sympathy for Dr. Taube's aims — that, with science taking so much of the public's money, we must countenance, even encourage, discussion of the relative validity and worthwhileness of the science which society supports.

## IV

I believe that criteria for scientific choice can be identified. In fact, several such criteria already exist; the main task is to make them more explicit. The criteria can be divided into two kinds: internal criteria and external criteria. Internal criteria are generated within the scientific field itself and answer the question: How well is the science done? External criteria are generated outside the scientific field and answer the question: Why pursue this particular science? Though both are important, I think the external criteria are the more important.

Two internal criteria can be easily identified: (1) Is the field ready for exploitation? (2) Are the scientists in the field really competent? Both these questions are answerable only by experts who know the field in question intimately, and who know the people personally. These criteria are therefore the ones most often applied when a panel decides on a research grant; in fact, the primary question in deciding whether to provide governmental support for a scientist is usually: How good is he?

I believe, however, that it is not tenable to base our judgments entirely on internal criteria. As I have said, we scientists like to believe that the pursuit of science as such is society's highest good, but this view cannot be taken for granted. For example, we now suffer a serious shortage of medical practitioners, probably to some extent because many bright young men who would formerly have gone into medical practice now go into biological research; government support is generally available for post-graduate study leading to the Ph.D. but not for study leading to the medical degree. It is by no means self-evident that society gains from more biological research and less medical practice. Society does not *a priori* owe the scientist, even the good scientist, support any more than it owes the artist or the writer or the musician support. Science must seek its support from society on grounds other than that the science is carried out competently and that it is ready for exploitation; scientists cannot expect society to support science because scientists find it an enchanting diversion. Thus, in seeking justification for the support of science, we are led inevitably to consider external criteria for the validity of science — criteria external to science, or to a given field of science.

# V

Three external criteria can be recognized: technological merit, scientific merit and social merit. The first is fairly obvious: once we have decided, one way or another, that a certain technological end is worthwhile, we must support the scientific research necessary to achieve that end. Thus, if we have set out to learn how to make breeder reactors, we must first measure painstakingly the neutron yields of the fissile isotopes as a function of energy of the bombarding neutron. As in all such questions of choice, it is not always so easy to decide the technological relevance of a piece of basic research. The technological usefulness of the laser came after, not before, the principle of optical amplification was discovered, and, in general, indirect technological or scientific benefits ("fallout") are not uncommon. But it is my belief that such technological bolts from the scientific blue are the exception, not the rule, that solving a technological problem by waiting for fallout from an entirely different field is rather overrated. Most programmatic basic research can be related fairly directly to a technological end at least crudely if not in detail. The broader question as to whether the technological aim itself is worthwhile must be considered again partly from within technology through answering such questions as: Is the technology ripe for exploitation? Are the people any good? It must also be dealt with partly from outside technology by answering the question: Are the social goals attained, if the technology succeeds, themselves worthwhile? Many times these questions are difficult to answer, and sometimes they are answered incorrectly: for example, the United States launched an effort to control thermonuclear energy in 1952 on a rather large scale because it was thought at the time that controlled fusion was much closer at hand than it turned out to be. Nevertheless, despite the fact that we make mistakes, technological aims are customarily scrutinized much more closely than are scientific aims; at least we have more practice discussing technological merit than we do scientific merit.

## VI

The criteria of scientific merit and social merit are much more difficult: scientific merit because we have given little thought to defining scientific merit in the broadest sense, social merit because it is difficult to define the values of our society. As I have already suggested, the answer to the question: Does this broad field of research have scientific merit? cannot be answered within the field. The idea that the scientific merit of a field can be judged better from the vantage point of the scientific fields in which it is embedded than from the point of view of the field itself is implicit in the following quotation from the late John Von Neumann: "As a mathematical discipline travels far from its empirical source, or still more, if it is a second and third generation only indirectly inspired by ideas coming from reality, it is beset with very grave dangers. It becomes more and more pure aestheticising, more and more purely *l'art pour l'art*. This need not be bad if the field is surrounded by correlated subjects which still have closer empirical connections or if the discipline is under the influence of men with an exceptionally well-developed taste. But there is a grave danger that the subject will develop along the line of least resistance, that the stream, so far from its source, will separate into a multitude of insignificant branches, and that the discipline will become a disorganized mass of details and complexities. In other words, at a great distance from its empirical source, or after much 'abstract' inbreeding, a mathematical subject is in danger of degeneration. At the inception the style is usually classical; when it shows signs of becoming baroque, then the danger signal is up."[3]

I believe there are any number of examples to show that Von

Neumann's observation about mathematics can be extended to the
empirical sciences. *Empirical* basic sciences which move too far
from the neighboring sciences in which they are embedded tend to
become "baroque". Relevance to neighboring fields of science is,
therefore, a valid measure of the scientific merit of a field of basic
science. In so far as our aim is to increase our grasp and understanding of the universe, we must recognise that some areas of basic
science do more to round out the whole picture than do others. A
field in which lack of knowledge is a bottleneck to the understanding
of other fields deserves more support than a field which is isolated
from other fields. This is only another way of saying that, ideally,
science is a unified structure and that scientists, in adding to the
structure, ought always to strengthen its unity. Thus, the original
motivation for much of high-energy physics is to be sought in its
elucidation of low-energy physics, or the strongest and most exciting
motivation for measuring the neutron capture cross sections of the
elements lies in the elucidation of the cosmic origin of the elements.
Moreover, the discoveries which are acknowledged to be the most
important scientifically, have the quality of bearing strongly on the
scientific disciplines around them. For example, the discovery of
X-rays was important partly because it extended the electromagnetic
spectrum but, much more, because it enabled us to see so much that
we had been unable to see. The word "fundamental" in basic
science, which is often used as a synonym for "important," can be
partly paraphrased into "relevance to neighboring areas of science."
I would therefore sharpen the criterion of scientific merit by proposing that, other things being equal, *that field has the most scientific merit which contributes most heavily to and illuminates most
brightly its neighboring scientific disciplines.* This is the justification
for my previous suggestion about making it socially acceptable for
people in *related* fields to offer opinions on the scientific merit of
work in a given field. In a sense, what I am trying to do is to extend
to basic research a practice that is customary in applied science:
a project director trying to get a reactor built on time is expected to
judge the usefulness of component development and fundamental
research which bears on his problems. He is not always right; but
his opinions are usually useful both to the researcher and to the
management disbursing the money.

## VII

I turn now to the most controversial criterion of all—social
merit or relevance to human welfare and the values of man. Two
difficulties face us when we try to clarify the criterion of social
merit: first, who is to define the values of man, or even the values of

our own society; and second, just as we shall have difficulty deciding whether a proposed research helps other branches of science or technology, so we will have even greater trouble deciding whether a given scientific or technical enterprise indeed furthers our pursuit of social values, even when those values have been identified. With some values we have little trouble: adequate defense, or more food, or less sickness, for example, are rather uncontroversial. Moreover, since such values themselves are relatively easy to describe, we can often guess whether a scientific activity is likely to be relevant, if not actually helpful, in achieving the goal. On the other hand, some social values are much harder to define: perhaps the most difficult is national prestige. How do we measure national prestige? What is meant when we say that a man on the moon enhances our national prestige? Does it enhance our prestige more than say, discovering a polio vaccine or winning more Nobel Prizes than any other country? Whether or not a given achievement confers prestige probably depends as much on the publicity that accompanies the achievement as it does on its intrinsic value.

Among the most attractive social values that science can help to achieve is international understanding and cooperation. It is a commonplace that the standards and loyalties of science are transnational. A new element has recently been injected by the advent of scientific research of such costliness that now it is prudent as well as efficient to participate in some form of international cooperation. The very big accelerators are so expensive that international laboratories such as CERN at Geneva are set up to enable several countries to share costs that are too heavy for them to bear separately. Even if we were not committed to improving international relations we would be impelled to cooperate merely to save money.

Bigness is an advantage rather than a disadvantage if science is to be used as an instrument of international cooperation: a $500,000,000 cooperative scientific venture—such as the proposed 1,000 Bev intercontinental accelerator—is likely to have more impact than a $500,000 Van de Graaff machine. The most expensive of all scientific or quasi-scientific enterprises—the exploration of space—is, from this viewpoint, the best–suited instrument for international cooperation. The exchange between President Kennedy and Chairman Khrushchev concerning possible increased cooperation in space exploration seems to have been well received and, one hopes, will bear ultimate fruit.

## VIII

Having set forth these criteria and recognising that judgments are fraught with difficulty, I propose to assess five different scientific and technical fields: molecular biology, high-energy physics, nuclear energy, manned-space exploration, and the behavioral sciences. Two of these fields, molecular biology and high-energy physics, are, by any definition, basic sciences; nuclear energy is applied science, the behavioral sciences are a mixture of both applied and basic science. Manned exploration of space, though it requires the tools of science and is regarded in the popular mind as being part of science, has not yet been proved to be more than quasi-scientific, at best. The fields which I choose are incommensurable: how can one measure the merit of behavioral sciences and nuclear energy on the same scale of values? Yet the choices between scientific fields will eventually have to be made whether we like it or not. Criteria for scientific choice will be most useful only if they *can* be applied to seemingly incommensurable situations. The validity of my proposed criteria depends on how well they can serve in comparing fields that are hard to compare.

Of the scientific fields now receiving public support, perhaps the most successful is molecular biology. Hardly a month goes by without a stunning success in molecular biology being reported in the *Proceedings of the National Academy of Sciences*. The most recent has been the cracking by Nierenberg and Ochoa of the code according to which triples of bases determine specific amino acids in the living proteins. Here is a field which rates the highest grades as to its ripeness for exploitation and competence of its workers. It is profoundly important for large stretches of other biological sciences—genetics, cytology, microbiology—and, therefore, according to my criterion, must be graded A+ for its scientific merit. It also must be given a very high grade in social merit, and probably in technological (that is, medical) merit—more than, say, taxonomy or topology. Molecular biology is the most fundamental of all the biological sciences. With understanding of the manner of transmission of genetic information ought to come the insights necessary for the solution of such problems as cancer, birth defects, and viral diseases. Altogether, molecular biology ought, in my opinion, to receive as much public support as can possibly be pumped into it; since money is not limiting its growth, many more post-graduate students and research fellows in molecular biology ought to be subsidized so that the attack on this frontier can be expanded as rapidly as possible.

The second field is high-energy physics. This field of endeavor originally sought as its major task to understand the nuclear force. In this it has been only modestly successful; instead, it has opened an undreamed-of subnuclear world of strange particles, a world in which mirror images are often reversed. The field has no end of interesting things to do, it knows how to do them, and its people are the best. Yet I would be bold enough to argue that, at least by the criteria which I have set forth—relevance to the sciences in which it is embedded, relevance to human affairs, and relevance to technology—high-energy physics rates poorly. The world of subnuclear particles seems to be remote from the rest of the physical sciences. Aside from the brilliant resolution of the $\tau$-particle paradox, which led to the overthrow of the conservation of parity, and the studies of mesic atoms (the latter of which is not done at *ultra*-high energy), I know of few discoveries in ultra-high-energy physics which bear strongly on the rest of science. This view must be tempered by the fairly considerable indirect fallout from high-energy physics—for example, the use of strong focusing, the development of ultra-fast electronics, and the possibility of using machines like the Argonne ZGS (Zero Gradient Synchrotron) as very strong, pulsed sources of neutrons for study of neutron cross sections. As for its bearings on human welfare and on technology, I believe it is essentially nil. These two low grades would not bother me if high-energy physics were cheap. But it is terribly expensive—not so much in money as in highly qualified people, especially those brilliant talents who could contribute so ably to other fields which contribute much more to the rest of science and to humanity than does high-energy physics. On the other hand, if high-energy physics could be strengthened as a vehicle for international cooperation—if the much-discussed intercontinental 1,000 Bev accelerator could indeed be built as a joint enterprise between East and West—the expense of high-energy physics would become a virtue, and the enterprise would receive a higher grade in social merit than I would now be willing to assign to it.

Third is nuclear energy, a field toward which I have passion and aspiration, and therefore am not unbiased. Being largely an applied effort, nuclear energy is very relevant to human welfare. We now realize that in the residual uranium and thorium of the earth's crust, mankind has an unlimited store of energy—enough to last for millions of years; and that with an effort of only one-tenth of our manned-space effort we could, within ten or fifteen years, develop the reactors which would tap this resource. Only rarely do we see ways of *permanently* satisfying one of man's major needs—in this case energy. In high-conversion ratio nuclear reactors we have such means, and we are close to their achievement. Moreover, we begin to see ways of applying very large reactors of this type to realise another great end, the economic desalination of the ocean. Thus, the time is very ripe for exploitation. Nuclear energy rates so highly in the categories of technical and social merit and timeliness that I believe it deserves strong support, even if it gets very low marks in the other two categories—its personnel and its relationship to the rest of science. Suffice it to say that in my opinion the scientific workers in the field of nuclear energy are good and that nuclear energy in its basic aspects has vast ramifications in other scientific fields.

Next on the list are the behavioral sciences—psychology, sociology, anthropology, and economics. The workers are of high quality; the sciences are significantly related to each other, they are deeply germane to every aspect of human existence. In these respects the sciences deserve strong public support. On the other hand, it is not clear to me that the behavioral scientists, on the whole, see clearly how to attack the important problems of their sciences. Fortunately, the total sum involved in behavioral science research is now relatively tiny—as it well must be when what are lacking are deeply fruitful, and generally accepted, points of departure.

Finally, I come to manned-space exploration. The personnel in the program are competent and dedicated. With respect to ripeness for exploitation, the situation seems to me somewhat unclear. Our "hardware" is in good shape, and we can expect it to get better—bigger and more reliable boosters, better communication systems, etc. What is not clear is the human being's tolerance of the space environment. I do not believe that either the hazards of radiation or of weightlessness are sufficiently explored yet positively to guarantee success in our future manned-space ventures.

The main objection to spending so much manpower, as well as money, on manned-space exploration is its remoteness from human affairs, not to say the rest of science. In this respect space (the exploration of very large distances) and high-energy physics (the exploration of very small distances) are similar, though high-energy physics has the advantage of greater scientific validity. There are some who argue that the great adventure of man into space is not to be judged as science, but rather as a quasi–scientific enterprise, justified on the same grounds as those on which we justify other non-scientific national efforts. The weakness of this argument is that space requires many, many scientists and engineers, and these are badly needed for such matters as clarifying our civilian defense posture or, for that matter, working out the technical details of arms control and foreign aid. If space is ruled to be non-scientific, then it must be balanced against other non-scientific expenditures like highways, schools or civil defense. If we do space research because of prestige, then we should ask whether we get more prestige from a man on the moon than from successful control of the water-logging problem in Pakistan's Indus Valley Basin. If we do space research because of its military implications, we ought to say so—and perhaps the military justification, at least for developing big boosters, is plausible, as the Soviet experience with rockets makes clear.

## IX

The main weight of my argument is that the most valid criteria for assessing scientific fields come from without rather than from within the scientific discipline that is being rated. This does not mean that only those scientific fields deserve priority that have high technical merit or high social merit. Scientific merit is as important as the other two criteria, but, as I have argued, scientific merit must be judged from the vantage point of the scientific fields in which each field is embedded rather than from that of the field itself. It we support science in order to maximize our knowledge of the world around us, then we must give the highest priority to those scientific endeavors that have the most bearing on the rest of science.

The rather extreme view which I have taken presents difficulties in practice. The main trouble is that the bearing that one science has on another science so often is not appreciated until long after the original discoveries have been made. Who was wise enough, at the time Purcell and Bloch first discovered nuclear magnetic resonance, to guess that the method would become an important tool in biochemistry for unravelling chemical structures? Or how could one have guessed that Hahn and Strassmann's radiochemical studies would have led to nuclear energy? And indeed, my colleagues in high-energy physics predict that what we learn about the world of strange particles will in an as yet undiscernible way teach us much about the rest of physics, not merely much about strange particles. They beg only for time to prove their point.

To this argument I say first choices are always hard. It would be far simpler if the problem of scientific choice could be ignored, and possibly in some future millennium it can be. But there is also a more constructive response. The necessity for scientific choice arises in "Big Science," not in "Little Science." Just as our society supports artists and musicians on a small scale, so I have no objection to—in fact, I strongly favor—our society supporting science that rates zero on all the external criteria, provided it rates well on the internal criteria (ripeness and competence) and provided it is carried on on a relatively small scale. It is only when science does make serious demands on the resources of our society—when it becomes "Big Science"—that the question of choice really arises.

At the present time, with our society faced with so much unfinished and very pressing business, science can hardly be considered its major business. For scientists as a class to imply that science can, at this stage in human development, be made the main business of humanity is irresponsible—and, from the scientist's point of view, highly dangerous. It is quite conceivable that our society will tire of devoting so much of its wealth to science, especially if the implied promises held out when big projects are launched do not materialize in anything very useful. I shudder to think what would happen to science in general if our manned-space venture turned out to be a major failure, if it turned out, for example, that man could not withstand the re-entry deceleration forces after a long sojourn in space. It is as much out of a prudent concern for their own survival, as for any loftier motive, that scientists must acquire the habit of scrutinizing what they do from a broader point of view than has been their custom. To do less could cause a popular reaction which would greatly damage mankind's most remarkable intellectual attainment — modern science — and the scientists who created it and must carry it forward.

## NOTES

1 As quoted by Dyson, Freeman J., in a review of Sweber, S.S., *Mesons and Fields*, in *Physics Today*, IX (May, 1956), pp. 32–34.

2 New York: Columbia University Press, 1961.

3 Heywood, R. B. (ed.), *The Works of the Mind* (University of Chicago Press, 1947), p. 196.

# 13

# The Scientist
# and National Policy

## MC GEORGE BUNDY

THE PROBLEM of talking to an audience of this kind is severe for a man with my absence of background in the sciences. One cannot talk about science as such, so one must talk about science and something else. I toyed with the idea of talking about science and the academic administrator, but the less I tell you about the trade secrets of academic administrators the more grateful my former colleagues will be. I played with the notion of discussing science and other cultures, a question sometimes framed as "science or culture," and sometimes as "science is culture." This is a topic everyone else has been discussing in the last few years, but I steered away from it, partly because it's too big and partly because I don't myself believe much in these distinctions between scientists and other parts of culture or society or politics; I think most of them are doubtful and misleading.

I thought also of talking about science and government, and especially about the interesting art of getting money out of government for science, but there is no point in my doing that in the presence of the great painless extractor, Alan T. Waterman, the most notable dentist of the progress of science that the government has ever been exposed to. Waterman's particular success is that he has taught the government to enjoy this process and even to claim the credit for it. In an article not long ago Robert Oppenheimer reported a calculation that if the *Physical Review* continued to grow at the rate of speed developed between 1945 and 1960, it would be as big as the earth in another hundred years. In the same

MC GEORGE BUNDY, *President of the Ford Foundation, was Special Assistant to the President for National Security Affairs when he delivered this address to the American Association for the Advancement of Science December 22, 1962, at Philadelphia. The text was first published in* Science, Vol. 139 (March 1, 1963), *pp. 805–809.*

way, money for science will soon consume the whole federal budget unless we can get Alan Waterman to retire.

After discarding these larger themes, either because they are non-themes or because there are people present who are better able to deal with them than I am, I concluded that it would be well for me to try to talk to a much narrower topic, the topic of the role of the scientist in the processes of judgment and action that go beyond science itself and affect other parts of public policy.

I do not think this is necessarily the largest role for a scientist in government. It can well be argued, and I think there is a good deal of force in the argument, that the largest single problem of scientists in their relation to the political process is to insure that science itself is understood, supported, and advanced. On this view, from the point of view of society itself, the progress of science is as large an issue as any that the scientist can concern himself with.

But I want to talk about a quite different topic, the problem of the relation between science and political judgment, when what is at issue is not the advancement of science but the protection of some other interest of the political power concerned. I suppose that one excuse for my trying to do this is that this is the kind of scientific participation in government with which I currently find myself associated. Most of what I have to say will find its most useful illustrations in the field of nuclear problems — nuclear testing, the search for a nuclear test ban, and the handling of nuclear weapons systems. And I know very well that much of what I say will be familiar to you, because nearly everything that can be said on this topic has been said.

About the only thing any one critic can do is to try to distinguish what he thinks are the helpful from the unhelpful commonplace propositions.

My own first proposition about the role of the scientist in these kinds of questions is that it is essential that he should be *there*. That really is a fairly simple proposition. But it carries somewhat more weight than that plain statement of it might suggest, because to be *there* in the process of government means more than one place, more than one role, and more than one moment in time. What I really mean to suggest by this first broad assertion is that all the kinds of there-ness which are relevant to the process of government should include the there-ness of the scientist whenever any component of the problem is essentially scientific in character.

I say that there is more than one place to be *there*. Government is an enormous layer cake with the sugar left out. It has all sorts of flavors and colors and mixtures in it, and it has been put together by a nongeometrical cook. There are therefore as many ways and as many places to be present in government as there are little balls in those models of large molecules which are so popular in your demonstrations to beginning students nowadays. And it is just as hard, unless you know the rules, to know just what you are doing in the molecule. Science has to be present not simply at the moment of crucial decision one minute before zero-hour. Science has to be present in the process of consideration which usually begins a very long way from the point or time of decision. And that is true not only in the obvious case of scientific research which may lead to development of a new weapon; it is true also if one is engaged in the problem of trying to design a section of a draft treaty which might eventually lead to the control of the weapon; and it is equally true, between these extremes of weapon design and disarmament, if one is concerned with the problem of the relation between one friendly government and another in their efforts to cooperate in the use of some such weapons system. Whether one is talking about initial research in a scientific laboratory on the West Coast, or about the preliminary staff studies, in the disarmament agency, of a new proposal for arms control, or about the framework of the relationships which connect us with the United Kingdom, there is no way of making progress effectively if there is not an intimate connection with the kind of knowledge, the kind of perception, the kind of awareness of possibility and impossibility which we associate with the scientist. So there are many places for the scientist to be *there*.

I also say that there are many roles. This is a point which is often ignored in the sterile debate as to whether scientists and other experts should be on tap or on top. It all depends. There are many situations in the management of government affairs in which it is best that the officer in charge should have a full technical background. I would myself hold that there is a very strong case for this kind of representation not only in the obviously technical jobs but in others. I think it has been a great reinforcement to the Atomic Energy Commission that in the last two years two of the commissioners have been scientists. While both of the new commissioners who are lawyers are friends of mine, I do not think that we should miss them as much as we should miss their two scientific colleagues, not because of any difference in natural ability or concern with the topic, but because in the framework of that particular assignment there is a special importance in the presence of men who understand the scientific basis from which this whole vast enterprise has developed.

On the other hand, when one gets to the negotiations in Geneva, or when one get to the level of presidential decision it is, I think, self-evident that no one giving advice—whether he be a scientist or nonscientist—can expect or should desire to take to himself that final responsibility which we call political, though it is true

that any given political judgment may have a heavy component—
perhaps a governing component—of science, or of law, or of economics, or of some other special kind of knowledge.

So that there is more than one way to be a scientist in this
process, and it is very dangerous to try to think of it in linear terms:
that there is this particular job which this kind of man does, and
there is only this one job. There are many jobs; they take many shapes.
They can be managing, they can be advisory, they can be conciliar,
they can be part time and full time. They can be professional in the
sense that the man must be an experienced long-term officer of
government, and they can be nonprofessional in the sense that he
comes in for a while and goes out. To make a theory of any one of
these multiple roles is, I think, to miss the complexity, the color,
and the wide range of meaning which this association should have
and is, I think, coming to have.

The one generalization I would offer is that it is of great importance that the scientist should be *there* through time, one way or
another. I do not mean in saying this to be critical of part-time
advisory committees or panels, which have often been of great
value, especially indeed in this very field of nuclear tests and nuclear
test bans.[1] But I do mean to say that government, like all other
human activities, is a process, and it is a process made up of a very
large number of steps. You cannot come in and out of government,
on a weekend, I'll-write-you-a-letter basis, and expect your opinions
to have the kind of impact which in your sense of virtue and of
rightness you think they deserve to have upon the process of
government. This is not a rule which is peculiar to the scientist; it is
equally true of the political scientist (a very advanced form of
nonscientist); it is true of newspaper editors; and it is true of politicians—in fact, it is perhaps pre-eminently true of politicians.
Nobody ever persuaded anybody of anything with one editorial.
Nobody ever made a lasting contribution to government by one visit
to Washington. We should not allow dramatic episodes—letters
from Einstein to FDR—to mislead us on this point. What really
bends the processes of government is continuous, sustained, and
intensive effort, generally uncertain at the beginning of what its
exact final outcome will be, always responsive to the situation as it
is, and continuously aware of the need to be on top of *that* situation,
and not of some abstract plan of what it ought to be, or was when one
once knew it, or would be if only the people in Washington had
more sense.

So much for my first general proposition. If I may take a moment
to give a judgment, let me say that we are making progress in the
government in developing the necessary there-ness of science, and
that you and your colleagues in your profession throughout the

country have made very great progress over the last twenty years in developing ways and means of responding, as a profession (or really as a set of professions), to this requirement. It's not an easy thing to do.

There is a special problem for the scientist in giving his time to other things than his science, even when what he is asked to do is impossible to conceive of except as an outgrowth of his learning. I myself have listened to the wailing and weeping of many very able wailers and weepers, telling me how a distinguished scientist's career is ruined if he is put on even the smallest interdepartmental committee, in a university in which everyone knows that the administration is dictatorial to begin with. This terror that you all have, of the destructive intrusion of the world upon your laboratories, is of course a proper terror, based on ample evidence from horrible case histories. That American science as a trade has been ready, even eager to find ways of filling the many different kinds of roles which I have just been sketching is a tribute to the sense of responsibility of scientists as scientists and of scientists as citizens.

My second general proposition is that it is very important that at the crucial points of counsel, judgment, decision, and action there be more than one scientist involved. This is true, I think, for a number of reasons. One of them is that government itself is not a monolith—it is the product of many different forces, as I have been suggesting, and each of these forces has a right to its own sense of what the scientific meaning of the problem is. As the problem comes to judgment, therefore, there is a reason for having more than one scientist in the discussion.

But there is another and somewhat deeper reason for this second rule. The task of the scientist advising on matters affecting the national security is in very considerable measure a task of translation, a task of communicating to a man who does not himself grasp and understand the real meaning of a subject, what its implications are and what its possibilities are. How big a bomb can you make? How long a time will it take? And what will its characteristics be? These problems, which became enormous for government in the early 1940s and which are with us still, cannot be decided out of his own internal knowledge by a political figure. It is very important for him not to be dependent upon a single channel of information even if on a surface impression it is only information that is at stake.

This is a form of translation, and all translation is an art. Translation from one language to another—for example, from English to French or French to German—has all of the splendid complexities and ambiguities which beguile the philologists. And in the same way it is no small task to present scientific propositions or scientific probabilities to laymen in language that does not mislead them.

Especially in new fields, where there is both uncertainty and great room for misunderstanding, the task of the expositor is a most demanding one. If there is only one man engaged in this process, a very dangerous burden falls upon both parties, both the expositor and his interlocutor. It is very difficult for either of them to have full confidence in his lonely process of communication, and when there is such full confidence it tends to be misplaced. We all know of exceptions. We know of men of such serenity of spirit, such clarity of mind, and such sympathy of audience that they are able to deal easily with this kind of problem of communication, but they are exceptions indeed. It is really quite simple and cheap (with all due respect for the value of your time) to enlarge the numbers of scientists engaged in exposition, and it helps the man who is reinforced.

I had this point brought home to me the other day in talking with Chairman Seaborg about some of his problems at the Atomic Energy Commission. He was saying that for his work as a scientist on the commission, leaving aside for the moment his special responsibilities as chairman, it was a great help that he had Commissioner Haworth with him. It's not that they have sharply different approaches to the topic (though that can also be important, as I shall be saying in a minute); it is rather that neither of them alone need feel the burden of assessing and translating technological meaning to laymen. They are able to check their judgments with each other, and to provide to others what we may call a binocular view of the situation. So without approving of all his illustrations I would not disapprove of the conclusion which Sir Charles Snow reached in his Godkin lectures two years ago: that an arrangement which places the whole of the apparatus of science as a community at the disposal of a single adviser is unsound.

There is, I think, a deeper and more intrinsic reason for opposing the notion of a single adviser. It is really against nature, in the sense that no one man *can* have a monopoly on relevant scientific information. If in fact it is scientific information, then unless it has just that moment been straightened out in some one man's work-room, more than one man understands it; more than one can have a crack at stating it, and there is no one expert. There are fields in which experts are fewer than they should be, and there are issues upon which one man for a while may be lonely and right, but broadly speaking it is not in the nature of science that it should have to come through only one man. In other fields sometimes there really is only one expert. There are ambassadors who really do have a unique perception of the behavior of the chiefs of government to whom they are accredited, and there are members of the executive branch and members of Congress who have a unique perception of the special political complexities to which they have given large sectors of their lives. But broadly speaking I think you would agree that it is in the nature of science that it has to do something which can be perceived and understood by more than one mind—if not, then it does not become a part of the corpus of science.

Third, and again this is very obvious but very easy to forget, it is of the highest importance that a scientist acting as a scientist in the processes of governmental decision should respect his calling. He should carefully limit the occasions upon which he speaks *ex cathedra*, in order not to lose his reputation for infallibility. This is obvious and has been said by many people; one of the most eloquent statements, by Van Bush, was printed in the journal of your society not very long ago.[2] But I think it's worth spelling out.

As a listener to science, let me say that there are many things that are important for the layman to understand which he does not automatically understand in his own ignorance. One of them is how much is *not* known, even to scientists. There is a tremendous pressure upon the political figure or the bureaucrat to press a scientific adviser for an answer. How many unappetizing electrons will a proposed high-altitude test spread around in distant sectors of the earth's environment? How many British astronomers will be angry? One could answer the second question, but not the first.

You all know, I suppose, the classic comment that Alfred North Whitehead made after a remarkable lecture on the cosmos by Bertrand Russell. It was a wonderful lecture and it left the audience in a state of total confusion, and Mr. Whitehead remarked in closing the proceedings, "We must be grateful to Lord Russell for the unequaled skill with which he has left the vast darkness of the subject unobscured." That is one of the necessary functions of the scientist in government. It goes without saying that it should be a deliberate and not an inadvertent success. What one means by probable accuracy, how normal it is to be off by an order of magnitude, how uncertain, at the edges, quantities are—these are things which non-scientists do not immediately appreciate and to which their attention must be directed.

The best expositors of science problems in the process of government are the men who are most modest, and I may illustrate the hazards by taking an example from a man whose comments and insights in this topic I, at least, find continuously challenging though not invariably persuasive. Let me read to you a little of what was said to you from this platform two years ago by Charles Snow. He was talking about what scientists know[3]:

> Scientists *know* certain things in a fashion more immediate and more certain than those who don't comprehend what science is. . . .
> I had better take the most obvious example. All physical

scientists *know* that it is relatively easy to make plutonium. We know this, not as a journalistic fact at second hand, but as a fact in our own experience. We can work out the number of scientific and engineering personnel needed for a nation-state to equip itself with fission and fusion bombs. We *know* that, for a dozen or more states, it will only take perhaps six years, perhaps less. Even the best informed of us always exaggerate these periods. . . .

We are faced with an either-or, and we haven't much time. The *either* is acceptance of a restriction of nuclear armaments. This is going to begin, just as a token, with an agreement on the stopping of nuclear tests. The United States is not going to get the 99.9-percent "security" that it has been asking for. This is unobtainable, though there are other bargains that the United States could probably secure. I am not going to conceal from you that this course involves certain risks. They are quite obvious, and no honest man is going to blink them. That is the *either*. The *or* is not a risk but a certainty. It is this. There is no agreement on tests. The nuclear arms race between the United States and the U.S.S.R. not only continues but accelerates. Other countries join in. Within, at the most, six years, China and several other states have a stock of nuclear bombs. Within, at the most, ten years, some of those bombs are going off. I am saying this as responsibly as I can. *That* is the certainty.

Now before I make a few critical comments, let me say that I think there is great reality in the danger of diffusion of nuclear weapons and the hazard that some of them might go off accidentally, or in a crisis that was relatively trivial. These are indeed very grave dangers; they demand, and I think in our government they have, the prayerful attention of political leaders and the constant effort of officers of the executive branch.

But it's not as simple as Snow made it. Moreover, he made it simple with the authority of a scientist, and in that, I suggest, there is great danger. What he did was to talk of what *can* happen, meaning what is physically possible, and it is true that several states can do these things, though it is probably not true that there are as many such states as he said, and probably not true that the time limit he set is long enough. But what is much more serious is that Sir Charles has omitted altogether the question whether those states *will* do what they *can* do. No government, to our imperfect knowledge, has moved newly into this process of the development of nuclear weapons in the two years since Sir Charles spoke. I doubt if Sir Charles himself would now predict that a dozen countries by 1966 will have these weapons, or even that "China and several other states" will by then "have a stock of nuclear bombs." The prediction, which he made as a scientist, dealt with political as well as with

scientific phenomena; it dealt with very complex questions of choice
and allocation of resources as well as with what was conceivably
possible, and it assumed certainties from possibilities. This I suggest
to you is a dangerous kind of thing to do.

The second error exemplified here is that of taking a problem
which has many gradations in shape and meaning and making it
an "either/or." Either we ban the bomb, preferably tomorrow, or
the world blows up, probably the day after tomorrow. Now again,
with no attempt to conceal or limit the unexampled hazards of the
time in which we live, or the degree to which they are increased
by continuing development and deployment of these kinds of instruments, nonetheless it is not that kind of a problem. It has not
been that kind of a problem over a seventeen-year period. People
do make more or less dangerous decisions about the kinds of
weapons they will have, and about whether they will have such
weapons at all. The phenomena of command and control, of discipline, of diplomatic tension and restraint, operate in less black-
and-white terms. Technology itself can work on both sides of the
equation, and one of the great issues for scientists in this field is
that they should assert and exert the influence of scientific method
upon the control as well as upon the explosion. These things, in
other words, are not quite that clear; one should not make them
wrongly clear while wearing the cloak of the profession.

So those are my three simple points. If there are enough scientists and they are on the scene in the right places, if they are not
given the overstrain of sole personal responsibility for interpreting
the meaning of science at a point of decisive significance, and if they
are careful not to overstate what is still the very large range of their
competence and their skill, they cannot but serve effectively and
with enormous influence in the process of government. But let me,
as a kind of coda, give you some general propositions that are *not*
true, some common fallacies that one runs into day in and day out.
One of them is that scientists should give advice on scientific subjects and keep away from military, political, social, and economic
topics. This happens to be nonsense. You can't stay away from military topics when the question with which you are concerned is the
design of a weapon. You cannot design a sensible weapon, a practicable one, one which is useful to the people for whom and with whom
you are cooperating, if you do not know what it is they are trying to
do. One of the first things that was learned—one of the great lessons,
I think—in the flowering of scientific cooperation with government
during the second world war was that there has to be an interpenetration of understanding such that a man can know what the other
man's problem is. It is madness to assume, as very many people
habitually do, that there is somehow an act of trespass if the scientist

shows himself alert to a problem which stretches beyond the purely technical problem. There is every reason for avoiding these narrow divisions.

This applies with equal clarity when you go the other way, incidentally (and this is not a point which scientists always so readily accept); the nonscientific partner has a right and an obligation to try to have some critical view of what the technological contribution can be. And in the same way it is nonsense to say that military men should stick to military matters. We get to wearing special hats in government; we get typed as character players; we are condemned by imagery and by expectation to as monotonous a life as the late Lionel Barrymore. Everybody knew good old Lionel. You know: here comes the scientist; he's going to give you scientific advice; he will probably forget his spectacles; he doesn't really understand ordinary things; he's a crusty old curmudgeon; but oh boy, he's great on diagnosis, and basically lovable too.

Well, the real world is not like that, and the moment people begin to construe it that way, they go wrong.

What is going on here is a process of communication among human beings. The problems do not divide apart that way. You don't solve the problem of nuclear weapons and their relation to the world by saying, "Here is a nuclear core—that's scientific; here is a nuclear weapon—that's military; here is a treaty—that's political." These things all have to live with each other. There are elements that are indeed military, or technological, or diplomatic, but the process of effective judgment and action comes at a point where you cannot separate them out.

It follows, I think, that it is also nonsense to talk about the political neutrality of scientists. Scientists are people, a fact which is frequently forgotten, but verifiable experimentally; they are bound to have feelings which for want of a better word we will call human. If they become deeply concerned with the development of a laboratory, or with the elaboration of an international proposal, or with an assessment of the real value of continued nuclear testing in this or that environment, it is inconceivable that they should be so inhuman as to have no personal judgment about the problem as a whole. It is important, obviously, that scientists and others should recognize that they do have personal judgments. But one should not suppose that this is in any way wrong, or even necessarily dangerous.

It is a simple but important fact of American life that in this whole great field of the exploitation of nuclear energy for military purposes there are schools of thought, among scientists as among others, which are essentially political. To pretend that they do not exist is to misunderstand much of the internal history of the government over the last fifteen years, to misunderstand why great injustices have been done to some notable individuals, and to fail to appreciate that there is great feeling, of a simple, human wicked sort, in these issues. The way to deal with this fact is to accept it, not to be startled by it;to live with it and to insure that there is a spectrum of feeling, attitude, and point of view, among scientists who are asked for their honest advice—a spectrum wide enough so that the final judgment of political authorities is not cramped by any arbitrary or accidental narrowness in technical counsel. Indeed, I would say that one element in the necessary thereness of the scientist is that there should be enough scientists, having enough ideas and enough ways of attacking problems, and enough notions of what it is that it is important to attack, so that a wide range of choice is always open to the political leaders. If the range of scientific counsel is limited, then the choices available to the politician may be fewer than he might wish, and the path of political action may be narrowed.

In this particular field of testing and test bans, incidentally, it has been the practice of this administration to seek a very wide range of advice. I think it's fair to say that there is no leading member of any of the great schools of thought whose views have not been heard with interest and respect. Strong differences of opinion do not mean that one man is wrong and sinful and the other man is right and virtuous; they only mean that these are the kinds of questions upon which human beings are bound to have sharp feelings and divisions. We must live with those things; we must accept them. The processes of government should allow for them, and scientists should not be cut off from these quite human activities either by their own image of themselves or by other people's picture of them.

And that, I think, is the wider point that I would make at the end. There is nothing in the experience, the training, and the discipline of the scientist that should cut him off from *any* responsible activity in the government—nothing but the fact that scientists are so busy, so eager to be back in the laboratory, and so few in number compared to the number of jobs that there are. I think that it would be worth your while to consider whether, as a profession, you should not enlarge still further your contribution to the processes of government. It may be important over the next ten or fifteen years that there should be more scientists who are ex-scientists, doing wholly unscientific things, acting as cabinet and subcabinet officers *without* a specific responsibility for research, serving on commissions that are *not* necessarily the Atomic Energy Commission, directing agencies that may *not* be just the National Science Foundation. For the interpenetrations of science and government, science and public policy, science and politics, are bound to increase, and the processes of communication from man to man, thick as they are and thickening steadily, are not yet as deep, as thick, as varied — are not, above all, as much taken for granted — as they need to be.

There is a still larger reason for being in favor of science and of scientists in this context — and this thought I will put as an affirmation, not as anything I know how to prove. I suggest that there is a wide, deep, and important coincidence between the temper and purpose of American national policy and the temper and purpose of American science. Our science and our society are deeply alike in their pragmatic, optimistic, energetic, and essentially cooperative view of the way in which useful things get done. They are alike, too, in having been exposed to great sophistication and great proliferation of responsibility, over a relatively short period of time. They are alike in having surpised the world by the measure of their success in responding to this new exposure, and there is good reason to suppose that in coming constantly closer together they will reinforce each other's high purposes. I think, in short, that there is no fundamental conflict between your existence as scientists and your existence as Americans.

## NOTES

1 Many of the members of these advisory panels are men whose long experience and continuing close involvement put them quite out of range of the present comment.

2 V. Bush, *Science* **134**, 1163 (1961).

3 C. P. Snow, *ibid.* **133**, 255 (1961).

*14*

# Future Needs for the Support of Basic Research

HARVEY BROOKS

*WHAT LEVEL of federal support is needed to maintain for the United States a position of leadership through basic research in the advancement of science and technology and their economic, cultural, and military applications?*

*What judgment can be reached on the balance of support now being given by the federal government to various fields of scientific endeavor, and on adjustments that should be considered, either within existing levels of overall support or under conditions of increased or decreased overall support?\**

The two questions posed by the House committee are exceedingly difficult to answer in any precise quantitative way. The general approach taken by this paper is that the answers can only be arrived at by successive approximations. We thus try to suggest some of the considerations and some of the mechanisms of choice that ought to be considered in determining levels of support for science.

I begin my paper discussing some of the problems involved in interpreting research and development statistics. Since current statistics must provide the basis for any future planning for science it is important that the limitations of these statistics be fully understood.

---

\*These two questions were put by the House Committee on Science and Astronautics to the Panel on Basic Research and National Goals appointed by the Committee on Science and Public Policy of the National Academy of Sciences and chaired by Professor George B. Kistiakowsky. This essay by Professor Brooks, Dean of Engineering Sciences at Harvard and a member of the President's Science Advisory Committee, was originally published, along with those of the other panel members, in Basic Research and National Goals, Washington, D.C., 1965. It is reprinted here by kind permission of the author and of the National Academy.

The second section deals with some of the reasons why the support of basic research is considered to be in the national interest, and why this support must be primarily a Federal responsibility. In this section we suggest some possible guidelines for future over-all support of academic rescarch.

In section III a conceptual scheme for considering the "science budget" is suggested. This involves an attempt to separate the requirements of big science from those of the individual investigator in the university. It suggests that the problem of relative allocation to fields is not one to be centrally determined, but rather a question of setting up suitable mechanisms for continuing decentralized choice. This section is concerned mainly with academic research.

The fourth section attempts to describe the difference between academic research and organized institutional research, and to explain the different mechanisms of choice and criteria that should apply to the latter as compared with the former.

## I. *Some Remarks on Research and Development Statistics*

Since much current discussion of Federal spending on science is based on financial and manpower statistics, it is important that the meaning and limitations of these statistics be fully understood. A recent report of the Organization of Economic Cooperation and Development has remarked that most countries have better statistics on poultry production than they do on the activities of their scientists and engineers. To some extent this is inevitable since the product of scientific activity is an elusive entity that defies measurement. Especially in basic research we have nothing but historical analogy to go on in evaluating the worth of the product, and even in purely scientific terms the value of any given piece of work often does not become fully apparent until several years after it is published. In many cases an unsuccessful experiment may have more lasting value than a successful one. A classic example is the famous Michelson-Morley experiment, which failed to detect the absolute motion of the earth through space and led directly to Einstein's formulation of the theory of special relativity, but not until many years later.

As a result of these features research activity is not very amenable to the ordinary methods of economic analysis. We can measure the "inputs" in financial terms or in terms of "professional man-years" of effort, but we have no comparable currency in which to measure the "output." We can see the continuing growth of our economy as primarily a product of technical innovation, but until very recently little of this innovation was clearly connected with organized research and development. No striking acceleration of economic growth has accompanied the dramatic growth of organized research in recent years. This is not very surprising in view of the large average time lag between research discoveries and their application. On the other hand, the sectors of the economy showing the largest percentage growth rates are in many cases those most heavily dependent on modern research. All the advanced industrial countries devote about the same proportion of their national income to civilian research and development. Thus we have no "controls" by which we may judge what would have happened to economic growth if there had been no research and development, nor do we have a way of measuring the relative importance, economically speaking, of the research relative to the development. Indeed, there is no economic "payoff" from research until it is incorporated in some kind of product, service, or process, and this won't happen to current research results, for the most part, for many years. Thus research, and particularly basic research, is a speculative investment in the relatively long-term future; its economic payoff has a longer incubation time than any other form of investment, except possibly education.

On the other hand, there are certain things that can be said about the current economic benefits of technical proficiency to the United States. For one thing, this country has an exceedingly favorable balance of trade in "technical know-how," as measured by international payments for royalties, licensing agreements, and management fees. Such payments net nearly half a billion dollars a year, and payments to the United States exceed, by a factor of nearly five, payments from the United States to all other countries. As another example, analysis of our exports clearly reveals that the proportion of products from industries that may be classed as "research intensive" is very much higher in our export trade than it is in the gross national product as a whole, suggesting that it is the industries based on technical know-how that generally compete most effectively in world markets. Analysis of the exports of other advanced nations indicates a similar bias toward products and services based on research. On the other hand, one must interpret these figures with some caution, since they must relate primarily to technical advances that took place before the present high Federal investment in research and development, and since technical progress in Europe and Japan was heavily retarded by the effects of World War II and its aftermath.

Because of the absence of valid economic measures for the product or benefits of research and development we are forced to measure it essentially in terms of its economic inputs, with the implicit assumption that in some sense the output will be proportional to the input. In terms of inputs, one thing is clear: research and development probably constitute one of our fastest-expanding forms of economic activity. Nevertheless, one must regard statistics of the past with great caution. Even within a span of a few years, there has been a tendency to include more and more activities under the category of research and development that were formerly looked upon as part of production or design or, in the military field, procurement. A few years ago, as a result of a reorganization, the category of research and development in the Defense Department was changed to "research, development, test, and evaluation." This placed the dividing line between development and procurement much further along in the weapons system cycle than had formerly been the case. Now sample production runs of weapons for evaluation, and the costs of expending them under simulated service conditions, are treated as part of research, development, test, and evaluation. Apart from this effect, which caused a discontinuous 20–30 percent jump in the apparent research and development budget of the Department of Defense, the general popularity of research and development probably resulted in a good deal of redefinition of many technical activities. Thus the growth of research and development in the last decade, while substantial, is probably not as rapid as indicated by the raw statistics.

On the other hand, there is much activity of a highly technical nature in the Federal Government which, while not classified as research and development, requires the participation and supervision of people with advanced technical training and experience. Many of the services performed by Government involve the collection of technical data on a more or less routine basis. Examples occur in weather forecasting, hydrographic and geological mapping, and collection of economic and population statistics. That the function of the Federal Government in our society is highly technical is indicated by the fact that nearly 50 percent of the professional civilian employees of the Federal Government are scientists, engineers, or health professionals, and the three highest grades of the civil service are even more heavily populated with people with technical backgrounds.

Similar problems arise when one talks about specific classes of activity, such as basic and applied research. In the first place, the motivations of the man who does research can, quite legitimately, be different from the man who supports it. In the second place, some basic research involves the design, construction, and operation of very large and complex equipment. The motivation for acquiring this equipment may be purely scientific, but much of the activity accompanying its design and use is indistinguishable from the more applied kinds of engineering or production. Thus, for example, in fiscal year 1964 the National Science Foundation reported a

Federal investment of about $1.6 billion in basic research. It turns out that nearly half of this amount was spent by the National Aeronautics and Space Administration and that approximately 80 percent of the National Aeronautics and Space Administration expenditure was for the design and procurement of scientific space vehicles, the operation of tracking ranges, and payments to military missile ranges for putting the vehicles into orbit. A significant part of the oceanography budget goes into simply keeping research vessels at sea, without any science. The operation of a large particle accelerator requires annually something like 10 percent of its capital cost, or perhaps as much as 30 percent if one includes the cost of continued updating of the equipment. Similar figures can be quoted for large optical telescopes or arrays and "dishes" for radio astronomy. These are operating costs that are required simply to make a facility available, with no consideration of the additional costs of the actual science to be done.

Why is it necessary to stress these logistic costs of research? Since they are incurred for the purpose of achieving basic research results, they are legitimately chargeable to basic research. Nevertheless, the impression conveyed by statistics that include such supporting costs can be quite misleading. A basic research budget that rises annually by 15 percent may appear to be adequate or even generous, but if most of this cost increase is merely to ensure the availability of certain new facilities, then the increased budget could actually be supporting the activities of fewer scientists. The situation would be a little like building a new department store that was so expensive to keep open that it was necessary to fire all the salesmen. This is not an academic issue. Much of the planning for new research facilities that took place in fiscal years 1962 and 1963 was based on an implicit assumption of continuing expansion of research budgets. Now, in fiscal years 1964 and 1965, when these facilities are just coming into operation, the expenses of merely making them available—without any science—are confronting fixed or even declining operating budgets for basic research. The political embarassment that would attend not using a facility already built makes it inevitable that the facilities are made available anyway, usually at the expense of the individual scientist who does not have large fixed costs. A recent calculation indicates that if the budget for oceanography continues to stay level, the cost of operating ships already planned but not yet completed will eventually consume almost the entire research budget. A similar situation appears to be developing in low-energy nuclear physics, and with respect to university computing facilities. In nuclear physics, for example, expenditures for facilities doubled between fiscal years 1962 and 1964, while operating expenditures increased only slightly and actually decreased in the university sector between 1963 and 1964. The point I am making is that simply to look at total budgets for basic research, or even their annual increments, can be highly misleading unless one knows something about the fixed availability costs that have been built into the program by past commitments for capital facilities. Where large availability costs are involved, the relation between research output and dollar input can be highly nonlinear, and hence measurements of basic research activity by dollar inputs can give a misleadingly reassuring impression as to the adequacy of support. Unfortunately, our present methods for collecting and classifying statistics on research expenditures are not sufficiently refined to reveal problems of this sort, or to draw clear-cut conclusions about the current situation. Subjective opinions of many individual scientists and research groups indicate that support for the individual investigator is becoming increasingly inadequate relative to his needs, but it is hard to prove this quantitatively, and even harder to establish that it is due to past commitments for facilities.

Classifications of research into basic and applied can also be misleading as to the type of manpower required. In the space example, a single experiment may involve the services of hundreds of technicians and skilled workmen, whereas only four or five scientists may be involved in the actual design of the instrumentation package and the analysis and interpretation of the data. The same amount of money in another field of research might finance the activities of fifty highly trained scientists. This issue is an important one because it is sometimes claimed that there is more money for basic research than the really competent people available to do it can spend wisely. This could be true, but I submit that it is a judgment that cannot be made in terms of total available funds, but only on a project-by-project basis. Two or three competent scientists can in some areas of research wisely command or direct the activities of a large number of less highly skilled people. In fact, one effect of increased research funds is that many scientists are able to buy from industry equipment that they would otherwise have to design and build themselves. The dollar input to their research is much larger than it would otherwise have been, but this does not necessarily mean that the research is more "expensive" if measured in terms of the research results obtained. The capital investment may not only enable the scientist to obtain more results for the same effort, but also may permit him to choose a much more significant problem or to obtain a much more conclusive answer. Just as capital investment embodying new technology improves the productivity of ordinary labor, so does it improve the productivity of scientific effort. Unfortunately, since it is the only thing that is quantifiable, there is a tendency to measure research in terms of man-years of effort or in terms of output of publishable papers. While the latter is certainly much more significant than the former, there is still too wide a variation in the information content and quality of scientific papers for paper publication to provide an accurate measure of research output.

Another statistic that is often quoted has to do with academic research. For a long time it was common practice to report only the total research and development support going into universities. However, in the postwar period many universities undertook the management of large applied laboratories or basic research institutes. Some of these, like Los Alamos, were remote from the campus and had no visible intellectual connection with the parent university. However, such clearcut cases were the exception; usually the relationship to the university was closer, as in the case of the Radiation Laboratory at Berkeley, the Cambridge electron accelerator, or even the Lincoln Laboratory at MIT. It has now become customary, however, to classify such organizations as federally financed research centers and exclude them in reporting the support of research in "universities proper." Nevertheless, there are many such organizations that employ faculty members part time and participate in the training of graduate students. Other organizations, such as the Brookhaven National Laboratory, the National Radio Astronomy Observatory, or the Kitt Peak National Astronomy Observatory, are not classified with universities at all, but nevertheless provide important facilities for university "user groups," including significant numbers of graduate students and faculty on temporary assignment. Conversely, there are some research activities within "universities proper" that are little more than research institutes with rather minimal intellectual connection with the rest of the university. The point here is that the line between "academic" and "nonacademic" research in universities — between universities proper and research centers — is not a sharp one if measured by involvement in the educational process. Yet, with respect to Federal research and development investment, the research centers account for something like 40 percent of all university research activity. With current emphasis on the connection between basic research and graduate education, there is a danger in completely eliminating the research center statistics from the overall picture, with the implication that the elimination or downgrading of such activities would have no effect on the educational function of the universities. In some cases this might well be so, but in others it would not be. There is equal hazard in the converse assumption that all the research funds going to universities proper are in support of graduate education and therefore required to maintain the quality of graduate training; unfortunately, we have discovered no quantitative way to measure the educational relevance of research funds.

Another statistic that may be misleading is the separation of Federal funds into contributions to "research" and "education." Thus, on the one hand, in reporting Federal research and development funds in universities proper, fellowship funds, research training grants, and certain types of institutional support are usually omitted, despite the fact that many of the individuals who receive stipends under such programs are actually engaged at least part time in research or in the supervision of student research. It is clear that a significant proportion of such funds contributes to the progress of research in universities. In the National Institutes of Health they amount to about 30 percent of all the funds contributed to universities, although they are less significant for other agencies. On the other hand, a very large proportion of the funds designated as "research" actually provide stipends for graduate students and postdoctoral research associates who, while engaged in research, are also receiving training. Indeed, since research experience is believed to be the most important and valuable part of advanced training in science, the separation between research and education funds is bound to be rather arbitrary and artificial.

Even the classification of research funds into Federal and non-Federal may be highly misleading. For example, procurement contracts in defense, space, and atomic energy permit business organizations to charge a small fraction of their independent research activity to procurement overhead and also allow technical work in connection with the preparation of development proposals, including unsuccessful proposals, as an overhead item. It has been estimated that the total funds channeled to industry in this way amount to close to $1 billion, about the same amount of money as flows from the Federal Government into universities proper for research, basic and applied. Yet this money is classified in the statistics as being financed by the private, not the public, sector. A good deal of private research is also financed out of the profits of military and space procurement. The proper classification of these activities is hard to decide. In the sense that the basic resource-allocation decisions are made in the private sector, regardless of the source of funds, the activity is correctly classified as private. On the other hand, the Government does exercise some surveillance over the expenditure of part of these funds. Furthermore, the extent and scope of the activity is strongly conditioned by decisions in the public sector.

In considering research in the university sector it is often forgotten that in practice, the salaries of faculty members engaged in research are paid largely by the university out of its own sources of funds, and are not a charge against Federal research and development budgets. This is in contrast to federally financed research centers and to research in private industry, where the Federal Government is routinely expected to bear the full costs. In addition, the universities make a major contribution in the form of unreimbursed indirect costs, estimated to exceed $60 million annually. In a sense that does not apply to any other sector to the same degree, the Federal contribution to university research is a contribution to a shared activity rather than procurement of a service at cost. Any increase in the Federal contribution to university research thus generally reflects an increased contribution from other sources as well.

In considering the totality of Federal research and development activities, there appears to be no unique way of breaking down expenditures into their significant components. Except possibly in the area of specific hardware development, most Federal research expenditures serve several purposes simultaneously, and most scientific activities relate to more than one traditional disciplinary categorization. The network of communications and organization in the technical community is so dynamic and complex that it is difficult to capture in a statistical snapshot at any one point in time, and even harder to characterize by fixed statistical categories over a period of time. In my personal view the most reliable and useful statistical categories are those that relate to institutional arrangements, such as universities, Federal research centers, and scientific departments or schools, rather than to such categories as basic and applied or to the various traditional scientific disciplines.

## II. *Why Should the Federal Government Support Basic Research?*

The House committee has asked at what level basic research should be supported in order to maintain our present position of leadership. As background for answering this question it is necessary to inquire why the Federal Government should support basic research in the first place, and what functions basic research serves in our society.

One can recognize four distinct functions of basic research, some of which also pertain to certain types of applied research. They are: cultural, economic, social, and educational.

### CULTURAL

Basic scientific research is recognized as one of the characteristic expressions of the highest aspirations of modern man. It bears much the same relation to contemporary civilization that the great artistic and philosophical creations of the Greeks did to theirs, or the great cathedrals did to medieval Europe. In a certain sense it not only serves the purposes of our society but *is* one of the purposes of our society. Science and technology together constitute the distinctive aspect of American culture that is most admired and imitated in the rest of the world, and I believe this admiration is connected with more than the economic and military power that derive from technology.

The attitude of the general public toward the space program suggests that this cultural aspect does enjoy a degree of public acceptance. While it is true that much of the public supports the space effort because it feels in a somewhat vague way that it is connected with military power, nevertheless there is a genuine sense of identification with the adventure of exploration into the unknown. To the scientists it may seem naive that the public should identify the space program, especially the man-in-space program, with science. To many, but by no means all, scientists the relative emphasis on the lunar-landing program appears as a distortion of scientific priorities and of intellectual values. Is manned exploration of the near solar system really worth a thousand times as much as probing the secrets of distant galaxies or the dramatic and intriguing quasi-stellar energy sources? Nevertheless, public acceptance of the space program must be regarded as in some sense a vote of confidence in intellectual exploration as such and a recognition of the desirability of public support for such exploration. This recognition is, by itself, a new political phenomenon, and may represent only the first step toward a wider and more informed public recognition of the desirability of social support of intellectual exploration for its own sake.

Any statement of a cultural motivation for the support of basic research raises, of course, much more serious issues of political philosophy than the other motivations listed. Why basic science but not art, music, and literature? Why not research in the humanities? If we support science for cultural reasons, how can we tell how much is enough? I think the only definite answer that can be given to these questions lies in the nature of science as a system of acquiring and validating knowledge. Science — especially natural science — has a public character that is still lacking in other forms of knowledge. The results of scientific research have to stand the scrutiny of a large and critical scientific community, and after a time those that stand the test tend to be accepted by all literate mankind. Outside the scientific community itself this acceptance tends to be validated by the practical results of science. If it works it must be true. There is no question that the successful achievement of an atom bomb provided a certain intellectual validation for nuclear physics, quite apart from its practical value. Part of the public character of science results from the fact that it is always in principle subject to independent validation or verification. It is like paper money that can always be exchanged for gold or silver on demand. Just because everybody believes that he can get gold for paper, nobody tries; so the public seldom questions the findings of science, just because it believes that they can always be questioned and revalidated on demand. This is much less true of other forms of knowledge and culture, which may be of equal social importance but are more subjective and more dependent on the vagaries of private tastes and value systems. It is just because science is a cultural activity generally believed to transcend private value systems that it becomes eligible for government support where other forms of cultural activities are not. The system of indirect public support through tax exemption has been used in the United States successfully to support cultural activities in areas where there is no consensus of values or tastes. This is possible because, although public funds are used, actual decisions as to what will be supported are left in private hands. It may well be that this situation should be regarded as temporary. Direct Government support of other forms of cultural expression is generally accepted in advanced countries other than the United States.

The basic difficulty with the cultural motivation for Federal support of basic research is that it does not provide any basis for quantifying the amount of support required. The amount of basic research that should be supported for purely cultural reasons is certainly a fraction of what should be supported for other reasons. It is currently believed that the talent for really creative basic work in science is exceedingly rare. I believe there is a most creative minority, possibly not more than 5 percent of all the active basic research scientists, who should receive support for their work for no other reasons than their demonstrated capacity for original and creative work. This highly selected group of people might be provided with some minimum level of research support with no strings attached. They would simply be backed up to some level, say $20,000 to $30,000 per year, to work on anything they thought worth doing. If they needed more than this, then their requirements would have to be justified in competition with others in terms of their specific proposed work and for other than purely cultural reasons. I believe the Government could reasonably commit something of the order of $100 million[1] a year to this type of completely free-wheeling research expenditure.

It must be remembered, however, that the work of this most creative group cannot be regarded as independent of the more run-of-the-mill kinds of research, as is sometimes implied. Important discoveries have sometimes been made by individuals who never did anything else of significance in their careers. The brilliant generalizations of giants often rest on the painstaking accumulation of data by less gifted individuals. The relative importance of brilliant and intuitive insight as compared with the more pedestrian hard work will vary from time to time with the circumstances of particular fields. For example, the progress of mathematics and theoretical physics is probably much more dependent on the insights of a few leaders of extraordinary ability than is the progress of experimental physics or chemistry. One cannot support only the geniuses and expect that science will continue to progress as though the workers in the vineyard were superfluous. However, it is certainly true that more than a merely cultural motivation should be required to justify the support of other than the few most highly gifted.

For the sake of its position of leadership it is essential that the Nation be prepared to invest heavily in equipment and facilities which place a few of its most talented groups at the "cutting edges" of modern scientific advance. No matter how talented the people, facilities that are second best are likely to leave them in the position of verifying exciting discoveries made by somebody else. The pre-eminence of the United States in nuclear physics owes much to the brilliance of its workers in this field, including many imported from other countries, but it owes even more to the superior equipment that generous Federal support, good planning, and high-class engineering have made possible. United States preeminence in many fields of science reflects not only the intellectual vigor of its scientists but also the excellence of its industrial base.

The United States has led the world in discoveries in optical astronomy almost since the turn of the century, and this is largely attributable to the foresight of some of the great private foundations that supported American astronomers in the construction of better instruments than existed anywhere else in the world. By contrast, in radio astronomy, despite a large investment, American instruments are inferior to some in Britain and Australia, with the result that the United States does not enjoy the clear lead in this field that it does in optical astronomy, despite the fact that the detection of radio waves from space was originally an American discovery.

Supporting basic science for purely cultural reasons, of course, pays dividends in other areas such as national prestige and the intellectual respect of the most influential groups in the rest of the world. Thus the purely cultural motivation supports the power and influence of the United States in the world and adds to the self-confidence of its own people. Nevertheless, paradoxically, supporting science solely for reasons of national prestige usually tends to corrupt it by distorting its scientific objectives and priorities, and thus ultimately to defeat the prestige objectives as well. This is generally an area where virtue is its own reward.


## ECONOMIC

There is now general acceptance among economists of the importance of technological innovation in economic growth. To an increasing extent such innovation depends upon the results of basic science, although the degree to which this is true is difficult to quantify. To an increasing degree also there is a disposition to regard organized research and development as an investment in new knowledge equivalent in some sense to the investment in fixed capital. Indeed, most capital investments incorporate some measure of technological innovation. According to some economists the rise in capital-to-labor ratio accounts for only a small part of increases in productivity; about 50 percent is ascribed to other factors lumped under the general heading of "technical progress," which probably incorporates about equal parts of research and education as well as such factors as managerial and marketing innovations. There is also general agreement that in a market economy the allocation of resources to the advance and spread of knowledge will tend to be less than the optimum required for maximum efficient long-term growth of the economic system as a whole. Moreover, the further removed research is from ultimate practical application the less likely it is to be supported in a market economy without either direct public subvention or private support induced by special tax incentives, which is also a form of public support. Thus, there appear to be strong economic reasons for Federal support of research, and especially basic research.

In comparing the United States with other advanced industrial countries one finds that, if one sets aside military research and development expenditures, our investment in research is about the same in terms of percentage of national income as that of other countries, including Japan, the Netherlands, the United Kingdom, Sweden, West Germany, and France. It is noteworthy that Federal support of basic research in universities is a smaller fraction of total university basic research than in any other advanced country. This is, of course, because the United States has no Federal university system, and also because it relies much more heavily than other nations on indirect public support via tax deductions for private contributions. It is also noteworthy that the Federal share of university basic research has remained almost constant at about 57 percent over the last ten years, despite the very large absolute increase. The fact that the Federal share of total research support in universities has increased is thus attributable solely to the increase in applied research, largely in the medical and engineering areas. Thus, in relation to our national investment in higher education, it does not appear that the Federal contribution to basic research in universities is in any way exceptionally large.

Since World War II there has been increasing recognition of the potential economic benefits of supporting science on its own terms without any commitment to specific applications. Politically, however, this commitment has always been made with some reserve. The National Science Foundation, the only agency with a clear mandate to support basic research as such, had a long struggle to come into existence, and an even longer struggle to attain a significant budget for research. Even today it accounts for only a little more than 10 percent of the support of research in universities proper—nearer 20 percent of the truly basic research. It also accounts for about 10 percent of all federally supported basic research. On the other hand, the Congress has been quite liberal in permitting the mission-oriented agencies to support basic research related to their missions, and the interpretation of mission-relatedness has been reasonably broad. If it had not been for this fact, United States science would not have attained the reputation for world leadership that it enjoys today.

In several fields Federal support for mission-related basic research has been of decisive importance for United States technological leadership, even in the field of civilian applications. Although the transistor was invented in private enterprise, Federal support for university solid-state research played an important role in creating an environment in which the transistor could be rapidly exploited and developed. Federally supported research also greatly accelerated the development of high-speed computers, and much of the pioneering work on computers was done in universities. Federal support of aeronautical research, largely in inhouse laboratories, was inportant for United States leadership in the development of modern civilian aircraft. Undoubtedly, Federal support for basic research in the medical sciences and biochemistry has accelerated the development of new drugs by industry. Support by the Atomic Energy Commission of basic nuclear research that was not obviously relevant to weapons or nuclear power has been largely responsible for the maintenance of United States leadership in this field.

On the other hand, in only three fields—agriculture, mineral resources, and civilian nuclear power—has the Federal Government explicitly supported applied research aimed at development of the civilian economy.

SOCIAL

In many areas, including public health and national defense, there is a recognized Federal responsibility. In these areas the Federal Government has generally been quick to utilize research in support of its missions, including a substantial amount of basic research. In fact, for the most part, basic research support has tended to derive from these special missions rather than from any overt policy concerning the desirability of social support for research. More recently, beginning with the National Advisory Committee for Aeronautics in 1920 and extending through the Atomic Energy Commission and the National Aeronautics and Space Administration, the Government has recognized a special responsibility for exploiting certain advanced technologies in the national interest. In these cases it was recognized that the technologies were sufficiently new and unappreciated so that they would not be adopted and adequately supported as part of the missions of existing Federal agencies or private institutions. They needed hothouse cultivation, as it were, before they could grow and mature on their own. In each example of such an agency, however, there was a strong military overtone to the justification; it is doubtful whether the National Advisory Committee for Aeronautics, the Atomic Energy Commission, or the reincarnation of the National Advisory Committee for Aeronautics in the National Aeronautics and Space Administration would ever have been justified without a quasi-military incentive. However, once there, their additional roles in economic growth gradually came to be appreciated.

It is clear that with increased urbanization and industrialization, our country is developing a number of problems that can only be faced on a national basis—for example, education, air pollution, water resources, weather forecasting and control, pesticides, radioactive wastes, public recreation, natural resources, air traffic control, highway safety, and urban transportation. The degree of Federal responsibility in these areas will always tend to be a matter for political debate, but there is greater consensus that the Federal Government has a responsibility for seeing that the foundations of knowledge are laid in these areas than there is that it has an operational responsibility. Research related to these social goals tends to be recognized as a Federal responsibility even when operation or regulation is delegated to the State or local level or to private enterprise. If applied research for these purposes is a Federal responsibility, it is clear that the basic research that underlies it must also be recognized as a Federal responsibility. Except in the areas of health and national security, however, there is still little appreciation of the contribution that uncommitted basic research can and should make to these goals. What is called basic research in many areas of Federal civil responsibility is still rather narrowly oriented in terms of obvious relevance to the immediate goal. Such oriented basic research is vital, but not sufficient. The rather rigid interpretation of relevance to mission that exists in the research in the older civilian agencies is in sharp contrast to the broader interpretation that is followed in national defense and health.

The difficulty with this motivation for Federal basic research is that criteria for the amount and character of basic research that should be supported in connection with social goals is difficult to establish. Clearly it is proper that research as a whole in these areas should compete on an equal basis with alternative means of achieving the same goals. Perhaps the only reasonable criterion is to relate the basic research effort of an agency to its total applied or development effort, possibly in terms of some percentage of the applied effort. Any such criterion, however, should involve some smoothing of fluctuations to take into account the larger time frame of basic research. The fractional effort on basic research will inevitably be strongly dependent on the breadth of the mission of an agency and on the magnitude of the total effort and its degree of dependence on relatively new or recently discovered scientific knowledge. I would suggest that in many instances 10 to 15 percent of the applied effort might be a good rule of thumb for the basic research effort. However, it is difficult to mount a viable basic research effort when the applied research is too fragmented into small units, as it is, for example, in the Department of the Interior, the Department of Agriculture, and the Department of Commerce (except for the National Bureau of Standards). In such cases it might make more sense for these departments to "task" the National Science Foundation with basic research in certain broad areas of relevance to the total mission of the department. It also seems rather important that not all the research, either basic or applied, be inhouse. Exclusively inhouse research often appears to be more efficient in the short run, since the people involved can be more closely channeled into research areas that meet the short-range requirements of the mission, but in the long run a purely inhouse research effort tends to cut the agency off from the scientific community. Not only is the scientific and educational community unaware of its problems, but its own people lose awareness of the opportunities that new developments in basic science present in the applied research it is doing. It always tends to define its own subject matter too narrowly.

EDUCATION

The intimate connection between basic research and graduate education has been repeatedly stressed in recent years. In engineering, medicine, agriculture, and several other areas, applied research is equally as important as advanced training, and there is danger that this fact may be forgotten in identifying the universities too exclusively with basic research. In particular, there is a tendency in the universities to regard the application of science as a lower order of intellectual activity than pure science, an attitude that tends to impede the healthy flow of talent between basic and applied science, which has been one of the characteristic features of American science contributing to its vitality. On the other hand, it is true that even in applied research the universities ought to focus on the longer-range goals, the things that are likely to become economically viable several years away, and that have the greatest generality in application. Research apprenticeship is the most essential part of graduate education beyond the master's level, whether it be in pure or applied science.

There is a broader sense in which research activity contributes to education. Research itself is defined as "learning work"—the production of new knowledge. While much of this knowledge is made explicit and public by publication in the technical literature, the individuals engaged in advancing knowledge acquire skills and perspectives that greatly transcend the sum of the information appearing in their publications. The contribution of a Fermi or a Von Neumann to our society is far greater than that of the bound volumes of their collected works or even than their influence on their students. A great scientist becomes a teacher of his whole culture. The people who devote most of their lives to research become a national human resource, available in emergencies to turn their attention to many problems outside their own immediate fields of interest. The rapid application of microwave radar during the early years of World War II was largely the work of nuclear physicists, even though the basic invention had been conceived several years earlier by engineers in Government laboratories. What was needed for the exploitation, however, was not just the invention itself but a whole complex of experience with advanced electronic techniques and with the integration of these techniques into an operable system. The nuclear physicists who had been working with accelerators possessed this kind of experience, and were able in an emergency to turn it to military applications. Through the decade of the 1930s they had been unknowingly educating themselves, in a sense, for just this moment. It is doubtful whether any explicit or conscious form of education would have been as effective as their own continuing involvement in basic science. What applied to radar was even more evident in the case of nuclear weapons, since only those previously engaged in nuclear research, chemical kinetics, radiochemistry, and other fundamental fields had the accumulated skills necessary to preceed with projects in this field. The contribution of the engineering management skills of American industry—especially of the chemical engineering industry—was also indispensable, but without the intellectual leadership and vision of the basic scientists the project would neither have been undertaken nor carried to a successful conclusion. The development of the electronic computer in the early postwar years owed much to the high-speed electronic-circuit techniques in which nuclear physicists had trained themselves in order to sharpen the tools of their own basic research.

Not all individuals who receive advanced training in basic research remain in basic sciences. Some enter basic research in industry or Government but then move on to applied science or technology in the course of their careers, often following a basic-research development or technique through into its applications. Many techniques now common in industry, such as high-vacuum technology, low temperatures, X-ray diffraction, spectroscopy, nuclear-reactor physics and neutron instrumentation, radioisotopes, electron microscopy, had their origin as techniques of basic research. Hence, there is a demand in industry for people trained as basic scientists in such fields who then find their careers in applications. The staffing of major new technological or scientific programs such as nuclear power and nuclear weapons, space research, oceanography, or atmospheric sciences has come from people with original training in basic research in physics, chemistry, mathematics, or biology. This transfer of people forms one of the major vehicles for the translation of basic science into applied science and technology, as well as for the creation of new disciplines. Thus, basic science tends to be a net exporter of people into other more applied fields of science or into technology. Too little is known, actually, about the transfer of people between fields and the influence of people receiving basic research training in one field on the development and success of other fields. It seems clear, however, that the training of people in the most advanced techniques and concepts of basic science is not only beneficial to the development of basic research itself and of graduate education, but also has an important influence on the development of technology and of new industry.

Other individuals trained in basic science may choose basic

research as a career but make important contributions on a part-time basis to technology and applied science. Von Neumann, a pure mathematician, formulated one of the key concepts of computer organization. Fermi, a pure physicist, conceived the idea of the nuclear chain reaction and played a leading role in its practical exploitation.

Many key ideas of military technology in the 1950s benefited from important contributions from basic scientists acting as amateur weaponeers. These people brought fresh viewpoints, new combinations of skills and techniques, and a broad vision of the potentialities of science to the weapons business. This contribution was often traceable to their basic research background. These contributions are an incidental benefit deriving from the vigorous support of basic research by the Federal Government, but they have played a significant role in the maintenance of United States preeminence in military technology.

Between the graduate student working as a research apprentice and the professor or laboratory scientist working at the frontiers of knowledge there has grown up a new group of post-doctoral research staff who also participate in the educational process, both as students and teachers. Such people have no formal part in the educational process; nominally, they are just research workers. They do not earn degrees and they do not teach classes. But they both help in the detailed guidance of graduate students and deepen their own knowledge in their chosen fields. Many university departments now have as many post-doctoral fellows as graduate students, largely supported out of federal research grants and contracts. Most of them stay only a few years and then move on to more permanent academic posts as full-fledged teachers. Because of their lack of formal academic status, we know very little about this group, although their support constitutes a very significant fraction of the total research money going into universities. In some other countries—notably Sweden, the United Kingdom, Japan, and the U.S.S.R.—there exists more formal recognition of the status of the post-doctoral student in the form of the D. Sc. degree, a sort of super-degree awarded on the basis of a body of significant contributions to the scientific literature.

The advantage of discussing the educational purposes of basic research is that this is the criterion for research support that is easiest to quantify. To an increasing degree United States policy has been evolving toward a consensus that, at least in science, society as a whole should be prepared to underwrite the opportunity for every individual to carry his education as far as he is willing and able to go.

Thus, by extrapolating long-term cultural trends, we are able to estimate fairly well how many people will be seeking graduate education in science and engineering during the next decade. The people who will do so are already in high school and college today, so there is not too much guesswork involved. The estimates of annual growth in the number of graduate students vary between 5 and 10 percent. The number has been about 8 percent for the last two years, but for the most part these students have not yet entered the research phase of their graduate study, so the full load on university research budgets has not yet been felt.

One can use the above figures to set a floor to the university research support required in the next ten years if one makes certain plausible assumptions, as follows:

1) The percentage of college graduates seeking graduate education in science will remain relatively constant or grow slightly. (Actually the Gilliland Panel* assumed a slight growth in engineering and a slight decline in mathematics relative to the number of undergraduate majors in these fields.)

2) The student-professor ratio will remain about the same as at present.

3) The ratio of post-doctoral students to graduate students will not grow beyond its present value.

4) The percentage of the total budget going into the support of large facilities, either construction or operation, or the support of research institutes relatively divorced from teaching but still in "universities proper" will remain about as at present.

5) Because of the increased sophistication of research— including such items as more automatic data taking and data processing, greater use of computers, and greater availability of sophisticated instrumentation for purchase rather than local construction—the cost of research per man-year of research effort will increase at an annual rate of 5 percent in constant dollars.

6) The contribution to research in universities from State, local, and private sources will increase at the same rate as the Federal contribution, so that the Federal share will not change.

With these assumptions one arrives at a university research requirement that rises at the rate of 13 to 15 percent annually. It is interesting to note that this figure agrees rather closely with projections of requirements for the optimum scientific development of selected fields of science made by certain committees of the National Academy of Sciences, which will report later.

It is important to note that almost all the assumptions in the above projection are conservative. For example, during the past

---

*See President's Science Advisory Committee, *Meeting Manpower Needs in Science and Technology.* The White House. Dec. 12, 1962 — Ed.

ten years, with relatively little growth in the number of graduate students, the research investment per Ph. D. granted one year later has increased by a factor of 2.5. This represents an increase of 10 percent a year on a per-man-year cost basis, nearly twice what is assumed above for the next decade. We are not sure of all the reasons for this growth. We suspect it is due mainly to a change in the character of universities that has been going on for the last thirty or forty years, and that was probably accelerated by the availability of Federal research funds. Research has become an increasingly important part of the purpose of more and more American universities, as it has been of European and British universities for many years. Although university faculties have probably increased by less than 30 percent during this period, Ph. D. faculty has more than doubled. Furthermore, the population of post-doctoral research associates and to some extent the growth of research institutes with permanent research staff or research professors have caused research costs on a per-Ph. D. basis to rise rather rapidly. However, it is to be noted that, because of the upward trend of salaries in the last ten years, the normal annual increase in cost per man-year of scientific effort has been more like 7 than 5 percent. The difference between 10 and 7 percent, or 3 percent, thus represents the cost of the general change in the character of the research economy of universities, and is not really dramatic. In the above projection we are assuming essentially that this long-range cultural trend will stabilize, a somewhat doubtful assumption. On the other hand, it is also true that the last decade was a period of rapid inflation of academic salaries, which had fallen seriously behind the cost of living during the postwar inflation. Academic salaries, at least for scientists, have now reached approximately their prewar position, and it is doubtful whether the inflation of the past decade will continue. Easing off of defense development expenditures may also take some of the inflationary supply-demand pressure off scientific salaries generally, especially in view of the projected increase in the supply of Ph. D.'s. The assumptions regarding the post-doctoral population are also probably conservative. On the other hand, this is the part of the academic research budget with the greatest flexibility; its size tends to be adjustable to the total funds available. A disproportionately large fraction of post-doctoral staff is probably of foreign origin, although many of them ultimately remain in the United States and take academic or industrial posts. With respect to the increased research orientation of university and college faculties, the assumptions are almost certainly conservative. As older professors oriented primarily to classroom teaching retire, they are likely to be replaced by younger men who expect to combine teaching and research. To an increasing degree it is expected that undergraduates may participate in research. Many formerly purely undergraduate institutions are talking about expanding into graduate work, if only to attract faculty of the requisite competence to maintain the quality of their undergraduate programs. Several areas of the country, especially in the South, are just at the beginning of recognizing the importance of research in the functions of a university. These expectations are not really taken into account in the estimate of 15 percent a year given above. They will not be satisfied unless one of several things happens:

1) Research funds for universities are increased faster than 15 percent a year.

2) There is a substantial cutback in support of new major research facilities at universities, and support going to postdoctoral associates and career research staff.

3) Other sources of financial support for research become available, possibly as a result of tax incentives to induce greater contributions to university research from industry, or special Federal programs to encourage matching research funds from States.

4) The declining post-education job market for scientists and engineers induces college graduates to seek other careers outside of the technical fields, so that present estimates of the demand for graduate education are grossly inflated.

In my opinion (3) and (4) appear highly unlikely. It is remarkable, in fact, that the non-Federal contribution to academic science has been able to keep pace as well as it has in the recent past. Most experts on fiscal and tax policy doubt that tax incentives could be designed to result in substantially increased allocation of resources to graduate education and research. In fact, the present tax system already provides many built-in mechanisms for transferring resources from the profit to the non-profit sectors of the private economy.

Cutbacks in defense spending may produce temporary effects along the lines of (4). On the other hand, historical experience does not suggest that the demand for graduate education is very sensitive to the short-term job market. In fact, it is entirely possible that lack of post-education opportunities may induce the opposite effect. The decline in the short-term financial advantage of going to work immediately after the baccalaureate might induce more people to continue their training, as tended to occur during the depression. In the past the massive Federal investment in research and development has scarcely influenced the fraction of college students choosing science; its effect has been mainly on the quality of the training available.

In my opinion it would be very unfortunate for United States science if any drastic change along the lines of (2) took place. The United States position of world leadership in science is highly dependent on the possession of research tools with greater capability than any in the world, and on the existence of a few outstandingly creative groups built up over a long period of time, which often set the pattern and stimulate the efforts of smaller groups throughout the country and train a disproportionate fraction of the people who become leaders and innovators in basic research in other institutions. The research-associate group in major centers often serves as the source of faculty for new centers.

Furthermore, an attempt to create new centers of excellence or achieve a wider geographical distribution of research funds primarily at the expense of existing centers of excellence would be of no service either to science or to graduate education. The inhibition of the best groups could not be compensated in leadership terms by better support of numerous other groups of a high but lesser level of competence. Inevitably it is the graduate schools of the leading institutions that set the standards to which the newer graduate schools aspire and by which they can be measured, and which must provide many of the leaders required to establish new centers of excellence. The wider diffusion of research support is an important and desirable goal, but we should not attempt to achieve it so fast that we destroy or degrade the excellence we have already achieved.

Possibility (1) may be worthier of more serious consideration. It could be achieved without as rapid an overall increase in research funds if support for nonuniversity basic research were held back, e.g., in research centers. On the other hand even here the jeopardy to our leadership position would have to be carefully considered. The principal difficulty in this area is that it is much harder to judge quality in the research centers than in the individual university research projects. Large research institutions tend to have a different social ecology than smaller university research groups. They are less individualistic, and the whole tends to be greater than the sum of the parts. At their best they provide an environment that may exploit the talents of people of average ability much more effectively than if they were entirely on their own on a university faculty. On the other hand, great laboratories tend to be evaluated by the best work that they produce, and, when support is given on an institutional basis, a few excellent groups or individuals can often "front" for the whole organization, even though the total product may not be too impressive in relation to the numbers of scientists involved and the resources used. We have not yet learned how to apply the same rigorous standards to large research organizations that we do to individual research projects in universities. On the other hand, many of these organizations have a purpose other than mere excellence in basic research. It may be necessary for them to do some basic research, even if only of average quality, in order to keep a staff of the requisite level of competence to fulfill their applied mission. On the other hand, with a rising supply-demand ratio for technical people, it should no longer be necessary for such organizations to offer complete freedom of research to rather average people in order to attract them to the organization in the first place. A general tightening up in quality standards of the larger research enterprises both inside and outside universities seems both feasible and desirable in the coming decade. However, it is not clear that the real savings that might be effected in this way would be sufficient to cover the expansion required for education without substantial annual increases in the allocation of funds to basic research. In any event, very close scrutiny of major projects in space, geophysics, and other areas seems called for, not only to evaluate their intrinsic scientific merits but also to consider their impact on the rest of science. In the past, such ventures have been enthusiastically supported by the scientific community on the tacit assumption that there was no competition between these projects and the general support of "little science." This assumption is valid to only a limited extent, and tends to become less valid as research and development becomes a larger fraction of the national budget and of the budgets of individual agencies. This is because research budgets become more and more competitive with other activities within predetermined agency ceilings. As mentioned previously, such projects also imply commitments for operating funds merely to keep the facilities available without supporting any science.

To summarize, on the basis of educational requirements alone, it appears that a minimum annual rate of increase for university research support of 13–15 percent will be required for the next decade if the United States is to meet its announced goals for graduate education. This implies that by 1970 the Federal money being channeled into "universities proper" should be of the order of at least $2.3 billion, of which about $1.2 billion will be for basic research. It is to be emphasized that this projection is based on very conservative assumptions regarding the development of universities in the next decade. If these assumptions do not apply, the requirements are likely to be substantially larger, and can be met only by increased research budgets or by reprograming substantial funds from the Federal support of non-education-related research. Alternatively, it is possible that the educational goals are unrealistic and should be revised downward, but this is so contrary to past cultural trends that I find it difficult to accept. One would have to demonstrate that there is some other intellectual activity that would be much more socially productive, and that would require a radically different kind of educational preparation. It should also be noted that if these goals for research support are to be met, either the budget of the National Science Foundation will have to be increased much faster than is currently envisioned (probably of the order of 30 percent a year or more) or the responsibility of the mission-oriented agencies for graduate research training as such will have to be more explicitly recognized in national budgeting.

## III. *Criteria for the Support of Various Fields of Basic Research in Universities*

A great deal has been written recently about criteria for support of various fields of basic science. I have already indicated that the small percentage of scientists representing the most talented and creative people should essentially be supported to do whatever they think best, within the financial limits indicated previously, since their own self-directed efforts are likely to be more useful to society than anything anybody of lesser talent could think of asking them to do. However, the people I am talking about probably represent only a small fraction (of the order of 5 percent) of those capable of doing competent and significant basic and applied research. The question of criteria, then, applies only to the activities of these less-than-top people. Even in this area it is my belief that the criteria are considerably less important than who applies them, that the fundamental problem of resource allocation within basic research is who makes the important decisions and how they are made. For example, to what extent should the cutting up of the pie among fields be left exclusively to the scientific community? At what level of detail should the financial decisions be made by the people not actually doing the work? Should resources be allocated to institutions and then divided within the institutions, or should they be allocated to broad fields and then divided within the field with the aid of representative groups of experts entirely from within the field regardless of institutional affiliation? To what degree should the system of choice be mixed, that is, with all allocation partly by institution and partly by field? If mixed, what are the proper proportions? What kind of guidelines should expert advisory committees be given? What kind of criteria, if any, apart from intrinsic scientific merit should be used? Should the definition of intrinsic scientific merit be left implicit rather than explicit — as something that every competent scientist knows intuitively but cannot express? To what extent should judgments in special fields be left entirely to the specialists in those fields, and to what extent should the judgment of fellow scientists from neighboring fields be brought to bear?

In trying to answer these questions, I should like to try to describe an idealized resource-allocation system for basic research. In doing this I am concerned primarily with university basic research, which for purposes of this discussion, however, should include major installations outside of universities, such as Brookhaven, Green Bank, or Kitt Peak, insofar as they exist primarily to serve the university community.

For the purposes of this discussion I feel that research funds should be placed in the following general classifications, which are quite separate conceptually if not organizationally:

1) The capital costs of major equipment, including in general the cost of properly housing it. By major equipment I mean the kind of equipment that would not ordinarily be provided on a research grant. The amount of money involved might vary from field to field, but I am thinking of something at least of the order of several hundred thousand dollars. In general, I have in mind really major facilities like oceanographic ships, the Mohole platform, space tracking stations, or particle accelerators. This category would include the costs of any major refurbishing or updating of such equipment.

2) That part of the operating costs of major facilities or equipment needed to make them available to the scientific community, exclusive of the cost of specific scientific work. This would include such items as ship-operating costs in oceanography, the costs of power, expendable supplies, maintenance personnel, and resident operating staff for big accelerators, the costs of computers, the logistic costs of scientific space vehicles including the cost of procurement, launching, and tracking of a given vehicle, but exclusive of the cost of the instrument package and data analysis and interpretation.

3) The strictly scientific costs, including small permanent and expendable equipment, salaries of technical personnel, computer charges where the computer is shared by many users, publication costs, general administrative overhead, etc.

In my opinion the budgets for items (1) and (2) should be rather carefully segregated from (3). Together, they constitute what Professor Kistiakowsky has referred to in his paper as "big science." The decisions regarding allocations under (1) are the only decisions regarding allocations between fields of science that should be made at the highest levels of government, e.g., by the Bureau of the Budget and the Congress or by the agency head. They should be made with the advice of the scientific community, but it should be recognized that they are inevitably quasi-political decisions. They are the basic investment decisions of the Federal Government, and they are the decisions that determine the scientific priorities for many years ahead. They are also the decisions in which the price of error is highest. In general, science-allocation decisions are less crucial because there are many investigators working independently in the same general area, and so mistakes in the decisions of one investigator tend to be compensated for by the successes of others, and the proposal-evaluation system gradually eliminates the unsuccessful ideas and investigators by a sort of free market of ideas. For the big projects involving many investigators, however, choices are much more irretrievable, and there is often no way of telling whether an alternative choice would have been better until a substantial investment has been made. For example, if the recommendations of the various panels on high-energy physics with respect to what machines should be built prove wrong, the consequence could be the loss of United States leadership in this field for a generation. Even if the Government were prepared to retrieve the mistake by writing off the original investment and building a new machine at greatly increased expense, the time lost might be a serious setback to United States leadership. With respect to science these are the same sorts of crucial decisions as the choice of an intercontinental ballistic missile system is for the preservation of national security. They are the fundamental strategic decisions of basic science, and for them criteria something like those proposed by Weinberg seem appropriate. In this regard I second the views expressed by Kistiakowsky in his paper. They should be widely debated in the scientific community and elsewhere from every angle; they should ultimately be made in a highly visible and public way.

When the decisions in category (1) are made, their consequences in terms of category (2) should be clearly spelled out and understood, and should form part of the basis of the decision as to whether to go ahead. In projecting research budgets into the future, category (2) funds should be separately identified as such. In many cases, it would be wisest if they were not included in the ordinary individual research proposal, although this is an administrative question that may have to be decided in each individual case. It is my feeling however, that the inclusion of fixed availability charges in individual research proposals tends greatly to confuse and complicate the proposal-evaluation process. In many cases it may be desirable to divide the availability charges between two budgets, with only a nominal charge to the individual research proposal.

Category (1) decisions also have implications for category (2) funds. It would make little sense to build facilities if support were not available for scientists to use them. On the other hand, I feel that scientific work with large facilities should not receive a specious priority just because of the political embarrassment entailed by lack of full utilization of a facility. Actually, once the commitment for the capital cost of facilities and their basic operating costs has been made, individual scientific experiments done with such facilities should compete on an equal basis in terms of scientific merit with other work that does not employ large facilities. Conversely, once the commitment to build and operate a facility has been made, I do not believe meritorious scientific work should be penalized before evaluation panels by having to bear the full category (2) costs related to the facility.

The above discussion takes care of category (1) and category (2) costs. The budgeting process should attempt to arrive at an overall Government-wide level for category (3) costs in universities. This will, of course, be a sum of agency budgets, and each agency will be expected to project its category (3) costs as a budget line item. In the National Science Foundation budget, for example, this would be approximately the basic research support category, although certain of the category (2) costs of particle accelerators and oceanographic ships might be excluded and budgeted under another category, and, as detailed below, certain other program costs might be included. The category (3) part of the total Federal budgets – the part for university research, that is – should then be evaluated against the 15-percent-a-year growth standard mentioned earlier. I am not saying that we must have 15-percent growth every year, or that we should limit ourselves to 15-percent growth in each year. Obviously, no part of the Federal budget can be sacred, and the amount of each category can be determined only in the light of the state of the economy, fiscal policy, tax revenues, and other global considerations. I am saying only that the 15-percent growth of category (3) Government-wide should provide a more adequate index than we now have of how we are doing in research support. Because of the confusion of "science" with category (1) and (2) expenses, which merely build the store and keep it open but don't sell any goods, our present system of budgeting doesn't tell us how much science we are buying.

At this point one must decide how to allocate the money in category (3) between disciplines and institutions. There appear to be several bases for this. Since the level of support in category (3) is being compared against a standard derived from the requirements of graduate and post-doctoral education, it ought to include not only basic research support funds, but also fellowship funds, general research support funds, and some proportion of science development funds, institutional base grants, and research training grants. In other words, it ought to include the total funds being channeled into higher education by the Federal Government that are related primarily to research and research training, as opposed to capital investment, and to graduate and post-doctoral research training or undergraduate research activities as opposed to formal teaching activities or curriculum development.

Taking the total of category (3) we now have the question of how it should be divided among the following categories of support:

(a) Project grants to individual professors or small groups of professors;

(b) Programmatic or coherent area grants to large groups or whole departments;

(c) Institutional grants, either on the basis of a formula or on the basis of specific selection criteria;

(d) Direct support of personnel, including graduate and post-doctoral fellowships, faculty fellowships, or career research awards, awarded on the basis of national competition;

(e) Direct support of personnel, but at the decision of the institution rather than on the basis of national competition between individuals in a discipline.

In this listing, the operative question is whether selection is on the basis of national competition within a discipline, or is primarily cross-disciplinary with award to institutions on either a formula or competitive basis. (a), (b), and (d) are regarded as falling in the first category, (c) and (e) in the second. My own present belief is that the country has a bit overdone the matter of project support, to the point where many institutions have abnegated their responsibility for and influence over their own research activities and institutional development. Therefore, I would be inclined to recommend a gradual transition to a situation in which about 25 percent of category (3) is direct support of personnel, category (d); about 25 percent is institutional support, categories (e) and (c); and about 50 percent project support [including both (a) and (b)]. It seems to me the exact division between (a) and (b) is a matter for individual agency decision and negotiation with grantee institutions. It may well vary from agency to agency. As nearly as one can determine, the fiscal year 1963 figures corresponding to the recommendation above are as follows:

*Percent*

| | |
|---|---|
| Direct research and development support (including project and coherent area or program grants and contracts) | 68 |
| Institutional program (NSF institutional base grants and NIH general research support) | 10 |
| Training (including fellowships, training grants, career awards, and post-doctoral fellowships) | 16 |
| Construction | 6 |

This still leaves open the question of allocation to disciplines. This presents no problem with regard to category (c) above, since the allocation is largely up to the institution. With respect to categories (d) and (e) I tend to be opposed, in principle, to too closely defined categorical fellowships such as those offered by the National Aeronautics and Space Administration and the Atomic Energy Commission. My observation is that students are cannier in choosing the right fields than any government administrator, and that, by and large, it is best to support the brightest people and let them choose the most promising and exciting fields, relying on the competitive salesmanship of different disciplines and the external scientific labor market to determine the actual allocation indirectly. In practice, the flexibility with which the National Aeronautics and Space Administration traineeships have been administered has apparently so far avoided what might ultimately prove to be a difficult and embarrassing problem.

If our policy is essentially to support the brightest people irrespective of field, then both government and the universities must give more attention to systematic presentation of the opportunities and promise of various fields, not only in terms of intellectual excitement but also with respect to occupational demand and social utility. I suggest that this method is superior to providing categorical fellowship support for rather narrowly defined fields. Obviously, the method of allocation on the basis of merit without reference to field is an ideal that can only be approached because of the limitations under which the mission-oreinted agencies work. It might well be that some government-wide pooling of fellowship applications would be worth considering in this connection.

With respect to categories (a) and (b) there will obviously be variations from agency to agency. My feeling is that, to the degree it is consistent with the agency's mission, each agency should allocate support in accordance with its estimate of the requirements of the academic community, as judged by proposal pressure and the informal advice of its program officers and consultants. Intrinsic scientific merit should be the most heavily weighted but by no means the only criterion of selection, with each agency supporting projects having a distribution of topics centered about those most closely related to its mission, but by no means confined to these. Application of this principle may actually force some gradual reallocation of resources. Of all the Federal agencies, the National Science Foundation is the one that has the clearest obligation to respond primarily to the estimated needs of the academic community. There is, of course, a good deal of positive feedback between known availability of funds and proposal pressure. It is necessary to invent mechanisms to discount such effects. In this connection, widely representative advisory panels extending over several different disciplines, such as the divisional committees of the

National Science Foundation or the institute advisory councils of the National Institutes of Health, must play a key role. These groups should be made more aware of the total resource-allocation problem, so that they become less inclined to promote only their own fields. Committees of the National Academy of Sciences appointed to analyze the needs of broad scientific fields and coordinated by an overall committee such as the Committee on Science and Public Policy should also play a key role in this connection. Federal agencies concerned primarily with civilian applied research should take more initiative in requesting that appropriate kinds of research be encouraged by the National Science Foundation.

There is a general problem with respect to research support and research priorities that deserves mention at this point. One aspect of it is discussed in the paper by Dr. Teller. One of the unfortunate sideeffects of the generous support of university research in the last ten years has been a tendency to denigrate the intellectual respectability of applied research. Perhaps this has always been present in the basic research community, but the size and influence of this community has reached the point where its viewpoints affect the self-image of applied scientists, engineers, and doctors, and especially the attitudes of young people toward their future careers. The generous support for academic basic research recommended in this and other papers in this series is predicated on the assumption that the healthy development of applied science and technology requires the continual infusion of people trained in basic research. Thus, to an increasing degree, many people trained in universities will be expected to move gradually into more applied areas as their careers mature. If the effect of their university training is to inculcate attitudes that make it too difficult for students to move into applied work, much of the benefit of their training will be lost to society and the justification for public support of basic research in connection with graduate education may ultimately be called into question. It is doubtful whether the long-term influence of university viewpoints on the attitudes and careers of students is as serious or as permanent as is sometimes represented. Basic research support outside of universities has been increasing rapidly at a time when the supply of new Ph. D.'s was relatively constant from year to year. As a result the opportunities for students trained in basic research to stay in basic research have been greater than ever before. This appears to be especially true in physics and biology. In chemistry, where the supply of Ph. D.'s is much larger in relation to the demand, a career in applied work is generally more acceptable. Looking toward the next decade, it appears that the situation in physics will tend to become much more like that of chemistry. I believe that the changing job market will tend to moderate the attitude of students. Still, I am in agreement with Professor Teller that there is a serious need to improve the intellectual status of applied work. This is most likely to occur when first-rate people go into applied work and provide the heroes or models that inspire youngsters. Experience shows that it is very difficult to make any intellectual activity respectable by definition, as opposed to example.

With regard to selection criteria for basic research proposals, I should like to suggest the following in approximate order of priority. Obviously, the relative importance of these criteria will vary between the National Science Foundation and the mission-oreinted agencies:

1) Quality of the people proposing the research, evaluated on the basis of their past performance as judged by their professional peers and by people in adjacent disciplines. In this instance, one must be careful to avoid development of a "closed system," since those who are supported will tend to acquire a reputation that will facilitate acquisition of more support. For this reason it is particularly important that the support system provide adequately for the support of new investigators.

2) Novelty, prospects for new generalizations or important changes in outlook, and degree of penetration into important and previously unexplored territory. In this connection, emphasis must be placed on the importance of new tools. Almost every new research tool has opened up unexpected richness of phenomena. No matter how tight research budgets become, it would be dangerous to forego the construction of really new research tools. Emphasis in research support should be on achieving new understanding or generalizations, and not merely the assembling of new data for their own sake. Measurements should be informed by hypotheses or expectations.

3) Relevance to recognized practical problems, assuming there is a reasonable prospect of progress. This criterion must be applied with caution and good judgment. Applied too narrowly and unimaginatively it can result in the support of rather trivial and pedestrian research. There is always a tendency to support applied research projects that are really basic research, but whose intrinsic scientific merit does not make them competitive with other basic research proposals. To the degree that relevance to practical problems is claimed as a basis of support, certain hard questions should be asked. What is a solution to the problem worth? How critical is a particular piece of information to the solution? What is the probability of success? What is the probability of unanticipated development or byproducts? In answering these questions, the advice of people with experience in the practical problems involved should be sought, as

well as the advice of people concerned only with the intrinsic scientific merit of the work.

4) Educational value, in both the strict sense and in the broader sense of extending the capabilities of bright people or groups of people. Will the research tend to stretch the limits of an existing technology that is likely to have other applications? Will it exploit a new technology not previously available as a basic research tool? Will it help maintain a standby capability in terms of people whose activities may become nationally critical in the future, as in the nuclear weapons laboratories? Will it help train graduate students, and enhance our resources for graduate education?

The preceding discussion has been concerned primarily with the criteria that should be used in allocating resources to basic and applied research in universities as well as to fellowships and other forms of support that indirectly subsidize research. The criteria suggested apply not only to what Dr. Kistiakowsky discussed as "little science," but also to "big science" insofar as it is primarily connected to universities and graduate education. In the area of academic research the emphasis is on the autonomy of science and on primarily scientific criteria of choice, although certainly other considerations such as potential relevance to the mission of the supporting agency must be given significant weight. However, it must be recalled that less than 50 percent of all the basic research supported by the Federal Government is conducted in universities proper. We must now discuss the criteria for support of basic research that is not connected with graduate education.

## IV. *Institutional Research*

The term "institutional research" is designed to cover a broad spectrum of activities ranging from university-based research institutes to industrial laboratories. Basically it is characterized by the fact that the great majority of the scientists are full-time career research workers not engaged in classroom teaching. As pointed out above, the social ecology of these institutions differs from that of universities proper, and judgments concerning their support should be based on different criteria. Institutes of this sort can be further subdivided into two types:

1) Those primarily concerned with basic research, having the aim of advancing some generally defined broad area of scientific knowledge, or perhaps a group of such areas, but usually connected by some common theme or object of study.

2) Those primarily concerned with an applied objective usually related to the mission or missions of some Federal agency.

Sometimes a single laboratory may combine both functions in some degree; for our purposes it should then be considered as two separate institutions. The great national and Government laboratories usually fall in category (2), as do industrial laboratories. The only exceptions are laboratories like Brookhaven, the Green Bank Radio Astronomy Observatory, or the Kitt Peak Observatory. These are really extensions of university research. They have a service function in relation to universities, but their career research staffs are independent scientists in their own right. In a sense, however, they still serve an instructional function in that they help train graduate students and faculty members and post-doctoral associates in the newest techniques of their science. They can also undertake research problems demanding greater continuity and cooperative effort than is possible in a university department with other responsibilities. The basic research laboratories in category (1) should not be judged by the same criteria as those used in connection with universities. In the first place, as Dr. Kistiakowsky has suggested in his paper, greater scientific productivity should be expected of such groups, since they do not have other responsibilities. In the second place, they should truly serve their function of supplementing and assisting the universities; the resident staffs should not be so large as to preempt the facilities for their own experiments. It seems to me that in periods of limited research funds the expansion of such institutes should have lower priority than the expansion of university-based research, which is more closely related to teaching. The local management should be given great freedom and should be promised continuity of support but not necessarily continually expanding support. The creation and support of such institutes ought to be based on general criteria for the support of various fields of "big" science along the lines suggested by Dr. Weinberg. In terms of quality, such institutions ought to be subjected to standards similar to those applied to university groups. Insofar as they carry out independent basic research, such institutions ought to concentrate on types of research requiring special facilities, an unusually programmatic or long-term type of approach involving the closely coordinated activities of many senior scientists, or other basic research activities that are unsuitable for the individualistic style of university research. Conversely, universities should concentrate on types of research that lend themselves to the individualistic approach.

Most of the great national laboratories fall in category (2), i.e., they have an applied mission. It is entirely right and proper that such laboratories should do a substantial amount of basic research, since experience shows that participation in basic research enables them to attract better people, to keep their staffs alert to new scientific developments of potential importance to their missions, and generally to perform better. However, the total support for such establishments should be based on the national importance of their applied missions and on their long-run success in performance. The fraction of support that goes into basic research should be largely a local management decision. On the other hand, such a laboratory should not receive increased support for basic research purely on the basis of the excellence of its scientific work or the number of papers published by its staff in reputable scientific journals. These may be indications of the general quality of the laboratory, but are not enough by themselves to justify its support. If this policy is followed, increased support for freewheeling research activities should be provided essentially as a reward for success in the performance of the applied mission, thus serving to give the whole staff a stake in the applied goals of the organization rather than setting up a status system in the laboratory that isolates the basic research from the rest of the laboratory. The so-called "independent research" supported by several agencies as part of the overhead on procurement contracts with profit organizations contains such a built-in incentive for success in its applied objectives, and a somewhat similar incentive system might be encouraged with respect to non-profit institutions doing applied work.

A special problem has arisen in connection with support of basis research by the Federal Government in industrial laboratories. Not only do many agencies support project contracts with industrial laboratories on a somewhat similar basis as that applied to project grants to university groups, but whole laboratories exist primarily by performing research services for Federal agencies. Some of this project activity represents excellent scientific work. On the other hand, there is a real question in my mind whether the basic research project contract is the proper mechanism for supporting industrial groups. This is especially true when research proposals from these groups are evaluated primarily on the basis of intrinsic scientific interest or merit rather than on the basis of their potential contribution to a specific applied objective. It is hard to lay down hard-and-fast rules in this matter, but, in general, it is my opinion that institutional-type support is preferable for industrial groups. In this type of support the basic research is supported by the local management as part of a general program aimed at an applied objective. Government laboratories and federally supported research centers also occasionally attempt to supplement the support from their parent agencies by seeking basic research contracts with other Government agencies in competition with academic research groups. In principle, this is undesirable; I would be strongly opposed, however, to blanket rules or regulations concerning it, and it would be unwise to alter abruptly the system of support that has grown up over the years. Such a sudden change would be unnecessarily disruptive. I feel, however, that this is a general area that the Congress may wish to examine, and that agencies now supporting industrial and Federal laboratories under small project grants and contracts should be encouraged to devise new support mechanisms more consonant with the institutional character of these organizations. The extent of this type of project support is not known at present, but it has an open-ended character that could make it a potential drain on tight basic research budgets if it were not carefully watched.

Occasionally, it is advantageous for agencies to make contracts with industrial organizations with a view to exploiting unique industrial skills in getting rather specific jobs done, usually in relation to some broader applied program or to provide needed tools or materials for university basic research. Examples might be the growing of crystals for experimental purposes or the development of new research equipment for which the potential market may be insufficient to justify private financing of the development costs. I have no criticism of contracts of this type.

## V. *Concluding Comments*

The basic thesis of this paper adds up to the conclusion that the concept of a total science budget, which is implied by the questions asked by the House committee, is probably not a very meaningful or significant one. Only in the restricted area of academic basic research does the concept of a government-wide "science budget" make a certain amount of sense. Even here it is essential to separate out the costs of major equipment—both the capital costs and the cost of keeping it available for the use of the scientific community. The rest of the "science budget" ought to be considered in a different context, in which the value of research and development is judged in competition with alternative means of achieving the same objectives. In these areas I think that the Congress and the administration ought to consider primarily the total resources that it is worthwhile to devote to a general objective, and then regard as tactical rather than strategic the decision as to what fraction of these resources should go into research and development. Inevitably, such decisions are quasi-political and must be settled by debate among the various groups concerned; the voice of the scientists should be heard but should not be conclusive in this part of the debate. Basic research outside of universities—more than 50 percent of the total—should be judged in terms of its potential contribution to the missions of specific agencies.

NOTES

1 Some scientists may derive
their support through working
in close association with the
outstanding 5 percent; thus it
is not legitimate to extrapolate
the $100 million for the 5 per-
cent to $2 billion for the total
pool.

# 15

# Knowledge and Power

## Science in the Service of Society

PHILIP H. ABELSON

AT PLATTSBURGH today we pause on a new threshold of man's destiny. A new institution is evolving here, and part of it, the fine new science building, is the immediate reason for our presence. Such an occasion is a time for stocktaking. Where are we heading? How will this developing college and its facilities fit into the world of tomorrow? In the course of my talk I intend to enumerate some of the challenges that can be foreseen. But I believe that we can grasp the spirit of the future more firmly if we approach it from the perspective of the past and the present. Then we will see that one word characterizes our present civilization. It is change. Further analysis shows that this century has witnessed an increased rate of change, and that the prime force in this new development has been science.

A few centuries ago Western society was static and authoritarian. The individual—his needs and aspirations—was of secondary importance. The obligation of the individual was to accept the world as it was. Disease, hunger, drudgery, indignity, natural calamities, war—these were man's portion. There was little hope that man himself might change his world.

Change was slow in coming. But with the Renaissance and the Reformation, men in all walks of life began to question the established order. In science, Copernicus and Galileo overturned a fixed image of the universe and the earth's relation to it. Later Isaac Newton developed the laws that dominated physics for two centuries

PHILIP H. ABELSON *is the director of the Carnegie Institution's Geophysical Laboratory and the editor of* Science. *This address was delivered at the dedication of a new science facility at State University College, Plattsburgh, New York, on April 24, 1965.*

and served as a springboard to modern science. Men glimpsed the glory of the free pursuit of truth; they gained faith in their power to learn through observation; their eyes lifted to new horizons.

The leaders of the Enlightenment in America, the architects of our freedom, were men who understood and practiced the unity of learning. To them, the new science was one of the humanities, important to the intellectual equipment of the educated man. Their convictions were expressed in Thomas Jefferson's assertion that "knowledge is power, knowledge is safety, knowledge is happiness."

Benjamin Franklin was a man of astonishing versatility. Among his many distinctions is that he was a great scientist. His research in electricity was one of the triumphs of human intellect. Franklin also had a keen awareness of the future role of science in human affairs. Let me quote a striking passage from a letter he wrote in 1780:

> The rapid progress true science now makes occasions my regretting sometimes that I was born too soon. It is impossible to imagine the height to which may be carried, in a thousand years, the power of man over matter. We may perhaps learn to deprive large masses of their gravity, and give them absolute levity, for the sake of easy transport. Agriculture may diminish its labor and double its produce; all diseases may by sure means be prevented or cured, not excepting even that of old age, and our lives lengthened at pleasure even beyond the antediluvian standard. O that moral science were in as fair a way of improvement, that men would cease to be wolves to one another, and that human beings would at length learn what they improperly call humanity!

Thomas Jefferson was one of the most articulate spokesmen of the period of the Enlightenment. He had an unfaltering faith in man's essential goodness, in his ability to learn and, through learning, to improve himself materially, morally, and spiritually. To Jefferson, science was an essential part of the life of an educated man. He himself was a talented botanist and paleontologist, and he had a deep interest in archeology, astronomy, cartography, meteorology, ethnology, geology, mineralogy, horticulture, mathematics, medicine, and zoology.

Those who followed the founding fathers were not nearly so broad in their interests or competence—perhaps because of the times and the needs. During the nineteenth century and the early part of the twentieth the challenges were the western frontier and the exploitation of the wealth of this land. These needs coincided with the Industrial Revolution, and as a result the nation was oriented toward doing rather than thinking. Science became identified with gadgetry, and so in the popular mind it remains today. In our emphasis on doing we were remarkably successful, and our inventors prepared the way for the affluent society. About forty years ago some of the visionary industrial corporations like General Electric began exploiting science purposefully. Since that time science has contributed even more importantly to industrial advances. It has also become essential to better health, to our position in international trade, and to our defense and safety. During the last two decades research and development have become crucial to the nation's economy. Our increasing abundance almost universally rests on science. We often note statements by company officers that a large fraction of their business is in products that did not exist ten years ago and that have come out of the laboratories. All of you could name some of the products, but let me remind you of just a few of the developments of the last twenty-five years: the wonder drugs; tranquilizers; polio vaccine; synthetic rubber; foamed plastics; new fibers; synthetic adhesives; synthetic gems; paints and corrosion-resistant coatings; high-fidelity sound reproduction; television; new methods of printing and reproduction, such as Xerox; color photography and almost instantaneous photography; transistors; magnetic tape; new materials like pure titanium, tantalum, and zirconium; nuclear reactors; nuclear-powered submarines; jet aircraft, artificial earth satellites; the electronic computer.

Benjamin Franklin was a wise and imaginative scholar, but even his vision was limited. He spoke of doubling the produce of agriculture. Much more than that has been accomplished. In the United States at the time of the American Revolution it was necessary for about 90 percent of the people to be engaged in agriculture if sufficient food was to be produced. Today only about 7 percent of the population are so engaged, and the fraction is dropping.

One of the most profound changes that science has brought is in life expectancy. To persons living today in the United States this development may not seem dramatic. However, those living in certain countries of the world are all too aware of the grim aspects attending a life expectancy of thirty. Nevertheless, many who are here can remember a time when even in this country life was uncertain. I can recall from my own youth the sadness which which we attended the funeral of a playmate. An only child, he was intelligent and handsome. He was struck down by a disease that modern medicine handles routinely. I remember another family of small children suddened rendered motherless by a disease that today is only a nuisance. In the small community in which I lived four contemporaries were struck by polio. One died; three survived, but with crippling deformities. Modern medicine has now eliminated many hazards for the individual. Other serious medical problems, like cancer and mental disease, remain, of course, but they too will yield at least in part to the advances made possible by science.

Science and technology have made outstanding contributions to our economic strength on the international scene. We are able to maintain a position of prestige and influence because we can devote large sums to foreign aid and to the support of military forces abroad. Although we do have some problems with the gold drain and with balance of payments, the situation would be completely impossible were it not for our strength in producing research-intensive products derived from laboratory studies. In the period January to September 1962, for example, the value of exports of synthetic fibers and goods made from them, and of chemicals and related products, reached the annual rate of $1.9 billion, while the corresponding value of imports was $0.5 billion. Other contributors to our favorable balance of trade included industrial machinery, electrical apparatus, and aircraft. All together, research-intensive products were exported at the rate of $10.5 billion while the rate for corresponding imports was $2.2 billion.

As I am sure that most of you realize how heavily our nation depends on science and technology for its security, I shall not dwell on the defense aspect. However, the necessity of bringing every potential talent to the service of the nation during World War II set in motion a series of events that has affected developments since then.

With World War II a great change in the support of science began. Large-scale, militarily oriented research projects were established in connection with a number of universities. There were at least two reasons for this. The academic community was a chief reservoir of initiative and scientific talent; and universities had both the organization and the good name desirable in a sponsor for the expenditure of large sums of money. Among the many university-based enterprises leading to useful military hardware during World War II were the development of radar techniques in the Radiation Laboratory at MIT; the participation in atomic bomb development by the universities of California and Chicago and by Columbia University; proximity fuse work at the Johns Hopkins University; and rocket propulsion at California Institute of Technology. All these programs contributed crucial technological advances and were decisive in giving us advantages in weapons capabilities. The atomic bomb came late in the war and did not have so much effect on the course of the conflict as some of the other weapons had, but the detonation at Hiroshima was dramatic enough to leave the average man with a profound impression of the power of science. All too soon the Cold War began, and with it the fear that an enemy might make important discoveries faster than we. The stage was set for the massive support of scientific research in this country. After World War II, one of the major areas in which there was large-scale increase in the support of academic research was the field of biology and medicine. It was a natural outgrowth of popular belief in the magical capabilities of science. If man could manufacture an atomic bomb, surely he could reduce heart disease, conquer mental illness, and cure cancer. The Congress is made up of men in an age group in which disease is a familiar menace. They are inclined to favor advances in medicine.

In view of the wartime accomplishments at universities it was almost inevitable that government efforts to encourage more research should focus on academic institutions. Various mechanisms for the distribution of funds (including outright grants and contracts) were devised and employed. The total sums allocated for such purposes expanded rapidly, doubling approximately every four years during the period 1947–1963. Today, nonprofit institutions — mainly universities — receive about $1.5 billion annually from the government. Consequently, research activity has burgeoned. There are more working scientists, and more creative output, than ever before. If we look objectively at our status in all branches of science this nation's emergence as an international leader is abundantly evident.

Awards of Nobel Prizes furnish an important measure of outstanding accomplishments. In the first thirty years of this century, Americans received only four of ninety-two awards. In the decade 1951 to 1960, men in this country received twenty-seven of fifty-two.

Another measure of recognition is the eagerness with which foreign students seek opportunities for research in the United States. Loss of British scientists to this nation has been so marked as to become a political issue in the United Kingdom. In part, this movement of scientists has been motivated by the availability of funds, bur really first-class men, when choosing a position, give most weight to excellence of association. Hence, Britain's anxieties are a high form of praise of our status in research activities.

From this sketch of the impact of science and technology we see that many crucial segments of our life and of society are now dependent on the fruits of research and development. The impacts are likely to increase. It has become national policy to support research development on a large scale. It has become national policy to create knowledge. Therefore, large numbers of scientists are being supported. Indeed, 90 percent of all the scientists who have ever lived are living today. They are hard-working scholars, provided with excellent facilities and equipment. They are producing knowledge at an unprecedented rate. As a result of the application of this knowledge, civilization will be changed. What are the trends in research, and how are they likely to affect mankind?

One of the most active research areas today is solid-state physics.

Out of such work came the transistor, and then masers and lasers. The transistor seems almost like a piece of magic. A small chip of pure solid material can control an electric current in much the way that radio tubes do. More recently, the magic has increased, for now complex electric circuits can be encompassed in a tiny bit of material. This work is progressing rapidly at present. The masers and lasers also open new opportunities. The laser is particularly useful; it produces monochromatic light that can be sharply focused. Lasers have already been used in medicine, in the repair of detached retinas, for instance. They are likely to be used in long-distance communication both on earth and in space. Laser beams have been bounced off the moon and detected back on earth. Communication with other solar systems will probably be via laser beams.

Another remarkable development is in the field of super-conductors. At low temperature certain conductors have been found to carry electricity with no loss. This discovery could make the long-distance transmission of power practicable. Moreover, new materials have been developed that are superconductors in the presence of a large magnetic field, opening up all kinds of new technical possibilities.

A great improvement in global communication is now as good as guaranteed. The communication satellites will permit transmission of telephone messages and television programs. Eventually the cost of both services will decrease markedly. Eventually, also, it will become possible to dial numbers between continents.

Automation and computers, already important, will have even greater significance in the future. Computers are taking over more and more clerical tasks. They are serving as essential management tools. They are being incorporated as remarkably good methods of controlling manufacturing processes. Their use in information retrieval and indexing is likely to be important. Beyond that, new computers are likely to be designed for maximum effectiveness in specific applications. Employed in scientific efforts such computers would facilitate new discoveries.

Most people are aware of the promise of nuclear energy. Not so many know how far and successfully the possibilities are being exploited. Electrical energy can now be produced from the atom less expensively than it can be generated from coal. Cheap energy, therefore, can be made available almost anywhere in the world, not just near cheap fossil fuels. The cost of nuclear energy is steadily being reduced. Developments in progress will make it even less expensive and far more abundant. With very low-cost power, applications like the desalting of sea water become feasible.

Chemistry is continuing to discover new useful chemicals such as plastics and finding new ways of rearranging molecules. Out of these efforts will come improvements in food, clothing, shelter, and almost every familiar object of everyday life. Chemistry will be applied in many ways in the study of other scientific problems. Purer solid chemicals, for example, may well lead to new solid-state devices. One challenging subject for investigation is our own planet. It will be studied by both chemical and physical means.

The chemistry of the earth constitutes an important field, with many discoveries to be made. The earth itself is a huge laboratory in which chemical changes are constantly occurring. These changes lead to unusual concentrations of large quantities of relatively rare elements to form economically valuable ore deposits. Our understanding of the processes involved is still primitive. Hidden ore deposits pose a challenge to the geophysicist to devise better means of locating them. Man must forever be interested in the study of the earth; economic necessity alone guarantees that. The earth is one of our great resources, and its chemical content must increasingly condition life upon it. Accordingly, man will make every effort to understand the processes that alter composition, not only on the crust but in the deep interior as well. Great mystery lies there, for the depth to which man can send exploratory equipment is limited. Yet he will continue to probe by geophysical methods, including seismologic investigations. A major untapped potentiality is study of the rocks under the ocean bottom. These rocks, representing 70 percent of the area of the earth, have scarcely been looked at. The recently successful Mohole drilling indicates that it is technically feasible for man to drill into the bottom of the ocean, even in the deepest of water, and to bring back cores for study. Such cores could reveal much about the past history of life, could help settle the question of continental drift, and might well lead to considerable economic opportunities.

Of great possible significance are materials on the deep-sea floor. Among them are manganese nodules (nominally worth $45 to $100 a ton), which contain not only manganese but such other elements as copper, cobalt, nickel, molybdenum, vanadium, zinc, and zirconium. The total reserves of these nodules have been estimated to be $10^{12}$ tons. To put a value on these reserves would be meaningless, but clearly a resource of fantastic magnitude is involved. To exploit it will require more information about the distribution of the nodules and a better understanding of their composition as a function of the ocean region in which they occur— as well as initiative in the development of practical harvesting techniques.

On the continental shelves are also potentially valuable mineral concentrations that have received little attention, including placer deposits of drowned beaches. Diamond-bearing gravels off the coast of southwest Africa are an example. Recently, substantial quantities of gold-bearing sands have been found in sea areas off Alaska. Tin ores have been found off Malaysia, and magnetite-rich sands are being mined near Japan.

In addition, oil and gas of the continental shelves are now being exploited, in the Gulf of Mexico and off California, for example. And the rocks underlying the North Sea, which are being intensively explored, give promise of yielding a rich harvest of natural gas. I feel certain that the next twenty years will bring increased widespread exploitation of the oceans and the ocean floor. Indeed, the vast resources under the ocean are likely to become the next great cause of international controversy.

Another development of high significance is likely to arise in the field of weather modification. I believe that weather modification is already possible, not on a local but on a global scale. During the last century, man has appreciably changed the composition of the planetary atmosphere through the burning of fuels. In the past twenty years, the rate of alteration of the environment has increased strikingly. Man's potential capacity to change his planet has increased even more and is likely to continue to increase.

The temperature of the earth is controlled by the balance between the energy received from the sun and that lost back into space. Visible light passes through the atmosphere to the surface of the earth, where some of it is absorbed, heating the ground. This energy is reradiated as infrared radiation. The atmosphere is kept warm because substances like carbon dioxide absorb infrared radiation from earth. Carbon dioxide acts like glass in a greenhouse. If its concentration rises, the greenhouse effect is likely to increase, producing a warmer climate.

Another method of influencing the weather is exemplified by an event which occurred in 1883. In that year the volcano Krakatoa erupted with sufficient violence to throw fine dust into the stratosphere, where it reflected the sun's light so that less than the usual intensity of radiation penetrated to the earth. Nearly three years elapsed before part of the dust settled, and during those three years the temperature of the earth was lowered by about a degree. This was the opposite phenomenon to the greenhouse effect. The energy involved in the eruption of Krakatoa, though substantial, was not greater than man could produce by nuclear devices. Indeed, man, if he wished, could drastically lower the temperature of the earth by injecting material into the high atmosphere.

There is a possibility that this will be done inadvertently. I am sure that all of you have seen the contrails of present-day jet planes which are caused when water vapor condenses to form ice crystals. The temperatures at 30,000 feet are usually far below freezing. The future supersonic jets will fly at perhaps 90,000 feet. They will burn large amounts of fuel and will produce corresponding quantities of water vapor. The contrails of supersonic jets will probably be much more voluminous than the trails with which we are familiar. Moreover, the ice crystals will tend to persist. The contrails will gradually spread, and the solar radiation reaching the earth may be attenuated.

I have outlined a number of developments in the physical sciences. Cumulatively, they will be very important. Yet I believe that, on a large overall view, some of the greatest challenges in science today are in biology. With large-scale support and a vast new array of instruments, with the application of chemistry and physics to biology, and with the fine talent that is now devoted to that field, it is certain that biological sciences have some of their most flourishing years of discovery ahead of them.

The area in which most vital advances are being made today is molecular biology. The details of the genetic code are being worked out, though the problem may be more difficult than was anticipated. Very active research is being carried out on the mechanisms by which information in the chromosome is converted into an ordered sequence of amino acids in proteins. Success in this area has stimulated interest in the processes by which the fertilized egg differentiates and grows into an adult animal.

Perhaps the greatest research frontier of our times lies in the investigation of nervous systems, especially of the human mind and the way it functions. There is increasing evidence that leading scientists from many fields are beginning to concentrate on these problems. The area presents difficulties, but its importance guarantees first-class efforts.

Related to the study of the mental process is work in the behavioral sciences. It would be bold to suggest that this field can be conquered by laboratory science, but major contributions will be made, and such tools as electronic devices and computers will be helpful.

Since no one knows what discoveries will be made, it is impossible to outline the practical consequences. We can get an inkling, however. Therefore, I will use a sort of poetic license during the next few moments to sketch some possibilities. Some new experiments indicate that man may find himself in a position to deliberately change the genetic content of developing embryos, possibly for the better. Suppose the bio-sciences succeeded in developing a fetal therapy such that the I.Q. of a person could be raised, say, ten to twenty points. Think what that would mean. A nation would be given an intellectual advantage over its competitors. A 20-point shift would ease the financial (and human-emotional) burden of

the low I.Q.'s and their relatives. If the shift were linear and applied
to the high end of the scale it would give us the biggest push of all—
more creative talent. Ten Einsteins, twenty Fermis, in one generation, and perhaps even a Newton every decade. Possibly this will
be the way to solve multidisciplinary problems; for we all recall
how Fermi could invade a new field and conquer it with his
genius. But even without the contributions of top genius, the production of more creative talent would give us an edge in the science
race.

As another example, consider the possibilities inherent in perfection of a memory-sharpening drug. It is not impossible. Once we
understand the mechanism of data storage and retrieval in the human
brain, we may be able to develop therapeutic aids. The achievement of such possibilities would give man greater power to control
his future, but it would also demand far more wisdom than he has
so far seemed able to supply. Another factor that will influence
biological research is the long-term value to society of abolishing
diseases like cancer and malfunctions like mental illness. The
emotional and financial costs of cancer on a worldwide basis each
year are enormous. Unless further progress is made soon, there are
many in this audience who will go through the emotional trauma of
watching a loved one die of cancer. Having experienced this myself,
I hope you will all be spared. Cures for this disease would be perhaps
the greatest contribution this generation could make to humanity.

I have spoken of some of the products of science and technology
and their effects on society. Let me summarize and provide perspective before proceeding further.

A few hundred years ago, man was little above the other animals.
He was at the mercy of forces he did not understand and could not
control. Today, he is master of his destiny. He has the power to
change his environment even on a planetary scale. To some extent,
he can already control his own evolution. Not content with the vast
powers at his disposal, he has harnessed science as an agent for
further change. The weight of the resources of great nations is
committed to speeding further innovations.

When we attempt to predict the future, our imaginations fail
us. Even so wise a man as Benjamin Franklin, visionary as he was,
underestimated the changes that were to occur. Indeed, the record
of predictions made concerning science and technology has been
one of consistent underestimate. I have little confidence in my own
crystal ball. I believe, however, that part of the future can be
inferred by examining present trends. For instance, the use of computers seems destined to expand, bringing with it far more automation than has been employed thus far. A further harnessing of

science and technology will produce an even more affluent society.

The course of events in the biological and behavioral areas is less predictable. Progress in medicine, however, is certain. What we cannot gauge is the effect of discoveries that will surely be made in genetics and in the study of the human mind.

I believe that the potential for discovery of revolutionary knowledge is great in biology—greater even than in the physical sciences. The tools and the concepts of physics and chemistry will, of course, have important roles in the new findings. There are many unsolved mysteries in biology. I am sure there are many mysteries of which we are not yet even aware. The one safe prediction is that we are destined to learn more about biological and social phenomena, and that the knowledge will give man vastly increased power in managing his destiny.

In my discussion so far I have emphasized the material aspects and products of science. Most observers who view the subject do likewise. Those who are not highly trained in science are likely to have the impression that scientists are essentially a special breed of mechanics. Lost to sight is the vast, beautiful structure of knowledge that has been erected. Lost to sight is the cumulative creative effort of thousands of devoted scholars. Men from every walk of life can appreciate to some degree the great works of art. The Rijksmuseum in Amsterdam, with its "Night Watch," leaves the visitor with an enhanced awareness of the dignity of man. Only a few men realize that the structure of science has been erected by men fully as creative as the greatest artists or poets. Moreover, the creative activity of one great man can be perfected and added to by others. Even individuals of lesser genius can add their smaller but valid share to the total. To those who can form a judgment the greatest significance of science lies in its contribution to the dignity of man. The edifice of knowledge is visible only to those who have knowledge. Others live out their lives half-blind to the world around them. The physicist who knows why the sky is blue sees a bluer, more beautiful sky. The astronomer studying stars a billion light years away perceives special grandeur in the organization of the heavens. The paleontologist stopping at a road cut can identify bones of animals that lived and died 500 million years ago. In his mind he can know the environment in which they lived, can reconstruct their mode of living and their internal anatomy, and can list their enemies. The chemist contemplating the structure of matter can see an aesthetic simplicity in the ordered relationships of more than a million known chemical compounds. He knows that he can, at will, prepare any of these million entities. The biochemist studying living processes sees broad patterns common to men, mice, and microorganisms. He knows that many of the same building blocks are employed in all forms of life.

These examples could be multiplied manyfold. Even so, I could suggest only the most superficial view of the beauty of the edifice of knowledge.

This afternoon, I have hastily reviewed the changing impact of science on human affairs. I have briefly sketched some of its cultural significance. Now I ask how education has responded to these evolving patterns. The answer must be "not vigorously." Indeed, the response has been far more effective in the secondary schools than in the institutions of higher learning. Few colleges are as alert as Plattsburgh in providing an exposure to science. Instead, as science has become more important to society, it has become less a part of the curriculum of so-called liberal education. The tendency was already apparent in the last century to Thomas Huxley, who maintained, and rightly, that a liberally educated person is one capable of making a criticism of life — of evaluating the environment and making enlightened judgments. By Huxley's standards, many of today's graduates are not educated.

I would not advocate trying to make every bright student a scientist. I would not recommend cramming many science courses into every student. But there surely is a better middle ground than we have reached so far. One error should be avoided. Too many science courses for nonscientists are watered-down versions of the beginning course for majors, taught by bored, condescending professors who couldn't care less. A partial solution might be to have educated humanists teach some of the science courses for nonscientists. One approach is by way of the history of science. Today, an increasing number of excellent scholars are addressing themselves to the history and philosophy of science. These men have the potential of developing a new kind of treatment of the relation of science to human affairs.

In the years ahead, science will play an increasingly important role. If the knowledge and power of science are wisely used, a golden age of humanity can be achieved, and maintained. But it is by no means guaranteed. The coin of knowledge and power has another side, namely, responsibility and decisions.

Let us examine a few of the many decisions man will face. Among them will be the problem of what to do with leisure. The talented and the educated will find much of interest to do. They will have agreeable employment and the opportunity to be creative in many ways. But what of the less well endowed? There will be fewer chances for them, fewer ways for them to have a useful role in society. Man's ego will not let him rest. If he is to be content, he must feel that his life has significance, that something he does or something he is has importance. Otherwise, he becomes deeply discontented. If this happens on a large scale, the climate is prepared for riot and anarchy. How are the masses to occupy themselves? Shall it be with bread and circuses, with tranquilizers in the form of alcohol or pills?

A better alternative is education and creative activity of some kind for all. We are already in the midst of a long-term trend toward more years of schooling. Ultimately, it may be desirable for education to continue for most of the individual's life.

We are in the midst of a population explosion made possible by science and technology. Are we to permit the population to increase to the fantastic levels that technology would permit? And what of pollution of the environment?

I have mentioned only a few problems. Many more will arise. Man now has the knowledge and power to shape his future. He cannot escape from the need for decisions. Even the refusal to make judgments and take action is itself a decision.

Who will make the decisions? Will it be a broadly informed electorate, or will it be a narrow oligarchy at the seat of highly centralized power? My feeling is that we are much closer to George Orwell's 1984 than most people realize. In fact, we are about on schedule in arriving there. I believe that we can avoid this catastrophe, but only if we achieve a greater maturity and sense of responsibility in our decision-making. The relationship of society to science has been summed up for us in a dramatic passage by J. Bronowski:

> We live in a world which is penetrated through and through by science. . . . The scholar who disdains science may speak in fun, but his fun is not quite a laughing matter. To think of science as a set of special tricks, to see the scientist as the manipulator of outlandish skills — this is the root of the poison mandrake which flourishes rank in the comic strips. There is no more threatening and no more degrading doctrine than the fancy that somehow we may shelve the responsibility for making the decisions of our society by passing it to a few scientists armored with a special magic . . . the dream of H. G. Wells, in which the tall elegant engineers rule, with perfect benevolence, a humanity which has no business except to be happy . . . is the picture of a slave society and should make us shiver whenever we hear a man of sensibility dismiss science as someone else's concern. The world today is made, it is powered by science; and for any man to abdicate an interest in science is to walk with open eyes towards slavery.[1]

And so we see the question starkly posed. Is man to march erect, conscious of his dignity and proud of the privilege of being part of a great developing culture? Or is he to function like some slave in an ant colony? The question is a close one, but I believe that man has the qualities of greatness that will enable him to avoid the traps of slothfulness and decay.


NOTES

1 J. Bronowski, *Science and Human Values*, New York, 1956, pp. 12–13.

# SELECT BIBLIOGRAPHY

## THE THIRD CULTURE: SCIENCE IN SOCIAL THOUGHT

### General

Aron, Raymond. *War and Industrial Society*. London: Oxford University Press, 1958.

Bacon, Francis. *The New Atlantis*. Edited, with introduction and notes by Alfred B. Gough. Oxford: Clarendon Press, 1924.

Bellamy, Edward. *Looking Backward: 2000–1887*. New York: Modern Library, 1917.

Condorcet, Marie-Jean-A.-N.-C., Marquis de. *Fragment sur l'Atlantide, ou efforts combinés de l'espèce humaine pour le progrès des sciences*, in A. C. O'Connor and M. F. Arago, eds. *Oeuvres de Condorcet*, Vol. 6. Paris: F. Didot frères, 1847.

Dillenberger, John. *Protestant Thought and Natural Science*. Garden City, N.Y.: Doubleday & Co., 1960.

Dubos, René. *The Dreams of Reason: Science and Utopias*. New York: Columbia University Press, 1961.

Hayek, F. A. *The Counter-Revolution of Science: Studies in the Abuse of Reason*. New York: Free Press paperback, 1964.

Himmelfarb, Gertrude. *Darwin and the Darwinian Revolution*. New York: Anchor paperback, 1962.

Huxley, Aldous. *Brave New World*. New York: Bantam paperback, 1955.

———. *Brave New World Revisited*. New York: Harper & Brothers, 1958.

Huxley, Thomas H. "Science and Culture" (1880), in *Science and Education*. New York: P. F. Collier & Son, 1893; Philosophical Library, 1964.

Juenger, Friedrich Georg. *The Failure of Technology: Perfection Without Purpose*. Hinsdale, Ill.: Henry Regnery, 1949.

Lindsay, Robert Bruce. *The Role of Science in Civilization*. New York: Harper & Row, 1963.

Manuel, Frank E. *The New World of Henri Saint-Simon*. Cambridge, Mass.: Harvard University Press, 1956.

Musil, Robert. *The Man Without Qualities*. Translated by E. Wilkins and E. Kaiser. New York: Coward-McCann, 1953–.

Renan, Ernest, *The Future of Science*. London: Chapman & Hall, 1891.

Santillana, Giorgio de. *The Crime of Galileo*. Chicago: University of Chicago Press, 1955; Phoenix paperback, 1963.

Skinner, B. F. *Walden Two*. New York: Macmillan paperback, 1962.

### The "Two Cultures" Controversy

Arnold, Matthew. "Literature and Science," in *Discourses in America*. London: Macmillan & Co., 1885.

Bowling, H. M. "The 'Two Cultures' Are One," *New Scientist*, Vol. VI (December 3, 1959), pp. 1118–1119.

Eisely, Loren. "The Illusion of the Two Cultures," *American Scholar* (Summer 1964), pp. 387–399.

Green, Martin. "Lionel Trilling and the Two Cultures," *Essays in Criticism*, Vol. XIII, No. 4 (October 1963), pp. 375–385.

Huxley, Aldous. *Literature and Science*. New York: Harper & Row, 1963.

Jones, W. T. *The Sciences and the Humanities, Conflict and Reconciliation*. Berkeley: University of California Press, 1966.

Kling, Merle. "The Intellectual: Will He Wither Away?" *New Republic*, Vol. CXXXVI (April 8, 1957), pp. 14–15.

Lakoff, Sanford A. "The Nth Culture Problem," *Bulletin of the Atomic Scientists*, Vol. XX (May 1964), pp. 21–23.

Leavis, F. R. *Two Cultures? The Significance of C. P. Snow*. With an essay on Sir Charles Snow's Rede lecture by Michael Yudkin. New York: Pantheon Books, 1963.

Prior, Moody E. *Science and the Humanities*. Evanston, Ill.: Northwestern University Press, 1962.

Snow, C. P. *The Two Cultures: And A Second Look; An Expanded Version of The Two Cultures and the Scientific Revolution*. New York: Mentor Books, 1964.

Trilling, Lionel. "Science, Literature & Culture: A Comment on the Leavis-Snow Controversy," *Commentary*, Vol. XXXIII, No. 6 (June 1962), pp. 461–477.

## CASES AND CONTROVERSIES

Alexander, William M. "Influences of the Atomic Scientists on the Enactment of the Atomic Energy Act of 1946." Unpublished Ph.D. dissertation, University of Oregon, 1963.

Alsop, Joseph and Stewart. *We Accuse. The Story of the Miscarriage of American Justice in the Case of J. Robert Oppenheimer*. New York: Simon & Schuster, 1954.

Birkenhead, Frederick W. F. S., 2nd Earl of. *The Professor and the Prime Minister*. Boston: Houghton Mifflin, 1962. Another view of relations between Churchill and Lindemann. See also C. P. Snow, *Science and Government*.

Blackett, P. M. S. *Studies of War: Nuclear and Conventional*. New York: Hill & Wang, 1962.

Bylinsky, Gene, and William E. Howard. "The Hot Rocket to Nowhere," *Saturday Evening Post*, Vol. CCXXXVI (November 9, 1963), pp. 78–81. Report on the project to develop a nuclear-powered rocket.

Carper, Edith. *The Reorganization of the Public Health Service*. Indianapolis: Bobbs Merrill, 1965 (Inter-University Case Program series, No. 89).

Carson, Rachel. *Silent Spring*. Boston: Houghton Mifflin, 1962; Crest paperback, 1964.

Clark, Ronald W. *Tizard*. Cambridge, Mass.: MIT Press, 1965. See also Sanford A. Lakoff, "The Tizard Record," *Bulletin of the Atomic Scientists*, Vol. XX, No. 1 (January 1966), pp. 39–41.

Diamond, Edwin. *The Rise and Fall of the Space Age*. Garden City, N.Y.: Doubleday & Co., 1964.

Etzioni, Amitai. *The Moon-Doggle: Domestic and International Implications of the Space Race*. Garden City, N.Y.: Doubleday & Co., 1964.

Fogelman, Edwin. *Hiroshima: The Decision to Use the A-Bomb.* New York: Chas. Scribner's Sons, 1964. Designed to be used as instructional material.

Fox, Irving K. and Isabel Picken. *The Upstream-Downstream Controversy in the Arkansas-White-Red Basins Survey.* University, Ala.: University of Alabama Press, 1960 (Inter-University Case Program series, No. 55).

Friedman, S. "The Rand Corporation and Our Policy Makers," *Atlantic,* Vol. CCXII (September 1963), pp. 61–68.

Groves, Leslie R. *Now It Can Be Told: The Story of the Manhattan Project.* New York: Harper & Row, 1962.

Harris, Richard. *The Real Voice.* New York: The Macmillan Co., 1964. Study of the Kefauver investigation into the drug industry.

Joravsky, David. "The Lysenko Affair," *Scientific American,* Vol. CCVII (November 1962), pp. 41–49.

Jungk, Robert. *Brighter than a Thousand Suns: A Personal History of the Atomic Scientists.* Translated by James Cleugh. New York: Harcourt, Brace & World, 1958; Black Cat paperback, 1962.

Lawrence, Samuel A. *The Battery Additive Controversy.* University, Ala.: University of Alabama Press, 1962 (Inter-University Case Program series, No. 68). Reprinted in Bock, Edwin A., and Alan K. Campbell, eds. *Case Studies in American Government.* Englewood Cliffs, N.J.: Prentice-Hall, 1962.

Leopold, Luna and Thomas Maddox. *The Flood Control Controversy.* New York: Ronald Press, 1954.

Lessing, Lawrence. "Laws Alone Can't Make Drugs Safe," *Fortune,* Vol. LXVII (March 1963), pp. 122–125 ff.

Maass, Arthur A. *Muddy Waters: the Army Engineers and the Nation's Rivers.* Cambridge, Mass.: Harvard University Press, 1951.

Mintz, Morton. *The Therapeutic Nightmare.* Boston: Houghton Mifflin, 1965. Critical view of government supervision of the drug industry.

Moorehead, Alan. *The Traitors: The Double Life of Fuchs, Pontecorvo, and Nunn May.* London: Hamish Hamilton, 1952.

Owens, John R. *A Wildlife Agency and its Possessive Public.* Indianapolis: Bobbs Merrill, 1965 (Inter-University Case Program series, No. 87).

Rothschild, J. H. *Tomorrow's Weapons: Chemical and Biological.* New York: McGraw-Hill, 1964.

Stratton, Owen and Philip Sirotkin. *The Echo Park Controversy.* University, Ala.: University of Alabama Press, 1959 (Inter-University Case Program series, No. 59).

Sullivan, Walter, ed. *America's Race for the Moon: The New York Times Story of Project Apollo.* New York: Random House, 1962.

Taubenfeld, Howard J., ed. *Space and Society: Studies for the Seminar on Problems of Outer Space, Sponsored by the Carnegie Endowment for International Peace.* Dobbs Ferry, N.Y.: Oceana Publications, 1964.

Tillet, Paul. *Doe Day: the Antlerless Deer Controversy in New Jersey.* New Brunswick: Rutgers University Press, 1963.

U.S. Atomic Energy Commission. *In the Matter of J. Robert Oppenheimer: Transcript of Hearing before Personnel Security Board,* April 12–May 6, 1954. Washington, D.C.: Government Printing Office, 1954.

Van Dyke, Vernon. *Pride and Power: The Rationale of the Space Program.* Urbana, Ill.: University of Illinois Press, 1964.

Voss, Earl H. *Nuclear Ambush: The Test-Ban Trap.* Chicago: Henry Regnery, 1963.

Wengert, Norman. *Natural Resources and the Political Struggle*. Garden City, N.Y.: Doubleday, 1955 (Short Studies in Political Science, No. 24).

## The Fluoridation Controversy

Burns, James MacGregor. "The Crazy Politics of Fluorine," *New Republic*, Vol. CXXVIII (July 13, 1953), pp. 14–15.

Coleman, James S. *Community Conflict*. New York: Free Press, 1957.

Davis, Morris. "Community Attitudes toward Fluoridation," *Public Opinion Quarterly*, Vol. XXIII (Winter 1959–1960), pp. 474–482.

Exner, Frederick B., and George L. Waldbott. *The American Fluoridation Experiment*. New York: Devin-Adair, 1957. The case against.

Gamsun, William A. "The Flouridation Dialogue: Is It Ideological Conflict?" *Public Opinion Quarterly*, Vol. XXV (Winter 1961), pp. 526–537.

Gulick, Luther H. "Who Are We To Believe?" [A letter from Gulick to Abe Stark, President of the City Council, City of New York.] *Public Administration Review*, Vol. XVII (Spring 1957), pp. 106–110.

Mausner, Bernard and Judith, "A Study of the Anti-Scientific Attitude," *Scientific American*, Vol. 192 (February 1955), pp. 35–39.

McNeil, Donald R. *The Fight for Fluoridation*. New York: Oxford University Press, 1957.

Paul, Benjamin D., William Gamsun, and S. Stephen Kegeles, Issue eds. "Trigger for Community Conflict: The Case of Fluoridation," *Journal of Social Issues*, Vol. 17, no. 4 (1961), pp. 1–18.


## GOVERNING SCIENCE

### General

Bethe, Hans. *Science: An Interview on the American Character*. Santa Barbara, Calif.: Center for the Study of Democratic Institutions, 1963.

Bush, Vannevar. *Science, The Endless Frontier*.Washington, D.C.: Government Printing Office, 1945; reprinted by the National Science Foundation, 1960.

Denny, Brewster C. "Science and Public Policy: A Literature in Search of a Field," *Public Administration Review*, Vol. XXV, No. 3 (September 1965) pp. 239–248.

Dupré, J. Stefan, and Sanford A. Lakoff. *Science and the Nation: Policy and Politics*. Englewood Cliffs, N.J.: Spectrum paperback, 1962.

Dupree, A. Hunter. *Science in the Federal Government: A History of Politics and Activities to 1940*. Cambridge, Mass.: Harvard University Press, 1957; Harper Torchbooks paperback, 1957.

Gilman, William. *Science: U.S.A*. New York: Viking Press, 1965.

Hailsham, Quintin M. H., 2nd Viscount. *Science and Politics*. London: Faber & Faber, 1963.

Price, Don K. *The Scientific Estate*. Cambridge, Mass.: Harvard University Press, 1965.

———. *Government and Science: Their Dynamic Relation in American Democracy*. New York: New York University Press, 1954; Oxford University Press paperback, 1962.

———. "Organization of Science Here and Abroad," *Science*, Vol. CXXIX (March 20, 1959), pp. 759–765.

Schrader, Rudolf. *Science and Policy: On the Interaction of Scientific and Political Affairs.* Oxford: Pergamon Press, 1963.

Seitz, Frederick. "Science and Government," *Physics Today,* Vol. XVI (December 1963), pp. 28–32.

## Science in the Executive and Congress

*Biomedical Science and Its Administration: A Study of the National Institutes of Health.* Washington, D.C.: Government Printing Office, 1965.

Green, Harold P., and Alan Rosenthal. *Government of the Atom: The Integration of Powers.* New York: Atherton Press, 1963.

Greenfield, Meg. "Science Goes to Washington," *The Reporter,* Vol. XXIX (September 26, 1963), pp. 20–26.

Hewlett, Richard S., and Oscar E. Anderson, Jr. *The New World, 1939/1946.* Vol. I of *A History of the Atomic Energy Commission.* University Park, Penna.: Pennsylvania State University Press, 1962.

Kerr, James R. "Congressmen as Overseers: Surveillance of the Space Program." Unpublished Ph.D. dissertation, Stanford University, 1963.

McCamy, James L. *Science and Public Administration.* University, Ala.: University of Alabama Press, 1960.

Newman, James R. and Byron S. Miller. *The Control of Atomic Energy.* New York: Whittlesey House, 1948.

National Science Foundation. *Federal Organization for Scientific Activities, 1962* (NSF 62–37). Washington, D.C.: Government Printing Office, 1963.

Seaborg, Glenn T., and Daniel M. Wilkes. *Education and the Atom: An Evaluation of Government's Role in Science Education and Information, Especially as Applied to Nuclear Energy.* New York: McGraw–Hill, 1964.

U.S. Congress, House Committee on Science and Astronautics, Subcommittee on Science, Research, and Development. *Hearings.* 88th Congress, 1st Session. Washington, D.C.: Government Printing Office, 1963. See particularly the statement of Jerome B. Wiesner, "Federal Research and Development: Policies and Prospects," pp. 90–109.

U.S. Congress, House Select Committee on Government Research. *Hearings,* parts 1 and 2. 88th Congress, 1st and 2nd Sessions. Washington, D.C.: Government Printing Office, 1963–1964.

Uyeki, Eugene S., and Frank B. Cliffe, Jr. "The Federal Science-Administrator," *Science,* Vol. CXXXIX (March 29, 1963), pp. 1267–1270.

Whitnah, Donald. *A History of the United States Weather Bureau.* Urbana: University of Illinois Press, 1961.

## The Scientist as Adviser

Cox, Donald W. *America's New Policy Makers: The Scientists' Rise to Power.* Philadelphia & New York: The Chilton Co., 1964.

Dubridge, Lee A. "Policy and the Scientists," *Foreign Affairs,* Vol. XLI (April 1963), pp. 571–588.

Gilpin, Robert. *American Scientists and Nuclear Weapons Policy.* Princeton, N.J.: Princeton University Press, 1962.

———, and Christopher Wright, eds. *Scientists and National Policy Making.* New York: Columbia University Press, 1963.

Grodzins, Morton and Eugene Rabinowitch, eds. *The Atomic Age: Scientists in National and World Affairs.* New York: Basic Books, 1963.

Hays, Samuel P. *Conservation and the Gospel of Efficiency.* Cambridge, Mass.: Harvard University Press, 1957.

Lapp, Ralph E. *The New Priesthood: The Scientific Elite and the Uses of Power.* New York: Harper & Row, 1965.

Leiserson, Avery. "Scientists and the Policy Process," *American Political Science Review,* Vol. LIX, No. 2 (June 1965), pp. 408–416.

Lilienthal, David E. *The Journals of David E. Lilienthal.* New York: Harper & Row, 1964. Vol. I, The TVA Years, 1935–1945; Vol. II, The Atomic Energy Years, 1945–1950.

————. "A Skeptical Look at Scientific Experts," *The New York Times Magazine* (September 29, 1963), pp. 23ff.

Schiff, Ashley L. *Fire and Water: Scientific Heresy in the Forest Service.* Cambridge, Mass.: Harvard University Press, 1962.

*Science, Scientists and Politics.* Santa Barbara, Calif.: Center for the Study of Democratic Institutions, 1963. See especially untitled articles by Sherwin Chalmers and Robert M. Hutchins.

Smith, Alice Kimball. *A Peril and A Hope: The Scientists' Movement in America: 1945–47.* Chicago: University of Chicago Press, 1965.

Strauss, Lewis L. *Men and Decisions.* Garden City, N.Y.: Doubleday & Co., 1962.

Wiesner, Jerome B. *Where Science and Politics Meet.* New York: McGraw–Hill, 1965.

## The Economics of Research and Development

Machlup, Fritz. *The Production and Distribution of Knowledge in the United States.* Princeton: Princeton University Press, 1963.

Marshall, A. W. and W. H. Meckling. *Predictability of the Costs, Time and Success of Development.* Santa Monica: Rand Corporation, 1959.

Nelson, Richard R. "The Economics of Invention: A Survey of the Literature," *The Journal of Business,* Vol. XXXII, No. 2 (April 1959) pp. 100–127.

————."The Simple Economics of Basic Scientific Research," *Journal of Political Economy,* Vol. LXVII, No. 3 (June 1959), pp. 297–306.

Organization for Economic Cooperation and Development. *Science, Economic Growth and Government Policy.* Paris, The Organization, 1963.

Solo, Robert A. "Gearing Military R and D to Economic Growth," *Harvard Business Review* (Nov.-Dec. 1962), pp. 49–60.

*The Rate and Direction of Inventive Activity: Economic and Social Factors.* A Report of the National Bureau of Economic Research. Princeton, N. J.: Princeton University Press, 1962.

## Defense Contracting

Dupré, J. Stefan, and W. Eric Gustafson."Contracting for Defense: Private Firms and the Public Interest," *Political Science Quarterly,* Vol. LXXVII (June 1962), pp. 161–177.

Hill, L. S. *Some Observations on the Application of PERT Cost to the TFX Program.* Santa Monica, Calif.: Rand Corporation, 1964.

Hitch, Charles J., and Roland N. McKean. *The Economics of Defense in the Nuclear Age.* Cambridge, Mass.: Harvard University Press, 1960.

Kaysen, Carl. "Improving the Efficiency of Military Research and Development," *Public Policy*, Vol. XII (1963), pp. 219–273. See, in the same volume, Paul W. Cherington, "Kaysen on Military Research and Development: A Comment," pp. 274–285, and J. Stefan Dupré, "The Efficiency of Military Research and Development: Kaysen, Cherington, and the Budget Bureau," pp. 286–301.

Peck, Merton J. and Frederic M. Scherer. *The Weapons Acquisition Process: An Economic Analysis.* Boston: Division of Research, Harvard Business School, 1962.

*Research & Development Contracting.* Washington, D.C.: The National Law Center of George Washington University and Federal Publications, Inc., 1963.

Scherer, Frederic M. *The Weapons Acquisition Process: Economic Incentives.* Boston: Division of Research, Harvard Business School, 1964.

Smith, Richard A. "The $7-Billion Contract that Changed the Rules," *Fortune*, Vol. LXVII (March 1963), pp. 96–101ff.; (April 1963), pp. 110–111ff. A report on the awarding of the TFX contract.

Stover, Carl F. *The Government Contract System as a Problem in Public Policy.* Menlo Park, Calif.: Stanford Research Institute, 1963.

U.S. Bureau of the Budget. *Report to the President on Government Contracting for Research and Development.* Washington, D.C.: Office of the White House Press Secretary, 1962.

## Industrial Research

Comanor, William S. "The Economics of Research and Development in the Pharmaceutical Industry." Unpublished Ph.D. dissertation, Harvard University, 1963.

Hitch, Charles J. *The Character of Research and Development in a Competitive Economy.* P–1297 (May 13, 1958). Santa Monica, Calif.: Rand Corporation, 1958.

Holloman, J. Herbert. "Science, Technology, and Economic Growth," *Physics Today*, Vol. XVI (March 1963), pp. 38–46.

Kornhauser, William. *Scientists in Industry: Conflict and Accommodation.* Berkeley, Calif.: University of California Press, 1962.

Mason, E. S., ed. *The Corporation in Modern Society.* Cambridge, Mass.: Harvard University Press paperback, 1959. See particularly Jacob Schmookler, "Technological Progress and the Modern American Corporation," pp. 141–165.

Mees, C. E. K., and J. A. Leermakers. *The Organization of Industrial Scientific Research.* 2nd ed. New York: McGraw-Hill, 1950.

Mullenbach, Philip. *Civilian Nuclear Power: Economic Issues and Policy Formation.* New York: Twentieth Century Fund, 1963.

## Basic Research and Manpower

*Basic Research and National Goals, A Report to the Committee on Science and Astronautics, U.S. House of Representatives, by the National Academy of Sciences, 1965.* Washington, D.C.: Government Printing Office, 1965. An exceptionally good collection of papers by fifteen panelists convened by the Committee on Science and Public Policy of the NAS.

David, Henry. *Manpower Policies for a Democratic Society: The Final Statement of the [National Manpower] Council.* New York: Columbia University Press, 1965.

Kistiakowsky, George B., *et al. Federal Support of Basic Research.* Washington, D.C.: National Academy of Science, 1964.

National Science Foundation. *Scientists, Engineers, and Technicians in the 1960's: Requirements and Supply.* (NSF 63–34). Prepared by the U.S. Department of Labor, Bureau of Labor Statistics. Washington, D.C.: Government Printing Office, 1964.

Orlans, Harold. *The Effects of Federal Programs on Higher Education: A Study of 36 Universities and Colleges.* Washington, D.C.: Brookings Institution paperback, 1962.

## International Ramifications

Deutsch, Karl W. "The Impact of Science and Technology on International Politics," *Daedalus,* Vol. LXXXVIII (Fall 1959), pp. 669–685.

Haskins, Caryl P. *The Scientific Revolution and World Politics.* New York: Harper & Row, 1964.

Jessup, Philip C., and Howard J. Taubenfeld. *Controls for Outer Space and the Antarctic Analogy.* New York: Columbia University Press, 1959.

Murra, Kathleen O. *International Scientific Organizations.* Library of Congress, 62–64648. Washington, D.C.: Government Printing Office, 1962.

Rand Corporation. *International Political Implications of Activities in Outer Space.* [A report of a conference, October 22–23, 1959.] Santa Monica, Calif.: Rand Corporation, 1960.

Sprout, Harold H. "Geopolitical Hypotheses in Technological Perspective," *World Politics,* Vol. XV, No. 2 (January 1963), pp. 187–212.

Sullivan, Walter. *Assault on the Unknown: The International Geophysical Year.* New York: McGraw-Hill, 1961.

## Scientific Organization Abroad

Ballard, B. G. "The Organization of Scientific Activities in Canada," *Science,* Vol. CXXIX (March 20, 1959), pp. 754–759.

De Witt, Nicholas. "Reorganization of Science and Research in the U.S.S.R.," *Science,* Vol. CXXXIII (June 23, 1961), pp. 1981–1991.

———. "Soviet Brainpower," *International Science and Technology* (January, 1962), pp. 33–38.

———. *Soviet Professional Manpower: Its Education, Training, and Supply.* Washington, D.C.: National Science Foundation, 1955.

Encel, S. "Financing Scientific Research in Australia," *Science,* Vol. CXXXIV (July 28, 1961), pp. 260–266.

Hailsham, Quintin M. H. *Science and Politics.* London: Faber and Faber, 1963.

Hiscocks, E.S. "Organization of Science in the United Kingdom," *Science,* Vol. CXXIX (March 13, 1959), pp. 689–693.

Joravsky, David. *Soviet Marxism and Natural Science, 1917–1932.* New York: Columbia University Press, 1961.

Korol, Alexander G. *Soviet Research and Development: Its Organization, Personnel, and Funds.* Cambridge, Mass.: MIT Press, 1964.

Nieburg, H.L. "EURATOM: A Study in Coalition Politics," *World Politics,* Vol. XV (July 1963), pp. 597–622.

Organization for Economic Cooperation and Development. *Country Reports on the Organization of Scientific Research.* Paris, The Organization, October 1963.

―――. *Science and the Policies of Governments.* Paris, The Organization, 1963.

―――. *O.E.C.D. Policies for Science and Education: Country Reviews* [by place]. Paris, The Organization, 1962–.

Piganiol, Pierre, and Louis Villecourt. *Pour une politique scientifique.* Paris: Flammarion, 1963.

Polach, Jaroslav G. *Euratom: Its Background, Issues and Economic Implications.* Dobbs Ferry, N.Y.: Oceana Publications, 1964.

Snow, C. P. *Science and Government.* Cambridge, Mass.: Harvard University Press, 1961.

*Survey: A Journal of Soviet and East European Studies,* "Report on Soviet Science," No. 52 (July 1964).

## THE OVERVIEW

### General

Barber, Bernard. *Science and the Social Order.* With a Foreword by Robert K. Merton. New York: Collier Books, 1962.

――― and Walter Hirsch, eds. *The Sociology of Science.* New York: The Free Press, 1962.

Barzun, Jacques. *Science; The Glorious Entertainment.* New York: Harper & Row, 1964.

―――. *The House of Intellect.* New York: Harper & Row, 1959.

Berkner, Lloyd V. *The Scientific Age: The Impact of Science on Society.* Trumbull Lectures. New Haven: Yale University Press, 1964.

Born, Max. *Physics and Politics.* New York: Basic Books, 1962.

Bronowski, Jacob. *Science and Human Values.* Rev. ed. with a new dialogue "The Abacus and the Rose." New York: Harper Torchbooks paperback, 1965.

―――. *The Common Sense of Science.* Cambridge, Mass.: Harvard University Press, 1958; Modern Library paperback, 1960.

―――. *The Dilemma of the Scientist.* London: National Peace Council 1955.

―――. "The Educated Man in 1984." (Closing address to the Education Section of the British Association for the Advancement of Science, 1955.)

―――. *Lessons of Science.* London: Fabian Publications, V. Gollancz, 1951.

Cohen, I. Bernard. *Science, Servant of Man; a Layman's primer for the Age of Science.* Boston: Little, Brown, 1948.

Glass, H. Bentley. *Science and Ethical Values.* Chapel Hill, N.C.: University of North Carolina Press, 1965.

Kaplan, Norman (ed.). *Science and Society.* Chicago: Rand McNally, 1965.

Lang, Daniel. *An Inquiry into Enoughness: Of Bombs and Men and Staying Alive.* New York: McGraw-Hill, 1965.

Piel, Gerard. *Science in the Cause of Man.* Rev. ed. New York: Alfred A. Knopf, 1962.

Polanyi, Michael. *The Logic of Liberty: Reflections and Rejoinders.* London: Routledge & Kegan Paul, 1951.

———. *Personal Knowledge: Towards a Post-Critical Philosophy.* Chicago: University of Chicago Press, 1958.

———. *The Planning of Science.* (Society for Freedom in Science, Occasional Pamphlet No. 4, February, 1946.) Oxford: Potter Press, 1946; also in *Political Quarterly,* Vol. XVI (October 1945), pp. 316–328.

———. "Pure and Applied Science and their Appropriate Forms of Organization," *Dialectica,* Vol. X, No. 3 (September 1956), pp. 231–242.

———. *Rights and Duties of Science.* (Society for Freedom in Science, Occasional Pamphlet No. 2, June, 1945.) Oxford: Potter Press, 1945.

———. *Science, Faith and Society.* London. Oxford University Press, 1946.

———. *The Study of Man.* Chicago: University of Chicago Press, 1959.

Price, Derek J. de Solla. *Little Science, Big Science.* New York: Columbia University Press, 1963.

Rabinowitch, Eugene. *The Dawn of a New Age: Reflections on Science and Human Affairs.* Chicago: University of Chicago Press, 1963.

Szent–Györgyi, Albert. *Science, Ethics and Politics.* New York: Vantage Press, 1963.

Szilard, Leo. *The Voice of the Dolphins, and Other Stories.* New York: Simon & Schuster, 1961.

Walker, Charles R. (assisted by Adelaide G. Walker). *Modern Technology and Civilization: An Introduction to Human Problems in the Machine Age.* New York: McGraw–Hill, 1962.

## Science as Profession

*American Behavioral Scientist.* Special issue on "Science, Scientists, and Society," Vol. VI, No. 4 (December 1962).

Ashby, Sir Eric. *Technology and the Academics: An Essay on Universities and the Scientific Revolution.* London: Macmillan & Co., 1958.

Ben-David, Joseph and Awraham Zloczower. "Universities and Academic Systems in Modern Societies," *Archives européennes de sociologie,* Vol. III (1962), pp. 45–84.

Eiduson, Bernice T. *Scientists: Their Psychological World.* New York: Basic Books, 1962.

Glaser, Barney G. *Organizational Scientists: Their Professional Careers.* Indianapolis: Bobbs Merrill, 1964.

Hill, Karl B., ed., with Everett Mendelsohn, Anne Roe, Royden C. Saunders, Jr., Albert F. Siepert, Norman Kaplan, Herbert A. Shepard. *The Management of Scientists.* Boston: Beacon Press, 1964.

Holton, Gerald. "Scientific Research and Scholarship: Notes Toward the Design of Proper Scales," *Daedalus,* Vol. XCI (Spring 1962), pp. 362–399. Reprinted as "Modes for Understanding the Growth and Excellence of Scientific Research," in Stephen R. Graubard and G. Holton, eds. *Excellence and Leadership in a Democracy.* New York: Columbia University Press, 1962.

Hornig, Donald F. "The American Scientific Scene," *Transactions, American Geophysical Union,* Vol. XLVI, No. 2 (June 1965), pp. 337–381.

Knapp, R. H., and H. B. Goodrich. *Origins of American Scientists: A Study Made Under the Direction of a Committee of the Faculty of Wesleyan University.* Chicago: University of Chicago Press, 1952.

Orth, Charles D., 3rd, Joseph C. Bailey, and Francis W. Wolek. *Administering Research and Development: The Behavior of Scientists and Engineers in Organizations.* Homewood, Ill.: Richard D. Irwin and the Dorsey Press, 1964.

Roe, Anne. *The Making of a Scientist.* New York: Dodd, Mead, 1961 (Apollo editions, A–23).

―――. *A Psychological Study of Eminent Biologists.* Washington, D.C.: American Psychological Association, 1951.

―――. *A Psychological Study of Eminent Psychologists and Anthropologists.* Washington, D.C.: American Psychological Association, 1953.

Rossi, Peter H. "Researchers, Scholars and Policy Makers: The Politics of Large-Scale Research," *Daedalus* (Fall 1964), pp. 1142–1161.

Strauss, Anselm L., Lee Rainwater, *et al. The Professional Scientist: A Study of American Chemists.* Chicago: Aldine Publishing Co., 1962.

## PERIODICALS

*The Advancement of Science,* bimonthly. The British Association for the Advancement of Science.

*AAAS Bulletin,* quarterly. American Association for the Advancement of Science.

*American Scientist,* quarterly. Society of the Sigma Xi.

*Aviation Week,* weekly.

*Bioscience,* monthly. American Institute of Biological Sciences.

*Bulletin of the Atomic Scientists,* monthly (except July and August). Educational Foundation for Nuclear Science, Inc.

*Euratom,* quarterly. European Atomic Energy Community.

*Impact of Science on Society,* quarterly. United Nations Educational, Scientific and Cultural Organization.

*International Science and Technology,* monthly.

*Minerva,* quarterly. England.

*Missiles and Rockets,* weekly.

*Nature,* weekly. England.

*New Scientist,* weekly. England.

*Physics Today,* monthly.

*Science,* weekly. American Association for the Advancement of Science.

*Science News Letter,* weekly.

*Scientific American,* monthly.

*Scientist and Citizen,* ten times a year. Greater St. Louis Citizen's Committee for Nuclear Information.

*Technology and Culture,* quarterly.

*Washington Science Trends,* weekly.

# Name Index

# Subject Index

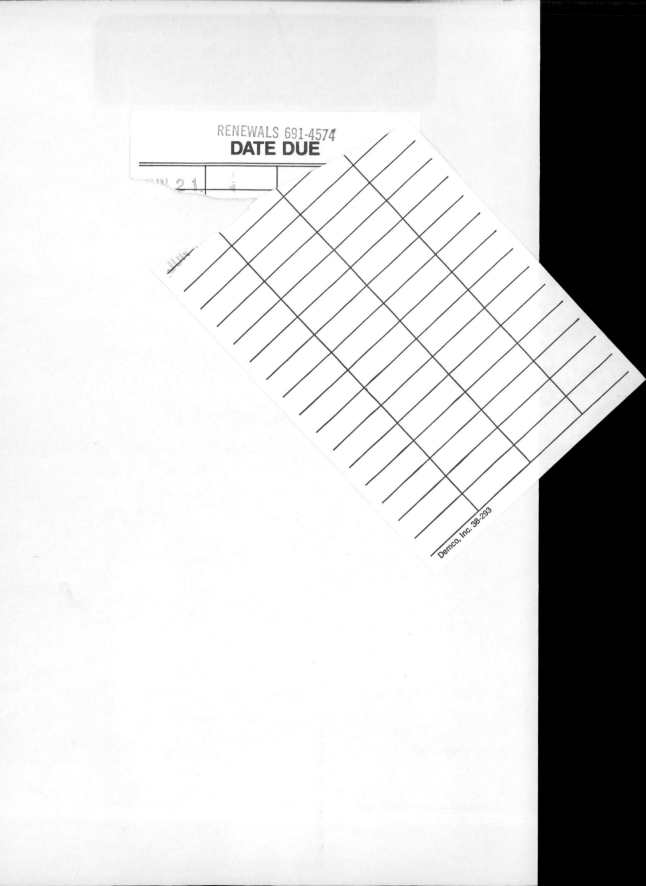